TEACHER'S EXAMINATION GUIDE

ALGEBRA is a comprehensive course in first-year algebra, covering the standard scope-and-sequence topics.

The new and innovative full-color design, use of photographs, color bands, and tinted boxes, highlight the features of the text.

ARITHMETIC REVIEW
(See pages xiii–xv)
Operations with whole numbers, fractions, decimals, and percent are reviewed before Chapter 1.

READY FOR   (See page 189)
Exercises keyed to previous sections preview skills needed in the upcoming chapter.

CHAPTER OPENING
(See page 228)
An attractive full-color photograph begins each chapter.

LESSON DEVELOPMENT
(See pages 194–195)
Lessons are made up of single-concept components, each using the unique *Example/Try This* format.

EXERCISE SETS
(See pages 170–171)
Three levels of exercises make up each exercise set: *Exercises, Extension,* and *Challenge.*

REVIEWS AND TESTS
(See pages 186–188)
Each chapter ends with a *Chapter Review,* keyed to the sections of the chapter, and a *Chapter Test.* Four *Cumulative Reviews* are spaced throughout the text. These are truly cumulative, reviewing concepts back to Chapter 1.

CALCULATORS   (See page 314)
Using a Calculator, with examples and practice problems, shows how to use calculators to solve algebra problems.

CAREERS   (See page 501)
Attractive full-color pages show algebra in different careers. Applications problems are included.

CONSUMER APPLICATIONS
(See page 354)
Arithmetic and algebra skills are applied to consumer topics.

COMPUTER ACTIVITIES
(See pages 536–551)
Ten BASIC programming lessons show how to use computers to solve algebra problems.

SUPPLEMENTS
(See pages T95–T96)
Material for applications, practice, enrichment, computers and video cassette reviews provide a complete teacher support package.

Teacher's Edition

ALGEBRA

MERVIN L. KEEDY
MARVIN L. BITTINGER
STANLEY A. SMITH
LUCY J. ORFAN

ADDISON-WESLEY PUBLISHING COMPANY
MENLO PARK, CALIFORNIA   READING, MASSACHUSETTS   LONDON
AMSTERDAM   DON MILLS, ONTARIO   SYDNEY

ABOUT THE PHOTOGRAPHS

The full-color photographs that appear on the cover and on the first page of each chapter serve to illustrate a variety of well-designed and manufactured objects in the physical world. As the students in your class learn algebraic skills and apply them in applications problems, the photographs will remind them of the many uses that mathematics has in today's world. The photographs illustrate applications in the following categories.

ARCHITECTURE AND ENGINEERING   The cover and the first pages of Chapters 8 and 11 show parts of the Golden Gate Bridge in San Francisco, California. The first pages of Chapters 1 and 13 show the World Trade Center in New York City.

MANUFACTURING AND INDUSTRY   The first page of Chapter 2 is a photograph of a textile mill in North Carolina. A variety of storage tanks are shown at the beginning of Chapters 4, 12, and 14. The last are used to store natural gas. Chapter 6 begins with a photograph of two kinds of aluminum pipes.

RECREATION   The sailboats at the beginning of Chapter 5 and the tennis courts on the first page of Chapter 9 are examples of design in the leisure time industry.

TRANSPORTATION   The first page of Chapter 3 shows cars on the deck of a carrier in Portland, Oregon. Chapter 7 begins with a photograph of the side of a fishing boat. And, the first page of Chapter 10 shows railroad tracks in Chicago, Illinois.

ISBN 0–201–20335–9

ABCDEFGHIJKL–VH–89876543

CONTENTS

ORGANIZATION

Full-color photographs appear at the beginning of each chapter. Each section title is in a large colored band. Each subsection (its title in bright red print) covers a different objective. A complete list of objectives for the course is in the Objectives section of this Teacher's Edition.

EXAMPLES alternate with Try This Exercises in the unique Example/Try This format. The fully worked Examples show in detail how to work each exercise. Side comments explain what is being done in each step.

5–2 Differences of Two Squares

Recognizing Differences of Two Squares

For a binomial to be a difference of two squares, two conditions must be true.
a. There must be two expressions, both squares. Examples are $4x^2$, $9x^4$, 16, y^2.
b. There must be a minus sign between the two expressions.

EXAMPLE 1
Is $9x^2 - 36$ a difference of two squares?
a. The first expression is a square. $9x^2 = (3x)^2$
   The second expression is a square. $36 = 6^2$
b. There is a minus sign between them.
So, we have a difference of two squares.

TRY THIS Which of the following are differences of two squares?
1. $x^2 - 25$ 2. $x^2 - 24$ 3. $x^2 + 36$
4. $4x^2 - 15$ 5. $16x^4 - 49$ 6. $9x^6 - 1$

Factoring Differences of Two Squares

One special product concerns multiplying the sum and difference of the same expression.
$$(A + B)(A - B) = A^2 - B^2$$
We can reverse this equation to factor a difference of two squares.
$$A^2 - B^2 = (A + B)(A - B)$$

EXAMPLE 2
Factor.
$$x^2 - 4 = x^2 - 2^2 = (x + 2)(x - 2)$$
$$A^2 - B^2 = (A + B)(A - B)$$

TRY THIS Factor.
7. $x^2 - 9$ 8. $y^2 - 64$

Always look first for the greatest common monomial factor. Write it as the first factor. Then continue factoring.

EXAMPLES
Factor.

3. $49x^4 - 9x^6 = x^4(49 - 9x^2)$ Factoring out the common factor
   $= x^4(7 - 3x)(7 + 3x)$ Factoring a difference of two squares

4. $18x^2 - 50x^6 = 2x^2(9 - 25x^4)$
   $= 2x^2[3^2 - (5x^2)^2]$ Writing as a difference of two squares
   $= 2x^2(3 - 5x^2)(3 + 5x^2)$

TRY THIS Factor.
9. $32y^2 - 8y^6$ 10. $64x^4 - 25x^6$ 11. $5 - 20y^6$

Factoring Completely

Factor until factoring is no longer possible. This is called factoring completely.

EXAMPLE 5
Factor.

$1 - 16x^{12} = (1 - 4x^6)(1 + 4x^6)$ Factoring a difference of two squares
$= (1 + 2x^3)(1 - 2x^3)(1 + 4x^6)$ Factoring the first factor as a difference of two squares

Factoring Hints
1. Always look first for a common factor.
2. Always factor completely, even though such directions are not given.
3. Check by multiplying to see if you get the original polynomial.
4. Never try to factor a sum of squares.

TRY THIS Factor and check by multiplying.
12. $81x^4 - 1$ 13. $49x^4 - 25x^{10}$

TRY THIS EXERCISES are like the Examples that precede them. They draw students into the development of the lesson and provide immediate reinforcement of the concept or skill being learned. Try This Exercises cover all course objectives. Try This Exercises can be used

- as oral exercises for *immediate response.*
- as boardwork.
- as independent paper-and-pencil work.
- as oral exercises to *summarize* each section.
- as additional *review* before each chapter test.

Important information, such as problem-solving hints, definitions, and theorems, are highlighted in attractively tinted boxes.

PRACTICE

There are abundant exercises, with many applications problems throughout.

Exercise Sets are in three levels of difficulty:

EXERCISES are carefully written to match the Examples and Try This Exercises. These cover all the objectives of the course.

We can also use columns to multiply. We multiply each term on the top row by each term on the bottom. Then we add.

EXAMPLE 8

Multiply $4x - 3$ and $x - 2$.

$$
\begin{array}{r}
4x - 3 \\
x - 2 \\
\hline
4x^2 - 3x \qquad \text{Multiplying the top row by } x \\
- 8x + 6 \qquad \text{Multiplying the top row by } -2 \\
\hline
4x^2 - 11x + 6 \qquad \text{Adding}
\end{array}
$$

TRY THIS Multiply.

16. $(5x + 3)(x - 4)$ 17. $(2y - 3)(3y - 5)$

4–6	

Exercises

Multiply.

1. $6x^2$ and 7 2. $5x^2$ and -2 3. $-x^3$ and $-x$
4. $-x^4$ and x^2 5. $-x^5$ and x^3 6. $-x^6$ and $-x^2$
7. $3x^4$ and $2x^2$ 8. $5x^3$ and $4x^5$ 9. $7t^3$ and $4t^3$
10. $10a^2$ and $3a^2$ 11. $-0.1x^6$ and $0.2x^4$ 12. $0.3x^3$ and $-0.4x^6$

13. $-\frac{1}{3}x^3$ and $-\frac{1}{3}x$ 14. $-\frac{1}{4}x^4$ and $\frac{1}{5}x^8$ 15. $-4x^2$ and 0

Multiply.

16. $3x$ and $-x + 5$ 17. $2x$ and $4x - 6$
18. $4x^2$ and $3x + 6$ 19. $5x^2$ and $-2x + 1$
20. $-6x^2$ and $x^2 + x$ 21. $-4x^2$ and $x^2 - x$
22. $3y^2$ and $6y^4 + 8y^3$ 23. $4y^4$ and $y^3 - 6y^2$
24. $3x^4$ and $14x^{50} + 20x^{11} + 6x^{57} + 60x^{15}$
25. $5x^6$ and $4x^{32} - 10x^{19} + 5x^8$
26. $-4a^7$ and $20a^{19} + 6a^{15} - 5a^{12} + 14a$
27. $-6y^8$ and $11y^{100} - 7y^{50} + 11y^{41} - 60y^4 + 9$

Multiply.

28. $(x + 6)(x + 3)$ 29. $(x + 5)(x + 2)$

170 CHAPTER 4 POLYNOMIALS

30. $(x + 5)(x - 2)$ **31.** $(x + 6)(x - 2)$

32. $(x - 4)(x - 3)$ **33.** $(x - 7)(x - 3)$

34. $(x + 3)(x - 3)$ **35.** $(x + 6)(x - 6)$

36. $(x - 5)(2x - 5)$ **37.** $(x + 3)(2x + 6)$

38. $(2x + 5)(2x + 5)$ **39.** $(3x - 4)(3x - 4)$

40. $(3y - 4)(3y + 4)$ **41.** $(2y + 1)(2y - 1)$

42. $\left(x - \frac{5}{2}\right)\left(x + \frac{2}{5}\right)$ **43.** $\left(x + \frac{4}{3}\right)\left(x + \frac{3}{2}\right)$

Extension

44. $(a + b)^2$ **45.** $(a - b)^2$

46. $(2x + 3)^2$ **47.** $(5y + 6)^2$

Find the area of the shaded regions.

48.
$14y - 5$
$6y$

49.
$21t + 8$
$3t - 4$
$4t$ $2t$

50. A box with a square bottom is to be made from a 12 inch square piece of cardboard. Squares with side x are cut out of the corners and the sides are folded up. Express the volume and the surface area of the box as polynomials.

x x
x x
12
x x
x x
12

Challenge

Compute.

51. a. $(x + 3)(x + 6) + (x + 3)(x + 6)$ **52. a.** $(x - 2)(x - 7) + (x - 2)(x - 7)$
   b. $(x + 4)(x + 5) - (x + 4)(x + 5)$ **b.** $(x - 6)(x - 2) - (x - 6)(x - 2)$

53. a. $(x + 5)(x - 3) + (x + 5)(x - 3)$ **54. a.** $(x + 7)(x - 8) + (x - 7)(x + 8)$
   b. $(x + 9)(x - 4) - (x + 9)(x - 4)$ **b.** $(x + 2)(x - 5) - (x - 2)(x + 5)$

Use the results of Exercises 51 – 54 to do Exercises 55 – 57.

55. If a and b are positive, how many terms are there in
$(x - a)(x - b) + (x - a)(x - b)$?

56. If a and b are positive, how many terms are there in
$(x + a)(x - b) + (x - a)(x + b)$?

57. If a and b are positive, how many terms are there in
$(x + a)(x - b) - (x + a)(x - b)$?

4–6 Multiplication of Monomials and Binomials **171**

EXTENSION problems may be slightly more difficult, or integrate the lesson with previous lessons for continued review and added depth. Frequently they include problem solving and applications.

CHALLENGE provides more difficult problems or new ideas that are beyond the scope of a middle track course. These are often applications.

APPLICATIONS

Colorfully highlighted features throughout the text show the many applications of algebra.

CAREERS in boxed full-color pages show algebra being used in the computer industry, space travel, graphic arts, health care, finance, the automobile industry, and the shipping industry. Applications problems are included.

USING A CALCULATOR shows how to use calculators and apply problem-solving techniques in algebra.

CONSUMER APPLICATIONS apply arithmetic and algebra skills to topics such as shopping in a supermarket, using credit cards, managing a checking account, finding total earnings, and buying on sale.

COMPUTER ACTIVITIES introduce programming in BASIC. They contain programs for solving algebra problems.

CAREERS/Automobile Industry

You see a great-looking new car whiz past on the freeway. After determining the make and model, you are likely to begin framing some mathematical questions.

If you are interested in auto performance, you may wonder how quickly this car accelerates from 0 to 50 mph. If you are concerned with fuel economy, you may wonder how many miles per gallon the car delivers.

who drive them on the job or for pleasure.

Complex algebraic equations are used to tell auto designers how effectively a newly-designed car will hold the road on a twisty course.

the ground. The eyes of a driver in a van are 2.4 meters above the ground. Using the formula $V = 3.5\sqrt{h}$, find out how much farther to the horizon the van driver can see. (See Section 12–9.)

2. Designers have found that a heavy-duty braking system cuts stopping distance for one model of car by 20%. Using this information, revise the formula used to approximate the speed of a car that has left a skid mark of length L.

USING A CALCULATOR

The Square and Power Keys

Many calculators have a key marked x^2 or x^y. These keys can be used to find powers of numbers and to evaluate functions of degree greater than 1. The x^2 key replaces a number in the display with the square of that number. The x^y key is used to find the yth

---

CONSUMER APPLICATION/Determining Earnings

As an employee, the pay you receive may be determined in various ways.

Fixed Salary

You are paid a certain salary per year. This salary is paid on a regular basis, perhaps weekly, monthly, or bi-weekly (every two weeks). Usually you do not receive additional pay for working extra hours.

COMPUTER ACTIVITIES

Writing Expressions and Numbers in BASIC

In order to use a computer, we must use a computer language. One of the most common computer languages is called BASIC. There are different versions of BASIC, so minor changes may be necessary for a particular computer.

In BASIC, as in algebra, variables are quantities whose value may change. A BASIC variable can be specified by a single letter, or a single letter followed by a single digit.

```
X   Y   Y8   A1   P2
```

There are five arithmetic operations in BASIC.

Operation	Basic Symbol
Exponentiation	^
Multiplication	*
Division	/
Addition	+
Subtraction	–

In BASIC we write

P^2	as	P ^ 2
$3X$	as	3 * X
$Y \div 2$	as	Y / 2
$S + 4$	as	S + 4
$X - Y$	as	X – Y

We evaluate BASIC expressions just as we do algebraic expressions. For example, when P = 5,

P ^ 2	means 5^2	or 25
3 * P	means 3×5	or 15
P / 2	means $5 \div 2$	or 2.5
P + 4 + 8	means $5 + 4 + 8$	or 17

To represent numbers in BASIC we use signs and decimal points, but not commas. We do not use fractional notation. Here are some examples.

```
-29   7.92   4923   .666666667
```

EVALUATION

Many opportunities for ongoing review and maintenance of skills are available throughout the text.

ARITHMETIC REVIEW (xiii–xv) provides practice with operations with whole numbers, fractions, decimals, and percent.

READY FOR exercises (keyed to sections of preceding chapters) provide a preview of skills from preceding lessons that will be needed in the following chapter.

CHAPTER REVIEWS at the end of each chapter are keyed to the sections of the chapter, and review all the important skills and concepts of the chapter.

CHAPTER TESTS follow the Chapter Reviews.

CUMULATIVE REVIEWS are each truly cumulative, reviewing skills and concepts back to Chapter 1.

This Teacher's Edition also provides Quizzes, at least two per chapter. The Teacher's Resource Book has two *Chapter Tests* per chapter, a *Mid-Year Test,* and an *End-Of-Year Test.*

Ready for Polynomials and Factoring?

1–5 Factor.

1. $6x + 6y$ **2.** $24w + 24z$ **3.** $4y + 28 + 12z$ **4.** $3w + 6z + 18$

2–7

5. $8x - 32$ **6.** $22 - 11y$ **7.** $3x + 18y - 6$ **8.** $4a + 16b - 6c$

3–1 Solve.

9. $x + 4 = -11$ **10.** $w - 8 = -2$

3–2

CHAPTER 4   Review

Review the material in the chapter. Then see how you have done by trying these review exercises. If you miss an exercise, restudy the indicated lesson.

4–1 Multiply.

1. $7^2 \cdot 7^4$ **2.** $y^7 \cdot y^3 \cdot y$ **3.** $(3x)^5(3x)^9$

CHAPTER 4   Test

Multiply.

1. $6^2 \cdot 6^3$ **2.** $x^6 \cdot x^2$ **3.** $(4a)^3(4a)^6$

Divide.

4. $\frac{3^5}{3^2}$ **5.** $\frac{x^3}{x^8}$ **6.** $\frac{a^{13}}{a^y}$

Simplify.

7. $(x^3)^2$ **8.** $(-3y^2)^3$ **9.** $(2a^3b)^4$

CHAPTERS 1–7   Cumulative Review

1–1 Write an algebraic expression for each of the following.

1. 7 less than twice y **2.** the difference of x and three times y

1–2 Simplify.

3. $\frac{1800}{156}$ **4.** $\frac{72xz}{90xy}$ **5.** $\frac{144ab}{108abc}$

1–3, 1–4 Evaluate.

6. $x^2 - 5$ for $x = 3$ **7.** $(y - 1)^2$ for $y = 6$.

1–5 Multiply.

8. $3(2x + y)$ **9.** $4(3x + 4y + z)$

1–5 Collect like terms.

10. $7a + 7b + a + 7c$ **11.** $x + 2y + 2z + x$

1–6 Solve.

12. $x + \frac{5}{6} = \frac{17}{12}$ **13.** $2.3y = 12.88$

1–7 Translate to an equation and solve.

14. A scale drawing shows a bolt enlarged 5 times. If the drawing is 3.7 cm long, how long is the actual bolt?

2–2 Use $<$, $>$, or $=$ to write a true sentence.

15. $-10 \quad -14$ **16.** $-3.1 \quad -3.15$ **17.** $0.01 \quad 0.1$

2–3, 2–4 Simplify.

18. $-\frac{1}{2} + \frac{3}{8} + (-6) + \frac{3}{4}$ **19.** $-2.6 + (-7.5) + 2.6 + (-7.5)$

20. $-6.1 - (-3.1) + 7.9 - 3.1 + 1.8$ **21.** $-7 - 2x + 5 - (-x) - 1$

2–5 Multiply.

22. $-\frac{2}{3}\left(\frac{18}{15}\right)$ **23.** $\frac{3}{5} \cdot \left(-\frac{3}{5}\right) \cdot \left(\frac{-25}{9}\right)$ **24.** $-2 \cdot (-7) \cdot (-3) \cdot 0$

2–6 Divide.

25. $\frac{-4}{3} \div \left(-\frac{2}{9}\right)$ **26.** $-6.262 \div 1.01$ **27.** $-\frac{72}{108} \div \left(-\frac{2}{3}\right)$

290 CHAPTER 7 GRAPHS AND LINEAR EQUATIONS

TEACHER'S RESOURCE BOOK

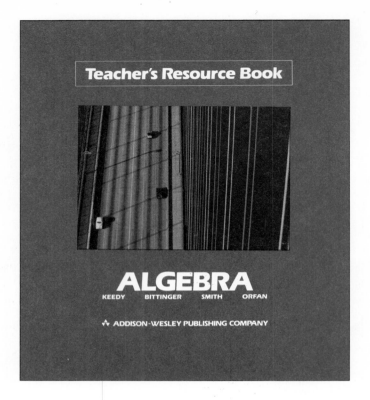

The Teacher's Resource Book, a supplement unique to the Addison-Wesley Algebra program, contains 176 pages of teaching aids to help fit the course to the special needs of any class.

Packaged in a convenient three-ring binder, these blackline masters provide a range of handouts from testing to computer worksheets.

Arithmetic Reviews provide ample maintenance of arithmetic skills.

Chapter Tests include two tests for each chapter. The free response chapter tests are like the chapter tests in the text. The multiple-choice chapter tests help prepare students for the PSAT and other standardized tests. Also included are a *Mid-Year Test* and an *End-of-Year Test*.

Skills Practice (two to four worksheets for each chapter) are like the first level of Exercises in the text, providing more practice with important algebra skills.

Applications (two to four worksheets for each chapter) complement the applications and special features of the text. These contain career and consumer applications, problem-solving refreshers, and calculator problems.

Computer Projects provide further opportunities to use the introduction to BASIC programming in the text.

TEACHER'S EDITION

The Teacher's Edition contains two parts:

128 pages at the front of the text with references, guides, and teaching suggestions; and the annotated Student Edition containing answers in blue for ready identification.

Material in the front of the text includes the following:

Tips for Teachers
This unique feature contains tips on classroom organization and management. New teachers will find this material very practical and experienced teachers may also find additional ideas.

Objectives
Section objectives for the entire course are listed.

Quizzes
This section contains at least two quizzes for each chapter.

Teaching Suggestions
Numerous suggestions serve a variety of teacher needs. Their easy-to-locate format makes them helpful sources of teaching ideas.

Assignment Guide
Daily assignments are given for three levels of courses for each semester. Assignment days for review, testing, and supplemental material are included.

Reference to Supplements
This chart lists supplementary features in the Student Edition, the Teacher's Edition, the Teacher's Resource Book, and other supplements. It also indicates where each of the features, such as Skills Practice, Applications, and Computer Projects, may be used.

Additional Answers
Answers for most exercises appear overprinted on student pages. Answers too long for the student pages are in the front part of this Teacher's Edition.

Computer Tips

Computer Programming

A one-semester course in computer programming is probably the fastest way to become familiar with how computers work and the types of problems they are used to solve. Most community colleges offer such a course. It may be called "Computer Programming in BASIC" or "Introduction to Computer Programming."

If you are unfamiliar with computers, invite a teacher from your school or district to teach a brief course in computer programming. Perhaps a two-week session in the spring would be a good time to arrange for your guest computer teacher to take over your class.

If you wish some or all of your students to have actual hands-on computer programming experience, you should have access to enough computers so that each student can have 2 hours of computer time per week. The computers should be equipped with a printer for students to be able to hand in assignments.

If you have access to only a limited number of computers, you might have students take turns during the school year. There are many software programs available that students may use independently to learn the rudiments of programming.

Computer Literacy

A course in computer literacy usually consists of a short history of computers, a description of the hardware—the parts of a computer and what they do, examples of applications of computers, and an introduction to systems analysis, the science of setting up problems so that they can be programmed into and solved by a computer. Some community colleges offer a course in computer literacy, although such courses may vary greatly in their content.

The basic elements of computer literacy can be self-taught by using books or magazine articles. One such book is *Computers and Data Processing* by Capron and Williams (Benjamin/Cummings, 1982). Your librarian may be able to suggest others.

To help your students become "computer literate" have each one be responsible for preparing a 20-minute report.

Testing and Record Keeping

Commercially-produced software management programs can be helpful to school administrators or anyone who wishes to monitor the progress of more than 50 students.

Keep in mind that these record keeping or management programs almost always require that you use multiple-choice form tests. If you prefer to use standard form, or free-response tests, you may wish to continue to use traditional testing materials.

A computer can be used to correct tests for you only if (1) you also have a card reader and (2) you use multiple-choice tests in which students fill in circles on separate answer cards. The Chatsworth card reader is probably the most commonly used at this time.

There are a few software programs available that include either randomly generated test items or test items pulled from a master test bank. A program of this type will help you construct tests for special purposes such as make-up tests or tests for students covering highly-individualized curriculums.

Interactive Practice and Problem Solving

There are an ever-increasing number of commercially produced software diskettes for your students to use along with their algebra textbooks and worksheets. As you begin to choose among the wide variety of diskettes, the following points may be helpful.

Check with other teachers in your school or district for recommended software. If a particular diskette has worked well for another teacher, it will probably work for you also.

If your school or district has a media or computer specialist, that person may be a good source for recommendations and evaluations.

Before deciding to purchase a diskette, check to see exactly how many diskettes you will need at one time. Companies do not allow copying diskettes, but may provide backup diskettes, review copies, and discounts on multiple purchases.

Many magazines now include reviews of software as well as textbooks. The Computing Teacher includes a Software Reviews section. Also, Purser's Magazine is a publication specifically designed to evaluate software.

REFERENCES:

Robert Taylor, Editor: *The Computer in the School: Tutor, Tool, Tutee,* Teachers College Press, 1980. This book contains three papers by Alfred Bork, four papers by Thomas Dwyer, four papers by Arthur Luehrmann, four papers by Seymour Papert, and four papers by Patrick Suppes.

Morsund, David, *Precollege Computer Literacy: A Personal Computing Approach,* International Council for Computers in Education (ICCE), c/o Dept. of Computer and Information Science, University of Oregon, Eugene, OR 94703, 1981.

Lathrop, Ann and Bobby Goodson, *Courseware in the Classroom: Selecting, Organizing, and Using Education Software.* Menlo Park, CA: Addison-Wesley, 1983.

The Computing Teacher, International Council for Computers in Education (ICCE), University of Oregon, Eugene, OR 97403.

The Mathematics Teacher, November 1981 issue on Microcomputers, National Council of Teachers of Mathematics (NCTM), Reston, VA 22091.

Purser's Magazine, P.O. Box 466, El Dorado, CA 95623.

Calculator Tips

Computation

Although your students will not be using calculators in every class period, each student should have access to a calculator with at least a memory and a square root key.

Most likely, your students will not all be using the same type of calculator. Near the beginning of the school year, set aside part of a class to discuss the different types of calculators. You might choose a problem from the previous day's class and have several different students explain how they would solve it on different calculators.

Whether or not you allow students to use calculators when they are taking quizzes and tests is, of course, an individual decision. Keep in mind that the tests available with this program, and most teacher-constructed tests, were designed to be worked without calculators. Their emphasis is, appropriately, on algebraic concepts and skills rather than on arithmetical proficiency.

If you begin to integrate student use of calculators into your curriculum, you may find you are spending less time on some topics. For example, working square roots by hand or using a table of logarithms are skills that the majority of algebra teachers spend less time on than in the past. Use this extra time to increase your emphasis on problem solving and applying algebraic skills to real-world situations.

Problem Solving

If each of your students has access to even a simple, four-function calculator, you can take advantage of this tool to more effectively teach problem solving. When students are encouraged to use calculators for tedious or lengthy computations, they are often more willing to tackle new or apparently difficult problems; they can begin to concentrate on solving problems rather than finding answers.

Consumer applications offer good opportunities to show students the advantages of mastering the use of a calculator. Problems in percent and compound interest are good examples.

Having calculators available in your classroom can give you opportunities to incorporate discovery learning into your instruction. Students can be encouraged to use "guess and check" or successive approximation methods as they approach new problems.

Calculators are also helpful in teaching students the rudiments of mathematical modeling. As they learn to translate ever more complex real-world problems into mathematical statements, they will also see more reasons for learning algebraic concepts and skills.

Organizing Your Chalkboard Work

- Place the topic of the lesson or daily objective at the top left-hand side of the board.
- Use colored chalk to emphasize key words or concepts. For example, place the LCM in a different color.

Classroom
Organization
Tips

- Organize your boardwork so that it is sequential and easy to follow from left to right.
- Use grids, compass, protractor, and straightedge when applicable.
- Use Try This Exercises as additional examples.
- Be sure to allow "copy" time for your students before you erase to continue instruction.
- Take the opportunity to walk to the back of the room to scrutinize your own boardwork.

Suggestions for Bulletin Boards

- Using computer paper or brick paper as background, make a "Math Graffiti" board, showing the many mathematical symbols.
- Use string art to produce a variety of designs. Metallic thread against black paper shows up well.
- Use photographs or illustrations from periodicals to show examples of math in nature: flowers, honeycombs, crystals, and the like. Also illustrate math in structures such as buildings, bridges, and aqueducts.
- Do a "Problem of the Week" board. Post a problem to be solved during the week and have students deposit solutions in an envelope attached to the board. Problems may be chosen from Extension or Challenge exercises or from the Applications section in the Teacher's Resource Book.
- Use graphs of equations and inequalities to match color-coded algebraic statements.
- Use a Venn diagram or a tree diagram to show the relationship of the subsets of the real number system, including rationals, irrationals, integers, and whole numbers.
- Display students' homework papers that show good format, directions well followed, or improvement.

Organization of the Student Notebook

A lightweight looseleaf notebook divided into three sections for reviews or drills, classwork, and homework is a simple, yet effective, means of organization. Dividers can be used to separate sections. A student assignment sheet can precede the initial divider.

The numbering of reviews or drills and homework assignments is recommended. Several days of review exercises may be included on a single sheet. Each homework assignment should begin on a new sheet of paper to simplify collection or grading.

The classwork section can contain vocabulary lists, class-notes, sample problems, and exercises completed in class, all in chronological order. A specific title for each new topic or skill can be printed on the chalkboard and in the student notebook to focus attention on the objective.

Students will need instruction during the first few weeks on managing notebook and assignment sheet entries as well as notetaking skills. Taking time to explain procedures and making cursory checks will both prove wise investments.

The collection and grading of notebooks two or three times during each grading period encourages students to maintain their algebra papers carefully. The lengthy task of checking notebooks is simplified by preparation of a checklist. Plan to evaluate the completeness of the student assignment sheet, three or four specific items from each of the three sections, and the overall neatness, sequence, and organization of the notebook.

Determining Algebra Student Placement

Give an Algebra Prognosis Test to incoming Algebra 1 students in spring, if possible, or on the first day of class. Use the prognosis test, previous reading and basic math tests, teacher recommendations, and student choice to evaluate student readiness.

If all your students are to be in the same level of algebra regardless of readiness, then use the tests to predict which students will need more arithmetic review or which should be assigned Extension or Challenge exercises.

REFERENCES:

Orleans-Hanna Algebra Prognosis Test, The Psychological Corporation, Harcourt Brace Jovanovich, 1982

Basic Skills Assessment Tests in Reading, Writing and Mathematics for Grades 7–12, Educational Testing Service, Addison-Wesley Publishing Company, 1978

Assignment Tips

Student Assignment Sheets

A quarterly record of assignments and grades maintained by the student and periodically checked by the teacher can be very helpful.

- A numbered sequence of assignments helps students keep papers in order and develop a system of organization.
- The recording of grades enables students to chart their progress and to spot missing work.
- This informal method of communicating with parents provides an ongoing form of reporting student achievement. Be sure to explain its purpose to parents during back-to-school night or parent conferences.
- It is recommended that the assignment sheet be printed on colored paper for easy reference.
- See the Student Assignment Sheet in the Teacher's Resource Book.

Homework Assignments

- The homework should take the average student 30 to 40 minutes. Motivate the better student with one or two challenge problems.
- Periodically assign a few problems from topics covered on previous days.
- After assigning homework try to begin exercises in class. Work problems step by step as a group or send six to eight students to work at the blackboard.
- Students can check their own problems by taking turns giving answers or writing problems on the board.
- The teacher should check that students do the homework. Papers may be collected daily or weekly.
- A mini quiz on homework can be given periodically in class by having students work three or four exercises taken from the past five or six assignments.
- The Assignment Chart in this Teacher's Edition gives suggestions for several levels of classes.

Reviewing Tips

Teaching Students How to Review for a Test

Students should be encouraged to study material for a test in the same sequence as concepts were presented. One strategy for algebra students includes the following steps.

- Review class notes, paying particular attention to properties, terminology, and sample problems.
- Rework problems originally missed on quizzes, tests, and homework assignments.
- Select from text and solve three Try This Exercises from the more difficult exercises in each Section. Solutions should be checked using the answer key in the back or homework. (Parents who wish to help are generally willing to select these problems for students.)

Students prepare excellent test questions. An assignment to write five questions for another classmate encourages the student to take an objective look at appropriate types of questions and reinforces skill development.

Reviewing for the PSAT

- A daily or twice weekly short PSAT review is more beneficial than a concentrated week review prior to the test.
- PSAT-style questions on arithmetic reasoning, algebra skills, and quantative comparisons will serve as an opportunity to discuss problem-solving strategies.
- A drill sheet of ten problems can be duplicated and distributed to students at the beginning of each week.
- A thirty-minute timed sample test could be administered periodically to simulate testing environment and evaluate student progress.
- Multiple Choice Chapter Tests in the Teacher's Resource Book give additional PSAT-style questions.

These three sources provide PSAT drill material.

Practice for the Scholastic Aptitude Test, Long Run Masters, CEBCO Standard Publishing, Fairfield, New Jersey, 1975.

Brownstein, Samuel C. and Mitchell Weiner, Barron's How To Prepare for the PSAT/NMSQT, Barron's, Woodbury, New York, 1981.

Posamentier, Alfred S., A Study Guide for the Mathematics Section of the Scholastic Aptitude Test, CEBCO Standard Publishing, Fairfield, New Jersey, 1975.

Grading Tips

Grading Homework

For homework to be an effective tool, it should not be graded on the basis of correct answers alone. Homework can be graded in various ways.

- Score 1 point for each problem worked, right or wrong.
- Assign a symbol (such as +) to each homework assignment that is complete. Other symbols (S,U) could signify satisfactory or unsatisfactory.
- A student's homework grade would be an A if 90% of the homework is scored +; a B if 80% of the homework is scored +; etc.
- Correct and grade one problem each day from all the homework problems assigned. Pick one problem from the homework each day as a "mini" quiz.

Always go over the assignments daily and answer any questions.

Assessing Partial Credit on Test Questions

- Before grading a test predetermine the point values for each skill being used within each test question.
- Assign higher point values for more difficult skills within a problem. For example, in solving a word problem give more points for setting up the equation and less for checking the answer. Actually solving the equation should be assigned a point value somewhere in between.
- Give credit for knowing the concepts and procedures learned. Do not over-penalize a student for a small calculation error—we all make "careless" errors.
- Check to see if the procedure from the point of an error is still mathematically correct for the incorrect values. Students should not be further penalized if they know the concepts.

Assessing Class Participation

1. Place your seating chart in an acetate folder.
2. Using a different colored transparency marker each day, mark on the chart when students give a good response to a question or when they explain work at the board.
3. Have every student go to the board at least twice a quarter and grade their explanation with seven to ten points.

4. At the end of the day or week transfer markings to your gradebook.

5. Wipe off your acetate. You're ready for another week.

Your acetate will help you to keep from relying on the same students during the week.

Scheduling Make-up Tests

One method of handling make-up tests which avoids the necessity of preparing individualized make-up tests for each student who misses a test is the following:

1. Provide no make-up tests for individual units throughout the grading period.

2. At the end of the grading period give a single make-up test which covers all topics taught during the period.

3. The student's grade on the test is used as a make-up grade for the unit test missed. (One test covers all material, but counts for different units for different students.)

4. If a student has not missed any chapter test during the grading period, the teacher has three choices.
   a. Dismiss the student from taking the test;
   b. Let the student treat the test as a review preparation for the final exam;
   c. For a student who does well on the test, substitute the score for a chapter test which had a lower score.

Parent-Teacher Conferences

Open communication between parents and teacher provides effective support for the student. Make parents aware that you are available to meet with them to discuss student performance. Here are a few suggestions for conducting a successful parent-teacher conference.

- Organize your paperwork and develop a brief list of points to be covered in advance. A folder containing the student's work is appropriate to share with parents.
- Briefly identify the strengths and weaknesses of the student. Rather than go over individual grades from your class record, concentrate on your overall observations.
- Make specific, concrete statements which offer suggested courses of action. Parents will want you to provide ways for them to assist their child. If homework is a problem,

Meeting
Tips

you may wish to explain the purpose of the student assignment sheet. For the student whose test performance is weak, sharing test review procedures is helpful.
- Parents appreciate a follow-up to the conference. Offering to send a note indicating progress is a successful way to close the conference.

REFERENCE:
Rudman, Masha Kabakow, "Evaluating Students: How To Do It Right," *Learning,* Vol. 7 (October, 1978): 50–53.

Conducting a Math Department Meeting
- Form an agenda of topics to be discussed and announcements to be made. Distribute agenda before the meeting, if possible.
- Try to focus on agenda topics only—keep the meeting brief.
- Withhold issues that could result in lengthy discussions until all other topics have been covered.
- Be sure to solicit comments from all members of the department in an effort to create a feeling of group decision.
- Call department meetings only when there are enough topics or a topic warrants group interaction. Often a communication system within the department is sufficient for announcements.

Planning a Class Presentation for a Supervisor
- If possible, at a pre-observation meeting, determine two or three goals. These will be the only goals that will be observed and discussed at a post-observation meeting. An example of a goal could be to increase student class participation.
- Use your typical class procedure so that students are at ease.
- Expect students to be less responsive and require more direction or repetition.
- Give only positive feedback to student responses.
- At a post-observation meeting, be prepared to give one or two points of self-evaluation and one new long-range goal for the next period.

Writing an Algebra Test

1. Write 60% of the questions in such a way that you feel the weakest student who has simply sat in class and paid attention should be able to answer them.

2. Write 10% of the questions so that you feel any "A" student should be expected to know them.

3. Design the remaining 30% of the test so that the level of difficulty follows a straight line curve from the level of the problems in step 1 to the difficulty of the problems in step 2.

4. Questions of the same type, such as multiple choice or true–false, should be grouped together to avoid confusing the student. Examples of directions for various item types are listed below.

   True–False   Indicate whether each of the following statements is true or false. Write plus (+) for true or zero (0) for false in the blank preceding each statement.

   Multiple Choice   Circle the letter of the phrase or numerical expression which *best* answers each of the following questions.

   Completion or Fill-In   In the appropriate blank, fill in the phrase, term, or numerical expression which best completes the sentence.

   Match   From Column B, select the term which best matches each expression in Column A. Write the letter which corresponds to your answer in the blank preceding each item in Column A. Use each letter only once.

5. Once the questions are decided upon, the test should be arranged so that the questions flow from the easiest to the most difficult. Students who experience success with the first questions on a test will perform more competently than they would if they had been unable to answer them correctly.

OBJECTIVES

The objectives in each Section correspond to the Subsections. For example, in Chapter 1, Section 1–1, the Subsections are Algebraic Expressions (page 1) and Writing Algebraic Expressions (page 2). The corresponding objectives are: to evaluate simple algebraic expressions, and to write algebraic expressions for English phrases.

The EXAMPLES, TRY THIS, and Exercises also correspond to each subsection and objective. For example, the first subsection and objective cover the EXAMPLES, TRY THIS, and Exercises shown below.

Subsection: Algebraic Expressions
Objective: To evaluate simple algebraic expressions
EXAMPLES 1–3   TRY THIS 1–4   Exercises 1–18

Chapter 1 Objectives

Evaluate simple algebraic expressions (p. 1)
Write algebraic expressions for English phrases (p. 2)
Write equivalent expressions using the commutative laws (p. 6)
Write equivalent expressions using the property of 1 (p. 7)
Find the simplest notation for a fractional expression (p. 9)
Write the product of factors in exponential notation (p. 12)
Evaluate expressions containing exponents (p. 13)
Calculate and evaluate expressions both with and without parentheses (p. 15)
Write equivalent expressions using the associative laws (p. 16)
Write equivalent expressions using the commutative and associative laws (p. 17)
Use the distributive law to multiply expressions of the form $a(b + c)$ (p. 20)

Use the distributive law to factor expressions of the form $ab + ac$ (p. 21)

Use the distributive law to collect like terms (p. 22)

Solve simple equations by trial (p. 25)

Solve equations of the type $x + a = b$ by subtracting a on both sides (p. 26)

Solve equations of the type $ax = b$ by dividing on both sides by a (p. 27)

Solve problems by first translating to equations (p. 29)

Find integers that correspond to various situations (p. 39)

Tell the order of two integers using the symbols $<$ or $>$ (p. 40)

Find the absolute value of any integer (p. 41)

Define a rational number as a ratio of two integers (p. 44)

Graph rational numbers on a number line (p. 44)

Tell the order of two rational numbers (p. 45)

Show that a number is rational by naming it as a ratio of two integers (p. 46)

Add rational numbers using a number line (p. 49)

Add rational numbers without using a number line (p. 51)

Find the additive inverse of a rational number (p. 53)

Solve problems involving addition of rational numbers (p. 54)

Subtract rational numbers using a number line (p. 57)

Subtract rational numbers without using a number line (p. 58)

Solve problems involving subtraction of rational numbers (p. 59)

Multiply rational numbers (p. 62)

Solve "moment" problems (p. 64)

Divide rational numbers (p. 68)

Find the reciprocal of any nonzero rational number (p. 69)

Rewrite division as multiplication using the reciprocal of the divisor (p. 70)

Use the distributive law of multiplication over subtraction (p. 73)

Use the distributive law to factor (p. 74)

Identify the terms of an expression (p. 74)

Use the distributive law to collect like terms (p. 75)

Chapter 2
Objectives

Find an expression, without parentheses, for the additive inverse of a sum (p. 77)
Subtract expressions, remove parentheses, and simplify (p. 78)
Simplify expressions having parentheses within parentheses (p. 79)
Translate problems involving percents to equations and solve them (p. 82)
Tell which properties of numbers guarantee that certain statements are true (p. 86)
Find axioms that guarantee that certain statements are true (p. 86)
Prove number properties (Optional) (p. 89)

Chapter 3 Objectives

Solve equations using the addition principle (p. 99)
Solve problems by translating to equations (p. 100)
Solve equations using the multiplication principle (p. 103)
Solve problems by translating to equations (p. 105)
Solve simple equations using both the addition and multiplication principles (p. 108)
Solve equations in which like terms are collected (p. 108)
Solve problems using both principles (p. 111)
Solve equations containing parentheses (p. 114)
Solve equations by first clearing of fractions or decimals (p. 115)
Solve problems involving equations containing parentheses (p. 116)
Solve problems by translating to equations (p. 120)
Solve a formula for a specified letter (p. 124)
Solve equations involving proportions (p. 128)
Prove simple if–then statements (Optional) (p. 131)
Write the converse of a given statement (Optional) (p. 132)
Solve equations by proving a statement and its converse (Optional) (p. 134)

Chapter 4 Objectives

Use exponents in multiplying (p. 143)
Use exponents in dividing (p. 144)
Use exponents in raising a power to a power (p. 145)
Identify the terms of a polynomial (p. 148)

Collect the like terms of a polynomial (p. 149)
Identify degrees of terms and degrees of polynomials (p. 150)
Identify coefficients of terms (p. 150)
Arrange a polynomial in descending order (p. 153)
Identify the missing terms in a polynomial (p. 154)
Evaluate a polynomial for a given value of a variable (p. 154)
Add polynomials (p. 157)
Solve problems involving addition of polynomials (p. 158)
Find the additive inverse of a polynomial (p. 163)
Rename an additive inverse of a polynomial (p. 163)
Subtract polynomials (p. 164)
Multiply two monomials (p. 168)
Multiply a polynomial by a monomial (p. 168)
Multiply two binomials (p. 169)
Multiply a trinomial and a binomial (p. 172)
Multiply any polynomials (p. 173)
Multiply two binomials mentally (p. 175)
Multiply the sum and the difference of two expressions mentally (p. 176)
Square a binomial mentally (p. 180)
Find special products (p. 181)

Chapter 5 Objectives

Factor monomials (p. 191)
Factor polynomials when the terms have a common factor (p. 192)
Recognize binomials that are a difference of two squares (p. 194)
Factor differences of two squares (p. 194)
Factor polynomials completely (p. 195)
Recognize trinomials that are squares of binomials (p. 197)
Factor squares of binomials (p. 198)
Factor trinomials of the type $x^2 + ax + b$ whose constant term is positive (p. 200)
Factor trinomials of the type $x^2 + ax + b$ whose constant term is negative (p. 201)
Factor trinomials of the type $ax^2 + bx + c$ (p. 204)
Factor polynomials with four terms by grouping (p. 207)
Apply a general strategy for factoring (p. 209)
Solve equations already factored, using the principle of zero products (p. 212)

Solve certain equations by factoring and then using the principle of zero products (p. 214)
Solve problems involving equations which can be factored (p. 217)

Chapter 6 Objectives

Evaluate a polynomial in several variables for given values of the variables (p. 229)
Identify the coefficients and degrees of the terms of a polynomial, and identify the degree of a polynomial (p. 230)
Arrange a polynomial in ascending or descending order (p. 230)
Add and subtract polynomials (p. 234)
Multiply polynomials (p. 234)
Multiply two binomials (p. 235)
Factor polynomials when the terms have a common factor (p. 239)
Factor differences of two squares (p. 239)
Factor trinomials (p. 240)
Factor by grouping (p. 241)
Solve equations with or without parentheses, where some letters are used as constants (p. 243)
Solve problems by first solving the formula for a certain letter and then evaluating (p. 247)

Chapter 7 Objectives

Plot points associated with ordered pairs (p. 259)
Determine the quadrant in which a point lies (p. 260)
Find coordinates of a point on a graph (p. 261)
Determine whether an ordered pair is a solution of an equation (p. 263)
Graph an equation with two variables (p. 264)
Graph linear equations using two points (p. 267)
Graph linear equations using intercepts (p. 268)
Graph linear equations with a missing variable (p. 269)
Find the slope of a line containing a given pair of points (p. 272)
Find the slope, if it exists, of horizontal and vertical lines (p. 274)
Find the slope of a line from an equation (p. 277)

Find the slope and y-intercept of a line from an equation (p. 278)
Use the slope and y-intercept to graph an equation (p. 279)
Write the equation of a line given the slope and y-intercept (p. 281)
Write the equation of a line given the slope and a point (p. 282)
Prove theorems related to slope (optional) (p. 285)

Identify a function (p. 295)
Use function notation (p. 296)
Draw graphs of functions (p. 300)
Recognize the graph of a function (p. 301)
Solve problems involving linear functions (p. 303)
Find an equation of variation given a description of direct variation and solve problems involving direct variation (p. 306)
Find an equation of variation given a description of inverse variation (p. 310)
Solve problems involving inverse variation (p. 311)

Chapter 8
Objectives

Determine whether an ordered pair is a solution of a system of equations (p. 321)
Solve a system of equations by graphing (p. 322)
Solve a system of two equations by the substitution method when one equation has a variable alone on one side (p. 325)
Solve a system of two equations by the substitution method when neither of them has a variable alone on one side (p. 326)
Solve problems by the substitution method after translating to systems of equations (p. 327)
Solve a system of equations using the addition method when no multiplication is necessary (p. 330)
Solve a system of equations using the addition method when the multiplication principle must be used first (p. 330)
Solve problems by the addition method after translating to a system of equations (p. 333)

Chapter 9
Objectives

Solve problems by translating them to systems of equations (p. 337)
Solve motion problems using the formula $d = rt$ (p. 343)
Solve coin and mixture problems (p. 349)

Chapter 10 Objectives

Determine whether a given number is a solution of an inequality (p. 361)
Solve inequalities using the addition principle (p. 361)
Solve inequalities using the multiplication principle (p. 365)
Solve inequalities using the addition and multiplication principles together (p.368)
Solve problems involving inequalities (p. 370)
Graph simple inequalities (p. 373)
Graph inequalities with absolute value (p. 374)
Solve inequalities in two variables (p. 377)
Graph inequalities in two variables on a plane (p. 377)
Graph systems of linear inequalities in two variables on a plane (p. 381)

Chapter 11 Objectives

Multiply fractional expressions (p. 391)
Simplify fractional expressions (p. 392)
Multiply fractional expressions and simplify (p. 393)
Divide fractional expressions and simplify (p. 395)
Divide a polynomial by a monomial (p. 397)
Divide a polynomial by a polynomial (p. 397)
Add or subtract fractional expressions having the same denominator (p. 401)
Add or subtract fractional expressions with denominators as additive inverses (p. 401)
Find the LCM of algebraic expressions (p. 404)
Add fractional expressions with different denominators (p. 405)
Subtract fractional expressions with different denominators (p. 406)
Simplify combined additions and subtractions of fractional expressions (p. 410)
Simplify complex fractional expressions (p. 410)

Solve fractional equations (p. 413)
Solve work, motion, and reciprocal problems involving fractional equations (p. 416)
Solve proportion problems (p. 418)
Prove theorems associated with multiplication and division (Optional) (p. 422)

Chapter 12
Objectives

Find principal square roots (p. 433)
Identify numbers as rational or irrational when named in radical notation (p. 433)
Identify numbers as rational or irrational when named by fractional or decimal notation (p. 434)
Approximate square roots using a table (p. 436)
Determine the valid replacements in radical expressions (p. 438)
Simplify radical expressions with a perfect square radicand (p. 439)
Multiply radical expressions (p. 441)
Factor radical expressions (p. 442)
Approximate square roots by factoring and using a table (p. 442)
Simplify radical expressions with perfect square factors (p. 445)
Simplify radical expressions where radicands are powers (p. 445)
Simplify radical expressions with perfect square numerators and denominators (p. 448)
Simplify to make the denominator a perfect square (p. 448)
Use a table to approximate square roots of fractions (p. 449)
Divide radical expressions (p. 452)
Rationalize denominators (p. 452)
Add or subtract with radical notation using the distributive law (p. 455)
Find the length of one side of a right triangle given the lengths of two sides (p. 459)
Solve problems involving right triangles (p. 461)
Solve equations with radicals (p. 465)
Solve problems involving radical equations (p. 466)

Chapter 13 Objectives

Write a quadratic equation in the standard form $ax^2 + bx + c = 0$ (p. 475)
Solve quadratic equations of the type $ax^2 = k$, $a \neq 0$ (p. 475)
Solve quadratic equations of the type $ax^2 + bx = 0$, $a \neq 0$, $b \neq 0$ (p. 476)
Solve quadratic equations of the type $ax^2 + bx + c = 0$, $a \neq 0$, $b \neq 0$, $c \neq 0$, by factoring (p. 478)
Solve equations of the type $(x + a)^2 = k$ (p. 478)
Solve applied problems involving quadratic equations (p. 479)
Write a quadratic expression as the square of a binomial (p. 482)
Solve quadratic equations by completing the square (p. 482)
Solve quadratic equations using the quadratic formula (p. 483)
Find approximate solutions of quadratic equations using a square root table (p. 485)
Solve certain fractional equations by first deriving a quadratic equation (p. 489)
Solve certain radical equations by first using the principle of squaring (p. 490)
Solve a formula for a given letter (p. 491)
Use quadratic equations in problem solving (p. 493)
Graph a quadratic function (p. 497)
Approximate the solutions of $ax^2 + bx + c = 0$ by graphing (p. 498)

Chapter 14 Objectives

Recognize similar triangles and write proportions based on the corresponding sides (p. 507)
Find a missing side of similar right triangles using proportions (p. 508)
Find the six trigonometric ratios for a right triangle (p. 509)
Find the sine of an acute angle of a right triangle to four decimal places (p. 512)
Find the cosine of an acute angle of a right triangle to four decimal places (p. 513)
Find the tangent of an acute angle of a right triangle to four decimal places (p. 513)
Find values of trigonometric functions using a table (p. 517)
Find an angle to the nearest degree using a table of trigonometric functions (p. 517)
Solve problems using trigonometric functions (p. 519)

There are alternate Chapter Tests in the **Teacher's Resource Book.** This material includes two tests for each chapter, a Mid-Year Test, and an End-of-Year Test.

This section contains 35 quizzes. Each chapter, except Chapter 14, has at least two quizzes, with emphasis on selections in the first half of each chapter.

Quizzes given in the first half of a chapter are an advantage to both students and teachers for two reasons: they highlight early difficulties within a limited range of concepts and they allow the student to demonstrate an understanding of skills and concepts.

QUIZ 1   Sections 1–1 to 1–3

Chapter 1 Quizzes

1. Evaluate $\frac{x + y}{3}$ for $x = 4$ and $y = 8$.
2. Evaluate $m^3 + 2$ for $m = 3$.
3. Suppose that x stands for some number and it is 10 more than another number. Write an expression for the smaller number.
4. Write an algebraic expression for the product of 8 and y.
5. Write an equivalent expression for $10 + ab$ using a commutative law.
6. Write an equivalent expression for $\frac{x}{5y}$ using $\frac{6}{6}$ for 1.
7. Write in exponential notation $(2d)(2d)(2d)(2d)$.
8. Simplify $\frac{2x}{8xyz}$.

ANSWERS: **1.** 4   **2.** 29   **3.** $x - 10$ **4.** $8y$

5. $ab + 10$, or $ba + 10$, or $10 + ba$ **6.** $\frac{6x}{30y}$

7. $(2d)^4$ or $16d^4$ **8.** $\frac{1}{4yz}$

QUIZ 2   Sections 1–4 to 1–5

1. Calculate $(7 + 2 \times 3) \times 3$.
2. Calculate $2 \times 3 - 8 \div 2$.
3. Calculate $25 - 2^4$.
4. Calculate $(101 - 98)^3$.
5. Use the associative law to rewrite $a + (b + 2x)$.
6. Evaluate $x(x + 2)$ for $x = 6$.
7. Multiply $4(6a + 2b + 1)$.
8. Factor $8a + 72$.
9. Collect like terms: $7a + 4a + a$.
10. Collect like terms: $8x^2 + 5x + 2x^2$.

ANSWERS: 1. 39   2. 2   3. 9   4. 27
5. $(a + b) + 2x$ 6. 48   7. $24a + 8b + 4$
8. $8(a + 9)$ 9. $12a$ 10. $10x^2 + 5x$

Chapter 2
Quizzes

QUIZ 3   Sections 2–1 to 2–2

Use either $<$ or $>$ to write a true sentence.

1. -4 ___ -1 2. $\frac{3}{7}$ ___ $-\frac{4}{7}$ 3. 2.01 ___ 2.2

Find the absolute value.

4. $|-4|$ 5. $|0|$ 6. $\left|-\frac{22}{7}\right|$

Show that each number is rational.

7. 0   8. -6.3 9. $-\frac{2}{3}$

10. Draw a number line showing these labels:
    $-2, -1, 0, 1, 2$.

On the number line, graph $-1\frac{1}{2}, \frac{7}{4}$, and $-\frac{9}{4}$.

ANSWERS: 1. $<$ 2. $>$ 3. $<$ 4. 4   5. 0
6. $\frac{22}{7}$ 7. $\frac{0}{1}$ (The denominator can be any nonzero
integer.)   8. $\frac{-63}{10}$ or $\frac{63}{-10}$ 9. $\frac{-2}{3}$ or $\frac{2}{-3}$

10. $-\frac{9}{4}$ $-1\frac{1}{2}$ $\frac{7}{4}$

number line with points at -2, -1, 0, 1, 2

QUIZ 4 Sections 2–3 to 2–4

Complete with "left" or "right."

1. To add $(-4) + (-6)$ on a number line, begin at -4 and move 6 units to the ___ .
2. The sum of $(-8) + (6)$ is to the ___ of 0.
3. The sum of $(6) + (-8)$ is to the ___ of 0.
4. The difference $(3) - (-8)$ is to the ___ of 0.
5. The difference $-2 - 10$ is to the ___ of 0.

Add.

6. $-7 + (-8)$ 7. $14 + (-19)$ 8. $0 + \left(-\frac{3}{4}\right)$
9. $-4.2 + 8.6$

Subtract.

10. $23 - 33$ 11. $-1 - 10$ 12. $-6 - (-12)$
13. $\frac{3}{4} - \left(-\frac{1}{4}\right)$

Simplify.

14. $12 + 3x - (-10) - 4x$ 15. $-6a - (-5a) - a$

ANSWERS: 1. Left   2. Left   3. Left   4. Right
5. Left   6. -15 7. -5 8. $-\frac{3}{4}$ 9. 4.4
10. -10 11. -11 12. 6   13. 1
14. $-x + 22$ 15. $-2a$

QUIZ 5 Sections 2–5 to 2–6

Multiply or divide.

1. $-\frac{2}{3} \cdot \frac{2}{3}$ 2. $(7)(-5.1)$ 3. $(-10)(-6)$
4. $(-6)(3)(-10)$ 5. $\left(\frac{1}{3}\right)(0)(1.4)$ 6. $36 \div \left(-\frac{1}{2}\right)$
7. $-100 \div (-20)$ 8. $0 \div 15$

Complete.

9. The reciprocal of $-\frac{1}{2}$ is ___ .
10. $\frac{x-1}{6} = (x-1) \cdot$ ___ .

ANSWERS: 1. $-\frac{4}{9}$ 2. -35.7 3. 60   4. 180
5. 0   6. -72 7. 5   8. 0   9. -2 10. $\frac{1}{6}$

QUIZ 6   Sections 2–7 to 2–8

1. Multiply $-5(a + 4b - c)$.
2. Factor $9x - 36$.
3. Collect like terms: $2a - 5c + 8a + 10c$.
4. Collect like terms: $3a + 7x + a - x$.
5. Simplify $-(x + y - z)$.
6. Simplify $12a - 4(3a - 1)$.
7. Simplify $[4(x - 6) - 1] - 3x$.
8. Simplify $[6(3 + 8) - 11] - [12 + 7(4 - 10)]$.

ANSWERS: **1.** $-5a - 20b + 5c$ **2.** $9(x - 4)$
3. $10a + 5c$ **4.** $4a + 6x$ **5.** $-x - y + z$
6. 4 **7.** $x - 25$ **8.** 85

Chapter 3
Quizzes

QUIZ 7   Sections 3–1 to 3–3

Solve and check.

1. $y - \frac{3}{4} = \frac{5}{8}$ 2. $4.8w = -1.2$

3. $5x - 7 = 3x + 9$

Translate to an equation and solve. Show the equation.

4. Five more than a number is -3.
5. A store has a sale on soft drinks at $\frac{2}{3}$ of the regular price. If a 1-liter bottle regularly sells for $1.29, what is the sale price?
6. If you multiply a number by 3 and then subtract 7, the result is twice the original number. What is the original number?

ANSWERS: **1.** $\frac{11}{8}$ **2.** -0.25 **3.** 8

4. $5 + n = -3; n = -8$ **5.** $x = 0.86$

6. $3n - 7 = 2n; n = 7$

QUIZ 8   Sections 3–4 to 3–6

Solve and check.

1. $5 - 2(m - 3) = 4(m + 7) - 5$

2. $\frac{3}{8}x - \frac{1}{4}x = 5 + \frac{3}{4}x$

3. Pickles sell for $0.79 a jar. Kathy had a pickle coupon for $0.25 off. If Kathy paid $4.49, how many jars did she buy?
4. The end-of-the-year car sale was for $\frac{1}{3}$ off the sticker price. Alice and Stanley paid $5638 for a car. What was the sticker price?
5. Solve $V = lwh$ for h.
6. Solve $Ax + By = C$ for y.

ANSWERS: **1.** -2 **2.** -8 **3.** 6   **4.** $8457
5. $h = \frac{V}{lw}$ **6.** $y = \frac{-Ax + C}{B}$

QUIZ 9   Sections 4–1 to 4–3

Simplify.

1. $(2x)^2 \cdot (2x)^5$ 2. $(-2x^2)^3$ 3. $\frac{7^3}{7^7}$
4. Collect like terms and arrange in descending order:
   $3w^2 - 2w + 7w - 5w^2 + 3$.
5. Evaluate for $x = -2$: $x^3 - x^2 - \frac{1}{2}x - 3$.
6. Identify the coefficients of each term:
   $3p^4 - 2p^2 + p$.

ANSWERS: **1.** $(2x)^7$ **2.** $-8x^6$ **3.** $\frac{1}{7^4}$
4. $-2w^2 + 5w + 3$ **5.** -14 **6.** 3, -2, 1

QUIZ 10   Sections 4–4 to 4–5

1. Add $w^4 - 2w^2 + 1$ and $-2w^3 + 5w^2 + 7w - 4$.
2. Add.
$$
\begin{array}{l}
\ \ 4x^4 \phantom{{}+x^3} + 2x^2 - \ x + 3 \\
-5x^5 + x^3 - \ x^2 + 4x \\
 5x^3 \phantom{{}-x^2} - 7x - 5 \\
\underline{3x^5 - 2x^4 \phantom{{}+x^3} + \ x^2 + 2x - 4} \\
\end{array}
$$
3. Find the additive inverse.
   $-2y^6 + 6y^2 - 2y + 1$
4. Subtract.
   $(7k^4 - 3k^2 + k - 3) - (3k^4 - 2k^3 + 1)$

5. Subtract.

$$
\begin{array}{l}
x^4 \quad\;\;\; + x^2 + \;\; x + 1 \\
\underline{\; - 2x^3 \quad\quad\;\; - 3x + 5}
\end{array}
$$

ANSWERS: **1.** $w^4 - 2w^3 + 3w^2 + 7w - 3$
2. $-2x^5 + 2x^4 + 6x^3 + 2x^2 - 2x - 6$
3. $2y^6 - 6y^2 + 2y - 1$ **4.** $4k^4 + 2k^3 - 3k^2 + k - 4$
5. $x^4 + 2x^3 + x^2 + 4x - 4$

QUIZ 11   Sections 4–6 to 4–8

Multiply.

1. $\frac{1}{2}x^4$ and $-5x$ **2.** $(2x + 4)\left(x + \frac{1}{2}\right)$
3. $(x^3 + 3x - 2)(x^2 - 2x + 1)$
4. $\left(2x - \frac{3}{4}\right)\left(2x + \frac{3}{4}\right)$ **5.** $(1 - 3x^2)(2 + x)$
6. $(3x - 5)(2x + 1)$

ANSWERS: **1.** $-\frac{5}{2}x^5$ **2.** $2x^2 + 5x + 2$
3. $x^5 - 2x^4 + 4x^3 - 8x^2 + 7x - 2$ **4.** $4x^2 - \frac{9}{16}$
5. $2 + x - 6x^2 - 3x^3$ **6.** $6x^2 - 7x - 5$

Chapter 5
Quizzes

QUIZ 12   Sections 5–1 to 5–2

Factor.

1. $3x^6 + 6x^4$ **2.** $a^6 - a$
3. $\frac{1}{3}a^3 - \frac{2}{3}a + \frac{1}{3}a^2$ **4.** $y^2 - 81$
5. $1 - 16x^2$ **6.** $5x^2 - 45$

ANSWERS: **1.** $3x^4(x^2 + 2)$ **2.** $a(a^5 - 1)$
3. $\frac{1}{3}a(a^2 - 2 + a)$ **4.** $(y + 9)(y - 9)$
5. $(1 - 4x)(1 + 4x)$ **6.** $5(x + 3)(x - 3)$

QUIZ 13   Sections 5–3 to 5–4

Factor.

1. $x^2 + 10x + 25$ **2.** $x^2 - 6x + 9$ **3.** $x^3 + 2x^2 + x$
4. $9x^2 - 30x + 25$ **5.** $x^2 - 7x + 6$ **6.** $x^2 - x - 72$

ANSWERS: **1.** $(x + 5)^2$ **2.** $(x - 3)^2$
3. $x(x + 1)^2$ **4.** $(3x - 5)^2$ **5.** $(x - 1)(x - 6)$
6. $(x + 8)(x - 9)$

QUIZ 14   Sections 5–5 to 5–7

Factor.

1. $49 - 28x + 4x^2$ **2.** $3a^2 + 4a - 7$
3. $6x^2 - 13x - 15$ **4.** $18a^2 - 13a + 2$
5. $7x^3 - 7x^2 + 4x - 4$ **6.** $27x^2 - 48$

ANSWERS: **1.** $(7 - 2x)(7 - 2x)$ **2.** $(3a + 7)(a - 1)$
3. $(6x + 5)(x - 3)$ **4.** $(9a - 2)(2a - 1)$
5. $(7x^2 + 4)(x - 1)$ **6.** $3(3x - 4)(3x + 4)$

QUIZ 15   Sections 6–1 to 6–2

1. Evaluate $3xy + 4xy^2 - 5x^2y$ for $x = 1$ and $y = -2$
2. Arrange in ascending powers of x:

$x^2y - x^3y^2 + xy + x^4y^5$.

3. Collect like terms:

$(6n^2 + 8mn) - (2n^2 + 9m^2) - mn + 8m^2$.

4. Multiply $2x^2 + 3xy - 4y^2$ by $5x^2 - xy$.
5. Multiply $(p^2 - n^2x)^2$.
6. Multiply $(a^2 + x - 1)(a^2 - x + 1)$.

ANSWERS: **1.** 20   **2.** $xy + x^2y - x^3y^2 + x^4y^5$
3. $4n^2 + 7mn - m^2$ **4.** $10x^4 + 13x^3y - 23x^2y^2 + 4xy^3$
5. $p^4 - 2p^2n^2x + n^4x^2$ **6.** $a^4 - x^2 + 2x - 1$

QUIZ 16   Sections 6–3 to 6–4

Factor.

1. $49m^2 - 36n^2$ **2.** $11x^8 - 11$
3. $6x^2 + 17xy + 12y^2$ **4.** $3x^2 + 6ax - 4a^2x - 8a^3$
5. $xy^4 + xy^3 - xy^2$ **6.** $18x^4 + 21x^2y - 22y^2$

Solve for a.

7. $x(x - a) = y(y - a)$
8. $(3a + 5y)(2a - 8y) = 2(3a^2 + 14y - 20y^2)$

Chapter 6
Quizzes

ANSWERS: 1. $(7m + 6n)(7m - 6n)$
2. $11(x^4 + 1)(x^2 + 1)(x + 1)(x - 1)$
3. $(3x + 4y)(2x + 3y)$
4. $(3x - 4a^2)(x + 2a)$
5. $xy^2(y^2 + y - 1)$
6. $(6x^2 + 11y)(3x^2 - 2y)$
7. $y + x$ 8. -2

Chapter 7 Quizzes

QUIZ 17   Sections 7–1 to 7–2

Complete.
1. $(-3, 2)$ is a point in quadrant ____ .
2. $(0, 6)$ is a point on the ____–axis.
3. The ____–coordinate of a point in quadrant IV is negative.
4. The point (____ , ____) is 4 units left of the origin and 3 units down.
5. Three solutions of $y - 2x + 5 = 0$ are $(0, \underline{})$, $(\underline{}, 8)$, and $(\underline{}, 0)$.
6. The graph of $y = -4x - 2$ does not pass through quadrant ____ .

ANSWERS: 1. II   2. y 3. y 4. $(-4, -3)$
5. $-5, \frac{13}{2}, \frac{5}{2}$ 6. I

QUIZ 18   Sections 7–3 to 7–4

Complete.
1. The standard form of $3x = y - 6$ is ____ .
2. To find the x-intercept in $2x = 3y + 1$, let ____ = 0.
3. The graph of $y = -7$ is a line parallel to the ____–axis.
4. The graph of $x = 0$ coincides with the ____–axis.
5. The slope of the line through $(-1, 5)$ and $(2, 10)$ is ____ .
6. The slope of the line $y = 2$ is ____ .

ANSWERS: 1. $3x - y + 6 = 0$ 2. y 3. x 4. y
5. $\frac{5}{3}$ 6. 0

1. Write $7x + 2y - 3 = 0$ in slope-intercept form.
2. The graph of $y = -7x + \frac{1}{3}$ crosses the y-axis at the point (____, ____).
   Write the equation for the lines in problems 3 and 4 in slope-intercept form.
3. Slope 2, through the point $(0, 6)$
4. Through the points $(8, 5)$ and $(1, -2)$
5. In the point-slope equation $y - y_1 = m(x - x_1)$, the given point has coordinates (____, ____).

ANSWERS: **1.** $y = -\frac{7}{2}x + \frac{3}{2}$ **2.** $\left(0, \frac{1}{3}\right)$

3. $y = 2x + 6$ **4.** $y = x - 3$ **5.** (x_1, y_1)

Chapter 8 Quizzes

Is each correspondence a function?

1. $1 \rightarrow 6$
   $\rightarrow -6$
   $2 \rightarrow 5$

2. $1 \rightarrow A$
   2
   3

3. $x \rightarrow 1$
   $y \rightarrow 2$
   $z \rightarrow 3$

For the function $f(x) = 10x - 1$ in problems 4 and 5:
4. Find $f(10)$.   5. Find $f(0)$.
6. The graph of $h(x) = |x|$ contains the point $(-2, $____$)$.

ANSWERS: **1.** No   **2.** Yes   **3.** Yes   **4. 99**
5. -1 **6.** 2

Translate into linear equations with two variables.

1. The yearly cost of maintaining a car is $480, increased by 18¢ for each mile driven.
2. To have a pizza delivered, there is a $1 charge plus $4.50 for each pizza.

Write equations of variation.

3. The weight of a beam varies directly as its length.
4. The brightness of a light varies inversely with the number of bulbs and directly as the size of the batteries.

5. Solve: The time, t, to drive from A to B varies inversely as the speed r. It takes 5 hours at 50 mi/h. How long could it take at 60 mi/h?

ANSWERS:　**1.** $C = 480 + 0.18$ m　**2.** $C = 1 + 4.5$ p
3. $w = kl$　**4.** $b = \dfrac{ks}{n}$　**5.** $\dfrac{25}{6}$ hrs or 4 hours 10 minutes

Chapter 9
Quizzes

QUIZ 22　Sections 9–1 to 9–3

1. Solve this system of equations graphically.
$$x - 3y = 3 \qquad x + y = -5$$

2. Check your answer in problem 1 by solving the system using the substitution method.

3. Solve this system of equations by the addition method.
$$3x + 4y + 2 = 0 \qquad 4x - 3y = -11$$

4. Translate to a system of equations and solve.
The sum of two numbers is 22. One number is 4 less than the other. Find the numbers.

ANSWERS:　**1.** $(-3, -2)$　**2.** $(-3, -2)$
3. $(-2, 1)$　**4.** 9 and 13

QUIZ 23　Sections 9–4 to 9–6

1. Mark's dog is 6 years older than his cat. In 4 years the dog will be twice as old at the cat. How old is each animal now?
2. Two bicyclists leave town at the same time, going in opposite directions. One pedals at a rate of 4 km per hour faster than the other. In $3\frac{1}{2}$ hours they will be 98 km apart. How fast does each one pedal?
3. Tickets to the auto show were $2.00 for children and $4.50 for adults. Three hundred people attended and $900 was collected. How many of each type of ticket were sold?

ANSWERS:　**1.** Dog, 8 yr; cat 2 yr　**2.** 16 km/h and 12 km/h　**3.** 180 children, 120 adults

QUIZ 24   Sections 10–1 to 10–3

Determine whether the given number is a solution of the inequality.

1. $x > -2$
   a. 0   **b.** -3 **c.** 5   **d.** -2
2. $y \leq 5$
   a. 0   **b.** -2 **c.** 5   **d.** 10
3. $w \geq 4$
   a. 0   **b.** 4   **c.** -2 **d.** 10
4. $z < -4$
   a. 0   **b.** -10 **c.** -4 **d.** 2

Solve these inequalities.

5. $5x - 7 \geq 4x - 5$ 6. $-5x < 25$
7. $3x + 7 \leq 7x - 5$

ANSWERS: **1. a.** Yes   **b.** No   **c.** Yes   **d.** No
2. a. Yes   **b.** Yes   **c.** Yes   **d.** No
3. a. No   **b.** Yes   **c.** No   **d.** Yes
4. a. No   **b.** Yes   **c.** No   **d.** No
5. $x \geq 2$ **6.** $x > -5$ **7.** $x \geq 3$

QUIZ 25   Sections 10–4 to 10–6

Solve by translating to an inequality.

1. The sum of 3 consecutive odd integers is less than 59. What is the greatest possible set of 3 numbers?

Tell whether the graph of each inequality has points on both sides of zero, is totally to the left of zero, or is totally to the right.

2. $x > -2$
3. $-3x - 2 \leq 8$
4. $|x| < 5$

Tell whether the graph of each half-plane includes the origin.

5. $3x - 5y \geq 15$
6. $x + y \geq -2$

ANSWERS: **1.** 17, 19, 21   **2.** Both sides
3. Right side   **4.** Both sides   **5.** No   **6.** Yes

Chapter 11
Quizzes

1. Simplify $\dfrac{8x^2 - 2x}{20xy - 5y}$.

2. Multiply $\dfrac{2x - 3}{4x} \cdot \dfrac{4x^2}{4x^2 - 9}$.

3. What is the reciprocal of $\dfrac{2x + 3}{x - 1}$?

4. Divide: $\dfrac{x^2 - 2x + 1}{x + 1} \div \dfrac{x^2 - 1}{x + 1}$.

ANSWERS: **1.** $\dfrac{2x}{5y}$ **2.** $\dfrac{x}{2x + 3}$ **3.** $\dfrac{x - 1}{2x + 3}$

4. $\dfrac{x - 1}{x + 1}$

QUIZ 27   Section 11–3

Divide.

1. $(8x^4 + 6x^3 + 12x^2 - 10x) \div (-2x)$
2. $(2x^3 + 3x^2 - 7x + 6) \div (x + 3)$
3. $(x^5 + 4x^3 - 3x^2 - 2) \div (x^2 + x + 2)$
4. $(x^3 - y^3) \div (x - y)$

ANSWERS: **1.** $-4x^3 - 3x^2 - 6x + 5$

2. $2x^2 - 3x + 2$ **3.** $x^3 - x^2 + 3x - 4 + \dfrac{-2x + 6}{x^2 + x + 2}$

4. $x^2 + xy + y^2$

QUIZ 28   Sections 11–4 to 11–5

1. Subtract $\dfrac{3a + 8}{x^2 - 5} - \dfrac{5a - 6}{x^2 - 5}$.

2. Add $\dfrac{2}{x - 1} + \dfrac{2x}{1 - x}$.

3. Find the LCM of $x^2 - 9,\ 6,\ -5x$.

4. Add $\dfrac{3a + 1}{a - 7} - \dfrac{2a + 1}{3a - 21}$.

5. Find the LCD: $\dfrac{x^2}{x^2 - 25} + \dfrac{x}{2x + 10} - \dfrac{6}{3x - 15}$.

ANSWERS: **1.** $\dfrac{-2a + 14}{x^2 - 5}$ **2.** -2

3. $-30x(x^2 - 9)$ **4.** $\dfrac{7a + 2}{3a - 21}$ **5.** $(2)(3)(x^2 - 25)$

QUIZ 29   Section 11–6 to 11–7

1. Simplify $\dfrac{2}{a + 1} - \dfrac{3a + 2}{a^2 + 2a + 1} + \dfrac{7a}{6(a + 1)^2}$.

2. Solve $\dfrac{1}{a} = \dfrac{1}{8-a}$.

3. Solve $\dfrac{x-1}{2} - \dfrac{x+1}{3} = 1$.

ANSWERS: 1. $\dfrac{a}{6(a+1)^2}$ 2. $a = 4$ 3. $x = 11$

QUIZ 30   Sections 12–1 to 12–2

Write true or false.
1. $\sqrt{121} = 11$ and -11 2. $\sqrt{35}$ is irrational.
3. -13 is a square root of 169.
4. The real numbers include the rational numbers.
5. $26.045131\overline{13}$ is a rational number.
6. $7.06006000600006\ldots$ is an irrational number.
7. $\sqrt{-25}$ represents a real number.
8. $\sqrt{(-12)^2} = 12$

ANSWERS: 1. False   2. True   3. True
4. True   5. True   6. True   7. False   8. True

QUIZ 31   Sections 12–3 to 12–4

1. Multiply $\sqrt{100} \cdot \sqrt{9}$.
2. Multiply $\sqrt{11} \cdot \sqrt{3}$.
3. Factor and simplify $\sqrt{72}$.
4. Factor and simplify $\sqrt{121a^2}$.
5. Use $\sqrt{7} \approx 2.65$ to find $\sqrt{252}$.
6. Simplify $\sqrt{5t^2 + 30t + 45}$.
7. Simplify $\sqrt{x^{19}}$.
8. Simplify $\sqrt{98x} \cdot \sqrt{2}$.

ANSWERS: 1. 30   2. $\sqrt{33}$ 3. $6\sqrt{2}$
4. $11 \cdot |a|$ 5. ≈ 15.9 6. $|t+3| \cdot \sqrt{5}$
7. $|x^9|\sqrt{x}$ 8. $14\sqrt{x}$

QUIZ 32   Sections 12–5 to 12–7

1. Simplify $\sqrt{\dfrac{75}{27}}$.

2. Rationalize the denominator: $\sqrt{\dfrac{2}{3}}$.

3. Simplify $\dfrac{\sqrt{7}}{\sqrt{5}}$.   4. Simplify $\dfrac{\sqrt{11}}{\sqrt{5a}}$.

Add or subtract.

5. $2\sqrt{8} - \sqrt{24} + \sqrt{18}$ **6.** $\sqrt{5} - \sqrt{\frac{1}{5}}$

ANSWERS: **1.** $\frac{5}{3}$ **2.** $\frac{1}{3}\sqrt{6}$ **3.** $\frac{1}{5} \cdot \sqrt{35}$

4. $\frac{1}{5a}\sqrt{55a}$ **5.** $7\sqrt{2} - 2\sqrt{6}$ **6.** $\frac{4}{5}\sqrt{5}$

Chapter 13 Quizzes

QUIZ 33   Sections 13–1 to 13–3

Solve.

1. $4x^2 = 49$ **2.** $6x^2 - 9x = 0$
3. $x^2 - x - 12 = 0$ **4.** $6x^2 - 7x - 5 = 0$

Solve by completing the square.

5. $x^2 - 10x - 2 = 0$

ANSWERS: **1.** $\frac{7}{2}, \frac{-7}{2}$ **2.** $0, \frac{3}{2}$ **3.** $4, -3$

4. $\frac{5}{3}, \frac{-1}{2}$ **5.** $5 + 3\sqrt{3}, 5 - 3\sqrt{3}$

QUIZ 34   Sections 13–4 to 13–6

1. Solve by using the quadratic formula.
   $6x^2 + 5x - 6 = 0$

2. Solve $\dfrac{9}{x + 1} - \dfrac{1}{x - 1} = 2.$

3. Solve $\sqrt{x + 11} = x - 1.$

ANSWERS: **1.** $\frac{2}{3}, \frac{-3}{2}$ **2.** 2   **3.** 5 (-2 is not a root.)

Chapter 14 Quizzes

QUIZ 35   Sections 14–1 to 14–3

Complete.

1. In a pair of similar triangles, the lengths of the corresponding sides are ____ .

2. You can solve the proportion $\frac{a}{c} = \frac{b}{d}$ by multiplying on both sides by ____ .

For an acute angle A in right triangle ABC:

3.   Sine $A = \dfrac{\text{length of} \underline{\quad}}{\text{length of} \underline{\quad}}$

4.   Cosine $A = \dfrac{\text{length of} \underline{\quad}}{\text{length of} \underline{\quad}}$

5. Tangent $A = \dfrac{\text{length of} \underline{\quad}}{\text{length of} \underline{\quad}}$

ANSWERS: **1.** proportional   **2.** *cd*
3. opposite side, hypotenuse   **4.** adjacent side,
hypotenuse   **5.** opposite side, adjacent side

TEACHING SUGGESTIONS

Chapter 1

INTRODUCTION   Chapter 1 is designed to plunge students into algebra. Immediately, they evaluate and simplify expressions, use exponents and grouping symbols, solve simple equations, and solve problems.

These basic skills are different from the students' arithmetic course. Yet, they are attractive and simple enough so that students can be impressed with their own progress.

VOCABULARY
variable (p. 1)   exponent (p. 12)
algebraic expression (p. 1)   term (p. 21)
evaluate an expression (p. 1)   factor (p. 21)
equivalent expression (p. 7)   equation (p. 25)
base (p. 12)

SECTION 1–1

BACKGROUND MATERIAL   In arithmetic, operation symbols usually require students to do something.

3 + 4 means "add 4 to 3 and get 7"

In algebra, $3 + 4$, or $x + 3$, or $a + b$ are themselves numbers. We say that $x + 3$ is the number of dollars, or that $a + b$ is the perimeter. If and when students find values for a and b they can do the computation. In algebra, that computation is less a goal than knowing the structure to compute with.

FOCUS ON STUDENT QUESTIONS
    Question: In the expression $3 + m - 2 + m$, can the first m equal 6 and the second m be something else, like 4?
    Answer: No. The variable in any one expression has the same value every time it occurs.

    Question: In $a + b + 7$, can a equal 4 and b also be 4?
    Answer: Yes. In saying that $a = 4$, we put no restrictions on the value of b.

TEACHING SUGGESTION   Teachers may find a quick review of set notation helpful. Use Sets and Symbols on page 5.

ORAL EXERCISES   Teachers use Try This Exercises in three different ways: as Oral Exercises after all Examples of a section are explained; as Oral Exercises following each group of Examples of a section; and as a Self-Check for additional review.

   Most Try This answers are found in the back of the student book. Additional answers for graphs and proofs are found in the front of the Teacher's Edition with the Additional Answers section.

TEACHING SUGGESTION   Preparation for commutative property. Suppose a person has 14 baskets, each with 27 ears of corn. Another person has 27 baskets, each with 14 ears of corn. Even though you have not computed the total number of ears, do you believe they have the same number of ears? If so, you believe the commutative property for multiplication.

CAPSULE REVIEW   Teachers may want to review the reasons why division by zero is prohibited.

Multiplication statement	Division statements	
$3 \times 7 = 21$	$21 \div 7 = 3$	$21 \div 3 = 7$
$8 \times 0 = 0$	$0 \div 0 = 8$	$0 \div 8 = 0$
$5 \times 0 = 0$	$0 \div 0 = 5$	$0 \div 5 = 0$
$9 \times 0 = 0$	$0 \div 0 = 9$	$0 \div 9 = 0$

Note that we have three different answers so far for $0 \div 0$. We say $0 \div 0$ is *indeterminate* and exclude it from arithmetic because it does not have a unique answer.

   But, what about $7 \div 0$ or $8 \div 0$ or $10 \div 0$? Such expressions come from multiplications like

   $0 \times ? = 7 \quad 0 \times ? = 8 \quad 0 \times ? = 10$

There are no such products, so dividing a nonzero number by 0 has *no meaning* in mathematics.

   Page 69 of Chapter 2 will give more detail on division by zero.

BACKGROUND MATERIAL   The operations of $+$, $-$, $\times$, $\div$ are all defined for two numbers. These four operations are called binary operations. How can we work with more than two numbers? The associative laws give the answer.

$$3 + 7 + 4 = (3 + 7) + 4$$

The binary operation $+$ tells us $3 + 7$ is 10. The binary operation $+$ tells us $10 + 4$ is 14. Also,

$$3 + 7 + 4 = 3 + (7 + 4) = 3 + 11 = 14$$

The real message of the associative law is a rule on how to deal with three numbers.

FOCUS ON STUDENT QUESTIONS
  Question: What about $8 - 6 - 1$?
  Answer: We take operations in order:

$$(8 - 6) - 1 = 2 - 1 = 1.$$

Notice this is not the same as

$$8 - (6 - 1) = 8 - 5 = 3.$$

There is no associative law for subtraction, nor for division.

  Question: Is $(8 + 2)^2 = 8^2 + 2^2$?
  Answer: $(8 + 2)^2 = 10^2 = 10 \cdot 10 = 100.$

It is easy to see this is not the same as $8^2 + 2^2 = 64 + 4 = 68$. Students learn ways to simplify $(8 + 2)^2$ in Chapter 5 without working inside parentheses first.

TEACHING SUGGESTIONS   Show students how powers may be large even with small numbers. For example,

$$9^1 = 9, \; 9^2 = 81, \; 9^3 = 729, \ldots, \; 9^9 = 387{,}420{,}489$$

Mention that 100^{100} is 200 digits long.

CAPSULE REVIEW   Teachers may want to review factorization. A quick numerical exercise is simply to factor integers.

	Possible student responses
20	4×5, 10×2, 20×1, $2 \times 2 \times 5$
17	17×1, 1×17

Some numbers like 20 can be factored several ways, and sometimes with more than two factors. Other numbers, prime numbers such as 17, can only be factored by using

1 as a factor. A prime factorization of 20 is $2 \times 2 \times 5$ since all factors are prime numbers.

If more work is needed on prime factorization, see Prime Factors on page 130. Teachers may want to delay this review until Chapter 5 on factoring.

TEACHING SUGGESTION   Just as factor is used to name a number in multiplication, *term* is used to name a number in addition. To build this vocabulary, ask students to give the number of terms in Examples 9 through 12.

SECTION 1–7

BACKGROUND MATERIAL   Solving word problems is valuable in Chapter 1 for several reasons.
- It emphasizes the importance of such problems.
- It emphasizes that algebra is not merely letters and rules. Algebra is based on the need to develop problem-solving techniques.
- These problems are simple translations from English sentences into equations.
- Most of the resulting equations are simpler than those solved in Section 1–6, so students build confidence.

TEACHING SUGGESTIONS   As students begin writing equations, it is recommended that they always identify the variable. It is important that this variable stand for a *number*. In Try This 4, for example, x does *not* stand for Ty Cobb. Instead x stands for the *number* of home runs hit by Ty Cobb. Later, students will have problems in which the number of tickets and the value of tickets must be found. Letting x = tickets leads to confusion.

One of the values of learning algebra is to develop logical abilities. Making distinctions of this kind is one of those logical abilities.

SELF-CHECK   Try This Exercises may be used as written review. The Try This Exercises correspond to the objectives listed for each section. Most Try This answers are found in the back of the student book. Additional answers to graphs and proofs are found in the front of the Teacher's Edition with the Additional Answers section.

In this chapter there are 84 Try This Exercises. Teachers might assign every third Try This Exercise or assign the last Try This Exercise of each subsection.

Chapter
End
Material

CHAPTER 1 REVIEW   Teachers use Chapter Reviews in three different ways: as midchapter homework assignments prior to section quizzes; as chapter-end homework assignments and a basis for student questions prior to the Chapter Test; and as review assignments to maintain skills while teaching later chapters.

The odd-numbered Chapter Review answers are in the back of the student book.

Chapter 2

READY FOR INTEGERS AND RATIONAL NUMBERS?
The first group of "Ready for" Exercises appears on page 37. The Exercises are keyed to earlier sections. If students have difficulty with any exercises, they can review the indicated sections.

VOCABULARY

integer (p. 39)	irrational number (p. 47)
negative number (p. 39)	real number (p. 47)
natural number (p. 39)	additive inverse (p. 53)
whole number (p. 39)	reciprocal (p. 69)
absolute value (p. 41)	distributive laws (p. 73)
ratio (p. 44)	axiom (p. 86)
rational number (p. 44)	theorem (p. 87)

SECTION 2–1

FOCUS ON STUDENT QUESTIONS
  Question: Are the positive integers and zero really exactly the same thing as the whole numbers in arithmetic?
  Answer: No, not at all. It is true that they work in exactly the same way. We don't need to label the positive integers with a plus sign. However, whole numbers simply tell a quantity. Integers always indicate a quantity *and* a direction. Graphing on the number line makes this easier to understand.

COMPUTER SIMULATION   You can simulate a computer program that arranges a set of numbers from smallest to largest. Consider these four numbers.

    13   -12 5 -17

Is number $1 <$ number 2? If yes, go on. If no, exchange.

    -12 13   5 -17

Is number 2 < 3? If yes, go on. If no, exchange.

$\quad$ -12 $\quad$ 5 $\quad$ 13 $\quad$ -17

Is number 3 < number 4? If yes, go on. If no, exchange.

$\quad$ -12 $\quad$ 5 $\quad$ -17 $\quad$ 13

So far, this process guarantees the greater integer is in the fourth position. Start again with number 1 and number 2.

$\quad$ -12 $\quad$ 5 $\quad$ -17 $\quad$ 13 $\quad$ O.K.
$\quad$ -12 $\quad$ -17 $\quad$ 5 $\quad$ 13 $\quad$ exchanged

This process guarantees the next greater integer is in the third position.

$\quad$ -17 $\quad$ -12 $\quad$ 5 $\quad$ 13 $\quad$ exchanged.

This process guarantees the next greater integer is in the second position. The smallest integer must be in the first position.

Question: How many comparisons must be made with 4 numbers to arrange in order?

Answer: $3 + 2 + 1 = 6$

Question: Is there a pattern here?

Answer: Begin with the number 1 less than the number of entries. For 3 entries, begin with 2. Now add decreasing consecutive positive integers. $2 + 1 = 3$ comparisons. This is easy to check.

BACKGROUND MATERIAL $\quad$ Between any two rational numbers there is another—their average. It is easy for students to accept that this first average is a rational number. Have students find the average of the first number and the first average, and so on. This introduces an *infinite set of rational numbers* that is completely contained in an interval, instead of one going off into outer space.

FOCUS ON STUDENT QUESTIONS

Question: Isn't a rational number the same as a fraction?

Answer: Rational numbers are special fractions—those that fulfill the definition on page 40.

Question: Are there any fractions that are not rational numbers?

Answer: π, $\frac{\sqrt{2}}{6}$, $\frac{\sqrt{3}}{4}$, and all the numbers you will learn more about in Chapter 12 called irrational numbers.

SECTION 2–2

TEACHING SUGGESTIONS   In arithmetic, students often round off quotients if the division did not come out evenly. Consequently, some students may not have the background to appreciate the infinite decimals in Example 8 on page 41.

Change to decimal form: $\frac{1}{3}, \frac{1}{6}, \frac{1}{9}$. These are infinite decimals $0.33\overline{3}$, $0.66\overline{6}$, and $0.11\overline{1}$.

Change to decimal form: $\frac{1}{11}, \frac{2}{11}, \frac{3}{11}$. These have a 2-digit repeating pattern: $0.09\overline{09}$, $0.18\overline{18}$, and $0.36\overline{36}$.

Every fraction that doesn't terminate has a repeating pattern of digits in its decimal form.

$\frac{1}{13}$ has 6 digits; $\frac{2}{13}$ has 6 digits; $\frac{1}{17}$ has 16 digits.

CHALLENGE   Ask students if they can find a fraction that has more than 16 digits in the repeating portion of its decimal form. There are many. The denominator will be a prime number, but not all prime denominators have long repeating parts. For example, $\frac{1}{19}$ has an 18-digit repeating pattern.

CALCULATOR SUGGESTIONS   Show $\frac{1}{19}$ as a repeating decimal using a calculator. (See preceding paragraph.)

Enter: ① ÷ ⑲   ⊜
Display: 1   19   0.052631578

There are 8 digits of the pattern, including the first digit, zero. The last digit, 8, may have been rounded.

Let's try adding on to the pattern. Choose the last two digits 7 and 8. Think of this part as 0.78. Find the nearest fraction, with 19 as denominator, that approximates 0.78.

Enter: ⑮ ÷ ⑲   ⊜
Display: 15   19   0.789473684

The new pattern will be *joined* with the first approximation. The closer approximation is now
$\frac{1}{19} \approx 0.0526315789473684$.

Again choose the last two digits. Find the nearest fraction, with 19 as denominator, that approximates 0.84.

Enter: ⑯ ÷ ⑲   ⊜
Display: 16   19   0.842105263

The last 5 digits show the start of a repeating pattern. Join this pattern.

$$\frac{1}{19} = 0.\overline{052631578947368421}$$

ORAL PREPARATION FOR EXERCISES   Have students answer these questions orally in class before assigning exercises as homework.

Exs.   1– 8   Predict: Will the answer be negative, positive, or 0?

Exs.   9–28   Select the problems that will have negative answers.

Exs. 29–34   What numbers will you group together before you add?

Exs. 58–62   Suggest that students make substitutions of their choice for the variables. After several substitutions they should be able to make a "prediction."

TEACHING SUGGESTIONS   The definition of subtraction on page 57 may be unfamiliar, but students should realize that it says what they have always known. However, $m - n$ must be thought of as an expression that names a number—not as a direction to do something.

We say that "$7 - 2$" is the number we add to 2 to get 7. Ask:

What is "$8 - 3$"?   What is "$x - 4$"?
What is "$10 - x$"?   What is "$m - n$"?

FOCUS ON STUDENT QUESTIONS

Question: In $- 3 - 2$ does the second minus sign mean subtraction or does it mean the 2 is negative?

Answer: We must have an operation sign, so the second sign means subtraction: $- 3 - (2)$.

TEACHING SUGGESTIONS   The fact that the product of two negative numbers is positive is often considered mysterious to students. First, go through the presentation in the text showing the patterns of signs. Then ask, if $(- 3)(- 4)$ is not positive, could it be negative? If $(- 3)(- 4) = - 12$, then $- 12 \div (- 3) = - 4$. But we already know that $(- 3)(4) = - 12$, which implies that $- 12 \div (- 3) = 4$. This means the division problem $- 12 \div (- 3)$ has two different answers—an impossibility in mathematics.

Another visualization of the product of two negative numbers follows. A piece of movie film shows a person building a brick wall at the rate of 4 bricks per minute.

Run the film forward (+) for 3 minutes. You see 12 bricks added (+) to the wall.

$3 \times 4 = 12$

Run the film backward (−) for 3 minutes. You see 12 bricks removed (−) from the wall.

$(-3)(4) = -12$

Now suppose another film shows the person *removing* bricks from a brick wall at the rate of 4 bricks per minute. Use − 4 for removing. Run the film forward (+) for 3 minutes. You see 12 bricks removed.

$(3)(-4) = -12$

Run the film backward for 3 minutes. What do you see?

$(-3)(-4) = 12$ 12 bricks added

SECTION 2–6

ORAL PREPARATION FOR EXERCISES   Have students answer these questions orally in class before assigning exercises as homework.

Exs.   1–20 Tell the sign of the answer: negative, positive, or 0.

Exs. 21–26 Tell which numbers have negative reciprocals.

Exs. 49–62 Tell the sign of the answer: positive, negative, or zero.

CALCULATOR SUGGESTIONS   When a problem includes only addition and subtraction, or only multiplication and division, students calculate the answer by entering the numbers and operations as they appear from left to right. Then (on most calculators) press the equal key.

Problem: $35.1 + 16.02 - 0.8 + 3.7$

Enter: 35.1 ⊕ 16.02 ⊖ 0.8 ⊕ 3.7 ⊜

Display: 35.1   16.02 51.12 0.8 50.32 3.7 54.02

Practice Problem: $42 + 378 - 93 - 16 + 49$

Answer: 360

In the next example, first change the fraction $\frac{1}{2}$ to the decimal 0.5.

Problem: $3.5 \times 0.7 \div 5 \times \frac{1}{2}$

Enter: 3.5 ⊗ 0.7 ⊘ 5 ⊗ 0.5 ⊜

Display: 3.5   0.7 2.45 5 0.49 0.5 0.245

Practice Problem: $76 \div 5 \times 2.3 \div \frac{3}{4}$

Answer: 46.613

TEACHING SUGGESTIONS   For Example 3, ask students for the meaning of "rose 16%."
Possible answers: The price is now 16% more than before. Or, if the price were y, it is now $y + 16\%$ of y. Or, if the price were y, it is now 116% of y. Chart and compare.

number	16% of y	16% more than y
y	$0.16(y)$	$y + 0.16(y) =$ $y(1 + 0.16) =$ $y(1.16)$

Teachers may want to review percents at this time using the worksheets in the Teacher's Resource Book.

Chapter 3

INTRODUCTION   This chapter provides a carefully sequenced development of linear equation solving. Students who have had a prealgebra course may feel that they "know" all about solving equations. Usually such students are unsure of the roles of the addition and multiplication principles; consequently these are stressed in this chapter.

VOCABULARY
solution (p. 99)
solve (p. 99)
addition principle (p. 99)
equivalent equations (p. 100)
multiplication principle (p. 103)
consecutive integers (p. 116)
formula (p. 124)
ratio (p. 128)
proportion (p. 128)
prime factor (p. 130)
if–then statement (p. 131)
antecedent (p. 131)
consequent (p. 131)
converse (p. 132)

SECTION 3–1

TEACHING SUGGESTION Students need to understand when enough information is available to solve a problem. Consider this problem.

> Chris had 87 more votes than Bill. How many did Bill have?

We can write $C = B + 87$, but we cannot find Bill's total unless we know Chris's number of votes.

ORAL PREPARATION FOR EXERCISES Have students answer these questions orally in class before assigning exercises as homework.

Exs. 1–30 Tell what number should be added to each side in using the addition principle.

Exs. 31–35 Tell what the variable would represent in each problem.
Sample 33. Let x be the amount she could lift when she started.

SECTION 3–2

BACKGROUND MATERIAL Procedures for solving equations in some later chapters give both valid and invalid solutions. Thus it is important to have students check results here as groundwork for later checking. In general, there are two purposes for checking: to see whether our solving procedure gave a valid result and to see whether we have made a mistake in the solving process. Until a number has been checked, we do not know whether it is a solution.

TEACHING SUGGESTIONS In Example 4 on page 104, the equation could also be written as $-\frac{5}{4}x = \frac{3}{8}$. Section 2–10 stated the symmetric property: if $a = b$, then $b = a$.

ORAL PREPARATION FOR EXERCISES Have students answer these questions orally in class before assigning exercises as homework.

Exs. 1–36 Tell what number will be used as a multiplier.

Exs. 37–46 Tell what quantity the variable should stand for in each problem.

SECTION 3–3

TEACHING SUGGESTIONS Using the multiplication principle first will be explained in Section 3–4, Examples 3 and 4.

In Example 4 on page 108, show students the first step of the check. Does

$$6\left(\tfrac{8}{3}\right) + 5 - 7\left(\tfrac{8}{3}\right) = 10 - 4\left(\tfrac{8}{3}\right) + 3?$$

CALCULATOR SUGGESTIONS   Students can use calculators to solve equations. They need to know how to use the clear keys on their calculators.

Most calculators have one or two clear keys. If there is just one clear key, it is marked C or C/CE. If there are two clear keys, they are marked CE and C, or CE and CLR, or C and AC. The first key clears just the display; the second clears the display, the processor, and the storage.

Example 1.   In this example, a mistake is made in entering 4.5. Then the clear entry key is used to clear the display and correct the mistake.

Problem: 3.1 + 0.8 − 4.5
Enter: 3.1 ⊕ 0.8 ⊖ 45 CE 4.5 ⊜
Display: 3.1   0.8 3.9 45   0   4.5 0.6

Example 2.   If the display of a calculator shows a number, it is a good idea to press the clear (or all clear) key before beginning a calculation. Suppose the calculator shows 318 on the display.

Problem: 3.72 × 8
Enter: 318 Ⓒ 3.72 ⊗ 8   ⊜
Display: 318   0   3.72   8   29.76

If your calculator has just one clear key (marked C or C/CE), press it once to clear just the display. Press it twice to clear the display, the storage, and the processor.

ORAL PREPARATION FOR EXERCISES   Have students answer these questions orally in class before assigning exercises as homework.

Exs. 1–48 Tell the first step to take in solving each equation.
           Sample 1. Add −6 to both sides.
Exs. 49–64 Tell what quantity the variable will represent.
           Sample 49. Let x be the length of the smaller piece.

TEACHING SUGGESTIONS   Example 3 on page 115 contains a common error spot. Students often fail to multiply

SECTION 3–4

whole numbers by the multiplier of each side when they are simplifying. Thus in Example 3, some students may forget to multiply $2x$ by 6 in the third step.

ORAL PREPARATION FOR EXERCISES   Have students answer these questions orally in class before assigning exercises as homework.

Exs.   1–24 Tell the first step in solving each equation.
Exs. 25–42 What will the multiplier be so that no fractions remain?
Exs. 43–60 Represent all the unknown quantities using a single variable as the basis for each expression. *Sample*   47. Let x, $x + 1$, and $x + 2$ be the three numbers (not x, y, and z).

SECTION 3–6

BACKGROUND MATERIAL   The solution of $ax + b = c$ at the bottom of page 124 is completely general and shows the operations to be carried out regardless of the numbers that might be used for a, b, and c. This emphasizes once again that in algebra we are more interested in the method than in the arithmetic.

APPLICATIONS: FORMULAS   The result of Exercise 3, $r = \frac{d}{t}$, can be used to discuss what is meant by "miles per hour," that is, distance per unit of time. Section 3–7 will use such rates in problem solving.

SECTION 3–7

TEACHING SUGGESTIONS   A ratio of two different kinds of measure is a *rate*. In problems a single ratio is often expressed in two ways. For example, it takes 2.5 liters of gasoline to drive 145 kilometers. This gives the ratio

$$\frac{2.5\,\ell}{145\text{ km}}.$$

How much will be required to go 1160 kilometers? This would be the ratio

$$\frac{x\,\ell}{1160\text{ km}}.$$

Assuming the car uses gas at the same rate throughout the trip, the ratios are the same.

$$\begin{array}{c} \text{Gas} \rightarrow \\ \text{Kilometers} \rightarrow \end{array} \frac{2.5}{145} = \frac{x}{1160} \begin{array}{c} \leftarrow \text{Gas} \\ \leftarrow \text{Kilometers} \end{array}$$

To solve, multiply by the LCM, which is 1160.

$$1160 \cdot \frac{2.5}{145} = 1160 \cdot \frac{x}{1160}$$

$$20 = x$$

Thus 20 liters will be required.

CUMULATIVE REVIEW CHAPTERS 1–3   Teachers use Cumulative Reviews in three different ways: as homework assignments and basis for student questions prior to a quarter or semester test; as review assignments to maintain skills while teaching later chapters; and as review material for a quarter make-up test. See **Tips for Teachers** in this Teacher's Edition for hints on scheduling make-up tests.

Other Cumulative Reviews are given for Chapters 1–7, Chapters 1–10, and Chapters 1–14.

Chapter 4

VOCABULARY
polynomial (p. 148)
monomial (p. 148)
terms of a polynomial (p. 148)
binomial (p. 149)
trinomial (p. 149)
like terms (p. 149)
degree (p. 150)
coefficient (p. 150)
leading term (p. 150)
leading coefficient (p. 150
descending order (p. 153)
ascending order (p. 153)
evaluating a polynomial (p. 154)
additive inverses (p. 163)
square of a binomial (p. 180)

SECTION 4–1

TEACHING SUGGESTIONS   The first law of exponents, page 143, is simply a statement of a shortcut—capitalizing on an observation. If students have trouble using this rule, remind them to visualize the multiplication written out, and then to count factors.

On page 144, the statement of the second law of exponents may seem technical, with so many restrictions on a,

m, and n. It is more important that students understand Examples 8–11 following the statement. Note that

$$\frac{a^m}{a^m} = a^0 = 1.$$

LOOKING AHEAD   Teachers may want to introduce the concept of negative exponents. (See also Challenge Exercise 55.)

$$
\begin{array}{lll}
10^2 & = 10 \times 10 = 100.0 \\
10^1 & = 10 & = \ 10.0 \\
10^0 & = 1 & = \ \ \ 1.000 \\
10^{-1} & = \frac{1}{10} & = \ \ \ 0.1000 \\
10^{-2} & = \frac{1}{10 \times 10} & = \ \ \ 0.01000
\end{array}
$$

SECTION 4–2

TEACHING SUGGESTIONS   As the examples show, an expression is a polynomial if it can be written in any of the following ways: as a sum of monomials, with no roots of variables, or with no variables in denominators. If students say an expression is not a polynomial, they should tell which part of the definition has not been satisfied.

FOCUS ON STUDENT QUESTIONS
   Question: Is this expression a polynomial?
   Answer:

$\frac{2}{5}x^2$	Yes. It's O.K. to have a fractional cofficient.
$\sqrt{3x^2} + \sqrt{2x}$	Yes. It's O.K. to have a root for a coefficient.
$\frac{2x^2}{5}$	Yes. This is equivalent to $\frac{2}{5}x^2$.
2	Yes. Think of it as $2x^0$

TEACHING SUGGESTION   Make sure students understand that in some polynomials the constant term is missing, as in $5x^3 - 14x^2 + 2x$. See Try This 7.

SECTION 4–4

BACKGROUND MATERIAL   Students should be permitted to use either method for adding polynomials. It's important for them to eventually feel comfortable with the "mental rearrangement" method. Students arrive at this stage at different rates.

LOOKING AHEAD   This subtraction skill comes up again in the long division of polynomials (Section 11–3) and in solving systems of equations (Section 9–3).

TEACHING SUGGESTIONS   The multiplication format in Example 8 on page 170 is an excellent one for letting students develop confidence with multiplication. Some teachers let students use this format until they voluntarily switch to the less space-consuming format of Example 7.

There are four patterns when binomials are multiplied.

$(x + 6)(x + 8) = x^2 + 14x + 48$
$(x - 6)(x + 8) = x^2 + 2x - 48$
$(x + 6)(x - 8) = x^2 - 2x - 48$
$(x - 6)(x - 8) = x^2 - 14x + 48$

When the binomial signs are both positive or both negative, the sign of the constant term of the product is positive. When the binomial signs are unlike, the sign of the constant term of the product is negative. These patterns will be emphasized in Chapter 5 on Factoring.

LOOKING AHEAD   The pattern in Exercises 25–27 is from Pascal's triangle. This is discussed again on page 245.

ARITHMETIC CONNECTION   Show students how the pattern for a difference of squares can help them find some products of numbers.

$7 \cdot 9 = (8 - 1)(8 + 1) = 64 - 1 = 63$
$10 \cdot 12 = (11 - 1)(11 + 1) = 121 - 1 = 120$

The product of numbers that differ by 2 is just one less than the square of the number between them. That is, $7 \cdot 9 = 8^2 - 1$. Have students find products such as $99 \cdot 101$ $(= 9999)$, $79 \cdot 81$ $(= 6399)$, $11 \cdot 13$ $(= 143)$.

ORAL PREPARATION FOR EXERCISES   Have students answer these questions in class before assigning exercises as homework.

Exs. 1– 4 How many terms in the product?
Exs. 5–58 Give the value of the O-term plus the I-term using FOIL.

Chapter 5

INTRODUCTION   Factoring as a skill, is not directly related to any skill students learned in arithmetic. There, a major process was division: one number (the dividend) was given, one factor was given (the divisor). The goal was to find the other factor. Here, the students are given an expression and asked to find factors—without any hint as to what one of them should be.

Factoring can be thought of as an intermediate skill. As a process it is applied to expressions to change the form of the expression from an indicated sum of terms to an indicated product. Usually we factor in the hope that succeeding steps will show that the expression can be simplified (Chapters 5 and 6), or that a least common multiple can be found (Chapter 11), or that a radical expression contains perfect powers as factors (Chapter 12).

VOCABULARY
common factor (p. 192)
difference of two squares (p. 194)
trinomial squares (p. 197)
principle of zero products (p. 212)
if–and–only–if statement (p. 212)

SECTION 5-1

TEACHING SUGGESTIONS   The factorizations on page 192 show some fractional numbers. Students should understand that we are factoring over the set of integers for most problems. Example 6 and Try This 7 are included to show students that if a fraction is factored out, the other factor may be free of fractions and "simpler" to work with.

For Example 7, we follow this method to find a common factor of $9x^4 + 12x^2 - 2$.

1. Is there a common integer factor among the coefficients?
   No.
2. Is there a variable common to all three terms?   No.
3. Therefore, there is no common factor.

EXTENSION   In arithmetic two numbers are relatively prime if they have no common factor other than 1. Consider 14 and 9, $14 = 2 \cdot 7$ and $9 = 3 \cdot 3$. There is no common factor—even though each number has factors and neither is prime. The numbers are *relatively prime*.

Consider the polynomials $2p^2 + 2$ and $2p$ (Exercise 34). $2p^2 + 2 = 2(p^2 + 1)$ and $2p = 2 \cdot p$. Two polynomials are relatively prime if they have no common factor, other than *constants*. The polynomials are *relatively prime*.

TEACHING SUGGESTION   Since fractions are given in the Extension Exercises, it is correct to use fractions to solve them. Students should add $\frac{1}{4}$, $\frac{1}{9}$, $\frac{1}{16}$, and so on to their list of squares. Good algebra students learn to recognize squares of rational numbers, like $\frac{1}{121} = \left(\frac{1}{11}\right)^2$.

FOCUS ON STUDENT QUESTIONS
   Question: Try This 3 says $x^2 + 36$ is not a difference of squares. Can we write it as $x^2 - (-36)$ to make it a difference of squares?
   Answer: This new expression is a difference, but (-36) is not a square in the system of real numbers.
   Question: In Try This 4, can we write $4x^2 - (\sqrt{15})^2$? Is this the difference of two squares?
   Answer: Yes it is. But, introducing square roots at this time doesn't make things simpler.

EXTENSION   For Exercises 53–56, use a substitution technique.
53. Factor $(x + 3)^2 - 9$. Let $y = x + 3$.

$$y^2 - 9 = (y + 3)(y - 3)$$
$$= [(x + 3) + 3][(x + 3) - 3]$$
$$= (x + 6)x$$

When factoring is restricted to the set of integers, the Fundamental Theorem of Arithmetic guarantees positive integers can be factored in only one way. This is *not* true for rational numbers. (See Exercises 46–52.) Compare these two methods of factoring the expression in Exercise 46.

$$3x^2 - \frac{1}{3} \qquad\qquad 3x^2 - \frac{1}{3}$$
$$= 3(x^2 - ?) \qquad = \frac{1}{3}(?x^2 - 1)$$
$$= 3\left(x^2 - \frac{1}{9}\right) \qquad = \frac{1}{3}(9x^2 - 1)$$
$$= 3\left(x + \frac{1}{3}\right)\left(x - \frac{1}{3}\right) \qquad = \frac{1}{3}(3x + 1)(3x - 1)$$

TEACHING SUGGESTIONS   Two people shaking hands with each other is considered one handshake. A chart like the one below may be helpful for Exercises 25–27.

No. of people	No. of handshakes
2	1
3	3
4	6
⋮	⋮
n	$\frac{1}{2}(n^2 - n)$

Chapter 6

BACKGROUND MATERIAL   Polynomials in two variables as well as polynomials in one variable cannot involve the variable in the denominator nor in a radical expression. Because of the added complexity of having more than one variable, we must expand the idea of degree and ascending order.

TEACHING SUGGESTIONS   In Example 9, a student may see x^2 in the first and fourth term, and a in the second and third term.

$$x^2(y^2 + b) + a(y^2 + b) = (x^2 + a)(y^2 + b)$$

Chapter 7

INTRODUCTION   The concepts in this chapter blend algebra and geometry. Graphing concepts can be applied to many algebraic ideas. In this course graphing concepts appear again with linear functions (Section 8–2), systems of equation (Section 9–1), inequalities (Sections 10–6 and 10–7), and quadratic functions (Section 13–7).

VOCABULARY

ordered pair (p. 259)	quadrant (p. 260)
axes (p. 259)	standard form (p. 267)
x-axis (p. 259)	y-intercept (p. 268)
y-axis (p. 259)	x-intercept (p. 268)
origin (p. 259)	slope (p. 272)
coordinates (p. 259)	rise (p. 272)

x-coordinate (p. 259)   run (p. 272)
y-coordinate (p. 259)   slope-intercept equation (p. 278)
abscissa (p. 259)   point-slope equation (p. 282)
ordinate (p. 259)

TEACHING SUGGESTION After students are familiar with graphing points with integer coordinates, let them find points whose coordinates are rational numbers. Such points appear in Exercises 20, 22–23.

SECTION 7–1

TEACHING SUGGESTIONS Up to now students have seen equations that, most of the time, had only one solution. Equations in two variables have an infinite number of solutions. After Example 3, ask students if they can find other solutions than the three given. Ask how many solutions they think the equation has. Because the method given at the top of page 264 says we choose any value for x, and since there are an infinite number of possible values for x, there must be an infinite number of solutions.

In Example 4 we draw a line between two graphed points. We say that if we continued to plot points, they would fall on the line we draw. Later, students will need to be careful about this assumption for nonlinear graphs.

SECTION 7–2

BACKGROUND MATERIAL The standard form includes equations in which one of the variables is 0. What if both x and y are 0, for example, $0 \cdot x + 0 \cdot y = 9$? This is impossible since $0 + 0$ is not equal to 9 or any other number except 0. The only possibility is $0x + 0y = 0$ or $0 = 0$. We do not want to include this equation as a linear equation. Consequently, the definition on page 267 specifically says a and b may not both be 0.

SECTION 7–3

TEACHING SUGGESTION As students work through Example 1, they should be aware that the same slope would be found by counting down from $(-4, 3)$ and then across to $(2, -6)$. The slope is

$$\frac{\text{rise}}{\text{run}} = \frac{\text{change in } y}{\text{change in } x} = \frac{-9}{6} = -\frac{3}{2}.$$

SECTION 7–4

BACKGROUND MATERIAL Earlier we had the general form for linear equations. Now we have the slope-intercept form. Familiarity with the slope-intercept form of the

SECTION 7–5

straight line in the form $y = mx + b$ is an important concept in beginning algebra.

Note that the letter b used for the y-intercept $(0, b)$ is not the same value as the letter b in $ax + by = c$.

COMPUTER SUPPLEMENTS   *Computer Graphing Experiments 1, Algebra One and Algebra Two,* by Lund and Andersen (Addison-Wesley 1982) provides a diskette and worksheets for graphing. The diskette has seven topics suitable for first-year algebra, Experiments 1–4 and 7–9. See also References to Supplements in this Teacher's Edition.

SECTION 7–6

TEACHING SUGGESTION   In the theorem on page 282, y_1, x_1 and m are *numbers* from the equation. Emphasize that x_1 and y_1 are not the variables x and y. They are known coordinates of a point.

Chapter 8

INTRODUCTION   This chapter contains the standard information on domain, range, $f(x)$ notation, function machines, the vocabulary of input–output, and the vertical-line test. It can be used at a later time in the course, if the teacher desires.

VOCABULARY

function (p. 295)	input (p. 295)
domain (p. 295)	output (p. 295)
range (p. 295)	$f(x)$ (p. 296)
value of a function (p. 295)	
linear function (p. 303)	
direct variation (p. 306)	
equation of direct variation (p. 306)	
variation constant (p. 306)	
inverse variation (p. 310)	
equation of inverse variation (p. 310)	

SECTION 8–2

TEACHING SUGGESTION   Students sometimes become confused about the distinction between a function and an equation. Of course, a function rule is usually a type of equation. But it is a specific type in that it is possible to write a set of pairs (input, output) for the variable. Thus

$x + 2 = 0$ is not a function rule. But $y = x + 2$ could be a function rule because each value selected for x yields a corresponding value for y.

Chapter 9

VOCABULARY
system of equations (p. 321)
solution (p. 321)
simultaneous equations (p. 321)
substitution method (p. 325)
addition method (p. 330)

SECTION 9–1

GET-READY EXERCISE   The idea that a single value of x and y satisfies both equations in a system can be reinforced by the following. Have students make up equations of their own. Let them choose x and y in advance and write true statements. Suppose $x = 3$ and $y = 1$. They could write this system.

$$2x + y = 7$$
$$x - y = 2$$

TEACHING SUGGESTION   Students should pay special attention to the boxed information on page 322, on ways two lines may or may not intersect.

Chapter 10

VOCABULARY
inequality (p. 361)
solution (p. 361)
addition principle for inequalities (p. 361)
multiplication principle for inequalities (p. 365)
half-plane (p. 378)
linear inequality (p. 379)
system of linear inequalities (p. 381)

SECTION 10–2

TEACHING SUGGESTIONS   The Multiplication Principle for Inequalities is perhaps the "trickiest" rule in first year algebra. When multiplying on both sides by a negative number, we must reverse the sign of the inequality.

One way to emphasize this principle is to begin with $x > -5$. Ask students if this is the same as $-5 < x$. Since the answer is yes, we can use the addition principle to find an inequality equivalent to $-5 < x$.

$$-5 < x$$
$$0 < x + 5 \quad \text{Adding 5 to both sides}$$
$$-x < 5 \qquad\quad \text{Adding } -x \text{ to both sides}$$

Since $-x < 5$ is equivalent to $-5 < x$ and $-5 < x$ is equivalent to $x > -5$, $-x < 5$ and $x > -5$ are equivalent.

SECTION 10–3

TEACHING SUGGESTION   An alternate way to solve the inequality in Example 1 is the following.

$$6 - 5y > 7, \ 6 > 5y + 7, \ -1 > 5y, \ -\frac{1}{5} > y$$

SECTION 10–5

GET-READY EXERCISES   Have students solve some equations involving absolute value and equality before Examples 4–7.
1. Solve $|x + 2| = 6$.

   $x + 2$ is either 6 or -6, since these are the only numbers that have an absolute value of 6. Therefore, $x + 2 = 6$ or $x + 2 = -6$. Solving each equation for x, we get $x = 4$ or $x = -8$.
2. Solve $|x - 3| = 7$. $x = 10$ or $x = -4$

SECTION 10–7

TEACHING SUGGESTION   This topic is one of the most satisfying to students, since they are able to deal with ideas that are truly complex. It is important that their success is not marred by falling into trivial errors, such as drawing graphs so small that the intersection point cannot be easily read.

Chapter 11

INTRODUCTION   For many teachers, the student's ability to deal with fractional expressions, especially addition with different denominators, is the true test of algebraic understanding. Certainly all previous skills come together in this chapter. The theory behind the skills, by contrast, is little different from that learned in arithmetic classes dealing with numerical fractions.

VOCABULARY
fractional expressions (p. 391)
least common multiple (p. 404)
complex fractional expression (p. 410)
fractional equation (p. 413)
proportion (p. 418)

SECTION 11–1

TEACHING SUGGESTION Establish classroom agreement about leaving expressions in factored form. Factored form must be found to be sure expressions have been simplified. It's convenient to leave answers this way.

SECTION 11–4

TEACHING SUGGESTIONS Fractions with denominators that are inverses of each other should be multiplied by $\frac{-1}{-1}$ so that the denominators become the same. This concept is used freely in succeeding lessons. Students may need to consider the following statements to become familiar with the concept.

$$-(a-b) = b-a \qquad \frac{1}{a-b} = \frac{-1}{b-a}$$

$$\frac{-1}{a-b} = \frac{1}{b-a} \qquad -\frac{1}{a-b} = \frac{1}{b-a}$$

SECTION 11–5

GET-READY EXERCISE Students should analyze the way they find least common multiples for numerical fractions. Use exponents to make this process as algebraic as possible. For example,

$$\frac{1}{24} + \frac{1}{36} + \frac{1}{42} = \frac{1}{2^3 \cdot 3} + \frac{1}{2^2 \cdot 3^2} + \frac{1}{2 \cdot 3 \cdot 7}$$

$$\text{LCD} = 2^3 \cdot 3^2 \cdot 7$$

$$\frac{1}{2^3 \cdot 3}\left(\frac{3 \cdot 7}{3 \cdot 7}\right) + \frac{1}{2^2 \cdot 3^2}\left(\frac{2 \cdot 7}{2 \cdot 7}\right) + \frac{1}{2 \cdot 3 \cdot 7}\left(\frac{2^2 \cdot 3}{2^2 \cdot 3}\right)$$

Each fractional name for 1 is constructed by comparing the existing denominator factors with the LCD factors. Students who can follow this review example will have less trouble doing the same thing with fractional expressions in algebra.

TEACHING SUGGESTION The remark in Example 9 is very important. One of the most common errors in subtracting fractional expressions is to subtract only part of the numerator. If students are required to write parentheses, they will be more likely to subtract correctly.

SECTION 11–6

TEACHING SUGGESTION   To solve fractional equations we multiply both sides by the LCD. This results in an equation without fractions. Remind students that this is the goal. They should stop and check their work if fractions remain.

SECTION 11–7

TEACHING SUGGESTIONS   A few students become confused in problems like Example 2. They may simplify each side and have two equal fractions:

$$\frac{x^2+6}{x} = -5 \qquad \text{or} \qquad \frac{x^2+6}{x} = \frac{-5x}{x}$$

While nothing wrong has been written, it is not so easy to see the next step. In the first equation they must multiply by x on both sides. In the second equation they must be able to say: If two fractions are equal and their denominators are the same, the numerators must be equal.

SECTION 11–8

TEACHING SUGGESTIONS   Some students may need more preparation for word problems. In Example 1, we are unable to translate directly into an equation. Instead we use the information given to create an equation. Have students work through a table like this, telling how much of the job each team would finish after the given number of minutes.

	A	B	Total
1 min	$\frac{1}{10}$	$\frac{1}{15}$	$\frac{5}{30}$
2 min	$2\left(\frac{1}{10}\right)$	$2\left(\frac{1}{15}\right)$	$\frac{10}{30}$
$\vdots$	$\vdots$	$\vdots$	$\vdots$
6 min	$6\left(\frac{1}{10}\right)$	$6\left(\frac{1}{15}\right)$	$\frac{30}{30}=1$

If t is the desired number of minutes, then

$$t\left(\frac{1}{10}\right) + t\left(\frac{1}{15}\right) = 1,$$

which is equivalent to the equation in the text.

APPLICATION: WILDLIFE POPULATION   The capture-recapture method in Example 4 has become a popular device for estimating various kinds of wildlife. There are a number of assumptions made. Your "what–if" students may enjoy creating as many assumptions as possible:

- No fish die, get caught, get eaten or born between the two catches.
- No fish is apt to get caught more readily than any other.
- Tagged fish disperse equally throughout the lake.
- The fish are caught singly at different points.

Chapter 12

VOCABULARY
square root (p. 433)
radical symbol (p. 433)
principal square root (p. 433)
rational numer (p. 433)
irrational number (p. 434)
real numbers (p. 435)
radical expressions (p. 438)
radicand (p. 438)
rationalize the denominator (p. 449)
hypotenuse (p. 459)
legs of a right triangle (p. 459)
Pythagorean Property (p. 459)
principle of squaring (p. 465)

SECTION 12–1

TEACHING SUGGESTION   The axioms listed on page 87 are valid for real numbers.

EXPLORING IDEAS   Students can easily understand that there are infinitely many rational numbers, and that there are infinitely many irrational numbers. But let them consider this: if you were to draw an infinite number of digits (0–9) from a box, recording each one to form a decimal, is it likely that you would have digits repeating in a pattern? Would you probably be recording a rational number or an irrational number? Some thought will show that, by comparison, rationals are very rare. In fact, rationals can be put into an infinite order, while the irrationals are too numerous to order.

SECTION 12-3

GET-READY EXERCISES As preparation for factoring radical expressions, have the class create lists of radical expressions containing a perfect square factor.

$\sqrt{2}$			$\sqrt{3}$		
$2\sqrt{2} = \sqrt{4 \cdot 2}$	$= \sqrt{8}$		$2\sqrt{3} = \sqrt{4 \cdot 3}$	$= \sqrt{12}$
$3\sqrt{2} = \sqrt{9 \cdot 2}$	$= \sqrt{18}$		$3\sqrt{3} = \sqrt{9 \cdot 3}$	$= \sqrt{27}$
$4\sqrt{2} = \sqrt{16 \cdot 2}$	$= \sqrt{32}$		$4\sqrt{3} = \sqrt{16 \cdot 3}$	$= \sqrt{48}$
$5\sqrt{2} = \sqrt{25 \cdot 2}$	$= \sqrt{50}$		$5\sqrt{3} = \sqrt{25 \cdot 3}$	$= \sqrt{75}$

You can make lists for $\sqrt{5}$, $\sqrt{6}$, $\sqrt{7}$, $\sqrt{10}$, and so on.

FOCUS ON STUDENT QUESTIONS
   Question: If $\sqrt{9} \cdot \sqrt{4} = \sqrt{36} = 6$ and if $\sqrt{9} \cdot \sqrt{4} = \sqrt{36} = \sqrt{(-6)^2} = -6$, what is wrong with this process?
   Answer: The last step: $\sqrt{(-6)^2} \neq -6$. Instead $\sqrt{(-6)^2} = |-6| = 6$.
   Question: If $\sqrt{-5} \cdot \sqrt{-4} = \sqrt{20}$, why is the answer "no real value"?
   Answer: Because $\sqrt{-5}$ and $\sqrt{-4}$ are not real numbers. It is not a legal step in the real number system to operate on these numbers. When the complex-number system is studied students will be able to work with quantities such as $\sqrt{-5}$. For now the original question is analogous to the following: In the system of whole numbers what is the value of $\frac{3}{5} \times \frac{10}{3}$? Answer: In the system of whole numbers it has no meaning.

SECTION 12-7

TEACHING SUGGESTION What is the additive inverse of $a + b\sqrt{c}$? Ask students for possible solutions. What is true of an additive inverse? It's the number we add to get 0.
   $a + b\sqrt{c} + x = 0$
Solve for x.
   $b\sqrt{c} + x = -a$, $x = -a - b\sqrt{c}$
Since the inverse of a is $-a$, and the inverse of $b\sqrt{c}$ is $-b\sqrt{c}$, the inverse of a sum of radical expressions is the sum of the inverses. Thus, the general rule we presented for rational numbers in Section 2-8 is also true for real numbers.

SECTION 12-9

BACKGROUND MATERIAL Because the converse of the Principle of Squaring is not true (for example, $2^2 = (-2)^2$ but $2 \neq -2$), we must use this principle with caution.

The paragraph at the bottom of the page shows that -1 is a solution of $x^2 = 1$, but is not a solution of the original equation.

CHALLENGE Find an equation with roots $4 + 3\sqrt{3}$ and $4 - 3\sqrt{3}$. First, find an equation with a root $4 + 3\sqrt{3}$.

$$x = 4 + 3\sqrt{3}$$
$$x - 4 = 3\sqrt{3}$$
$$x^2 - 8x + 16 = (3\sqrt{3})^2 = 9 \cdot 3 = 27$$
$$x^2 - 8x - 11 = 0$$

Ask the students to find an equation with root $4 - 3\sqrt{3}$. Since $(-3\sqrt{3})^2 = (3\sqrt{3})^2$, the equation is the same. $x^2 - 8x - 11 = 0$ is a solution.

Chapter 13

VOCABULARY

quadratic equation (p. 475)	discriminant (p. 486)
standard form (p. 475)	radical equations (p. 490)
compounding interest (p. 480)	quadratic function (p. 497)
completing the square (p. 482)	parabola (p. 497)
quadratic formula (p. 485)	line of symmetry (p. 497)

TEACHING SUGGESTION In Example 5 we see a solution of the equation that is not a solution of the word problem. If a positive fraction, or 0, had been a solution, these would have been rejected as well.

SECTION 13-2

APPLICATIONS: INTEREST The formula $A = P(1 + r)^t$ on pages 479–480 is used only for $t = 2$. The formula is valid for all values of t. It can be made more general by letting r be the interest rate for one period and letting t equal the number of periods. Thus, an annual rate of 12% compounded quarterly for 5 years would be expressed as $r = 0.12/4 = 0.03$ and $t = 20$.

LOOKING AHEAD Completing the square is a preparation for deriving the quadratic formula. This concept occurs again in the study of conic sections in second-year algebra.

SECTION 13-3

SECTION 13–4

BACKGROUND MATERIAL   The restriction that $a > 0$ serves two purposes.
1. If $a = 0$, the equation is not quadratic, but linear, and the $2a$ in the denominator of the formula renders it meaningless.
2. Having $a > 0$ avoids the use of absolute value in taking the square root of $4a^2$. The restriction $a > 0$ is not required in applying the formula.

SECTION 13–7

TEACHING SUGGESTIONS   It is important to know what a graph is going to look like. A student may make a trivial calculation error, such as including $(2, 11)$ instead of $(2, -5)$ as a point on the graph in Example 3. Connecting this point in some way to the others shows a lack of understanding of the two issues above.

Chapter 14

VOCABULARY
similar triangles (p. 507)
corresponding angles (p. 507)
corresponding sides (p. 507)
right triangle (p. 508)
trigonometric ratios (p. 509)
trigonometric functions (p. 512)
sine function (p. 512)
cosine function (p. 513)
tangent function (p. 513)

SECTION 14–1

GEOMETRY CONNECTION   Students may need some background on properties of triangles and similar triangles.
- The sum of the measures of the three angles of a triangle is 180°.
- In similar figures, corresponding angles always have the same measure.
- In similar triangles, corresponding sides *do not* have the same measure, unless the figures are actually the same.
- Although corresponding sides are not the same length, they are proportional, as shown in Example 1.
- In determining similarity for right triangles, only one other angle needs to be checked. The third pair automatically have the same measure because the three must total 180°.

COMPUTER ACTIVITIES

Overview

The Computer Activities may be used with or without a computer. For classes without access to a computer, students follow the steps of the sample programs. Students should tell what the computer will do at each step, supply the value of appropriate variables, and find the output. The exercises may also be worked without a computer. The exercises emphasize writing and understanding BASIC expressions and programs. If individual students have access to home computers, they may run the programs at home and report their results.

For classes with access to a computer, type and save the sample programs before class, or ask a student to do so.

List, discuss, and run the programs for each specific activity. If the system has a printer, program listings and printouts of output are valuable.

BASIC
Expressions

WRITING EXPRESSIONS AND NUMBERS IN BASIC (Use after Chapter 1.) It is important that students have a good understanding of algebraic expressions before BASIC statements are introduced. Teachers need to mention that variables A1 and A2 are different, just as x and y are different.

BASIC
Programs

INTRODUCTION TO BASIC PROGRAMS (Use after Section 3–6.) Make up a table with columns X, Y, Z, and rows giving BASIC statement line numbers. Write the values the computer will have for the variables at each line number of the program on page 537.

	X	Y	Z
10	5		
20	5	3	
30	5	3	2
40	5	3	2
50	5	3	2

The following is an explanation of what happens inside the computer when this program runs.

`10 LET X = 5`	Sets aside a storage location in the computer which it calls X and places the number 5 there. The number is represented by a series of 0's and 1's. (See The Binary System, page 223.)
`20 LET Y = 3`	The computer follows a similar procedure for Y and the value 3.
`30 LET Z = X - Y`	Subtracts Y from X, then stores the result in the location called Z.
`40 PRINT X, Y, Z`	Shows whatever values are in the locations called X, Y, and Z on the computer screen.
`50 END`	Tells the computer that the program is finished.

FOCUS ON STUDENT QUESTIONS

Question: Is spacing important?

Answer: The computer ignores spaces, with a few exceptions. However, a program must be readable. The line 4 0PRIN TX , Y,Z will work, but would not be easy to read or to find errors. Spaces do count within quotation marks of a PRINT statement.

Question: Do line numbers matter?

Answer: Yes. The computer puts the lines in numerical order first, no matter when they were typed. However, when two lines have the same line number, the computer accepts only the last one typed.

Question: What if I make a mistake?

Answer: If an error is made typing a line, press the DELETE or ← key until you reach the error. Then type the rest of the line. If you already pressed RETURN or ran the program, just type the line over. If the error was an incorrect line number, remove that line by typing that number and pressing RETURN. Use LIST to be sure you have all the lines.

Question: Will the following statements work in BASIC?

```
10 LET 5 = X
```

Answer: No, the variable must be on the left side.

```
20 LET X - Y = Z
```

Answer: No, the expression to be calculated must be on the right side of the equal sign. The left side is a variable in which to store the result.

```
30 LET B = 4X
```

Answer: No, the * must be used for multiplication.

```
40 PRINT HELLO
```

Answer: No, without quotation marks, the computer assumes HELLO is a variable. It may print 0 or an error message.

INPUT STATEMENTS (Use after Chapter 5.)   It should be stressed that

```
10 PRINT ''INPUT BASE AND HEIGHT''
```

does not tell the computer that input will be entered. Without this line, it would only print a question mark, and we might not know what quantities to enter. Without

```
20 INPUT B, H
```

the computer will type "INPUT BASE AND HEIGHT", but will not wait for input. It will either assign 0 for both the area and perimeter, or print an error message. Note that the program does not check whether the base and height are realistic values. We can enter zero or negative numbers, but P and A will still be calculated.

Parentheses may be used, but there are no brackets or braces. Extra levels of parentheses are used in place of brackets or braces.

READ AND DATA STATEMENTS (Use after Chapter 7.)
When a GO TO statement is encountered, the program tells the computer to go to that line number and continue from there. When a READ statement is encountered, the program instructs the computer to find and read from the DATA statement; the program does not actually go to the DATA statement. The program continues to the next line following the READ statement. A GO TO statement "transfers control of the program." A READ statement does not transfer control.

Students may use spacing in a DATA statement to separate groups of data. Line 60 on page 542 may be typed as follows:

```
60 DATA 4,-4, -3,-2,  3,5, 1,1,  -1,2, -2,4
```

This spacing presents a much clearer pattern for grouping the coordinates of the problem. It alerts students if they are missing a number or have extra numbers.

IF ... THEN STATEMENTS (Use after Section 10–1.)
Two concepts in this activity, equation-like forms and the IF–THEN form, appear different from concepts taught in algebra. Consider the following program which counts from one to ten.

```
10 LET X = 1
20 PRINT X
30 LET X = X + 1
40 IF X < = 10 THEN 20
50 END
```

The LET or assignment statement evaluates the right side of an equation and stores the result in the location named by the variable on the left. LET $X = X + 1$ adds 1 to X, then stores the result in X. If X were 1, then the new value of X is 2, and so on.

IF $X < = 10$ THEN 20 means if X is less than or equal to 10, then go to line 20. If the answer is no, then continue to the next line. We do not try to prove an If-then relationship as we did in Section 3–8. IF ... THEN statements are extremely useful in testing input values. The Area/Perimeter program on page 540 can be revised to accept only positive values for B and H. Two lines like these may be used:

```
25 IF B < = 0 THEN 20
26 IF H < = 0 THEN 20
```

LOOPS AND FOR ... NEXT STATEMENTS (Use after Section 12–1.) Here is another program that counts to 10. Compare it to the one in the Teaching Suggestions for IF ... THEN statements.

```
10 FOR X = 1 TO 10
20 PRINT X
30 NEXT X
40 END
```

Line 30 automatically increases the value of X by 1 and goes to the beginning of the loop on line 10. After printing the value of ten numbers, the NEXT X statement again increases the value of X by 1. This value of 11 is tested at the beginning of the loop. Since the value is too great, the program transfers control to the line following the end of the loop. In this case, the program ends and the value 11 does not print.

Students need to understand that INT(Q) means the integer part of Q for any positive number. Follow the program loop on page 545 for D = 1, 2, and 3. A table will help.

D	Q	INT(Q)	Output
1	16/1 = 16	16	1 and 16 are factors
2	16/2 = 8	8	2 and 8 are factors
3	16/3 = 5.33333	5	(no output)

PROGRAMS FOR QUADRATIC EQUATIONS (Use after Section 13–4.)   Lines 40 and 50 of the quadratic formula program on page 546 contain several levels of parentheses. Students should carefully match left and right parentheses. There must be an equal number of each. There is an error in the following statement.

```
40 LET X1 = (-B + SQR(B^2-4*A*C)/(2*A)
```

A second right parenthesis is needed after the C. A more serious error, however, may occur when the grouping is incorrect algebraically and the computer gets a wrong answer. Have students omit line 30. What happens when the computer tries to solve the third equation? An "illegal quantity" error will occur when the discriminant is negative.

The second program, on page 546, finds compound interest. Teachers may want students to find interest rates. Use Example 6 on page 491. Students can develop a program to calculate the interest rate using LET $R = SQR(A/P - 1)$ for one or more successive values of A or P.

PROGRAMS FOR QUADRATIC FUNCTIONS (Use after Chapter 13.)   The concepts of parabola, line of symmetry, and vertex are introduced here. The vocabulary need not be stressed. A simple drawing of a parabola, such as $y = x^2 + 4$, should be shown for clarification. The line of symmetry is the x-axis and the vertex is the point $(0, 4)$.

Enrichment
Programs

The SGN function finds the sign of a variable. For the quadratic function $y = x^2 + 4$, it would find the sign of the x^2 term to determine that the graph opens upward.

So (0, 4) is a minimum point and 4 is a minimum value.

Note that for Exercise 3, the graph is plotted sideways. Each line printed represents an increasing x-value and the computer tabs to each y-value.

PROGRAMS FOR SYSTEMS OF EQUATIONS (Use after Chapter 13.) This activity stresses the usefulness of nested loops—loops within loops—as a test for solutions. To test 11 values for x and 11 values for y, 121 ordered pairs must be tested. To search a file of license plates with three letters followed by three numbers, $26^3 \times 10^3$ or 17,576,000 combinations need to be tested. This is a difficult task without loops.

The solutions for the first program, $(1,2)$, $(1,-2)$, $(-1,2)$, $(-1,-2)$, may also be found using conventional methods. Multiply the second equation by 5 and add, or substitute $3X^2 + 1$ for Y^2 in the first equation and solve.

PROGRAMS FOR TRIGONOMETRY (Use after Chapter 14.) Consider two versions of the same program.

```
10 INPUT T              10 DEF FNS(T) = 16 * T^2
20 LET S = 16 * T^2     20 INPUT T
30 PRINT T,S            30 PRINT T,FNS(T)
40 GO TO 10             40 GO TO 20
```

The LET statement must be read each time new data is input. The DEF statement needs to be read only once. Exercise 2 may be extended to find the cosine and tangent values for angles to 90°. The program will end on a "divide by zero" error when the tangent of 90° is attempted.

Additional Programs

PROGRAM FOR SYSTEMS OF LINEAR EQUATIONS (Use after Section 9–3.) The standard form of a system of two linear equations is given in Exercise 51a on page 336:

$ax + by = c$

$dx + ey = f$

Input the coefficients a through f in the following program.

The program prints the solution as an ordered pair.

```
10 INPUT A,B,C,D,E,F
20 LET X = (C*E-B*F)/(A*E-B*D)
30 LET Y = (A*F-C*D)/(A*E-B*D)
40 PRINT ''THE SOLUTION IS
   ''('';X;'','';Y;'')''
```

Can the program be simplified? Since X is assigned in line 20, we can use the following substitution.

```
30 LET Y = (C-A*X)/B
```

If the lines are parallel or coincide, the program will get a "divide by zero" error. IF ... THEN statements inserted before line 20 can be used to avoid this. For coinciding lines, both the numerator and denominator in line 20 are zero. For parallel lines only the denominator is zero.

PROGRAM FOR RIGHT TRIANGLES (Use after Chapter 14.) Students can use the Pythagorean Property to write a program to find the lengths of sides of a right triangle. To find the length of a hypotenuse, use

```
LET C = SQR(A^2 + B^2).
```

To find the length of a leg, use

```
LET A = SQR(C^2 - B^2).
```

PROGRAM FOR RANDOM NUMBERS Random numbers between 0 and 1 can be generated using RND(0) or RND(1) for some systems. To generate random integers from 1 to 100, use INT(100*RND(0) + 1). Random numbers are the basis for many computer games.

PROGRAM FOR PRIME NUMBERS This program uses an array to print the prime numbers from 2 to 150 with the Sieve of Eratosthenes. The program marks each multiple of 2, 3, 5 and so on with a 1, then prints those that have not been marked.

```
10 DIM Z(150)
20 FOR X = 2 TO 75
30 IF Z(X) = 1 THEN 70
40 FOR Y = 2*X TO 150 STEP X
50 LET Z(Y) = 1
60 NEXT Y
70 NEXT X
```

Additional
Enrichment

```
80 FOR P = 2 TO 150
90 IF Z(P) = 0 THEN 110
100 PRINT P,
110 NEXT P
120 END
```

2	3	5
7	11	13
17	19	23
29	31	37
41	43	47
53	59	61
67	71	73
79	83	89
97	101	103
107	109	113
127	131	137
139	149	

ASSIGNMENT GUIDE

The following schedules of assignments are for minimum, regular, and advanced courses. The total number of days is based on 174, with 87 assignment days for each semester. Review and testing days are included at the end of each chapter. Assignment days for supplemental material in the student book are included as optional and starred. *Even* or *odd* exercises are shown as *e/o*.

The minimum course is recommended for students who plan to take one or two years of high school mathematics. It does not include Chapter 8 and 14, Sections 3–8, 7–7, 10–5 to 10–7, 11–9, 2–9, 12–9, 13–5 to 13–7.

The regular course is recommended for students who plan to take two or three years of high school mathematics. It does not include Sections 3–8, 7–7, 11–9, 14–3, and 14–4. The advanced course is recommended for students who will complete three or more years of high school mathematics.

MINIMUM COURSE

First Semester

Chapter	1	2	3	4	5	6	Supplements
Days	10	15	12	18	15	10	7*

Second Semester

Chapter	7	9	10	11	12	13	Supplements
Days	13	13	6	17	16	8	14*

REGULAR COURSE

First Semester

Chapter	1	2	3	4	5	6	7	Supplements
Days	9	14	11	13	13	8	9	9*

Second Semester

Chapter	8	9	10	11	12	13	14	Supplements
Days	7	10	10	17	13	13	2	15*

ADVANCED COURSE

First Semester

Chapter	1	2	3	4	5	6	7	8	Supplements
Days	9	12	10	11	11	8	9	7	10*

Second Semester

Chapter	9	10	11	12	13	14	Supplements
Days	10	10	16	12	13	7	19*

FIRST SEMESTER			
Day	Minimum Course	Regular Course	Advanced Course
1	1–1: 1–43 e/o	1–1: 1–57 e/o	1–1: 1–57 e/o, 58–63
2	1–2: 1–32 e/o	1–2: 1–46 e/o	1–2: 1–46 e/o, 47–48
3	1–3: 1–24 e/o	1–3: 1–39 e/o	1–3: 1–39 e/o, 40–45
4	1–4: 1–46 e/o	1–4: 1–37 e/o	1–4: 1–37 e/o, 38, 43, 47–59
5	1–5: 1–48 e/o	1–5: 1–48 e/o, 49–52	1–5: 1–56 e/o, 57
6	1–6: 1–36 e/o	1–6: 1–44 e/o	1–6: 1–44 mult. of 3, 45–47
7	1–7: 1–12	1–7: 1–27 e/o	1–7: 1–31 e/o
8	1–7: 13–23	Chapter 1 Review	Chapter 1 Review
9	Chapter 1 Review	Chapter 1 Test Ready for Ch. 2?	Chapter 1 Test Ready for Ch. 2?
10	Chapter 1 Test Ready for Ch. 2?	2–1: 1–38 e/o	2–1: 1–49 e/o, 50, 51
11	2–1: 1–31 e/o	2–2: 1, 2–37 e/o	2–2: 1, 2–37 e/o, 38, 39
12	2–2: 1, 2–25 e/o, 26, 27	2–3: 1–55 e/o	2–3: 1–67 e/o, 68
13	2–3: 1–52 e/o	2–4: 1–44 e/o	2–4: 1–68 e/o, 69–71
14	2–4: 1–36 e/o	2–4: 45–68 e/o	2–5: 1–57 e/o
15	2–4: 36–62 e/o	2–5: 1–48 e/o	2–6: 1–70 e/o, 71–76
16	2–5: 1–40 e/o	2–6: 1–48 e/o	2–7: 1–52 e/o
17	2–6: 1–44 e/o	2–6: 49–70 e/o	2–8: 1–42 e/o
18	2–6: 45–62 e/o	2–7: 1–44 e/o	2–9: 1–42 e/o
19	2–7: 1–26	2–8: 1–38 e/o	2–10: 1–18 e/o, 19–25
20	2–7: 27–44	2–9: 1–39 e/o	Chapter 2 Review
21	2–8: 1–34 e/o	2–10: 1–18	Chapter 2 Test Ready for Ch. 3?
22	2–9: 1–16	Chapter 2 Review	3–1: 1–41 e/o, 42–48
23	2–10: 1–18	Chapter 2 Test Ready for Ch. 3?	3–2: 1–58 mult. of 3, 59–61
24	Chapter 2 Review	3–1: 1–41 e/o, 42	3–3: 1–57 mult. of 3, 58–72 e/o
25	Chapter 2 Test Ready for Ch. 3?	3–2: 1–58 mult. of 3	3–4: 1–69 mult. of 3, 70
26	3–1: 1–35 e/o	3–3: 1–36 e/o	3–5: 1–21 e/o

FIRST SEMESTER			
Day	**Minimum Course**	**Regular Course**	**Advanced Course**
27	**3–2:** 1–42 e/o	**3–3:** 37–64 e/o	**3–6:** 1–41 e/o
28	**3–3:** 1–32 e/o	**3–4:** 1–38 e/o	**3–7:** 1–20 e/o, 21, 22
29	**3–3:** 33–57 e/o	**3–4:** 39–63 e/o	**3–8:** 1–24 e/o, 25–29
30	**3–4:** 1–30 e/o	**3–5:** 1–16 e/o	Chapter 3 Review
31	**3–4:** 31–52 e/o	**3–6:** 1–31 e/o	Chapter 3 Test Ready for Ch. 4?
32	Careers/Space Travel p. 136*	Careers/Space Travel p. 136*	Cum. Rev. Ch. 1–3*
33	**3–5:** 1–10	**3–7:** 1–20 e/o	**4–1:** 1–59 e/o, 50–52
34	**3–6:** 1–12	Chapter 3 Review	**4–2:** 1–49 e/o, 50–52
35	**3–6:** 13–25	Chapter 3 Test Ready for Ch. 4?	**4–3:** 1–39 e/o
36	**3–7:** 1–15	Cum. Rev. Ch. 1–3*	**4–4:** 1–36 mult. of 3, 37–47
37	Chapter 3 Review	**4–1:** 1–52 e/o	**4–5:** 1–42 e/o, 43–45
38	Chapter 3 Test Ready for Ch. 4?	**4–2:** 1–49 e/o	**4–6:** 1–42 mult. of 3, 44–58 e/o
39	**4–1:** 1–27	**4–3:** 1–39 e/o	**4–7:** 1–33 e/o
40	**4–1:** 28–42	**4–4:** 1–44 e/o	**4–8:** 1–77 e/o
41	**4–2:** 1–41 e/o	**4–5:** 1–32 e/o **4–6:** 1–21 e/o	**4–9:** 1–47 e/o, 48, 49
42	**4–3:** 1–34 e/o	**4–6:** 22–50 e/o	Chapter 4 Review
43	**4–4:** 1–22 e/o	**4–7:** 1–23 e/o	Chapter 4 Test Ready for Ch. 5?
44	**4–4:** 23–36 e/o	**4–8:** 1–52 e/o	**5–1:** 1–43 e/o
45	**4–4:** 23–36 e/o, 37, 38	**4–8:** 53–68	**5–2:** 1–65 e/o
46	**4–5:** 1–22	Consumer Application pp. 184–185*	**5–3:** 1–65 e/o
47	**4–5:** 23–32	**4–9:** 1–28	**5–4:** 1–50 e/o, 51
48	Consumer Application pp. 184–185*	**4–9:** 1–28	**5–5:** 1–66 e/o, 67
49	**4–6:** 1–23	Chapter 4 Review	**5–6:** 1–24 e/o, 25–27
50	**4–6:** 24–43	Chapter 4 Test Ready for Ch. 5?	**5–7:** 1–42 e/o, 43–45
51	**4–7:** 1–24 e/o	**5–1:** 1–38 e/o	**5–8:** 1–75 e/o

FIRST SEMESTER			
Day	**Minimum Course**	**Regular Course**	**Advanced Course**
52	**4–8:** 1–24	**5–2:** 1–59 e/o	**5–9:** 1–40 e/o
53	**4–8:** 25–58 e/o	**5–3:** 1–57 e/o	Careers/Graphic Arts p. 224*
54	**4–9:** 1–18	**5–4:** 1–44 e/o	Chapter 5 Review
55	**4–9:** 19–44	**5–5:** 1–61 e/o	Chapter 5 Test Ready for Ch. 6?
56	Chapter 4 Review	**5–6:** 1–24 e/o	**6–1:** 1–44 even
57	Chapter 4 Test Ready for Ch. 5?	**5–7:** 1–42 e/o	**6–2:** 1–75 e/o
58	**5–1:** 1–28 e/o	**5–8:** 1–50 e/o	**6–3:** 1–55 e/o
59	**5–2:** 1–41 e/o	**5–8:** 51–74 e/o	**6–3:** 56–86 e/o
60	**5–3:** 1–37 e/o	**5–9:** 1–24 odd	**6–4:** 1–50 e/o
61	**5–4:** 1–30 odd	**5–9:** 2–24 even, 25–35 e/o	Using a Calculator pp. 250–253*
62	**5–4:** 1–30 even	Careers/Graphic Arts p. 224*	**6–5:** 1–36 e/o, 37, 38
63	**5–5:** 1–51 e/o	Chapter 5 Review	Chapter 6 Review
64	**5–6:** 1–20 e/o	Chapter 5 Test Ready for Ch. 6?	Chapter 6 Test Ready for Ch. 7?
65	**5–7:** 1–32 odd	**6–1:** 1–35 e/o	**7–1:** 1–40 e/o
66	**5–7:** 1–32 even	**6–2:** 1–62 e/o	**7–2:** 1–40 e/o, 41
67	**5–8:** 1–32 e/o	Using a Calculator pp. 250–251*	**7–3:** 1–35 mult. of 3, 36–43
68	**5–8:** 33–64 e/o	**6–3:** 1–41 e/o	**7–4:** 1–40 e/o
69	**5–9:** 1–28 odd	**6–3:** 42–79 e/o	**7–5:** 1–47 e/o, 48
70	**5–9:** 1–28 even	**6–4:** 1–44 e/o	**7–6:** 1–32 e/o
71	Chapter 5 Review	**6–5:** 1–38 e/o	**7–7:** 1–2
72	Chapter 5 Test Ready for Ch. 6?	Chapter 6 Review	Chapter 7 Review
73	**6–1:** 1–28	Chapter 6 Test Ready for Ch. 7?	Chapter 7 Test Ready for Ch. 8?
74	**6–2:** 1–14	**7–1:** 1–38 e/o	**8–1:** 1–32 e/o, 33–39
75	**6–2:** 15–58 e/o	**7–2:** 1–40 e/o	Using a Calculator pp. 314–315*

FIRST SEMESTER			
Day	**Minimum Course**	**Regular Course**	**Advanced Course**
76	6–3: 1–29 e/o	7–3: 1–15 e/o	8–2: 1–24 e/o
77	6–3: 30–65 e/o	7–3: 16–41 e/o	8–3: 1–16
78	6–4: 1–32 e/o	7–4: 1–37 e/o	8–4: 1–28 e/o
79	6–5: 1–20	7–5: 1–47 e/o	8–5: 1–28 e/o
80	6–5: 21–36	7–6: 1–16 e/o	Careers/Finance, p. 316*
81	Using a Calculator pp. 250–251*	Chapter 7 Review	Chapter 8 Review
82	Chapter 6 Review	Chapter 7 Test	Chapter 8 Test
83	Chapter 6 Test	Using a Calculator pp. 252–253*	Computer Activities pp. 537–538*
84	Cum. Review 1–7*	Cum. Rev. 1–7*	Cum. Rev. 1–7*
85	Cum. Rev. 1–7*	Cum. Rev. 1–7*	Cum. Rev. 1–7*
86	Review Ch. 1–6	Review Ch. 1–7	Review Ch. 1–8
87	Mid-Year Test Ready for Ch. 7?	Mid-Year Test Ready for Ch. 8?	Mid-Year Test Ready for Ch. 9?

SECOND SEMESTER			
Day	**Minimum Course**	**Regular Course**	**Advanced Course**
1	7–1: 1–28 e/o	8–1: 1–32 e/o	9–1: 1–33 e/o
2	7–2: 1–15 e/o, 16–20	8–2: 1–21	9–2: 1–39
3	7–2: 21–33 e/o, 34, 35	8–3: 1–13	9–3: 1–28 e/o
4	7–3: 1–15 e/o	Using a Calculator pp. 314–315*	9–3: 29–44 e/o
5	7–3: 16–35 e/o	8–4: 1–26 e/o	9–4: 1–21 e/o
6	7–4: 1–15	8–5: 1–25 e/o	9–5: 1–21 e/o, 22
7	7–4: 16–30	Careers/Financial Institutions, p. 316*	Computer Activities pp. 548–549*
8	7–5: 1–18	Chapter 8 Review	9–6: 1–8
9	7–5: 19–36	Chapter 8 Test Ready for Ch. 9?	9–6: 9–26 e/o
10	7–6: 1–12	9–1: 1–26 e/o	Chapter 9 Review
11	7–6: 13–24	9–2: 1–35 e/o	Chapter 9 Test Ready for Ch. 10?

SECOND SEMESTER			
Day	**Minimum Course**	**Regular Course**	**Advanced Course**
12	Using a Calculator pp. 252–253	**9–3:** 1–28 e/o	**10–1:** 1–54 e/o
13	Chapter 7 Review	**9–3:** 29–44 e/o	**10–2:** 1–45 e/o, 46–48
14	Chapter 7 Test Ready for Ch. 9?	Consumer Application pp. 354–355*	Consumer Application pp. 354–355*
15	**9–1:** 1–12	**9–4:** 1–8	**10–3:** 1–49 e/o
16	**9–1:** 13–22 e/o	**9–4:** 9–17	**10–4:** 1–18
17	**9–2:** 1–12	**9–5:** 1–21 e/o	Careers/Agriculture p. 428*
18	**9–2:** 13–29 e/o	**9–6:** 1–8	**10–5:** 1–21 e/o, 22–29
19	**9–3:** 1–20 e/o	Computer Activities pp. 548–549*	**10–6:** 1–3, 4–43, mult. of 3
20	**9–3:** 21–40 e/o	Chapter 9 Review	**10–7:** 1–15 e/o
21	Computer Activities pp. 548–549*	Chapter 9 Test Ready for Ch. 10?	**10–7:** 16–27 e/o
22	**9–4:** 1–13 e/o	**10–1:** 1–48 e/o	Chapter 10 Review
23	**9–5:** 1–8	**10–2:** 1–45 e/o	Chapter 10 Test Ready for Ch. 11?
24	**9–5:** 9–14	**10–3:** 1–44 e/o	Cum. Rev. 1–10*
25	Consumer Application pp. 354–356*	**10–4:** 1–17	Cum. Rev. 1–10*
26	**9–6:** 1–8	Careers/Agriculture p. 428*	Using a Calculator p. 425–427*
27	**9–6:** 9–16	**10–5:** 1–21 e/o, 22–29	**11–1:** 1–49 e/o
28	Chapter 9 Review	**10–6:** 1–3, 4–36 mult. of 3	**11–2:** 1–28 e/o
29	Chapter 9 Test Ready for Ch. 10?	**10–7:** 1–12 e/o	**11–3:** 1–24
30	**10–1:** 1–40 e/o	**10–7:** 13–21 e/o	**11–3:** 25–42
31	**10–2:** 1–36 e/o	Chapter 10 Review	**11–4:** 1–22 e/o
32	**10–3:** 1–34 e/o	Chapter 10 Test Ready for Ch. 11?	**11–4:** 23–36 e/o
33	**10–4:** 1–13	Cum. Rev. 1–10*	**11–5:** 1–40 e/o
34	Careers/Agriculture p. 428*	Cum. Rev. 1–10*	**11–5:** 41–82 e/o
35	Chapter 10 Review	**11–1:** 1–35 e/o	**11–6:** 1–18

SECOND SEMESTER			
Day	Minimum Course	Regular Course	Advanced Course
36	Chapter 10 Test Ready for Ch. 11?	**11–1:** 36–46	**11–6:** 19–25
37	Using a Calculator p. 315*	**11–2:** 1–24 e/o	**11–7:** 1–30 e/o
38	Cum. Rev. 1–10*	**11–3:** 1–20	**11–8:** 1–15
39	Cum. Rev. 1–10*	**11–3:** 17–38 e/o	**11–8:** 16–27
40	**11–1:** 1–30 e/o	**11–4:** 1–20 e/o	**11–9:** 1–4
41	**11–1:** 31–44	**11–4:** 21–34	Consumer Application pp. 469–470*
42	**11–2:** 1–18 e/o	**11–5:** 1–36 e/o	Chapter 11 Review
43	**11–3:** 1–16	**11–5:** 67–79 e/o	Chapter 11 Test Ready for Ch. 12?
44	**11–3:** 17–34 e/o	Computer Activities pp. 542–543*	**12–1:** 1–57 e/o, 58–60
45	**11–4:** 1–15	**11–6:** 1–10	**12–2:** 1–40 e/o, 41
46	**11–4:** 16–30 e/o	**11–6:** 11–18	**12–3:** 1–50 e/o
47	Using a Calculator pp. 425–426*	**11–7:** 1–30 e/o	**12–3:** 51–85 e/o, 86
48	**11–5:** 1–30 e/o	**11–7:** 31–42 e/o	Computer Activities pp. 542–543*
49	**11–5:** 31–69 odd	**11–8:** 1–13	**12–4:** 1–66 e/o
50	**11–5:** 31–69 even	**11–8:** 14–24	**12–5:** 1–57 e/o
51	**11–6:** 1–10	Chapter 11 Review	**12–6:** 1–60 e/o
52	**11–7:** 1–15 e/o	Chapter 11 Test Ready for Ch. 12?	**12–7:** 1–57 e/o
53	**11–7:** 15–34 odd	**12–1:** 1–57 e/o	Computer Activities p. 544*
54	**11–8:** 1–10 odd	**12–2:** 1–36 e/o	**12–8:** 1–36 e/o
55	**11–8:** 11–20 odd	**12–3:** 1–50 e/o	**12–9:** 1–42 e/o
56	Chapter 11 Review	**12–3:** 51–77	Using a Calculator, p. 458*
57	Chapter 11 Test Ready for Ch. 12?	**12–4:** 1–59 e/o	Chapter 12 Review
58	**12–1:** 1–50 e/o	Consumer Application pp. 469–470*	Chapter 12 Test Ready for Ch. 13?
59	**12–2:** 1–24	**12–5:** 1–30 e/o	**13–1:** 1–33 e/o

SECOND SEMESTER			
Day	Minimum Course	Regular Course	Advanced Course
60	12–3: 1–30 e/o	12–5: 31–54 e/o	13–1: 34–57 e/o
61	12–3: 31–66 odd	12–6: 1–56 e/o	13–2: 1–30 e/o
62	12–3: 31–66 even	12–7: 1–51 e/o	13–3: 1–44 e/o
63	12–4: 1–30 e/o	12–8: 1–29 e/o	13–4: 1–33 e/o
64	12–4: 31–51	12–9: 1–31 e/o	13–4: 34–58 odd
65	12–5: 1–12	Chapter 12 Review	13–4: 34–58 even, 59–61
66	12–5: 13–30	Chapter 12 Test Ready for Ch. 13?	Careers/Automobile Industry, p. 501*
67	Consumer Application pp. 469–470*	13–1: 1–33 e/o	13–5: 1–30 e/o, 31–35
68	12–6: 1–24	13–1: 34–47 e/o	13–6: 1–20 e/o
69	12–6: 25–80	13–2: 1–46 e/o	13–7: 1–24 e/o
70	Computer Activities pp. 542–543*	Computer Activities pp. 545–546*	Using a Calculator pp. 502–503*
71	12–7: 1–42 odd	13–3: 1–24 e/o	13–7: 25–42 e/o, 43
72	12–7: 1–42 even	13–4: 1–33 e/o	Chapter 13 Review
73	12–8: 1–23 e/o	13–4: 34–58 odd	Chapter 13 Test Ready for Ch. 14?
74	Chapter 12 Review	Using a Calculator pp. 502–503*	14–1: 1–9 e/o, 10–15
75	Chapter 12 Test Ready for Ch. 13?	13–4: 34–58 even	14–2: 1–26 e/o, 27
76	13–1: 1–39 e/o	13–5: 1–30 e/o, 31	14–3: 1–36 e/o, 37
77	13–2: 1–30 e/o	13–6: 1–20 e/o	Computer Activities pp. 545–546*
78	13–2: 31–46	13–7: 1–24 e/o	Computer Activities p. 547*
79	13–3: 1–24 e/o	13–7: 25–39 e/o	Computer Activities pp. 550–551*
80	13–4: 1–24 e/o	Chapter 13 Review	14–4: 1–12
81	13–4: 25–42 odd	Chapter 13 Test Ready for Ch. 14?	14–4: 13–23
82	13–4: 25–42 even	14–1: 1–9 e/o	Chapter 14 Review
83	Chapter 13 Test	14–2: 1–26 e/o	Chapter 14 Test

SECOND SEMESTER			
Day	Minimum Course	Regular Course	Advanced Course
84	Cum. Rev. 1–14*	Cum. Rev. 1–14*	Cum. Rev. 1–14*
85	Cum. Rev. 1–14*	Cum. Rev. 1–14*	Cum. Rev. 1–14*
86	Review Ch. 1–13	Review Ch. 1–14	Review Ch. 1–14
87	End-of-Year Test	End-of-Year Test	End-of-Year Test

REFERENCES TO SUPPLEMENTS

APPLICATIONS
In the **Teacher's Resource Book** order code 20337, Applications 1–6 cover Career topics, Applications 7–12 cover Consumer topics, Applications 13–26 cover Problem Solving, and Applications 27–34 cover Calculator topics.

PRACTICE MASTERS
Making Practice Fun by Ray Chayo © 1978 Addison-Wesley order code 3836. A book of 113 blackline masters of activity-based practice. For remediation and reinforcement.

ENRICHMENT MASTERS
Math Motivators by Alfred S. Posamentier and Gordon Sheridan © 1983 Addison-Wesley order code 5582. A book of 38 blackline masters of Investigations in Algebra including one page of teacher resources for each investigation.

   The investigations referenced in the following charts relate directly to the indicated sections of the student book and may be assigned for independent student work. Other investigations may also be assigned at the teacher's discretion.

COMPUTER GRAPHING EXPERIMENTS
Computer Graphing Experiments, Volumes 1, 2, and 3 by Charles Lund and Edwin Andersen © 1982 Addison-Wesley order code 23465 for Volume 1 Algebra One & Two, order code 23470 for Volume 2 Trigonometric Functions, order code 23475 for Volume 3 Conic Sections, and order code 23480 for Volumes 1–3. An interactive Apple II or Apple II Plus program. Each volume contains a diskette, backup diskette, blackline master worksheets, plus answers and teacher notes. No programming knowledge is required.

   The experiments referenced in the following charts relate directly to the indicated sections of the student book and may be assigned for independent student work. Other experiments may be assigned at the teacher's discretion.

COMPUTERS: SUPPLEMENTARY READING
Using Computers in Mathematics by Gerald H. Elgarten, Alfred S. Posamentier, and Stephen E. Moresh © 1983 Addison-Wesley order code 10450. A textbook for an introductory computer course or a supplement to teach the BASIC language. All computer ideas are introduced in the context of mathematical concepts. The Instructor's Commentary, order code 10449, has 148 detailed lesson plans. The Solutions Manual, order code 10456, contains complete solutions.

The sections of this book referenced in the following charts relate directly to the indicated sections of the student book and are sources for supplementary computer programs. Other sections may also be helpful sources for the teacher.

VIDEO REVIEW
The *Addison-Wesley Video Cassette Reviews for Introductory Algebra* by Keedy, Bittinger © 1983. This series of videotape films consists of televised review lessons for first-year Algebra. Each cassette contains a review of 2–4 specific objectives.

The videotaped lessons are taught by a classroom teacher, Professor John Jobe, and can be used for students who missed class presentations or who need review.

Student Textbook

	Chapter 1		Chapter 2		Chapter 3		Chapter 4	
Sections	Sec. 1–1 to 1–3	Sec. 1–4 to 1–7	Sec. 2–1 to 2–4	Sec. 2–5 to 2–10	Sec. 3–1 to 3–3	Sec. 3–4 to 3–8	Sec. 4–1 to 4–5	Sec. 4–6 to 4–9
Chapter Review and Test		pp. 35–37		pp. 93–96		pp. 137–139		pp. 186–188
Computer Activities		pp. 536–537				pp. 537–539		

Teacher's Edition

Quizzes	1	2	3, 4	5, 6	7	8	9, 10	11
Teaching Suggestions	pp. T48-49	pp. T50-51, 77	pp. T52-55	pp. T55-57	pp. T57-59	pp. T59-61, 77	pp. T61-63	p. T63

Teacher's Resource Book

Arithmetic Reviews	1–4	5, 6	7, 8	9, 10	11	12		
Chapter Tests		1		2		3		4
Multiple Choice Chapter Tests		1		2		3		4
Mid-Year Test								
End-of-Year Test								
Skills Practice	1	2		3, 4	5	6	7, 8	9
Applications		13	1	14	7	15	2	16
Computer Projects					1	2	3	4

Other Supplementary Materials

Practice Masters	1–3	5–7, 10–12	4, 9, 14–16	8, 13, 17–20, 23	24–26	27, 29, 30	31–34	35–38
Enrichment Masters			p. 61		p. 37			p. 19
Computer Graphing Experiments								
Using Computers in Mathematics						Sec. 1–2 to 1–4		Sec. 1–7, 2–1

Student Textbook

	Chapter 5		Chapter 6		Chapter 7		Chapter 8	
Sections	Sec. 5–1 to 5–4	Sec. 5–5 to 5–9	Sec. 6–1 to 6–2	Sec. 6–3 to 6–5	Sec. 7–1 to 7–4	Sec. 7–5 to 7–7	Sec. 8–1 to 8–2	Sec. 8–3 to 8–5
Chapter Review and Test		pp. 225–226		pp. 255–257		pp. 288–289		pp. 317–319
Computer Activities		pp. 539–541				pp. 541–542		

Teacher's Edition

Quizzes	12, 13	14	15	16	17, 18	19	20	21
Teaching Suggestions	pp. T64-65	p. T66, 79	p. T66	p. T66	pp. T66-67	pp. T67-68, 79	pp. T68-69	

Teacher's Resource Book

Arithmetic Reviews								
Chapter Tests		5		6		7		8
Multiple Choice Chapter Tests		5		6		7		8
Mid-Year Test						Mid-Year Test		
End-of-Year Test								
Skills Practice	10	11, 12	13	14	15	16		17, 18
Applications	8	17	3, 27	18	9	19	10, 28	20, 29
Computer Projects	5	6, 7	8	9, 10	11	12	13	14

Other Supplementary Materials

Practice Masters	42, 43	28, 39–41,44,45	64, 65	66–70	47–50	52, 53		51, 82, 106, 107
Enrichment Masters		p. 11		p. 17		p. 21		
Computer Graphing Experiments						Vol. 1 Exp.1–4, 9–11		Vol. 1 Exp. 12
Using Computers in Mathematics						Sec. 2–7		

Student Textbook

	Chapter 9		Chapter 10		Chapter 11		Chapter 12	
Sections	Sec. 9–1 to 9–3	Sec. 9–4 to 9–6	Sec. 10–1 to 10–3	Sec. 10–4 to 10–7	Sec. 11–1 to 11–3	Sec. 11–4 to 11–9	Sec. 12–1 to 12–4	Sec. 12–5 to 12–9
Chapter Review and Test		pp. 357– 359		pp. 385– 389		pp. 429– 431		pp. 470– 473
Computer Activities			pp. 542– 544				pp. 544– 545	

Teacher's Edition

	Chapter 9		Chapter 10		Chapter 11		Chapter 12	
Quizzes	22	23	24	25	26, 27	28, 29	30, 31	32
Teaching Suggestions	p. T69		pp. T69-70, 80	p. T70	pp. T70-71	pp. T71-72	pp. T73-74, 80	pp. T74-75

Teacher's Resource Book

	Chapter 9		Chapter 10		Chapter 11		Chapter 12	
Arithmetic Reviews								
Chapter Tests		9		10		11		12
Multiple Choice Chapter Tests		9		10		11		12
Mid-Year Test								
End-of-Year Test								
Skills Practice	19	20	21	22	23, 24	25, 26	27	28-30
Applications	4	21	5	22	11, 30	23, 31	6	24
Computer Projects		15					16	

Other Supplementary Materials

	Chapter 9		Chapter 10		Chapter 11		Chapter 12	
Practice Masters	54–56	57–59	60–62	63	71, 72, 78	73–77, 79–81	83–87	88–91
Enrichment Masters				pp. 71, 73		pp. 29, 39, 47	p. 9	p. 69
Computer Graphing Experiments				Vol. 1 Exp. 5–8				
Using Computers in Mathematics		Sec. 2–5	Sec. 2–6	Sec. 2–3		Sec. 5–5	Sec. 2–2, 2–4, 5–1	Sec. 2–8 3–3

Student Textbook

	Chapter 13		Chapter 14				
Sections	Sec. 13–1 to 13–3	Sec. 13–4 to 13–7	Sec. 14–1 to 14–2	Sec. 14–3 to 14–4			
Chapter Review and Test		pp. 503–505		pp. 524–527			
Computer Activities		pp. 545–550		pp. 550–551			

Teacher's Edition

Quizzes	33	34		35			
Teaching Suggestions	p. T75	pp. T76, 81, 82	p. T76	p. T83			

Teacher's Resource Book

Arithmetic Reviews							
Chapter Tests		13		14			
Multiple Choice Chapter Tests		13		14			
Mid-Year Test							
End-of-Year Test				End-of-Year Test			
Skills Practice		31, 32	33	34			
Applications	12, 32	25, 33		26, 34			
Computer Projects	17	18, 19	20				

Other Supplementary Materials

Practice Masters	46, 92–95	96–101	109, 110	111, 112			
Enrichment Masters							
Computer Graphing Experiments							
Using Computers in Mathematics							

ADDITIONAL ANSWERS

Answers too long to be listed on student pages.

CHAPTER 1 Page 19
EXERCISE SET 1–4
38. $a + (b + 2)$, $(b + a) + 2$, $b + (a + 2)$
39. $3 + (x + y)$, $3 + (y + x)$, $(3 + y) + x$
40. $(5 + v) + w$, $5 + (w + v)$, $(5 + w) + v$
41. $(6 + x) + y$, $6 + (y + x)$, $(6 + y) + x$
42. $x \cdot (y \cdot 3)$, $(y \cdot x) \cdot 3$, $y \cdot (x \cdot 3)$
43. $a \cdot (b \cdot 5)$, $(b \cdot a) \cdot 5$, $b \cdot (a \cdot 5)$
44. $b \cdot (7 \cdot a)$, $(7 \cdot a) \cdot b$, $(7 \cdot b) \cdot a$
45. $(5 \cdot x) \cdot y$, $5 \cdot (y \cdot x)$, $(5 \cdot y) \cdot x$

Page 23
EXERCISE SET 1–5
1. $2b + 10$ 2. $4x + 12$ 3. $7 + 7t$
4. $6v + 24$ 5. $3x + 3$ 6. $7x + 56$
7. $4 + 4y$ 8. $9s + 9$ 9. $30x + 12$
10. $54m + 63$ 11. $7x + 28 + 42y$
12. $20x + 32 + 12p$ 13. $2(x + 2)$
14. $5(y + 4)$ 15. $5(6 + y)$ 16. $7(x + 4)$
17. $7(2x + 3y)$ 18. $6(3a + 4b)$
19. $5(x + 2 + 3y)$ 20. $9(a + 3b + 9)$

CHAPTER 2 Page 45
TRY THIS
2–5.

Pages 47–48
EXERCISE SET 2–2
2–5.

36–37.

38. Yes. If $\frac{a}{b} < \frac{c}{d}$, $\frac{a}{b} \cdot \frac{d}{d} < \frac{c}{d} \cdot \frac{b}{b}$; $\frac{ad}{bd} < \frac{cb}{bd}$; $\frac{ad}{bd} \cdot bd < \frac{cb}{bd} \cdot bd$ (bd is always positive); $ad < cb$. If $ad < cb$, then $ad \cdot \frac{1}{bd} < cb \cdot \frac{1}{bd}$; $\frac{ad}{bd} < \frac{cb}{bd}$; $\frac{a}{b} \cdot \frac{d}{d} < \frac{c}{d} \cdot \frac{b}{b}$; $\frac{a}{b} < \frac{c}{d}$. Let $a = -5$, $b = 23$, $c = -4$, $d = 27$, $ad = -135$, $bc = -92$; $bc > ad$, so $\frac{c}{d} > \frac{a}{b}$, or $\frac{-4}{27} > \frac{-5}{23}$.

Page 48
Special Topic: Subsets of the Rational Numbers
1. Answers may vary. Ex.: $N \subset W$, $N \subset I$, $N \subset R$, $W \subset I$, $W \subset R$, $I \subset R$ 2. Yes

Pages 49–51
TRY THIS
1.

2.

3.

4.

5.

6.

7.

8.

9.

10.

11.

Page 55
EXERCISE SET 2–3
1. -7 2. -3 3. -4 4. 5 5. 0 6. 0
7. -8 8. -10 9. -7 10. -13
11. -27 12. -35 13. 0 14. 0
15. -42 16. -41 17. -43 18. -80
19. -2 20. -7 21. 5 22. -11
23. $-\frac{25}{7}$ 24. $\frac{7}{19}$ 25. -11 26. 6
27. $\frac{7}{16}$ 28. $\frac{1}{84}$ 29. 39 30. -62 31. 50
32. 37.9 33. -1093 34. -1021

Page 57
TRY THIS
1.

2.

3.

Page 61
EXERCISE SET 2–4
69. Both of these. Subtraction is the addition of an inverse. **70.** No. For example: $7 - 2 \neq 2 - 7$. **71.** No, it is equal to -5; 5. If there is an even number of minus signs, the number is even; if there is an odd number of minus signs, the number is odd.

Page 67
EXERCISE SET 2–5
57. a. $2(10) + 2(9) + 2(8) + 2(7) + 2(6) + 2(5) + 2(4) + 2(3) + 2(2) + 2(1) - 10x = 0$, $10x = 110$, $x = 11$ lbs **b.** $20w = 110$, $w = 5.5$, 5.5 ft from the center.

Page 75
EXERCISE SET 2–7
11. $45x + 54y - 72$

Page 91
EXERCISE SET 2–10

24.	
$(-a)b = (-1 \cdot a)b$	Property of -1
$= -1(ab)$	Assoc. law
$= -ab$	Property of -1
$(-a)b = -ab$	Transitive

25.	
$-(a - b) = -[a + (-b)]$	Subtr. rule
$= -a + [-(-b)]$	Inverse of sum
$= -a + b$	Inverse of inverse
$= b + (-a)$	Comm.
$= b - a$	Subtr. rule
$-(a - b) = b - a$	Trans.

Page 94
CHAPTER 2 REVIEW
6–7.

CHAPTER 3 Page 130
SPECIAL TOPIC: PRIME FACTORS
1. $210 = 2 \cdot 3 \cdot 5 \cdot 7$ 2. $378 = 2 \cdot 3^3 \cdot 7$
3. $825 = 3 \cdot 5^2 \cdot 11$ 4. $1000 = 2^3 \cdot 5^3$
5. $6144 = 2^{11} \cdot 3$

Pages 132–135
TRY THIS
1. 1. $3x + 5 = 20$, Hypothesis; 2. $3x = 15$, Add. prin.; 3. $x = 5$, Mult. prin.; 4. If $3x + 5 = 20$, then $x = 5$, Statements 1–3.
4. 1. $x = 5$, Hypothesis; 2. $3x = 15$, Mult. prin.; 3. $3x + 5 = 20$, Add. prin.; 4. If $x = 5$, then $3x + 5 = 20$, Statements 1–3.

5.a. 1. $6y - 12 = 30$, Hypothesis; 2. $6y = 42$, Add. prin.; 3. $y = 7$, Mult. prin.; 4. If $6y - 12 = 30$, then $y = 7$, Statements 1–3.
5.b. 1. $y = 7$, Hypothesis; 2. $6y = 42$, Mult. prin.; 3. $6y - 12 = 30$, Add. prin.; 4. If $y = 7$, then $6y - 12 = 30$, Statements 1–3. **6.a.** 1. $8x + 17 = 81$, Hypothesis; 2. $8x = 64$, Add. prin.; 3. $x = 8$, Mult. prin.; 4. If $8x + 17 = 81$, then $x = 8$, Statements 1–3. **6.b.** $8(8) + 17 = 64 + 17 = 81$

Page 135
EXERCISE SET 3–8
1. 1. $8x - 12 = 68$, Hypothesis; 2. $8x = 80$, Add. prin.; 3. $x = 10$, Mult. prin.; 4. If $8x - 12 = 68$, then $x = 10$, Statements 1–3.
2. 1. $3x + 5 = 32$, Hypothesis; 2. $3x = 27$, Add. prin.; 3. $x = 9$, Mult. prin.; 4. If $3x + 5 = 32$, then $x = 9$, Statements 1–3.
3. 1. $\frac{x}{2} + 3 = 15$, Hypothesis; 2. $\frac{x}{2} = 12$, Add. prin.; 3. $x = 24$, Mult. prin.; 4. If $\frac{x}{2} + 3 = 15$, then $x = 24$, Statements 1–3.
4. $0.5x + 0.25 = 1.75$, Hypothesis; 2. $0.5x = 1.5$, Add. prin.; 3. $x = 3$, Mult. prin.; 4. If $0.5x + 0.25 = 1.75$, then $x = 3$, Statements 1–3. **9.** 1. $x = 10$, Hypothesis; 2. $8x = 80$, Mult. prin.; 3. $8x - 12 = 68$, Add. prin., 4. If $x = 10$, then $8x - 12 = 68$, Statements 1–3. **10.** 1. $x = 9$, Hypothesis; 2. $3x = 27$, Mult. prin.; 3. $3x + 5 = 32$, Add. prin.; 4. If $x = 9$, then $3x + 5 = 32$, Statements 1–3. **11.** $x = 24$, Hypothesis; 2. $\frac{x}{2} = 12$, Mult. prin.; 3. $\frac{x}{2} + 3 = 15$, Add. prin.; 4. If $x = 24$, then $\frac{x}{2} + 3 = 15$, Statements 1–3. **12.** $x = 3$, Hypothesis; 2. $0.5x = 1.5$, Mult. prin.; 3. $0.5x + 0.25 = 1.75$, Statements 1–3. **13.a.** 1. $3x + 5 = 14$, Hypothesis; 2. $3x = 9$, Add. prin.; 3. $x = 3$, Mult. prin. **13.b.** 1. $x = 3$, Hypothesis; 2. $3x = 9$, Mult. prin.; 3. $3x + 5 = 14$, Add. prin.
  14.a. 1. $4x + 8 = 19$, Hypothesis; 2. $4x = 11$, Add prin.; 3. $x = \frac{11}{4}$, Mult. prin. **14.b.** 1. $x = \frac{11}{4}$, Hypothesis; 2. $4x =$ 11, Mult. prin.; 3. $4x + 8 = 19$, Add. prin.
15.a. 1. $2m - 5 = 17$, Hypothesis; 2. $2m = 22$, Add. prin.; 3. $m = 11$, Mult. prin.
15.b. 1. $m = 11$, Hypothesis; 2. $2m = 22$, Mult. prin.; 2. $2m - 5 = 17$, Add. prin.
16.a. 1. $3y - 4 = 22$; 2. $3y = 26$, Add. prin.; 3. $y = \frac{26}{3}$, Mult. prin. **16.b.** 1. $y = \frac{26}{3}$, Hypothesis; $3y = 26$, Mult. prin.; 3. $3y - 4 = 22$, Add. prin. **17.a.** 1. $\frac{x}{2} - 4 = 8$, Hypothesis; 2. $\frac{x}{2} = 12$, Add. prin.; 3. $x = 24$, Mult. prin. **17.b.** 1. $x = 24$, Hypothesis; 2. $\frac{x}{2} = 12$, Mult. prin.; 3. $\frac{x}{2} - 4 = 8$, Add. prin. **18.a.** 1. $\frac{a}{3} + 6 = 9$, Hypothesis; 2. $\frac{a}{3} = 3$, Add. prin.; 3. $a = 9$, Mult. prin. **18.b.** 1. $a = 9$, Hypothesis; 2. $\frac{a}{3} = 3$, Mult. prin.; 3. $\frac{a}{3} + 6 = 9$, Add. prin. **19.a.** 1. $2(y - 1) - 7 = 5$, Hypothesis; 2. $2(y - 1) = 12$, Add. prin.; 3. $y - 1 = 6$, Mult. prin.; 4. $y = 7$, Add. prin. **19.b.** 1. $y = 7$, Hypothesis; 2. $y - 1 = 6$, Add. prin.; 3. $2(y - 1) = 12$, Mult. prin.; 4. $2(y - 1) - 7 = 5$, Add. prin. **20.a.** 1. $5(x - 2) + 8 = 3$, Hypothesis; 2. $5(x - 2) = -5$, Add. prin.; 3. $x - 2 = -1$, Mult. prin.; 4. $x = 1$, Add. prin. **20.b.** 1. $x = 1$, Hypothesis; 2. $x - 2 = -1$, Add. prin.; 3. $5(x - 2) = 5$, Mult. prin.; 4. $5(x - 2) + 8 = 3$, Add. prin. **21.a.** 1. $14 + 5m = -76$, Hypothesis; 2. $5m = -90$, Add. prin.; 3. $m = -18$, Mult. prin. **21.b.** $14 - 90 = -76$ **22.a.** 1. $8 + 5(y + 3) = 53$, Hypothesis; 2. $5(y + 3) = 45$, Add. prin.; 3. $y + 3 = 9$, Mult. prin.; 4. $y = 6$, Add. prin. **22.b.** $8 + 5(6 + 3) = 53$.
23.a. 1. $2(x - 3) - x = -2$, Hypothesis; 2. $2x - 6 - x = -2$, Distrib. law.; 3. $x - 6 = -2$, Distrib. law; 4. $x = 4$, Add. prin. **23.b.** $2(4 - 3) - 4 = -2$ **24.a.** 1. $3(y + 4) - 2y = -5$, Hypothesis; 2. $3y + 12 - 2y = -5$, Distrib. law; 3. $y + 12 = -5$, Distrib. law; 4. $y = 17$, Add. prin. **24.b.** $3(-17 + 4) - 2 \cdot (-17) = -5$.

Page 136

CAREERS: SPACE TRAVEL

3. $\frac{9}{5}(10) = 18$, 18 degrees below maximum Farenheit

CHAPTER 4 Page 162

EXERCISE SET 4–4

46. $ax^2 + bx + c$

$\underline{dx^2 + ex + f}$

$(a + d)x^2 + (b + e)x + (c + f)$

47. $a_nx^n + a_{n-1}x^{n-1} + \cdots + a_1x + a_0$

$\underline{+ b_nx^n + b_{n-1}x^{n-1} + \cdots + b_1x + b_0}$

$(a_n + b_n)x^n + (a_{n-1} + b_{n-1})x^{n-1}$

$+ \cdots + (a_1 + b_1)x + a_0 + b_0$

Page 174

EXERCISE SET 4–7

28.a. $x^3 - 1$ b. $x^3 + 2x^2 + 2x + 1$ c. $x^3 - 2x^2 + 2x - 1$ d. $x^3 + 1$ e. $-x^3 + 2x^2 - 2x + 2$ f. $-x^3 - 1$ g. $x^4 - 1$ h. $x^4 + 2x^3 + 2x^2 + 2x + 1$ i. $x^4 - 2x^3 + 2x^2 - 2x + 1$ j. $x^4 + 2x + 1$ k. $-x^4 + 2x^3 - 2x^2 + 2x - 1$ l. $-x^4 + 1$

CHAPTER 5 Page 193

EXERCISE SET 5–1

7. $x(x - 4)$ 8. $x(x + 8)$ 9. $2x(x + 3)$
10. $3x(x - 1)$ 11. $x^2(x + 6)$
12. $x^2(4x^2 + 1)$ 13. $8x^2(x^2 - 3)$
14. $5x^3(x^2 + 2)$ 15. $2(x^2 + x - 4)$
16. $3(2x^2 + x - 5)$ 17. $17x(x^4 + 2x^2 + 3)$
18. $16x(x^5 - 2x^4 - 3)$
19. $x^2(6x^2 - 10x + 3)$
20. $x(5x^4 + 10x - 8)$
21. $x^2(x^3 + x^2 + x - 1)$
22. $x^3(x^6 - x^4 + x + 1)$
23. $2x^3(x^4 - x^3 - 32x^2 + 2)$
24. $5(2x^3 + 5x^2 + 3x - 4)$
25. $0.8x(2x^3 - 3x^2 + 4x + 8)$
26. $0.5x^2(5x^4 - x^2 + 10x + 20)$
27. $\frac{x^3}{3}(5x^3 + 4x^2 + x + 1)$
28. $\frac{x}{7}(5x^6 + 3x^4 - 6x^2 - 1)$

Page 196

EXERCISE SET 5–2

30. $(x^2 + 1)(x + 1)(x - 1)$ 31. $(x^2 + 4)(x + 2)(x - 2)$ 32. $4(x^2 + 4)(x + 2)(x - 2)$
33. $5(x^2 + 4)(x + 2)(x - 2)$ 34. $(1 + y^4)(1 + y^2)(1 + y)(1 - y)$ 35. $(x^4 + 1)(x^2 + 1)(x + 1)(x - 1)$ 36. $(x^6 + 4)(x^3 + 2)(x^3 - 2)$
37. $(x^4 + 9)(x^2 + 3)(x^2 - 3)$
38. $\left(\frac{1}{4} + y\right)\left(\frac{1}{4} - y\right)$ 39. $\left(\frac{1}{5} + x\right)\left(\frac{1}{5} - x\right)$
40. $\left(5 + \frac{1}{7}x\right)\left(5 - \frac{1}{7}x\right)$ 41. $\left(2 + \frac{1}{3}y\right)\left(2 - \frac{1}{3}y\right)$
42. $(4 + t^2)(2 + t)(2 - t)$ 43. $(1 + a^2)(1 + a)(1 - a)$ 44. $4x^2(x + 1)(x - 1)$
45. $3x^3(x + 2)(x - 2)$ 46. $3\left(x + \frac{1}{3}\right)\left(x - \frac{1}{3}\right)$ 47. $2x\left(3x + \frac{2}{5}\right)\left(3x - \frac{2}{5}\right)$
48. $(x + 1.5)(x - 1.5)$ 49. $x\left(x + \frac{1}{1.3}\right)\left(x - \frac{1}{1.3}\right)$ 50. $(1.8x + 0.9)(1.8x - 0.9)$
51. $(0.8x + 1.1)(0.8x + 1.1)$
52. $2(0.8x + 1)(0.8x - 1)$ 53. $x(x + 6)$
54. $(y + 1)(y - 11)$ 55. $3(a - 1)(3a + 11)$
56. $4(y - 4)(y - 3)$ 57. $(y^4 + 16)(y^2 + 4)(y + 2)(y - 2)$ 58. $(x^8 + 1)(x^4 + 1)(x^2 + 1)(x + 1)(x - 1)$ 59. $\frac{1}{x^2}(x^2 + 1)(x + 1)(x - 1)$

Page 198

TRY THIS

9. $(x + 1)^2$ 10. $(x - 1)^2$ 11. $(x + 2)^2$
12. $(5x - 7)^2$ 13. $(4x - 7)^2$
14. $3(16x^2 + 40x + 25) = 3(4x + 5)^2$

Page 215

EXERCISE SET 5–8

26. $-\frac{1}{10}, \frac{1}{27}$ 27. 2, 6 28. $\frac{1}{21}, \frac{18}{11}$ 29. $\frac{1}{3}$, 20 30. 3, 50 31. 0, $\frac{2}{3}, \frac{1}{2}$ 32. 5, $-55, \frac{1}{5}$

CHAPTER 6 Page 237

EXERCISE SET 6–2

15. $6z^2 + 7zu - 3u^2$ 16. $x^3 - y^3$
17. $x^2y^2 + 3xy - 28$ 18. $p^3q^4 - 4p^2q^2 + 3pq^2 - 12$ 19. $a^4 + a^3 - a^2y - ay + a + y - 1$ 20. $tvx^2 + stx + rvx + rs$
21. $a^6 - b^2c^2$ 22. $m^4 + m^2n^2 + n^4$
23. $a^4 + a^2b^2 + b^4$ 24. $p^5q^4 - p^4 + 5p^2 - 3p^3q^4 - 6$ 25. $a^4 - b^4$ 26. $c^4 - d^4$

27. $12x^2y^2 + 2xy - 2$ **28.** $m^6n^2 + 2m^3n$
$- 48$ **29.** $12 - c^2d^2 + c^4d^4$ **30.** $30x^2$
$- 28xy + 6y^2$ **31.** $m^3 + m^2n - mn^2 - n^3$
32. $p^3 - p^2q + pq^2 - q^3$ **33.** $x^9y^9 - x^6x^6$
$+ x^5y^5 - x^2y^2$ **34.** $a^7b^7 + a^4b^5 - a^5b^4$
$- a^2b^2$ **35.** $x^2 + xy^3 - 2y^6$ **36.** $10s^2t^4$
$+ 3st^3 - 4t^2$ **37.** $9a^2 + 12ab + 4b^2$
38. $r^6t^4 - 8r^3t^2 + 16$ **39.** $9a^4b^2 - 6a^2b^3$
$+ b^4$ **40.** $p^8 + 2m^2n^2p^4 + m^4n^4$ **41.** a^2b^2
$+ 2abcd + c^2d^2$ **42.** $4a^6 - 2a^3b^3 + \frac{1}{4}b^6$
43. $-5x^3 - 30x^2y - 45xy^2$ **44.** $a^4 + 2a^2b$
$+ 4a^2 + b^2 + b^2 + 4b + 4$ **45.** $x^2 - y^2$
46. $4a^2 - b^2$ **47.** $c^4 - d^2$ **48.** $p^6 - 25q^2$
49. $a^2b^2 - c^2d^2$ **50.** $c^2 + 2cd + d^2 - 25$
51. $x^2 + 2xy + y^2 - 9$ **52.** $b^2 - a^2$ **53.** p^8
$- m^4n^4$ **54.** $a^2 - b^2 - 2bc - c^2$ **55.** a^2
$- b^2 - 2bc - c^2$ **56.** $9x^2 + 12x + 4 - 25y^2$
57. $9x^2 - 25y^2 - 10y - 1$ **58.** $h^2 - k^2$
$+ 8k - 16$

CHAPTER 7 Page 260
TRY THIS
1–6.

7–10.

Page 261
EXERCISE SET 7–1
1–15. odd

2–16. even

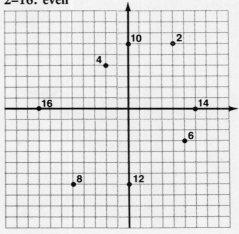

Page 265
TRY THIS
4.

5.

Pages 265–266
EXERCISE SET 7–2
16.

17.

18.

19.

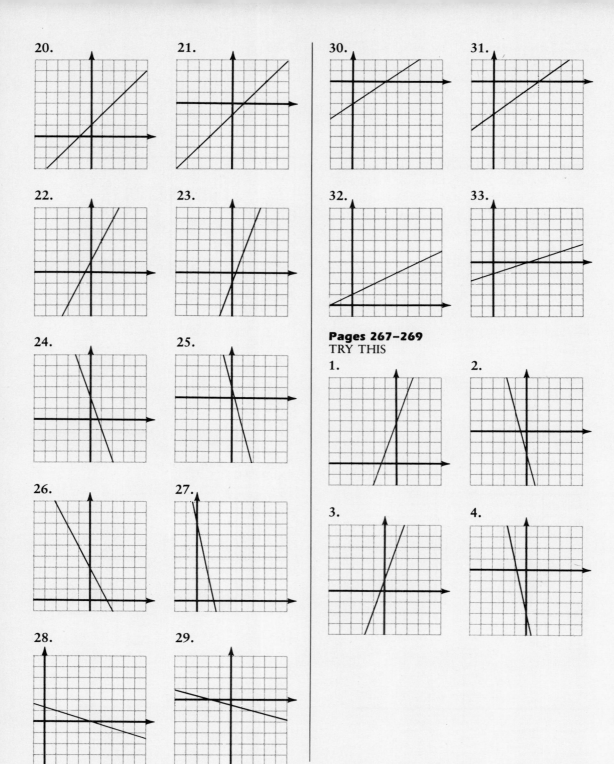

20.

21.

22.

23.

24.

25.

26.

27.

28.

29.

30.

31.

32.

33.

Pages 267–269
TRY THIS

1.

2.

3.

4.

5.

6.

1.

2.

7.

8.

3.

4.

9.

5.

6.

10.

11.

7.

8.

9.

10.

11.

12.

13.

14.

15.

16. $(0, -1)$, $(1, 0)$ **17.** $(0, -3)$, $(3, 0)$

18. $(0, -1)$, $\left(\frac{1}{2}, 0\right)$ **19.** $(0, -2)$, $\left(\frac{2}{3}, 0\right)$

20. $(0, -4)$, $(3, 0)$ **21.** $(0, -9)$, $(3, 0)$

22. $(0, 3)$, $\left(\frac{6}{7}, 0\right)$ **23.** $\left(0, \frac{5}{4}\right)\left(\frac{5}{3}, 0\right)$

24. $(0, -4)$, $(-1, 0)$ **25.** $(0, -3)(-1, 0)$

26. $\left(0, \frac{1}{3}\right)$, $\left(\frac{2}{3}, 0\right)$ **27.** $\left(0, \frac{5}{8}\right)$, $\left(\frac{5}{4}, 0\right)$

28. Vertical line through $(-4, 0)$ **29.** Vertical line through $(-3, 0)$ **30.** Horizontal line through $(0, -7)$ **31.** Horizontal line through $(0, -9)$ **32.** Vertical line through $(5, 0)$ **33.** Vertical line through $(7, 0)$

34. Horizontal line through $\left(0, \frac{1}{2}\right)$

35. Horizontal line through $\left(0, \frac{1}{4}\right)$

Page 271

42.

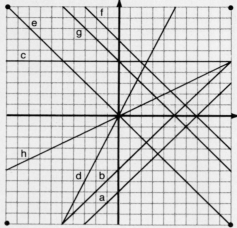

Page 273

TRY THIS

1.

2.

Pages 274–275

EXERCISE SET 7–4

1.

2.

3.

4.

5.

6.

7. 2 8. $\frac{5}{4}$ 9. $-\frac{9}{7}$ 10. $\frac{3}{7}$

Page 279
TRY THIS

10.

11.

12.

13.

Page 280
EXERCISE SET 7–5

28.

29.

30.

31.

32.

33.

34.

35.

36.

37–42.

1–3.

12.

13.

14.

1. The y-intercept of a line is the point where the line crosses the y-axis. Thus, the x-coordinate of the point is zero. Let $x = 0$ in the equation $y = mx + b$. $y = 0 \cdot x + b$, $y = 0 + b$, $y =$ b. Thus, b is the y-intercept.

2. Suppose that (x_1, y_1) and (x_2, y_2) are any two points on a vertical line. The slope of the line is $\frac{y_2 - y_1}{x_2 - x_1}$. Since the line is vertical, the x-coordinates are the same, so the slope is $\frac{y_2 - y_1}{0}$. Division by 0 is not allowed, so the line has no slope.

1. Given a nonvertical line containing the point (x_1, x_1) and having slope m, let (x, y) be any other point on the line. Then $m = \frac{y - y_1}{x - x_1}$. Multiplying each side of the equation by $x - x_1$ (Mult. prin.), we have $m(x - x_1) = y - y_1$, or $y - y_1 = m(x - x_1)$.

2. 1. Line with slope m and point $(0, b)$, Hypothesis; 2. $y - y_1 = m(x - x_1)$, Point-Slope equation; 3. $y - b = m(x - 0)$, Substitution; 4. $y = mx + b$, Add. prin.

1–2.

7.

8.

9.

108.

10.

14.

Pages 291–292
CUMULATIVE REVIEW 1–7

56. $8x^5 - 4x^4 + 28x^3$ **57.** $6x^2 - 7x - 20$
58. $a^2 - 9$ **59.** $12x^3 - 12x^2 + 7x - 2$
60. $2x^5 + x^3 - 6x^2 - x + 3$ **61.** $2 - 10x^2$
$+ 12x^4$ **62.** $6x^7 - 12x^5 + 9x^2 - 18$
63. $4x^6 - 1$ **64.** $64x^2 + 48x + 9$
65. $36x^2 - 60x + 25$ **66.** $4x^4 - 4x^3$
$- x^2 + 2x - 1$ **67.** $x(x - 4)$
68. $3x^2(2x^3 - 12x + 3)$ **69.** $4x(-12x^3$
$- x + 3)$ **70.** $(3x + 1)(3x - 1)$
71. $2(x + 3)(x - 3)$ **72.** $(4x^2 + 9)$
$(2x + 3)(2x - 3)$ **73.** $(x - 7)^2$
74. $(4x + 5)^2$ **75.** $2(3x - 4)^2$
76. $(x - 6)(x - 4)$ **77.** $(x - 7)(x + 5)$
78. $x(x - 7)(x + 3)$ **79.** $(2x + 1)$
$(4x + 3)$ **80.** $(3x - 2)(x + 4)$
81. $2(3x - 2)(x - 4)$ **82.** $(x^2 + 2)$
$(x + 1)$ **83.** $(x^3 - 3)(x + 2)$
84. $3(1 + 2x^3)(1 - 2x^3)$

Pages 292–293
CUMULATIVE REVIEW 1–7
100.

101.

102.

103.

CHAPTER 8   Page 300
TRY THIS
1.

2.

1.

2.

3.

4.

5.

6.

7.

8.

9.

10.

11.

12.

13.

Page 305
EXERCISE SET 8-3
15.

Page 313
EXERCISE SET 8-5
26. Graph lines in the first and third quadrants. It is the graph of a hyperbola passing through points $(1, 6)$, $(2, 3)$, $(3, 2)$, $(6, 1)$, $(-1, -6)$, $(-2, -3)$, $(-3, -2)$, $(-6, -1)$

Pages 317-318
CHAPTER 8 REVIEW
6.   7.

8.

12. $y = 3x$ 13. $y = \frac{1}{2}x$ 14. $y = \frac{4}{5}x$
16. $y = \frac{30}{x}$ 17. $y = \frac{1}{x}$ 18. $y = \frac{0.65}{x}$

Page 318
CHAPTER 8 TEST
3.   4.

CHAPTER 9 Page 322
TRY THIS
3.   4.

Page 323
EXERCISE SET 9-1
23. Vertical line through $(0, 3)$ and horizontal line through $(5, 0)$ intersecting at $(5, 3)$
24. Line through $(0, 0)$ and $(1, 3)$ intersecting line through $(0, 2)$ and $(1, -1)$ at $\left(\frac{1}{3}, 1\right)$
25. Infinitely many solutions.
26. No solutons.

Page 330
TRY THIS
1. $x = 3$, $y = 2$ 2. $x = 1$, $y = -1$

CHAPTER 10 Pages 374-375
TRY THIS
1.

2.

3.

4.

5.

6.

7.

8.

9.

10.

11.

Page 375
EXERCISE SET 10–5

1.

2.

3.

4.

5.

6.

7. $x > 5$ 8. $x > 6$ 9. $z < 7$ 10. $x < 8$
11. $t \leq -4$ 12. $x \leq -4$ 13. $x \geq 8$
14. $x < 4$ 15. $y < 7$ 16. $x \geq 5$ 17. $y > 3$
18. $x > 2$ 19. $y < 3$ 20. $t \leq 5$ 21. $x \geq \frac{1}{2}$

22. $-2 < x < 2$ 23. $-6 < y < 6$ 24. $-1 \leq t \leq 1$ 25. $-7 \leq x \leq 7$ 26. $y < -3$ or $y > 3$ 27. $t < -4$ or $t > 4$ 28. $x \leq -7$ or $x \geq 7$ 29. $y \leq -9$ or $y \geq 9$ 30. $-9 < x < 15$ 31. $-7 \leq x \leq 3$ 32. $x \leq -5$ or $x \geq 7$ 33. $x < -24$ or $x > 14$ 34. $-\frac{3}{2} < y < \frac{11}{2}$ 35. $-\frac{5}{4} < y < \frac{9}{4}$ 36. $x \leq -\frac{10}{3}$ or $x \geq \frac{8}{3}$ 37. $x \leq -\frac{15}{4}$ or $x > \frac{25}{4}$

Pages 378–380
TRY THIS

3.   **4.**

5.   **6.**

7.   **8.**

9.   **10.**

4.

5.

6.

7.

8.

9.

10.

11.

12.

13.

14.

15.

16.

17.

18.

19.
10
−10

20.

21.

22.

23.

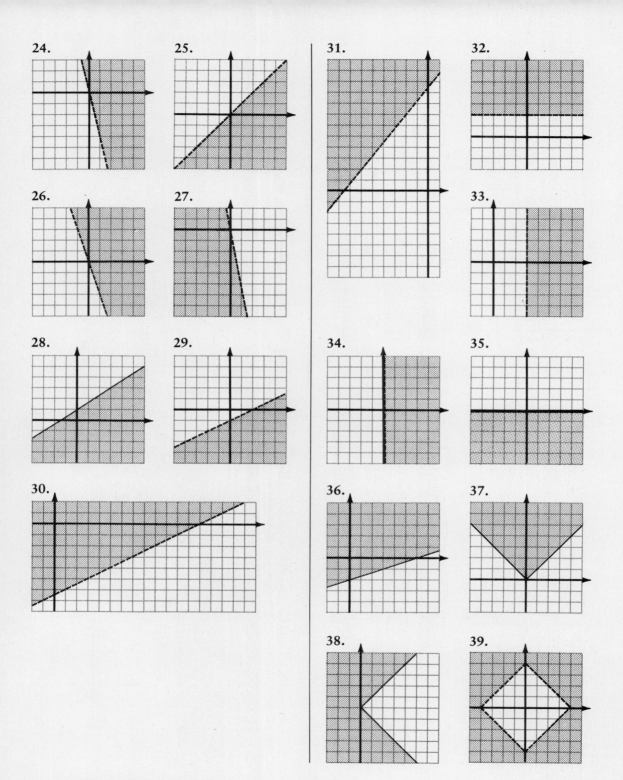

24.

25.

26.

27.

28.

29.

30.

31.

32.

33.

34.

35.

36.

37.

38.

39.

40.

Pages 382–383
TRY THIS

1.

2.

3.

4.

5.

6.

7.

8.

Page 384
EXERCISE SET 10–7

1.

2.

3.

4.

5.

6.

27.

Page 385
CHAPTER 10 REVIEW

15. All numbers less than or equal to 9
16. All numbers less than 1 **17.** All numbers between -2 and 2, including -2 and 2 **18.** All numbers greater than 4 or less than -2

22.

23.

24.

25.

Page 386
CHAPTER 10 TEST

10.

11.

12.

13.

14.

15.

Page 389
CUMULATIVE REVIEW 1–10

70.

71.

72.

73.

74.

75.

76.

77.

CHAPTER 11 Page 408
EXERCISE SET 11–5
72. $120(x + 1)(x - 1)^2$

Page 415
EXERCISE SET 11–7
44. LCM is $(a - b)^2(a + b)^2$

$$\frac{\left(\frac{ab}{a-b}\right)^2 - \left(\frac{ab}{a+b}\right)^2}{\left(\frac{ab}{a-b}\right)^2 + \left(\frac{ab}{a+b}\right)^2} =$$

$$\frac{a^2b^2(a+b)^2 - a^2b^2(a-b)^2}{a^2b^2(a+b)^2 + a^2b^2(a-b)^2} =$$

$$\frac{(a+b)^2 - (a-b)^2}{(a+b)^2 + (a-b)^2} = \frac{4ab}{2a^2 + 2b^2} = \frac{2ab}{a^2 + b^2}$$

Page 422
TRY THIS

1.

1. $ab\left(\frac{1}{a} \cdot \frac{1}{b}\right) = \left(ab \cdot \frac{1}{a}\right) \cdot \frac{1}{b}$	1. Assoc. prop.
2. $\qquad = \left(a \cdot \frac{1}{a} \cdot b\right) \cdot \frac{1}{b}$	2. Comm. prop.
3. $\qquad = \left(a \cdot \frac{1}{a}\right)\left(b \cdot \frac{1}{b}\right)$	3. Assoc. prop.
4. $\qquad = 1 \cdot 1$	4. Def. of recip.
5. $\qquad = 1$	5. Prop. of 1
6. $ab\left(\frac{1}{a} \cdot \frac{1}{b}\right) = 1$	6. Trans. prop.

3.

1. $\frac{a}{b} \cdot \frac{b}{a} = \left(a \cdot \frac{1}{b}\right)\left(b \cdot \frac{1}{a}\right)$	1. Division Thm.
2. $\qquad = \left(a \cdot \frac{1}{a}\right)\left(b \cdot \frac{1}{b}\right)$	2. Assoc., comm.
3. $\qquad = 1 \cdot 1$	3. Def. of recip.
4. $\qquad = 1$	4. Prop. of 1
5. $\frac{a}{b} \cdot \frac{b}{a} = 1$	5. Trans. prop.
6. The reciprocal of $\frac{a}{b}$ is $\frac{b}{a}$.	6. Def. of recip.

4.

1. $\frac{a}{b} = \frac{c}{d}$ $(b, d \neq 0)$	1. Hypothesis
2. $\frac{a}{b} \cdot bd = \frac{c}{d} \cdot bd$	2. Mult. prin.
3. $a\left(\frac{1}{b} \cdot b\right) \cdot d = c\left(\frac{1}{d} \cdot d\right) \cdot b$	3. Assoc., comm.
4. $a \cdot 1 \cdot d = c \cdot 1 \cdot b$	4. Def. of recip.
5. $ad = bc$	5. Prop. of 1, comm.

Page 424
EXERCISE SET 11–9

2.

1. $\frac{a}{c} = a \cdot \frac{1}{c}$ and $\frac{b}{c} = b \cdot \frac{1}{c}$	1. Division Thm.
2. $\frac{a}{c} - \frac{b}{c} = a \cdot \frac{1}{c} - b \cdot \frac{1}{c}$	2. Substitution
3. $\qquad = (a - b)\frac{1}{c}$	3. Distributive
4. $\qquad = \frac{a - b}{c}$	4. Division Thm.
5. $\frac{a}{c} - \frac{b}{c} = \frac{a - b}{c}$	5. Trans. prop.

Page 429
CHAPTER 11 REVIEW
9. $5x^2 - \frac{1}{2}x + 3$
10. $3x^2 - 7x + 4 + \frac{1}{2x + 3}$

CHAPTER 12 Page 437
EXERCISE SET 12–1
19. Irrational **20.** Irrational **21.** Irrational **22.** Irrational **23.** Rational
24. Rational **25.** Irrational **26.** Irrational
27. Rational **28.** Rational **29.** Irrational
30. Irrational **51.** 2 **52.** 5 **53.** $-5, -6$
54a. $\sqrt{73}$ **b.** $\sqrt{17}$ **c.** $\sqrt{59}$ **d.** $\sqrt{26}$
e. $\sqrt{3}$ **55.** $\sqrt{113}$ **56.** $\frac{x + y}{2}$ **57.** 1 is $(-1)^2$
and 1^3, 64 is 8^2 and 4^3.

CHAPTER 13 Pages 497–499
TRY THIS

1.

x	0	1	2	-2	3	-3
y	-1	0	3	3	8	8

2.

3.

4.

5.

4. ≈ − 0.8, ≈ 4.8

5. ≈ − 2.2, ≈ 0.2

6.

7.

Page 499
EXERCISE SET 13–7

1.

2.

8.

9.

3.

10.

11.

12.

13.

14.

15.

16.

17.

18.

19.

20.

21.

22.

23.

24.

Page 504
CHAPTER 13 REVIEW

30. Graph opens upward. Minimum point at $(0, -2)$.

32.

Page 505
CHAPTER 13 TEST

16. Graph opens upward. Minimum point at $(-2, -2)$. Passes through $(-4, 2)$, $(-3, 1)$, $(-1, -1)$, $(0, 2)$.

CHAPTER 14   Page 510
EXERCISE SET 14–1

1. Corresponding angles: $\angle B$ and $\angle E$, $\angle C$ and $\angle F$, $\angle A$ and $\angle D$; corresponding sides: $\overline{BC}$ and $\overline{EF}$, $\overline{CA}$ and $\overline{FD}$, $\overline{AB}$ and $\overline{DE}$.

2. Corresponding angles: $\angle Q$ and $\angle X$, $\angle R$ and $\angle Y$, $\angle P$ and $\angle W$; corresponding sides: $\overline{QR}$ and $\overline{XY}$, $\overline{RP}$ and $\overline{YW}$, $\overline{PQ}$ and $\overline{WX}$.

60.

61.

62.

99. All numbers greater than 9   **100.** All numbers less than 8   **101.** All numbers between −4 and 4, including −4 and 4
102. All numbers less than −3 or greater than 3   **103.** All numbers between −4 and 16, including −4 and 16   **104.** All numbers between −3 and 3, including −3 and 3

106.

107.

109.

110.

111.

COMPUTER ACTIVITIES   Page 539

7. Answers may vary. Any numbers may be used for N1 and N2.
```
10 LET N1 = 20
20 LET N2 = 30
30 PRINT N1 + N2, N1 − N2,
   N1 * N2, N1/N2
40 END
```

8. Answers may vary. Any numbers may be used for T1–T6.
```
10 LET T1 = 95
20 LET T2 = 80
30 LET T3 = 98
40 LET T4 = 72
50 LET T5 = 86
60 LET T6 = 92
70 LET S = T1 + T2 + T3 + T4
   + T5 + T6
80 LET A = S/6
90 PRINT "SUM IS " ;S,
   "AVERAGE IS " ;A
100 END
```

Page 541

3. Answers may vary.

```
10 PRINT "TYPE IN RADIUS
   OF A CIRCLE"
20 INPUT R
30 LET P = 3.14159
40 LET A = P*R^2
50 LET C = 2*P*R
60 PRINT "AREA = ";A,
   "CIRCUMFERENCE = ";C
70 END
```

Page 542

2–4. Answers may vary.

2.
```
10 REM EVALUATE EXPRESSION
20 READ X
30 PRINT 5 * X ^ 2 + 3 * X - 1
40 DATA 7,0,-2,100,15
50 END
```
Output: 265
      -1
      13
      50299
      1169

3.
```
10 REM ORDERED PAIR SOLUTIONS
20 READ X
30 LET Y = 3 * X - 1
40 PRINT "(";X;",";Y;")"
50 GO TO 20
60 DATA -5,0,33,-16,50
70 END
```
Output: (-5,-16)
      (0,-1)
      (34,101)
      (-16,-49)
      (50,149)

4.
```
10 REM PRINT N, ITS SQUARE,
   ITS CUBE
20 READ N
30 PRINT N, N ^ 2, N ^ 3
40 GO TO 20
50 DATA 13,-6,1000,-2,28
60 END
```

Output:

13	169	2197
-6	36	-216
1000	1000000	1E + 09
-2	4	-8
28	784	21952

Pages 543–544

3. Answers may vary.
```
25 IF X1 = X2 THEN 55
55 PRINT "THERE IS NO
   SLOPE"
56 GO TO 20
```
4. Answers may vary.
```
10 PRINT "NUMBER",
   "ABSOLUTE VALUE"
20 READ N
30 PRINT N,
40 IF N >= 0 THEN 60
50 LET N = -N
60 PRINT N
70 GO TO 20
80 DATA 35,-98,2.4,-73.9,-5,
   0,-1
90 END
```
Output:

NUMBER	ABSOLUTE VALUE
35	35
-98	98
2.4	2.4
-73.9	73.9
-5	5
0	0
-1	1

?OUT OF DATA ERROR IN 20

Page 545

2–5. Answers may vary.

2.
```
10 REM DISTANCE (KM) YOU
   CAN SEE
20 FOR H = 1 TO 10
30 LET V = 3.5 * SQR(H)
40 PRINT "WHEN H = ";H,
   "V= ";V
```

```
50  NEXT H
60  END
Output:
WHEN H = 1    V = 3.5
WHEN H = 2    V = 4.94974747
WHEN H = 3    V = 6.06217783
WHEN H = 4    V = 7
WHEN H = 5    V = 7.82623792
WHEN H = 6    V = 8.57321411
WHEN H = 7    V = 9.26012959
WHEN H = 8    V = 9.89949495
WHEN H = 9    V = 10.5
WHEN H = 10 V = 11.0679718
```

3.
```
10  REM EVEN OR ODD
20  PRINT "INPUT N"
30  INPUT N
40  IF N/2 = INT(N/2) THEN 70
50  PRINT N "IS ODD"
60  GO TO 80
70  PRINT N "IS EVEN"
80  END
```

4.
```
10  REM DISTANCE ON NUMBER
        LINE
20  READ N1, N2
30  LET D = ABS(N1 - N2)
40  PRINT "DISTANCE
        BETWEEN";N1;"AND";
        N2;"IS";D
50  GO TO 20
60  DATA -8,-92,-5,15,0,27,
        49,-4,-10,10
70  END
```

5.
```
10  REM SUM OF 25 INTEGERS
20  LET S = 0
30  FOR N = 1 TO 25
40  LET S = S + N
50  NEXT N
60  PRINT "THE SUM IS ";S
70  END
```

Pages 546–547

2.a. Output:
```
$500 GROWS TO $644.112501
$501 GROWS TO $645.400726
$502 GROWS TO $646.688951
$503 GROWS TO $647.977176
$504 GROWS TO $649.265401
$505 GROWS TO $650.553626
$506 GROWS TO $651.841851
$507 GROWS TO $653.130076
$508 GROWS TO $654.418301
$509 GROWS TO $655.706526
$510 GROWS TO $656.994751
```

b. Output
```
$1   GROWS TO $1.2321
$2   GROWS TO $2.4642
$3   GROWS TO $3.6963
$4   GROWS TO $4.92840001
$5   GROWS TO $6.16050001
$6   GROWS TO $7.39260001
$7   GROWS TO $8.62470001
$8   GROWS TO $9.85680002
$9   GROWS TO $11.0889
$10 GROWS TO $12.321
$11 GROWS TO $13.5531
$12 GROWS TO $14.7852
$13 GROWS TO $16.0173
$14 GROWS TO $17.2494
$15 GROWS TO $18.4815
```

3.
```
20  LET R = .15
30  LET T = 2
40  FOR P = 5000 TO 20000
        STEP 1000
Output:
$5000   GROWS TO $6612.5
$6000   GROWS TO $7935
$7000   GROWS TO $9257.5
$8000   GROWS TO $10580
$9000   GROWS TO $11902.5
$10000 GROWS TO $13225
$11000 GROWS TO $14547.5
$12000 GROWS TO $15870
$13000 GROWS TO $17192.5
$14000 GROWS TO $18515
$15000 GROWS TO $19837.5
$16000 GROWS TO $21160
$17000 GROWS TO $22482.5
```

```
$18000 GROWS TO $23805
$19000 GROWS TO $25127.5
$20000 GROWS TO $26450
```

Page 548

1. Output:
   ```
   LINE OF SYMMETRY IS X = 2.5
   VERTEX IS (2.5,5.5)
   MAXIMUM VALUE IS 5.5
   LINE OF SYMMETRY IS X = -1
   VERTEX IS (-1,-7)
   MINIMUM VALUE IS -7
   LINE OF SYMMETRY IS X = -2
   VERTEX IS (-2,7)
   MAXIMUM VALUE IS 7
   ```

2. `140 DATA 3,-24,50,1,-6,4`
   Output:
   ```
   LINE OF SYMMETRY IS X = 4
   VERTEX IS (4,2)
   MINIMUM VALUE IS 2
   LINE OF SYMMETRY IS X = 3
   VERTEX IS (3,-5)
   MINIMUM VALUE IS -5
   ```

3. The monitor will show the following:

   ```
                                *
                       *
              *
          *            *
       *
      *
        *
           *
                                *
   ```

4.a. `30 LET Y = X ^ 2 + .5 * X + 1`
  b. `30 LET Y = .25 * X ^ 2 + 16`

Page 549

1. Output for first program:
   ```
   (-1,-2) IS A SOLUTION
   (-1,2) IS A SOLUTION
   (1,-2) IS A SOLUTION
   (1,2) IS A SOLUTION
   ```
   Output for second program:
   ```
   0 + 0 = 0      0 + 2 = 2
   0 + 4 = 4      0 + 6 = 6
   0 + 8 = 8      0 + 10 = 10
   2 + 0 = 2      2 + 2 = 4
   ```

```
2 + 4 = 6      2 + 6 = 8
2 + 8 = 10     2 + 10 = 12
4 + 0 = 4      4 + 2 = 6
4 + 4 = 8      4 + 6 = 10
4 + 8 = 12     4 + 10 = 14
6 + 0 = 6      6 + 2 = 8
6 + 4 = 10     6 + 6 = 12
6 + 8 = 14     6 + 10 = 16
8 + 0 = 8      8 + 2 = 10
8 + 4 = 12     8 + 6 = 14
8 + 8 = 16     8 + 10 = 18
10 + 0 = 10    10 + 2 = 12
10 + 4 = 14    10 + 6 = 16
10 + 8 = 18    10 + 10 = 20
```

2.a. `40 IF 2 * Y ^ 2 - 3 * X ^ 2`
        `<> 6 THEN 70`
     `50 IF 5 * Y ^ 2 - 2 * X ^ 2`
        `<> 53 THEN 70`
  b. `40 IF X ^ 2 + 4 * Y ^ 2 <> 20`
        `THEN 70`
     `50 IF X * Y <> 4 THEN 70`
  c. `40 IF X ^ 2 + Y ^ 2 <> 25`
        `THEN 70`
     `50 IF 3 * X - 4 * Y <> 0`
        `THEN 70`

3.

```
**************************
*********************
****************
************
*********
******
****
***
**
***
***
*****
*********
************
******************
***********************
***************************************
*****************************************
```

4a. `30 LET Y = X ^ 2 + 4`
  b. `30 LET Y = X ^ 2 - X + 1`

5.   Answers may vary.
```
10  REM PRIMES 100 to 200
20  FOR X = 101 TO 200 STEP 2
30  FOR I = 3 TO SQR(X) STEP 2
40  IF X/I = INT(X/I) THEN 70
50  NEXT I
60  PRINT X,
70  NEXT X
80  END
```
Output:

101	103	107
109	113	127
131	137	139
149	151	157
163	167	173
179	181	191
193	197	199

Page 551

1.   Output for first program:

DEGREES	RADIANS	SINE
0	0	0
10	.174532778	.173648033
20	.349065556	.342019866
30	.523598333	.499999597
40	.698131111	.642787158
50	.872663889	.766043969
60	1.04719667	.866024961
70	1.22172944	.939692268
80	1.39626222	.984807548

Output for second program:

ANGLES:	40	50	90
SIDES:	9.64181415	11.4906667	15
AREA:	55.3954361		
ANGLES:	58	32	90
SIDES:	8.48048096	5.29919264	10
AREA:	22.4698512		
ANGLES:	25	65	90
SIDES:	2.62023322	5.61910828	6.2
AREA:	7.36168710		

2.
```
10  PRINT "DEGREES"; TAB
    (10);"COS"; TAB(24);
    "TAN"
    .
    .
30  FOR D = 0 TO 45 STEP 5
40  PRINT D; TAB(10); COS
    (D * C); TAB(24); TAN
    (D * C)
```

3.   Answers may vary.

4.   Answers may vary. For example, this function may be used to express angles in degrees:
```
DEF FNA(X) = X * 3.14159/180
```

ALGEBRA

MERVIN L. KEEDY
MARVIN L. BITTINGER
STANLEY A. SMITH
LUCY J. ORFAN

ADDISON-WESLEY PUBLISHING COMPANY

MENLO PARK, CALIFORNIA   READING, MASSACHUSETTS   LONDON
AMSTERDAM   DON MILLS, ONTARIO   SYDNEY

PHOTOGRAPHS

Cover: © 1976 Peter Fronk

© 1981 Jim Anderson / Woodfin Camp & Associates: 16 and 474
© Craig Aurness / West Light: 523 (left)
Ken Biggs / After-Image: 34 (right)
© Gianalberto Cigolini / The Image Bank West: 224
© Ruffin Cooper, Jr.: 294
© 1978 Jay Freis: 190
© 1976 Peter Fronk: 390
© 1979 Lowell Georgia / Photo Researchers Inc.: 523 (right)
© Alfred Gescheidt / The Image Bank West: 316 (right and left)
L.D. Gordon / The Image Bank West: 258
© George Hall: 98
© Erich Hartmann / Magnum Photos: 432
© Lawson L. Jones / After-Image: 501 (right)
© 1982 Roy King: 38
© 1982 Bruce Kurosaki / After-Image: 228
© 1981 John Lund: 142
NASA / The Image Bank West: 136 (right)
G. Palmer / The Image Bank West: 320
© 1980 Barrie Rokeach: 428 (right)
M. Salas / The Image Bank West: 287
Ken Sherman / Bruce Coleman Inc.: 136 (left)
Vince Streano / After-Image: 360
© William James Warren: 501 (left)
Frank Wing / The Image Bank West: 34 (left)
© Baron Wolman / Woodfin Camp & Associates: 428 (left)
© Baron Wolman: 506

ILLUSTRATION

Michel Allaire

TECHNICAL ILLUSTRATION

Sally Shimizu
Phyllis Rockne

DESIGN AND PRODUCTION

Design Office, San Francisco

ISBN   0–201–20334–0

ABCDEFGHIJK–VH–89876543

AUTHORS

MERVIN L. KEEDY
Mervin L. Keedy is Professor of Mathematics at Purdue University. He received his Ph.D. degree at the University of Nebraska and formerly taught at the University of Maryland. He has also taught mathematics and science in junior and senior high schools. Professor Keedy is the author of many books on mathematics. Most recently, he is co-author of *General Mathematics* (Addison-Wesley, 1983) and *Applying Mathematics* (Addison-Wesley, 1983).

MARVIN L. BITTINGER
Marvin L. Bittinger is Professor of Mathematics Education at Indiana University-Purdue University at Indianapolis. He earned his Ph.D. degree at Purdue University. He is the author of *Logic and Proof* (Addison-Wesley, 1980) and is co-author of *General Mathematics* (Addison-Wesley, 1983).

STANLEY A. SMITH
Stanley A. Smith is Coordinator, Office of Mathematics (K–12), for Baltimore County Public Schools, Maryland. He has taught junior high school mathematics and science and senior high school mathematics. He earned his M.A. degree at the University of Maryland. He is co-author of *General Mathematics* (Addison-Wesley, 1983) and *Applying Mathematics* (Addison-Wesley, 1983).

LUCY JAJOSKY ORFAN
Lucy Jajosky Orfan is Assistant Professor of Mathematics Education at Kean College of New Jersey. She earned her M.A. degree at New York University and her Ed.D. at Fairleigh Dickinson University. She currently teaches mathematics education courses at both the undergraduate and graduate level.

PREFACE

This text, *Algebra,* is for students who are ready for their first course in algebra. The authors have also published *Algebra and Trigonometry,* designed for students who have completed a first-year course in algebra. In both these books, skills are heavily emphasized, because without skills students cannot adequately cope with the concepts—the big ideas—that make algebra important.

Section Organization

Each section has alternating Examples and Try This exercises. Try This exercises are very much like the examples that precede them. They are carefully and strategically placed to draw students into an active development of the lesson. Immediate reinforcement of the concept or skill being learned is the goal. This kind of skill development builds success since the homework exercises grow directly from the Try This exercises.

Exercise Sets

Three levels of exercises are provided for each section. The first, labeled *Exercises,* provides problems that follow the same pattern as the Examples and Try This exercises. The second, labeled *Extension,* provides problems that combine single concepts presented in the Exercises into several-step problems. The third level, labeled *Challenge,* provides highly motivated students with problems that are related—sometimes in not so obvious ways—to the material of the lesson.

Applications

Much attention has been given to problems in which algebra is applied to situations arising from daily life. These appear not only in Exercise Sets for appropriate sections, but also in the *Career, Consumer Application,* and *Using a Calculator* features.

Computer Activities

This appendix contains a series of computer activities keyed to appropriate chapters. The activities provide an introduction to programming in the BASIC language.

On-Going Review

There are many opportunities for students to review previous concepts in order to maintain their skills at a high level. Before Chapter 1 there is an *Arithmetic Review,* reviewing operations with whole numbers, fractions, decimals, and percents. Before each of the other chapters there are *Ready For* exercises (keyed to preceding sections) providing review of skills needed in that chapter. In addition, each chapter has a *Chapter Review* (keyed to sections) and *Chapter Test.* There are also four Cumulative Reviews, each reviewing skills beginning with Chapter 1.

TO THE STUDENTS

Algebra, more than any other course you study, presents you with many new ideas. Nowhere else will you learn so many new skills. No other course presents such intense sequential development as your first course in algebra. In fact, every other course in mathematics you will ever take will be based on what you learn in this course, this year.

For some of you, algebra will open up new ways of seeing and thinking about events that happen in the world—the first step in formulating interests that will turn into lifelong careers. For you who plan to be scientists or engineers this is obviously true. But remember, everyone must be aware that numbers are around us everywhere, and dealing with them is important in surprisingly many careers. You who will work in business, the social sciences, history, psychology or health fields will find that information about the past and present—so often presented as data—must be analyzed, compared, researched, summarized, or restated in ways in which a mathematical understanding of what you are doing will deepen your knowledge and extend the usefulness of what you are doing.

Computers will also affect many of you during your lives. One of the skills needed to use and understand computers is the effective use of variables. Learning how to deal with variables and seeing their role in formulating statements may be the most important result of studying algebra for all of you, regardless of your future careers.

There are many other reasons to study algebra. One of these is that algebra is interesting for its own sake, the way a game or puzzle can be interesting. Whatever your goals, we hope this book will help you succeed in your studies, and will make this important year in your lives an interesting and enjoyable one.

The Authors

CONTENTS

CHAPTER 6   Polynomials in Several Variables

CHAPTER 7   Graphs and Linear Equations

CHAPTER 8　Functions and Variation

CHAPTER 9　Systems of Equations

CHAPTER 10　Inequalities

CHAPTER 11 Fractional Expressions and Equations

CHAPTER 12 Real Numbers and Radical Expressions

CHAPTER 13   Quadratic Equations and Functions

CHAPTER 14   Trigonometry

COMPUTER ACTIVITIES   535

ARITHMETIC REVIEW

Add.

1. 42
     + 56
     ———
      98

2. 879
     + 412
     ———
     1291

3. 1354
      2179
      6118
    + 2771
    ————
    12,422

Subtract.

4. 86
     − 12
     ——
      74

5. 75
     − 28
     ——
      47

6. 4003
     − 276
     ————
      3727

Multiply.

7. 23
     × 7
     ——
     161

8. 89
     × 30
     ——
     2670

9. 8342
     × 7000
     —————
     58,394,000

10. 709
      × 807
      ————
      572,163

Divide.

11. $9\overline{)162}$ 18

12. $18\overline{)3006}$ 167

13. $290\overline{)10,150}$ 35

Add. Simplify answers if possible.

14. $\frac{3}{7} + \frac{2}{7}$ $\frac{5}{7}$

15. $\frac{3}{8} + \frac{1}{6}$ $\frac{13}{24}$

16. $7\frac{1}{4}$
       $+ 8\frac{1}{4}$
       ———
       $15\frac{1}{2}$

17. $6\frac{3}{4}$
       $+ 9\frac{5}{8}$
       ———
       $16\frac{3}{8}$

18. $3\frac{1}{2}$
       $4\frac{2}{3}$
       $+ 7\frac{1}{4}$
       ———
       $15\frac{5}{12}$

Subtract. Simplify answers if possible.

19. $\frac{5}{9}$
       $- \frac{2}{9}$
       ——
       $\frac{1}{3}$

20. $\frac{5}{6}$
       $- \frac{2}{5}$
       ——
       $\frac{13}{80}$

21. $1\frac{7}{8}$
       $- \frac{3}{4}$
       ——
       $1\frac{1}{8}$

22. 7
       $- \frac{5}{8}$
       ——
       $6\frac{3}{8}$

23. $6\frac{1}{3}$
       $- 4\frac{7}{8}$
       ——
       $1\frac{11}{24}$

24. $12\frac{1}{4}$
       $- 4\frac{5}{8}$
       ——
       $7\frac{5}{8}$

Multiply. Simplify answers if possible.

25. $\frac{3}{4} \times \frac{3}{4}$ $\frac{9}{16}$ 26. $\frac{5}{8} \times 18$ $\frac{45}{4}$ or $11\frac{1}{4}$

27. $\frac{3}{5} \times \frac{5}{3}$ 1   28. $7 \times 3\frac{1}{3}$ $23\frac{1}{3}$

29. $3\frac{3}{7} \times 1\frac{1}{6}$ 4   30. $\frac{2}{3} \times \frac{5}{7} \times \frac{9}{14}$ $\frac{15}{49}$

31. $4\frac{1}{5} \times 3\frac{5}{7}$ $15\frac{3}{5}$ 32. $2\frac{3}{10} \times 3\frac{1}{3}$ $7\frac{2}{3}$

Divide. Simplify answers if possible.

33. $\frac{7}{12} \div \frac{7}{12}$ 1   34. $\frac{3}{4} \div 2$ $\frac{3}{8}$

35. $\frac{5}{9} \div \frac{5}{2}$ $\frac{2}{9}$ 36. $3\frac{1}{3} \div 1\frac{1}{4}$ $2\frac{2}{3}$

37. $3 \div \frac{1}{3}$ 9   38. $12\frac{1}{2} \div 2\frac{3}{4}$ $4\frac{6}{11}$

39. $\dfrac{\frac{5}{8}}{\frac{2}{5}}$ $1\frac{9}{16}$ 40. $\dfrac{\frac{3}{7}}{\frac{6}{11}}$ $\frac{11}{14}$

Add.

41. $0.5 + 0.35 + 1.5$ 2.35 42. $14 + 3.75 + 8.6$ 26.35

43.
```
    47.6
+    0.8
```
48.4

44.
```
    6.1
    3.48
+   0.5
```
10.08

Subtract.

45.
```
    8.9
-   0.76
```
8.14

46.
```
    37.009
-   18.473
```
18.536

47. $7 - 4.38$ 2.62 48. $11.2 - 6.09$ 5.11

Multiply.

49.
```
    8.75
×      6
```
5.25

50.
```
    0.75
×   0.003
```
0.00225

51.
```
    7.82
×    7.9
```
61.778

52.
```
    0.0004
×       57
```
0.0228

Divide. Round answers to the nearest hundredth, if necessary.

53. $7\overline{)8.1}$ 1.16   54. $0.08\overline{)396.7}$ 55. $1.1\overline{)0.44}$

54. 4958.75
55. 0.4

56. $\frac{5.82}{0.6}$ 9.7   57. $0.065\overline{)333}$ 58. $8\overline{)0.91}$

57. 5123.08
58. 0.11

Write each percent in decimal notation.

59. 13% 0.13 **60.** 9% 0.09 **61.** 100% 1   **62.** 0.5% 0.005

Write each number as a percent.

63. 0.25 25% **64.** 0.01 1% **65.** 0.175   **66.** 3 65. 17.5%
66. 300%

Find each percent.

67. 30% of 200 60   **68.** 15% of 48 7.2
69. 200% of 14 28   **70.** 1.2% of 35 0.42

1

CHAPTER ONE

Introduction to Algebra

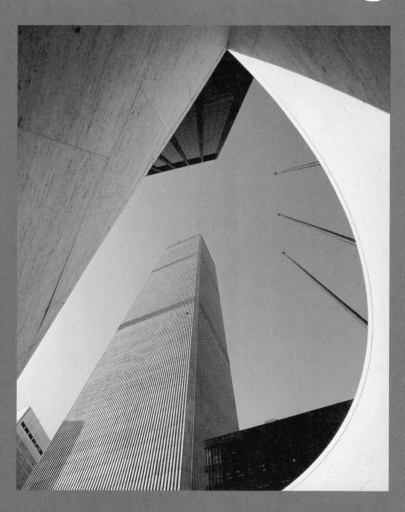

1–1 Symbols and Expressions

In this chapter you will begin to learn what algebra is like and how it works.

Algebraic Expressions

In algebra we use symbols that stand for various numbers. Such symbols are called variables. We can replace a variable with numbers. This is called substituting for the variable.

EXAMPLE 1
Mark is 3 years older than his sister Erin. If the variable x stands for Erin's age, then $x + 3$ stands for Mark's age. How old is Mark when Erin is

a. 6?   We substitute 6 for x in $x + 3$. We get $6 + 3$ or 9.
b. 10?   Substituting 10 for x in $x + 3$ gives $10 + 3$ or 13.
c. 15? $15 + 3 = 18$

TRY THIS   Maria has $5 more than Jose. If we use the variable n to stand for the number of dollars Jose has, then $n + 5$ stands for the number of dollars Maria has. How many dollars has Maria when Jose has
1. $3? $8   **2.** $25? $30   **3.** $16? $21

An algebraic expression is a symbol made up of variables, numerals, and operations signs. When we substitute for the variables and calculate the results, we get a number. This process is called evaluating the expression.

EXAMPLE 2
Evaluate the expression $3 \times y$ for $y = 5$ (y stands for 5). We substitute 5 for y.

$$3 \times y = 3 \times 5 = 15$$

The number we get when we evaluate an expression is called its value. The value of $3 \times y$ when y is replaced by 5 is 15.

EXAMPLE 3

Evaluate $\frac{x}{y}$ for $x = 10$ and $y = 5$ (x stands for 10 and y stands for 5).

$$\frac{x}{y} = \frac{10}{5} = 2 \qquad \text{Substitute 10 for } x, \text{ 5 for } y, \text{ and divide.}$$

TRY THIS Evaluate $\frac{2 \times p}{t}$ for the given values of p and t.

4. $p = 6$ and $t = 3$ $\quad_4$ **5.** $p = 7$ and $t = 5$ $\quad\frac{14}{5}$

Writing Algebraic Expressions

In algebra you will often need to write expressions using variables. To do this it helps to think of what you would do with specific numbers.

EXAMPLE 4

Suppose that y stands for some number. Write an expression that stands for twice (or two times) that number. Think of some number, say 8. What number is twice 8? 16. How did you get 16? You multiplied by 2. Do the same thing using a variable. Multiply y by 2. The answer is $y \times 2$. The answer could also be $2 \times y$ or $2 \cdot y$.

In Example 4 we used $\times$ for a multiplication sign as in arithmetic. We also used a dot.

$3 \cdot 7$ means 3×7
$3 \cdot a$ means $3 \times a$

When two letters or a number and a letter are written together, that also means that they are to be multiplied. Numbers to be multiplied are called factors. In algebra we usually write the numerical factor first and the variable factor second.

$5y$ means $5 \cdot y$ or $5 \times y$
ab means $a \cdot b$ or $a \times b$

EXAMPLE 5

Write an expression to stand for five more than some number. We use a variable to stand for "some number." To see how to write the expression, think of a number, say 6. Ask yourself, "What is 5 more than 6?" It is 11. How did you get 11? You added 5. You found $6 + 5$. Now do the same thing using the variable n. The expression is $n + 5$, or $5 + n$.

6. Suppose that y stands for some number. Write an expression for 7 times y. 7y

7. Write an expression that stands for 8 more than a number x. 8 + x or x + 8

EXAMPLE 6

Suppose that m stands for some number and it is five more than some other number. Write an expression for the smaller number. First think of a number, say 12. If it is 5 more than another number, what is the other number? It is 7. How did you get the other number? You subtracted 5 from 12, $12 - 5$. Do the same thing using m instead of 12. The smaller number is $m - 5$.

TRY THIS

8. Suppose that x stands for some number and it is 7 less than another number. Write an expression for the larger number. x + 7

9. Suppose that y stands for some number and it is 9 more than another number. Write an expression for the smaller number. y − 9

1–1	

Exercises

Substitute for the given value and calculate.

1. Theresa is 6 years younger than her husband Frank. If the variable x stands for Frank's age, then $x - 6$ stands for Theresa's age. How old is Theresa when Frank is 29? 34? 47? 58? 23, 28, 41, 52

2. It took Janice's younger brother Rick five times as long as Janice to solve the cube puzzle. If the variable q stands for Janice's time, then $5q$ stands for Rick's time. How long did Rick take if Janice took 30 seconds? 90 seconds? 2 minutes? 150 sec, 450 sec, 10 min

Evaluate.

3. $4 \cdot y$ for $y = 9$ 36

4. $8 \cdot m$ for $m = 3$ 24

5. $6x$ for $x = 7$ 42

6. $7y$ for $y = 7$ 49

7. $\frac{x}{y}$ for $x = 9$ and $y = 3$ 3

8. $\frac{m}{n}$ for $m = 14$ and $n = 2$ 7

9. $\frac{3 \cdot p}{q}$ for $p = 2$ and $q = 6$ *1*   10. $\frac{5 \cdot y}{z}$ for $y = 15$ and $z = 25$ *3*

11. $\frac{x + y}{5}$ for $x = 10$ and $y = 20$ *6*   12. $\frac{p + q}{2}$ for $p = 2$ and $q = 16$ *9*

13. $\frac{x - y}{8}$ for $x = 20$ and $y = 4$ *2*   14. $\frac{m - n}{5}$ for $m = 16$ and $y = 6$ *2*

15. $\frac{x}{y}$ for $x = 3$ and $y = 6$ $\frac{1}{2}$ 16. $\frac{p}{q}$ for $p = 4$ and $y = 16$ $\frac{1}{4}$

17. $\frac{5z}{y}$ for $z = 8$ and $y = 2$ *20*   18. $\frac{9m}{q}$ for $m = 4$ and $q = 18$ *2*

Write an algebraic expression for each of the following.

19. 6 more than b *b + 6*   20. 8 more than t *t + 8*

21. 9 less than c *c – 9*   22. 4 less than d *d – 4*

23. 6 greater than q *q + 6*   24. 11 greater than z *z + 11*

25. b more than a *a + b*   26. c more than d *d + c*

27. x less than y *y – x*   28. c less than h *h – c*

29. x added to w *w + x*   30. s added to t *t + s*

31. m subtracted from n *n – m*   32. p subtracted from q *q – p*

33. the sum or r and s *r + s*   34. the sum of d and f *d + f*

35. twice x *2x*   36. three times p *3p*

37. 5 multiplied by t *5t*   38. 9 multiplied by d *9d*

39. the product of 3 and b *3b*

40. A number y is 6 less than a larger number. Write an expression for the larger number. *y + 6*

41. A number m is 1 less than a larger number. Write an expression for the larger number. *m + 1*

42. A number x is 4 more than a smaller number. Write an expression for the smaller number. *x – 4*

43. A number h is 43 more than a smaller number. Write an expression for the smaller number. *h – 43*

Extension

Write expressions to represent the following.

44. A number x increased by three times y. *x + 3y*

45. A number y increased by twice x. *y + 2x*

46. A number a increased by 2 more than b. *a + b + 2*

47. A number that is 3 less than twice x. *2x – 3*

48. Your age in 5 years, if you are a years old now. *a + 5*

49. Your age two years ago, if you are b years old now. *b – 2*

50. A number x increased by itself. $x + x$

51. The area of a rectangle with length l and width w. lw

52. The perimeter of a square with side s. $4s$

53. Evaluate $\dfrac{x + y}{4}$ if $y = 8$ and x is twice y. 6

54. Evaluate $\dfrac{x - y}{7}$ if $y = 35$ and x is twice y. 5

55. Evaluate $\dfrac{y - x}{3}$ if $x = 9$ and y is three times x. 6

56. Evaluate $\dfrac{256y}{32x}$ for $y = 1$ and $x = 4$. 2

57. Evaluate $\dfrac{y + x}{2} + \dfrac{3 \cdot y}{x}$ for $x = 2$ and $y = 4$. 9

Challenge

Represent the required numbers in terms of the given variable.

58. If $w + 3$ is a whole number, what is the next whole number after it? $w + 4$

59. If $d + 2$ is an odd whole number, what is the preceding odd number? d

60. The difference between two numbers is 3. One number is t. What are two possible values for the other number? $t + 3, t - 3$

61. Two numbers are $v + 2$ and $v - 2$. What is their sum? $2v$

62. Two numbers are $2 + w$ and $2 - w$. What is their sum? 4

63. You invest n dollars at 10% interest. Write an expression for the number of your dollars in the bank a year from now. $n + 0.10n$

1. $\{4, 16, 36\}$ 2. $\{0, 1, 2, 3, 4, 5\}$

SETS AND SYMBOLS

We call a collection of numbers a set. Each number in the set is called an element. If A is the set of whole numbers less than 5, then

$$A = \{0, 1, 2, 3, 4\}.$$

If B is the set of odd whole numbers less than 8, then

$$B = \{1, 3, 5, 7\}.$$

The intersection of A and B are all the elements in A and in B. The symbol $\cap$ is read intersection.

$$A \cap B = \{1, 3\}$$

The union of A and B are all the elements in A or in B or both. The symbol $\cup$ is read union.

$$A \cup B = \{0, 1, 2, 3, 4, 5, 7\}$$

1. What is the intersection of the set of even whole numbers and the set K,

where $K = \{1, 4, 9, 16, 25, 36, 49\}$.

2. What is the union of the set of whole numbers less than 4 and the set of natural numbers less than 6?

3. Find the intersection and union of sets C and D where $C = \{1, 3, 5, 7, 9\}$ and $D = \{0, 1, 3, 7, 15, 31, 63\}$.

3. $\{1, 3, 7\}, \{0, 1, 3, 5, 7, 9, 15, 31, 63\}$

1–2 Properties of Numbers

In this lesson we begin to study number properties. You will see how they are used to help us work with algebraic expressions. There are several different kinds of numbers. Here are some that you already know.

> *Natural numbers* are the numbers used for counting, 1, 2, 3, 4, 5, and so on.
>
> *Whole numbers* are the natural numbers and 0. The whole numbers are 0, 1, 2, 3, and so on.
>
> *Numbers of arithmetic* are the whole numbers and the fractions, such as $\frac{2}{3}$, $\frac{4}{1}$, or $\frac{6}{5}$. All of these numbers can be named with fractional notation $\frac{a}{b}$, provided b is not 0.

Notice that all whole numbers are also numbers of arithmetic. In this chapter we will use the word number to mean the numbers of arithmetic.

The Commutative Laws

An expression for "two more than a number" is $x + 2$. The expression $2 + x$ names the same number. In multiplication, $2 \cdot x$ names the same number as $x \cdot 2$.

> **Commutative Laws**
>
> ADDITION
> For any numbers a and b, $a + b = b + a$. (We can change the order when adding without affecting the answer.)
>
> MULTIPLICATION
> For any numbers a and b, $ab = ba$. (We can change the order when multiplying without affecting the answer.)

The expressions $x + 2$ and $2 + x$ will have the same value for every number substituted for the variable. We know that by the commutative law of addition. Expressions that always have the same value are called *equivalent expressions*

EXAMPLES

Use a commutative law to write an equivalent expression.

1. $y + 5$ An equivalent expression is $5 + y$ by the commutative law of addition.

2. xy An equivalent expression is yx by the commutative law of multiplication.

3. $5 + ab$ An equivalent expression is $ab + 5$ by the commutative law of addition.

Another is $5 + ba$ by the commutative law of multiplication.

Another is $ba + 5$ by both commutative laws.

TRY THIS Use a commutative law to write an equivalent expression.

1. $x + 9$ $9 + x$ **2.** pq qp **3.** $xy + t$ $yx + t, t + xy,$ or $t + yx$

Properties of 0 and 1

Some simple but powerful properties of numbers are the properties of 0 and 1. We shall see some ways to use these simple properties in algebra and arithmetic.

Additive Property of 0

For any number a, $a + 0 = a$. (Adding 0 to any number gives that same number.)

The Property of 1

For any number a, $1 \cdot a = a$. (Multiplying a number by 1 gives that same number.)

There are many ways to name the number 1. Some of them follow.

$$\frac{5}{5} \qquad \frac{3}{3} \qquad \frac{26}{26}$$

Here are some algebraic expressions having the value 1 for all replacements, except that we do not divide by 0. (Later, in Chapter 2, we shall see why such division is not allowed.)

$$\frac{n}{n} \qquad \frac{x + 2}{x + 2} \qquad \frac{5y + 4}{5y + 4}$$

For any number a, except 0, $\frac{a}{a} = 1$.

EXAMPLE 4

Write an equivalent expression for $\frac{2}{3}$ by multiplying by 1. Use $\frac{5}{5}$ for 1. Recall from arithmetic that the product of two fractions equals the product of the numerators divided by the product of the denominators.

$$\frac{2}{3} = \frac{2}{3} \cdot 1 \quad \text{Using the property of 1}$$

$$= \frac{2}{3} \cdot \frac{5}{5} \quad \text{Using } \frac{5}{5} \text{ for 1}$$

$$= \frac{10}{15} \quad \text{Multiplying numerators and denominators}$$

TRY THIS

4. Write an equivalent expression for $\frac{7}{5}$ by multiplying by 1. Use $\frac{4}{4}$ for 1. $\frac{28}{20}$

Thinking about properties of numbers in arithmetic will show you how to write equivalent expressions. We can use the property of 1, for example, to write equivalent expressions.

EXAMPLE 5

Write an expression equivalent to $\frac{x}{2}$ by multiplying by $\frac{y}{y}$.

$$\frac{x}{2} = \frac{x}{2} \cdot \frac{y}{y} \quad \text{Using the property of 1}$$

$$= \frac{xy}{2y}$$

The expressions $\frac{x}{2}$ and $\frac{xy}{2y}$ will have the same value for all replacements of x and y. We do not divide by 0, so we will never replace y by 0.

TRY THIS

5. Write an expression equivalent to $\frac{y}{2x}$ by multiplying by $\frac{z}{z}$. $\quad \frac{yz}{2xz}$

Simplifying Expressions

The notation for a number that has the smallest possible numerator and denominator is called simplest fractional notation. We call the process of finding simplest fractional notation simplifying. We begin by writing a factorization of the numerator and the denominator. Then we use the property of 1.

EXAMPLES

6. $\dfrac{10}{15} = \dfrac{2 \cdot 5}{3 \cdot 5}$ Factoring numerator and denominator

     $= \dfrac{2}{3} \cdot \dfrac{5}{5}$ Factoring the fraction

     $= \dfrac{2}{3}$ Using the property of 1 (removing a factor of 1)

7. $\dfrac{36}{24} = \dfrac{6 \cdot 6}{4 \cdot 6}$ Factoring numerator and denominator

     $= \dfrac{3 \cdot 2 \cdot 6}{2 \cdot 2 \cdot 6}$ Further factoring

     $= \dfrac{3}{2} \cdot \dfrac{2 \cdot 6}{2 \cdot 6}$ Factoring the fraction

     $= \dfrac{3}{2}$ Using the property of 1

TRY THIS Simplify.

6. $\dfrac{18}{27}$ $\frac{2}{3}$ 7. $\dfrac{48}{18}$ $\frac{8}{3}$ 8. $\dfrac{56}{49}$ $\frac{8}{7}$

The factors in the numerator and denominator may not always "match." If they do not, we can always insert the number 1 as a factor. The property of 1 allows us to do that.

EXAMPLES

Simplify.

8. $\dfrac{18}{72} = \dfrac{2 \cdot 9}{4 \cdot 2 \cdot 9}$

$\quad = \dfrac{1 \cdot 2 \cdot 9}{4 \cdot 2 \cdot 9}$ Using the property of 1 (inserting a factor of 1)

$\quad = \dfrac{1}{4} \cdot \dfrac{2 \cdot 9}{2 \cdot 9}$ Factoring the fraction

$\quad = \dfrac{1}{4}$

9. $\dfrac{72}{9} = \dfrac{8 \cdot 9}{1 \cdot 9}$ Factoring and inserting a factor of 1 in the denominator

$\quad = \dfrac{8}{1} \cdot \dfrac{9}{9}$

$\quad = \dfrac{8}{1}$

$\quad = 8$

TRY THIS Simplify.

9. $\dfrac{27}{54}$ $\frac{1}{2}$ **10.** $\dfrac{48}{12}$ 4

Now let's simplify some algebraic expressions. We will use the property of 1 as in Examples 6–9.

EXAMPLES

Simplify.

10. $\dfrac{xy}{3y} = \dfrac{x \cdot y}{3 \cdot y}$ Factoring numerator and denominator

$\quad = \dfrac{x}{3} \cdot \dfrac{y}{y}$ Factoring the fractional expression

$\quad = \dfrac{x}{3}$ Using the property of 1 (removing a factor of 1)

11. $\dfrac{x}{5xy} = \dfrac{1 \cdot x}{5 \cdot x \cdot y}$ Inserting a factor of 1 in the numerator

$\quad = \dfrac{1}{5y} \cdot \dfrac{x}{x}$ Using the commutative property and factoring the fractional expression

$\quad = \dfrac{1}{5y}$

TRY THIS Simplify.

11. $\dfrac{5xy}{3x}$ $\frac{5y}{3}$ **12.** $\dfrac{m}{8mn}$ $\frac{1}{8n}$

Exercises

Write an equivalent expression using a commutative law.

1. $y + 8$ $_{8 + y}$ **2.** $x + 3$ $_{3 + x}$ **3.** mn $_{nm}$ **4.** ab $_{ba}$

5. $9 + xy$ **6.** $11 + ab$ **7.** $ab + c$ **8.** $rs + t$

Write an equivalent expression. Use the indicated name for 1.

9. $\frac{5}{6}$ Use $\frac{8}{8}$ for 1. $_{\frac{40}{48}}$ **10.** $\frac{9}{10}$ Use $\frac{11}{11}$ for 1. $_{\frac{99}{110}}$ **11.** $\frac{6}{7}$ Use $\frac{100}{100}$ for 1. $_{\frac{600}{700}}$

12. $\frac{y}{10}$ Use $\frac{z}{z}$ for 1. $_{\frac{yz}{10z}}$ **13.** $\frac{s}{20}$ Use $\frac{t}{t}$ for 1. $_{\frac{st}{20t}}$ **14.** $\frac{m}{3n}$ Use $\frac{p}{p}$ for 1. $_{\frac{mp}{3np}}$

Simplify.

15. $\frac{18}{45}$ $_{\frac{2}{5}}$ **16.** $\frac{16}{56}$ $_{\frac{2}{7}}$ **17.** $\frac{49}{14}$ $_{\frac{7}{2}}$ **18.** $\frac{72}{27}$ $_{\frac{8}{3}}$ **19.** $\frac{6}{42}$ $_{\frac{1}{7}}$ **20.** $\frac{13}{104}$ $_{\frac{1}{8}}$

21. $\frac{56}{7}$ $_{8}$ **22.** $\frac{132}{11}$ $_{12}$ **23.** $\frac{5y}{5}$ $_{y}$ **24.** $\frac{ab}{9b}$ $_{\frac{a}{9}}$ **25.** $\frac{x}{9xy}$ $_{\frac{1}{9y}}$ **26.** $\frac{q}{8pq}$ $_{\frac{1}{8p}}$

27. $\frac{8a}{3ab}$ $_{\frac{8}{3b}}$ **28.** $\frac{9p}{17pq}$ $_{\frac{9}{17q}}$ **29.** $\frac{3pq}{6q}$ $_{\frac{p}{2}}$ **30.** $\frac{51d}{17sd}$ $_{\frac{3}{s}}$ **31.** $\frac{9nz}{19tn}$ $_{\frac{9z}{19t}}$ **32.** $\frac{13rv}{3vh}$ $_{\frac{13r}{3h}}$

Extension

Tell which of the following expressions are examples of the commutative law.

33. $3t + 5$ and $3 \cdot 5 + t$ $_{No}$ **34.** $4x$ and $x + 4$ $_{No}$

35. $5m + 6$ and $6 + 5m$ $_{Yes}$ **36.** $(x + y) + z$ and $z + (x + y)$ $_{Yes}$

37. $bxy + bx$ and $yxb + bx$ $_{Yes}$ **38.** $ab + bc$ and $ac + db$ $_{No}$

39. $a + c + e + g$ and $ae + cg$ $_{No}$ **40.** $abc \cdot de$ and $a \cdot b \cdot c \cdot ed$ $_{Yes}$

Simplify.

41. $\frac{128}{192}$ $_{\frac{2}{3}}$ **42.** $\frac{pqrs}{qrst}$ $_{\frac{p}{t}}$ **43.** $\frac{33sba}{2(11a)}$ $_{\frac{3sb}{2}}$

44. $\frac{4 \cdot 9 \cdot 16}{2 \cdot 8 \cdot 15}$ $_{\frac{12}{5}}$ **45.** $\frac{36 \cdot (2rh)}{8 \cdot (9hg)}$ $_{\frac{r}{g}}$ **46.** $\frac{3 \cdot (4xy) \cdot (5)}{2 \cdot (3x) \cdot (4y)}$ $_{\frac{5}{2}}$

Challenge

47. Is there a commutative law for division of whole numbers? If not, give a counterexample. A counterexample shows one case where a rule is false. $_{No.(12 \div 4 \text{ does not equal } 4 \div 12)}$

48. Suppose we define a new operation $\odot$ on the set of whole numbers as follows: $a \odot b = 2a + b$. Find $3 \odot 4$ and $4 \odot 3$. Is $\odot$ commutative? That is, does $a \odot b = b \odot a$? $_{No. \ 2 \cdot 3 + 4 \neq 2 \cdot 4 + 3}$

5. $9 + yx$
$yx + 9$
$xy + 9$
6. $ab + 11$
$ba + 11$
$11 + ba$
7. $ba + c$
$c + ba$
$c + ab$
8. $t + rs$
$t + sr$
$sr + t$

Exponential Notation

Using Exponents

We can write shorthand notation for $10 \times 10 \times 10$ using exponents. When we use exponents we say the expression is written in exponential notation. For $10 \times 10 \times 10$ we write 10^3. We call the number 3 an exponent and we say that 10 is the base. The exponent tells how many times the base is used as a factor.

EXAMPLES
What is the meaning of each expression?

1. 3^5 3^5 means $3 \cdot 3 \cdot 3 \cdot 3 \cdot 3$ **2.** n^4 n^4 means $n \cdot n \cdot n \cdot n$
3. $(2n)^3$ $(2n)^3$ means $2n \cdot 2n \cdot 2n$ **4.** $(50x)^2$ means $50x \cdot 50x$

TRY THIS What is the meaning of each expression?

1. 5^4 **2.** x^5 **3.** $(5y)^4$ 1. $5 \cdot 5 \cdot 5 \cdot 5$ 2. $x \cdot x \cdot x \cdot x \cdot x$ 3. $5y \cdot 5y \cdot 5y \cdot 5y$

Ordinary notation for whole numbers is called decimal notation. We can use exponents to help explain decimal notation.

$$
\begin{aligned}
9345 = 9000 &&& + 300 && + 40 && + 5 \\
= 9 \times 1000 &&& + 3 \times 100 && + 4 \times 10 && + 5 \times 1 \\
= 9 \times 10 \times 10 \times 10 &&& + 3 \times 10 \times 10 && + 4 \times 10 && + 5 \times 1 \\
= 9 \times 10^3 &&& + 3 \times 10^2 && + 4 \times 10 && + 5 \times 1
\end{aligned}
$$

In order to keep the decreasing pattern of exponents we shall let 10^1 stand for 10 and 10^0 stand for 1. Thus, we have

$$9345 = 9 \times 10^3 + 3 \times 10^2 + 4 \times 10^1 + 5 \times 10^0.$$

We read exponential notation as follows. b^n is read the nth power of b, or simply b to the nth, or b to the n. b^2 may also be read b-squared. b^3 may also be read b-cubed. We are now ready to make a definition of exponential notation.

b^0 means 1, for any number b, except 0.
b^1 means b, for any number b.
If n is a whole number greater than 1, b^n means $\overbrace{b \cdot b \cdot b \cdot b \cdots b}^{n \text{ factors}}$.

Write in exponential notation.

5. $7 \cdot 7 \cdot 7 \cdot 7$ The answer is 7^4.

6. $n \cdot n \cdot n \cdot n \cdot n \cdot n$ The answer is n^6.

7. $2y \cdot 2y \cdot 2y$ The answer is $(2y)^3$.

8. $10x \cdot 10x$ The answer is $(10x)^2$.

TRY THIS Write in exponential notation.

4. $9 \cdot 9 \cdot 9$ 9^3 **5.** $y \cdot y \cdot y \cdot y \cdot y$ y^5 **6.** $4y \cdot 4y \cdot 4y$ $(4y)^3$

Evaluating Expressions

EXAMPLES

Evaluate each expression containing exponential notation.

9. x^4 for $x = 2$ **10.** y^2 for $y = 5$
   $x^4 = \quad ^4$ $y^2 = \quad ^2$
      $= 2 \cdot 2 \cdot 2 \cdot 2$ $= 5 \cdot 5$
      $= 16$ $= 25$

TRY THIS Evaluate each expression.

 7. a^2 for $a = 10$ 100   **8.** y^5 for $y = 2$ 32   **9.** x^4 for $x = 0$ 0
10. z^1 for $z = 4$ 4   **11.** p^{12} for $p = 1$ 1

EXAMPLES

Evaluate each expression. In evaluating an expression like $y^4 + 3$, we agree to evaluate y^4 first and then add 3.

11. $y^4 + 3$ for $y = 2$ **12.** $m^3 + 5$ for $m = 4$
   $y^4 + 3 = 2^4 + 3$ Substituting $m^3 + 5 = 4^3 + 5$ Substituting
         $= (2 \cdot 2 \cdot 2 \cdot 2) + 3$ $= (4 \cdot 4 \cdot 4) + 5$
         $= 16 + 3$ $= 64 + 5$
         $= 19$ $= 69$

TRY THIS Evaluate each expression.

12. $x^3 + 2$ for $x = 3$ 29   **13.** $n^5 + 8$ for $n = 2$ 40

Exercises

What is the meaning of each expression?

1. 2^4 **2.** 5^3 **3.** $(1.4)^5$ **4.** $(2.5)^4$ **5.** n^5 **6.** m^6

7. $(7p)^2$ **8.** $(11c)^3$ **9.** $(19k)^4$ **10.** $(104d)^5$ **11.** $(10pq)^3$ **12.** $(24ct)^3$

Write in exponential notation.

13. $10 \times 10 \times 10 \times 10 \times 10 \times 10$ 10^6 **14.** $6 \times 6 \times 6 \times 6$ 6^4

15. $x \cdot x \cdot x \cdot x \cdot x \cdot x \cdot x$ x^7 **16.** $y \cdot y \cdot y$ y^3

17. $3y \cdot 3y \cdot 3y \cdot 3y$ $(3y)^4$ **18.** $5m \cdot 5m \cdot 5m \cdot 5m \cdot 5m$ $(5m)^5$

Evaluate each expression.

19. m^3 for $m = 3$ 27   **20.** x^6 for $x = 2$ 32   **21.** p^1 for $p = 19$ 19

22. x^{19} for $x = 0$ 0   **23.** x^4 for $x = 4$ 256   **24.** y^{15} for $y = 1$ 1

Extension

Write each of the following with a single exponent.

For example, $\dfrac{3^5}{3^3} = \dfrac{3 \cdot 3 \cdot 3 \cdot 3 \cdot 3}{3 \cdot 3 \cdot 3} = 3 \cdot 3 = 3^2.$

25. $\dfrac{10^5}{10^3}$ 10^2 **26.** $\dfrac{10^7}{10^2}$ 10^5 **27.** $\dfrac{5^4}{5^2}$ 5^2 **28.** $\dfrac{2^6}{8^2}$ 1

29. Evaluate $x^3y^2 + zx$ for $x = 2$, $y = 1$, and $z = 3$.   14

30. Evaluate $c^2a^3 + ba$ for $a = 3$, $b = 1$, and $c = 2$.   111

31. Evaluate $x^2 + 2xy + y^2$ for $x = 7$ and $y = 8$.   225

$(3n)^3$ means $3n \cdot 3n \cdot 3n$, $3n^3$ means $3 \cdot n \cdot n \cdot n$. Evaluate $(3n)^3$ and $3 \cdot n^3$

32. when $n = 2$.   **33.** when $n = 3$.   **34.** when $n = 4$.   **35.** when $n = 5$.
216; 24   729; 81   1728; 192   3375; 375

Evaluate $(5p)^2$ and $5 \cdot p^2$

36. when $p = 4$.   **37.** when $p = 7$.   **38.** when $p = 11$.   **39.** when $p = 26$.
400; 80   1225; 245   3025; 605   16,900; 3380

Challenge

Write in exponential notation.

40. $x \cdot x \cdot x \cdot y \cdot y \cdot y$ x^3y^3 **41.** $3a \cdot 3a \cdot 3a \cdot 2b \cdot 2b$ $(3a)^3(2b)^2$

42. Find $x^{149}y$ for $x = 13$ and $y = 0$.   0   **43.** Find $x^{410}y^2$ for $x = 1$ and $y = 3$.   9

44. 10^{127} is one followed by how many zeros?   127   **45.** Find $(x^2)^2$ if $x = 3$.   81

The answers for the Extension section:
1. $2 \cdot 2 \cdot 2 \cdot 2$
2. $5 \cdot 5 \cdot 5$
3. $(1.4) \cdot (1.4) \cdot (1.4) \cdot (1.4) \cdot (1.4)$
4. $(2.5) \cdot (2.5) \cdot (2.5) \cdot (2.5)$
5. $n \cdot n \cdot n \cdot n \cdot n$
6. $m \cdot m \cdot m \cdot m \cdot m \cdot m$
7. $7p \cdot 7p$
8. $11c \cdot 11c \cdot 11c$
9. $19k \cdot 19k \cdot 19k \cdot 19k$
10. $104d \cdot 104d \cdot 104d \cdot 104d \cdot 104d$
11. $10pq \cdot 10pq \cdot 10pq$
12. $24ct \cdot 24ct \cdot 24ct$

The Associative Laws

Parentheses

Consider the expression $2 + 4 \times 5$. If we multiply 4 by 5 and add 2 we get 22. If instead we add 2 and 4 and then multiply by 5 we get 30. To show which operation to do first, we can use parentheses.

$$2 + (4 \times 5) = 22 \qquad (2 + 4) \times 5 = 30$$

But in algebra, if there are no parentheses, we multiply or divide first working from left to right, and then add or subtract working from left to right.

EXAMPLE 1
Calculate.

$$
\begin{aligned}
&15 - 2 \times 5 + 3 \\
&15 - \quad 10 \quad + 3 \qquad \text{Multiplying} \\
&\quad\ 5 \qquad\quad + 3 \qquad \text{Subtracting and adding, from left to right} \\
&\qquad\quad\ 8
\end{aligned}
$$

TRY THIS Calculate.

1. $5 + 2 \times 3$ ₁₁ **2.** $6 \times 2 + 3 \times 5$ ₂₇ **3.** $7 - 3 \times 2 + 5$ ₆

Always calculate within parentheses first. When there are exponents and no parentheses, simplify powers before multiplying or dividing.

EXAMPLES
Calculate.

2. $(3 \times 4)^2 = 12^4 \qquad$ Working within parentheses first
$\qquad\qquad = 144$

3. $3 \times 4^2 = 3 \times 16 \qquad$ There are no parentheses, so we find 4^2 first.
$\qquad\qquad = 48$

TRY THIS Calculate.

4. $(3 \times 5)^2$ ₂₂₅ **5.** 3×5^2 ₇₅ **6.** 4×2^3 ₃₂ **7.** $(4 \times 2)^3$ ₅₁₂
8. $4 + 2^2$ ₈ **9.** $(4 + 2)^2$ ₃₆ **10.** $(5 - 1)^2$ ₁₆ **11.** $5 - 1^2$ ₄

EXAMPLES

Evaluate each expression. We can also use parentheses when evaluating expressions.

4. $(3x)^3 - 2$ for $x = 2$

$$\begin{aligned}(3x)^3 - 2 &= (3 \cdot 2)^3 - 2 \quad \text{Substituting} \\ &= 6^3 - 2 \quad \text{Multiplying within parentheses first} \\ &= 216 - 2 \\ &= 214\end{aligned}$$

5. $(2 + x) \cdot (y - 1)$ for $x = 3$ and $y = 5$

$$\begin{aligned}(2 + x) \cdot (y - 1) &= (2 + 3) \cdot (5 - 1) \\ &= 5 \cdot 4 \quad \text{Working within parentheses first} \\ &= 20\end{aligned}$$

TRY THIS Evaluate each expression.

12. $(4y)^2 - 5$ for $y = 3$ 139 **13.** $6(x + 12)$ for $x = 8$ 120

14. $\dfrac{t + 6}{5t^3}$ for $t = 2$ $\frac{1}{5}$ **15.** $(x - 4)^3$ for $x = 6$ 8

16. $(4 + y) \cdot (x - 3)$ for $y = 3$ and $x = 12$ 63

Using the Associative Laws

EXAMPLES

Calculate and compare. Sometimes moving parentheses does not affect the value of the expression.

6. $3 + (7 + 5)$ Calculating within $(3 + 7) + 5$ Calculating within
  $3 + \quad 12$ parentheses first $10 \quad + 5$ parentheses first
    15 15

The two expressions are equivalent.

7. $3 \cdot (4 \cdot 2)$ $(3 \cdot 4) \cdot 2$
  $3 \cdot 8$ $12 \cdot 2$
    24 24

The two expressions are equivalent.

TRY THIS Calculate and compare.

17. $4 + (5 + 11)$ and $(4 + 5) + 11$ 20 **18.** $6 \cdot (3 \cdot 4)$ and $(6 \cdot 3) \cdot 4$ 72

When only addition is involved, parentheses can be placed any way we please without affecting the answer. When only multiplication is involved, parentheses can be placed any way we please without affecting the answer.

Associative Laws

ADDITION

For any numbers a, b, and c, $a + (b + c) = (a + b) + c$. (Numbers can be grouped in any manner for addition.)

MULTIPLICATION

For any numbers a, b, and c, $a \cdot (b \cdot c) = (a \cdot b) \cdot c$. (Numbers can be grouped in any manner for multiplication.)

EXAMPLES

Use an associative law to write an equivalent expression.

8. $y + (z + 3)$ An equivalent expression is $(y + z) + 3$ by the associative law of addition.

9. $5 \cdot (x \cdot y)$ An equivalent expression is $(5 \cdot x) \cdot y$ by the associative law of multiplication.

TRY THIS   Use an associative law to write an equivalent expression.

19. $a + (b + 2)$ 20. $3 \cdot (v \cdot w)$ 19. $(a + b) + 2$ 20. $(3 \cdot v) \cdot w$

When only additions or only multiplications are involved, parentheses may be placed any way we please. So, we very often omit them.

    For instance,

$$x + (y + 7) = x + y + 7$$
$$9 \cdot (u \cdot v) = 9 \cdot u \cdot v.$$

Using Laws Together

If addition or multiplication is the only operation in an expression, then the associative and commutative laws allow us to group and change order as we please. For instance, in a calculation like $(5 + 2) + (3 + 5) + 8$, addition is the only operation. So, we change grouping and order to make easy combinations $5 + 5 + 2 + 8 + 3 = 10 + 10 + 3 = 23$.

EXAMPLE 10

Use the commutative and associative laws to write at least three expressions equivalent to $(x + 5) + y$.

a. $(x + 5) + y = x + (5 + y)$ Using the associative law first
              $= x + (y + 5)$ and then using the commutative law
b. $(x + 5) + y = y + (x + 5)$ Using the commutative law and
              $= y + (5 + x)$ then the commutative law again
c. $(x + 5) + y = 5 + (x + y)$ Using the commutative law first
                                     and then the associative law

EXAMPLE 11

Use the commutative and associative laws to write at least three expressions equivalent to $(3 \cdot x) \cdot y$.

a. $(3 \cdot x) \cdot y = 3 \cdot (x \cdot y)$ Using the associative law first
              $= 3 \cdot (y \cdot x)$ and then the commutative law
b. $(3 \cdot x) \cdot y = y \cdot (x \cdot 3)$ Using the commutative law twice
c. $(3 \cdot x) \cdot y = x \cdot (y \cdot 3)$ Using the commutative law, then the associative,
                                     and then the commutative law again

TRY THIS Use the commutative and associative laws to write at least three equivalent expressions.

21. $4 \cdot (t \cdot u)$ **22.** $r + (2 + s)$

21. $(4 \cdot t) \cdot u$, $(t \cdot 4) \cdot u$, $u \cdot (4 \cdot t)$

22. $(r + 2) + s$, $(2 + r) + s$, $s + (r + 2)$, $s + (2 + r)$, $2 + (r + s)$

1–4

Exercises

Calculate.

1. $7 + 2 \times 6$ ₁₉   **2.** $11 + 4 \times 4$ ₂₇   **3.** $8 \times 7 + 6 \times 5$ ₈₆
4. $10 \times 5 + 1 \times 1$ ₅₁   **5.** $19 - 5 \times 3 + 3$ ₇   **6.** $14 - 2 \times 6 + 7$ ₉
7. $9 \div 3 + 16 \div 8$ ₆   **8.** $32 - 8 \div 4 - 2$ ₂₈   **9.** $7 + 10 - 10 \div 2$ ₁₂
10. $(5 \cdot 4)^2$ ₄₀₀   **11.** $(6 \cdot 3)^2$ ₃₂₄   **12.** $3 \cdot 2^3$ ₂₄   **13.** $4 \cdot 5^2$ ₁₀₀
14. $(8 + 2)^2$ ₁₀₀   **15.** $(5 + 3)^3$ ₅₁₂   **16.** $7 + 2^2$ ₁₁   **17.** $6 + 4^2$ ₂₂
18. $(5 - 2)^2$ ₉   **19.** $(3 - 2)^2$ ₁   **20.** $10 - 3^2$ ₁   **21.** $12 - 2^3$ ₄

Evaluate each expression.

22. $3 \cdot (a + 10)$ for $a = 12$ ₆₆   **23.** $b \cdot (7 + b)$ for $b = 5$ ₆₀
24. $(t + 3)^3$ for $t = 4$ ₃₄₃   **25.** $(12 - w)^3$ for $w = 7$ ₁₂₅
26. $(x + 5) \cdot (12 - x)$ for $x = 7$ ₆₀   **27.** $(y - 4) \cdot (y + 6)$ for $y = 10$ ₉₆

28. $(5y)^3 - 75$ for $y = 2$ ₉₂₅   **29.** $(7x)^2 + 59$ for $x = 3$ ₅₀₀

30. $\dfrac{y+3}{2y}$ for $y = 5$ $\frac{4}{5}$ **31.** $\dfrac{(4x)+2}{2x}$ for $x = 5$ $\frac{11}{5}$

32. $\dfrac{w^2+4}{5w}$ for $w = 4$ ₁   **33.** $\dfrac{b^2+b}{2b}$ for $b = 5$ ₃

Use the associative laws to write an equivalent expression for each of the following.

34. $(a + b) + 3$ **35.** $(5 + x) + y$ **36.** $3 \cdot (a \cdot b)$ **37.** $(6 \cdot x) \cdot y$

34. $a + (b + 3)$
35. $5 + (x + y)$
36. $(3 \cdot a) \cdot b$
37. $6 \cdot (x \cdot y)$

Use the commutative and associative laws to write three expressions that always have the same value.

38. $(a + b) + 2$ **39.** $(3 + x) + y$ **40.** $5 + (v + w)$

41. $6 + (x + y)$ **42.** $(x \cdot y) \cdot 3$ **43.** $(a \cdot b) \cdot 5$

44. $7 \cdot (a \cdot b)$ **45.** $5 \cdot (x \cdot y)$ **46.** $2 \cdot c \cdot d$

Extension

Find a value of the variable for which the two expressions do *not* have the same value. _{Answers may vary.}

47. $3x^2$; $(3x)^2$ _{Any number except 0}   **48.** $(a + 2)^3$; $a^3 + 2^3$ _{Any number except 0 or −2}

49. $\dfrac{x+2}{2}$; x _{Any number except 2}   **50.** $\dfrac{y^6}{y^3}$; y^2 _{Any number except 1. 0 is not acceptable.}

Write an algebraic expression for each of the following.

51. A number squared plus 7 _{$x^2 + 7$}

52. A number plus the square of 7 _{$x + 7^2$ or $x + 49$}

53. A number plus 7 with the result squared _{$(x + 7)^2$}

54. A number squared plus 7 squared _{$x^2 + 7^2$}

55. The numerator is 3 more than some number and the denominator is that number squared. _{$\frac{x+3}{x^2}$}

56. Two numbers are multiplied. One of them is 5 more than the other. _{$x(x + 5)$}

Challenge

57. Carole is twice as old as Victor was a year ago. If Victor's age is now x, write an expression for Carole's age. _{$2(x - 1)$}

58. Does $a(b + c) = ab + ac$? Try different values for a, b, and c. _{Always equal}

59. Is there an associative law for subtraction of whole numbers? for division of whole numbers? If not, give counterexamples.

_{Neither. $6 - (10 - 7) \neq (6 - 10) - 7$}
_{$10 \div (5 \div 5) \neq (10 \div 5) \div 5$}

The Distributive Law

Multiplying a Sum by a Factor

If we wish to multiply a sum of several numbers by a factor, we can either add and then multiply, or multiply and then add.

EXAMPLE 1

Compute two ways. $5 \cdot (4 + 8)$

$5 \cdot (4 + 8)$ Calculating within parentheses means adding and then multiplying.

$5 \cdot 12$

60

$(5 \cdot 4) + (5 \cdot 8)$ Calculating within parentheses means multiplying and then adding.

$20 + 40$

60

TRY THIS Calculate and Compare.

1 a. $4 \cdot (2 + 5)$ 28   **1 b.** $(4 \cdot 2) + (4 \cdot 5)$ 28   **2 a.** $(7 \cdot 7) + (7 \cdot 4)$ 77

2 b. $7 \cdot (7 + 4)$ 77   **3 a.** $6 \cdot (3 + 2 + 4)$ 54   **3 b.** $(6 \cdot 3) + (6 \cdot 2) + (6 \cdot 4)$ 54

The Distributive Law

For any numbers a, b, and c, $a(b + c) = ab + ac$.

In the statement of the distributive law we know that in an expression such as $ab + cd$, the multiplications are to be done first. We can also omit the multiplication dot before or between parentheses. So, instead of writing $(4 \cdot 5) + (3 \cdot 7)$ we can write $4 \cdot 5 + 3 \cdot 7$. Instead of $3 \cdot (x + 2)$ we can write $3(x + 2)$. However, in $a(b + c)$ we cannot omit the parentheses. If we did we would have $ab + c$ which means $(ab) + c$. For example, $3(4 + 2) = 18$, but $3 \cdot 4 + 2 = 14$.

EXAMPLES

We can use the distributive law to multiply with algebraic expressions.

2. $3(x + 2) = 3x + 3 \cdot 2$ Using the distributive law

$= 3x + 6$

3. $6(s + t + w) = 6s + 6t + 6w$

The parts of an expression such as $ax + ay + az$, separated by a plus sign, are called terms.

TRY THIS Multiply.

4. $5(y + 3)$ **5.** $4(x + y + z)$ **6.** $6(x + 2y + 5)$

Factoring

If we reverse the statement of the distributive law, we have the basis of a process called factoring: $ab + ac = a(b + c)$. To factor an expression means to write an equivalent expression which is a product.

EXAMPLE 4

$3x + 3y = 3(x + y)$ by the distributive law. When we write $3(x + y)$ we say that we have factored $3x + 3y$. To factor, look for a number that is a factor of every term. Then use the distributive law.

EXAMPLES

Factor.

5. $5x + 5y + 5z = 5(x + y + z)$ The common factor is 5.

6. $7y + 14 + 21z = 7 \cdot y + 7 \cdot 2 + 7 \cdot 3z$ The common factor is 7.
$$= 7(y + 2 + 3z)$$

7. $9x + 27y + 9 = 9 \cdot x + 9 \cdot 3y + 9 \cdot 1$ The common factor is 9.
$$= 9(x + 3y + 1)$$

TRY THIS Factor.

7. $5x + 10$ **8.** $12 + 3x$ **9.** $6x + 12 + 9y$ **10.** $5x + 10y + 5$

Factoring can be checked by multiplying. We multiply the factored expression to see if we get the original expression.

EXAMPLE 8

Factor and check by multiplying.

$$5x + 10 = 5(x + 2)$$
$$\text{Check: } 5(x + 2) = 5x + 5 \cdot 2$$
$$= 5x + 10$$

TRY THIS Factor and check by multiplying.

11. $9x + 3y$ **12.** $5 + 10x + 15y$ 11. $3(3x + y)$ 12. $5(1 + 2x + 3y)$

Collecting Like Terms

Terms such as $5x$ and $4x$, whose variable factors are exactly the same, are called like terms. Similarly, $3y^2$ and $9y^2$ are like terms. Terms such as $4y$ and $5y^2$ are not like terms. We often simplify expressions by using the distributive law to collect or combine like terms.

EXAMPLES

Collect like terms.

$$
\begin{aligned}
\textbf{9. } x + x &= 1 \cdot x + 1 \cdot x \quad \text{Using the property of 1} \\
&= (1 + 1)x \quad \text{Using the distributive law} \\
&= 2x
\end{aligned}
$$

$$
\begin{aligned}
\textbf{10. } 3x + 4x &= (3 + 4)x \\
&= 7x
\end{aligned}
$$

$$
\begin{aligned}
\textbf{11. } 2x + 3y + 5x + 2y &= 2x + 5x + 3y + 2y \\
&= (2 + 5)x + (3 + 2)y \\
&= 7x + 5y
\end{aligned}
$$

$$
\begin{aligned}
\textbf{12. } 5x^2 + x^2 &= 5x^2 + 1 \cdot x^2 \quad \text{Using the property of 1} \\
&= (5 + 1)x^2 \\
&= 6x^2
\end{aligned}
$$

TRY THIS Collect like terms.

13. $6y + 2y$ **14.** $7x + 3y + 5y + 4x$ **15.** $10p + 8q + 4p + 5q$ **16.** $7x^2 + x^2$

13. $8y$
14. $11x + 8y$
15. $14p + 13q$
16. $8x^2$

EXAMPLES

We can mentally collect terms and write only the answer.

13. $5y + 2y + 4y = 11y$

14. $3s + 4t + 7s + 5t = 10s + 9t$

15. $3x^2 + 7x^2 + 2y = 10x^2 + 2y$

TRY THIS Collect like terms.

17. $3x + 5x + 8y + 2y$ **18.** $5x + 4y + 4x + 6y$ **19.** $3s + 4s + 6w^2 + 7w^2$

17. $8x + 10y$
18. $9x + 10y$
19. $7s + 13w^2$

Exercises

Multiply.

1. $2(b + 5)$ 2. $4(x + 3)$ 3. $7(1 + t)$ 4. $6(v + 4)$

5. $3(x + 1)$ 6. $7(x + 8)$ 7. $4(1 + y)$ 8. $9(s + 1)$

9. $6(5x + 2)$ 10. $9(6m + 7)$ 11. $7(x + 4 + 6y)$ 12. $4(5x + 8 + 3p)$

Factor.

13. $2x + 4$ 14. $5y + 20$ 15. $30 + 5y$ 16. $7x + 28$

17. $14x + 21y$ 18. $18a + 24b$ 19. $5x + 10 + 15y$ 20. $9a + 27b + 81$

Factor and check by multiplying.

21. $9x + 27$ 22. $6x + 24$

23. $9x + 3y$ 24. $15x + 5y$

25. $8a + 16b + 64$ 26. $5 + 20x + 35y$

27. $11x + 44y + 121$ 28. $7 + 14b + 56w$

Collect like terms.

29. $9a + 10a$ 30. $12x + 2x$

31. $10a + a$ 32. $16x + x$

33. $2x + 9z + 6x$ 34. $3a + 5b + 7a$

35. $7x + 6y^2 + 9y^2$ 36. $12m^2 + 6q + 9m^2$

37. $41a + 90 + 60a + 2$ 38. $42x + 6 + 4x + 2$

39. $8a + 8b + 3a + 3b$ 40. $100y + 200z + 190y + 400z$

41. $8u^2 + 3t + 10t + 6u^2 + 2$ 42. $5 + 6h + t + 8 + 9h$

43. $23 + 5t + 7y + t + y + 27$ 44. $45 + 90d + 87 + 9d + 3 + 7d$

45. $\frac{1}{2}b + \frac{1}{2}b$ 46. $\frac{2}{3}x + \frac{1}{3}x$

47. $2y + \frac{1}{4}y + y$ 48. $\frac{1}{2}a + a + 5a$

21. $9(x + 3)$
22. $6(x + 4)$
23. $3(3x + y)$
24. $5(3x + y)$
25. $8(a + 2b + 8)$
26. $5(1 + 4x + 7y)$
27. $11(x + 4y + 11)$
28. $7(1 + 2b + 8w)$
29. $19a$
30. $14x$
31. $11a$
32. $17x$
33. $8x + 9z$
34. $10a + 5b$
35. $7x + 15y^2$
36. $21m^2 + 6q$
37. $101a + 92$
38. $46x + 8$
39. $11a + 11b$

40. $290y + 600z$
41. $14u^2 + 13t + 2$
42. $13 + 15h + t$
43. $50 + 6t + 8y$
44. $135 + 106d$
45. $1b$ or b
46. $1x$ or x
47. $\frac{13}{4}y$ or $3\frac{1}{4}y$
48. $\frac{13}{2}a$ or $6\frac{1}{2}a$

Extension

49. When you put money in the bank and draw interest, the amount in your account later on is given by the expression $P + Prt$, where P is the principal, r is the rate of interest, and t is the time. Factor the expression. $P(1 + rt)$

50. a. Factor $17x + 34$. Then evaluate both expressions when $x = 10$ (the value of x is 10). $17 \cdot 10 + 34 = 204$; $17(x + 2) = 17(12) = 204$

b. Will you get the same answer for both expressions no matter what the value of x? Why? Yes; distributive law

51. Find a simpler expression that always has the same value as $\dfrac{3a + 6}{2a + 4}$. (Hint: Factor numerator and denominator and factor the fractional expression.) $\frac{3}{2}$

52. Find a simpler expression that always has the same value as

$$\frac{4x + 12y}{3x + 9y}. \quad \tfrac{4}{3}$$

Challenge

Collect like terms if possible and factor the result.

53. $1x + 2x^2 + 3x^3 + 4x^2 + 5x$ $6x + 6x^2 + 3x^3 = 3x(2 + 3x + x^2)$

54. $q + qr + qrs + qrst$ $q(1 + r + rs + rst)$

55. $21x + 44xy + 15y - 16x - 8y - 38xy + 2x + xy$

$7x + 7xy + 7y = 7(x + xy + y)$

56. Expand $a\{1 + b[1 + c(1 + d)]\}$ (Hint: Begin with $c(1 + d)$ and work outwards.) $a + ab + abc + abcd$

57. Here is a number trick: Think of a number. Multiply it by 4. Add 8. Divide by 4. Subtract 2. Your answer is the original number. How do we know this? Let's write an algebraic expression showing what we did.

1. Multiply by 4   2. Add 8

$\downarrow$ $\downarrow$

$\dfrac{4a + 8}{4} - 2$

$\uparrow$ $\uparrow$

3. Divide by 4   4. Subtract 2

We can find a simpler expression that always has the same value.

$\dfrac{4(a + 2)}{4 \cdot 1} - 2$ Factoring numerator and denominator

$\dfrac{4}{4} \cdot \dfrac{a + 2}{1} - 2$ Writing the expression with a factor of 1

$\dfrac{a + 2}{1} - 2$ Using a property of 1

$a + 2 - 2 = a$ Using a property of 0

The trick uses the fact that 2 is $\frac{8}{4}$.

Make up a number trick, and show that it works by finding two expressions that always have the same value. Answers may vary.

1–6 Solving Equations

Equations are very important in algebra. In this lesson you will learn how to solve some very simple equations. Later you will learn to solve others.

Equations and Solutions

An equation is a number sentence with an equal sign ($=$) for its verb. Here are some examples.

$$3 + 2 = 5 \qquad 7 - 2 = 4 \qquad x + 6 = 13$$

An equation $a = b$ says that the symbols a and b stand for the same number. An equation may be true, or false, or neither.

EXAMPLES
Determine whether these equations are true, or false, or neither.

1. $3 + 2 = 5$ The equation is true.

2. $7 - 2 = 4$ The equation is false.

3. $x + 6 = 13$ The equation is neither true nor false because we don't know what number x represents.

TRY THIS Determine whether these equations are true, or false, or neither.

1. $3 \cdot 5 + 2 = 13$ 2. $4 \cdot 2 - 3 = 5$ 3. $y + 5 = 6$

1. False
2. True
3. Neither

Any replacement for the variable that makes an equation true is called a solution of the equation. To solve an equation means to find all of its solutions. One way to solve equations is by trial.

EXAMPLE 4
Solve $x + 6 = 13$ by trial.

If we replace x by 2 we get $2 + 6 = 13$, a false equation.
If we replace x by 8 we get $8 + 6 = 13$, a false equation.
If we replace x by 7 we get $7 + 6 = 13$, a true equation.

No other number makes the equation true, so the only solution is the number 7.

4. Find three replacements that make $y + 5 = 12$ false. Example: 1, 2, or 3

5. Find the replacement that makes $x + 5 = 12$ true. 7

Solve by trial.

6. $x + 4 = 10$ 6 **7.** $3x = 12$ 4 **8.** $3y + 1 = 16$ 5

Solving Equations of the Type $x + a = b$

Think of a very simple equation such as $x + 2 = 5$. We have added 2 to x to get 5. Since addition and subtraction are opposite operations, we can subtract 2 to "undo" the addition. The equation says that $x + 2$ and 5 represent the same number, so we subtract on both sides.

$$x + 2 - 2 = 5 - 2$$
$$x = 3$$

The solution of the equation $x = 3$ is obvious. It is also the solution of the original equation $x + 2 = 5$. We can check this by substituting 3 for x in the original equation. Now let us use this method to solve some equations that are not as simple.

> To solve an equation of the type $x + a = b$, subtract a on both sides of the equation.

EXAMPLE 5

Solve.

$$x + 17 = 50$$
$$x + 17 - 17 = 50 - 17 \quad \text{Subtracting 17 on both sides}$$
$$x = 33$$

We now check to see if 33 is really a solution.

Check: $\underline{x + 17 = 50}$ Writing the original equation

$$\begin{array}{c|c} 33 + 17 & 50 \\ \hline 50 & \end{array}$$ Substituting 33 for x

Calculating

Since the left-hand and right-hand sides match, 33 checks. It is the solution.

EXAMPLE 6

Solve.

$$x + 1.6 = 9.8$$
$$x = 9.8 - 1.6 \quad \text{Subtracting 1.6}$$
$$x = 8.2 \qquad\qquad \text{on both sides}$$

Check: $\dfrac{x + 1.6 = 9.8}{\begin{array}{c|c} 8.2 + 1.6 & 9.8 \\ 9.8 & \end{array}}$

The solution is 8.2.

TRY THIS Solve. Be sure to check.

9. $x + 47 = 119$ ₇₂ **10.** $x + 2.7 = 7.6$ ₄.₉ **11.** $x + \dfrac{3}{5} = \dfrac{4}{5}$ ⅕

Solving Equations of the Type *ax* = *b*

Multiplication and division are also opposite operations. To solve an equation $ax = b$, where x is multiplied by a, we can "undo" the multiplication by dividing on both sides by a.

> To solve an equation of the type $ax = b$, where a is not 0, divide by a on both sides of the equation.

EXAMPLE 7

Solve.

$$5x = 15$$
$$\dfrac{5x}{5} = \dfrac{15}{5} \quad \begin{array}{l}\text{Dividing by 5}\\ \text{on both sides}\end{array}$$
$$x = \dfrac{15}{5}$$
$$x = 3$$

Check: $\dfrac{5x = 15}{\begin{array}{c|c} 5 \cdot 3 & 15 \\ 15 & \end{array}}$ Substituting 3 for x

The solution is 3.

EXAMPLE 8

Solve.

$$4.7y = 40.42$$
$$y = \dfrac{40.42}{4.7} \quad \begin{array}{l}\text{Dividing by 4.7}\\ \text{on both sides}\end{array}$$
$$y = 8.6$$

Check: $\dfrac{4.7y = 40.42}{\begin{array}{c|c} 4.7(8.6) & 40.42 \\ 40.42 & \end{array}}$

The solution is 8.6.

TRY THIS Solve. Be sure to check.

12. $9y = 108$ ₁₂ **13.** $6y = 50$ ²⁵⁄₃ **14.** $2.6x = 11.7$ ₄.₅

1–6	

Exercises

Solve by trial.

1. $x + 17 = 32$ ₁₅   **2.** $y + 28 = 92$ ₆₄   **3.** $x - 7 = 12$ ₁₉   **4.** $y - 8 = 19$ ₂₇

5. $6x = 54$ ₉   **6.** $8y = 72$ ₉   **7.** $\frac{x}{6} = 5$ ₃₀   **8.** $\frac{y}{8} = 6$ ₄₈

9. $5x + 7 = 107$ ₂₀ **10.** $9x + 5 = 86$ ₉ **11.** $7x - 1 = 48$ ₇ **12.** $4y - 2 = 10$ ₃

Solve by subtracting on both sides. Be sure to check.

13. $x + 7 = 24$ **14.** $y + 26 = 43$ **15.** $x + 19 = 105$ 13. 17

16. $y + 37 = 212$ **17.** $x + 99 = 476$ **18.** $x + 112 = 1001$ 14. 17
                                                                                   15. 86
19. $x + 5064 = 7882$ **20.** $x + 4112 = 8007$ **21.** $x + 2.78 = 8.44$ 16. 175
                                                                                   17. 377
                                                                                   18. 889
22. $x + 3.04 = 4.69$ **23.** $x + \frac{1}{7} = \frac{6}{7}$ **24.** $x + \frac{3}{13} = \frac{11}{13}$ 19. 2818
                                                                                   20. 3895
                                                                                   21. 5.66
                                                                                   22. 1.65
                                                                                   23. ⁵⁄₇
                                                                                   24. ⁸⁄₁₃

Solve by dividing on both sides. Be sure to check.

25. $15x = 90$ ₆   **26.** $26z = 182$ ₇   **27.** $4x = 5$ ⁵⁄₄

28. $6y = 27$ ⁹⁄₂ or 4.5 **29.** $10x = 2.4$ 0.24   **30.** $9y = 3.6$ 0.4

31. $2.9y = 8.99$ ₃.₁   **32.** $5.5y = 34.1$ ₆.₂   **33.** $6.2y = 52.7$ ₈.₅

34. $9.4x = 23.5$ ₂.₅   **35.** $117t = 2106$ ₁₈   **36.** $193c = 4053$ ₂₁

Extension

Solve.

37. $5x + 3x = 10$ ⁵⁄₄   **38.** $9y + 4y = 26$ ₂

39. $225a = 27$ ³⁄₂₅   **40.** $1000x = 300$ ³⁄₁₀

41. $0.0592y = 0.4736$ ₈ **42.** $1.009x = 14.126$ ₁₄

43. $0.125n = 1$ ₈   **44.** $0.004t = 1$ ₂₅₀

Challenge   Answers may vary.

45. Write an equation which has *no* whole number solution. $3x = 2$

46. Write an equation for which *every* whole number is a solution. $x - x = 0$

47. Write an equation for the number of 12's that will give a product of zero. $12x = 0$

1–7 Solving Problems

We learn to solve equations to help us solve certain types of problems. To do that, we translate the problem situation to an equation and then solve the equation. The problems in this section are simple ones. You may be able to solve some of them without using equations, but it is better to practice with simple problems. Remember, you are learning how algebra works. Later, you will use the methods of algebra to solve harder problems.

EXAMPLE 1

What number added to 478 gives 1019? We translate the problem situation to an equation where x represents the unknown number.

$$\underbrace{\text{What number}}_{x} \quad \underbrace{\text{added to}}_{+} \quad \underset{478}{\downarrow} \quad \underset{=}{\downarrow} \quad \underset{1019}{\downarrow}$$

We now solve the equation.

$$x + 478 = 1019$$
$$x = 1019 - 478 \quad \text{Subtracting 478 on both sides}$$
$$x = 541$$

To check, we try our answer in the original problem . Does the number 541 added to 478 give 1019?

$$541 + 478 = 1019$$

The answer checks, and we have a solution to the problem. If we make a mistake in translating the problem to an equation, then checking in the equation does not reveal the mistake. We must check in the original problem to make sure the answer is a solution.

In Example 1 notice these things.
a. "What number" translates to a variable.
b. "added to" translates to a plus sign.
c. "gives" translates to an equals sign.

TRY THIS Translate to an equation and solve. Be sure to check.

1. What number added to 397 gives 1821? $x + 397 = 1821, 1424$

EXAMPLE 2

Nine times what number is 6426? Here we let y represent the number and we translate to an equation.

Nine times what number is 6426?

$$9 \cdot y = 6426$$

We have an equation. We now solve it.

$$9y = 6426$$

$$y = \frac{6426}{9} \quad \text{Dividing on both sides by 9}$$

$$y = 714$$

To check, we try our answer in the original problem. Is 9 times 714 actually 6426?

$$9 \cdot 714 = 6426$$

We have an answer to the problem.

TRY THIS Translate to an equation and solve. Be sure to check.

2. Sixteen times what number is 496? $16x = 496, 31$

3. Seven times what number is 168? $7x = 168, 24$

EXAMPLE 3

Sometimes it helps to reword a problem before translating.

One year a person earned a salary of $23,400. That was $1700 more than the previous year. What was the salary the previous year?

Let x = the previous year's salary. We reword and then translate.

New salary is $1700 plus previous year's salary.

$$23,400 = 1700 + x \qquad \text{No dollar signs in an equation}$$

We solve the equation.

$$23,400 = 1700 + x \quad \text{Subtracting 1700 on both sides}$$
$$23,400 - 1700 = x$$
$$21,700 = x$$

To check, we add 1700 to 21,700. We get 23,400, so $21,700 is the correct answer.

EXAMPLE 4

A solid state color television set uses about 420 kilowatt-hours (kwh) of electrical energy in a year. That is 3.5 times the amount of energy used by a black-and-white set. How many kwh does the black-and-white set use in a year?

Let x = the amount of energy used by the black-and-white set. We reword and translate.

3.5 times the amount of energy used by the black-and-white set is 420 kwh.

$$3.5 \cdot x = 420$$

We solve the equation.

$$3.5x = 420$$

$$x = \frac{420}{3.5} \quad \text{Dividing on both sides by 3.5}$$

$$x = 120$$

To check, we look at the original problem. Is 3.5 times 120 kwh actually 420 kwh? We multiply and see that it is. The answer is 120 kwh.

TRY THIS Translate to an equation and solve. Be sure to check.

4. Hank Aaron hit 755 home runs. That is 637 more home runs than were hit by Ty Cobb. How many home runs did Cobb hit? $\quad 755 = 637 + x, 118$

5. An investment grew to $14,500 after one year. That was 1.16 times the amount invested. How much was invested? $\quad 1.16x = 14,500; 12,500$

1–7	

Exercises

Translate to an equation. Then solve and check.

1. What number added to 60 is 112? $\quad 60 + x = 112, x = 52$

2. What number added to 45.3 is 53.1? $\quad 45.3 + x = 53.1, x = 7.8$

3. When 29 is added to a number the answer is 171. $\quad x + 29 = 171, x = 142$

4. When 123 is added to a number the answer is 987. $\quad x + 123 = 987, x = 864$

5. Seven times what number is 2233? $\quad 7x = 2233, x = 319$

6. Four times what number is 8944? $\quad 4x = 8944, x = 2236$

7. When 42 is multiplied by a number the answer is 2352. $42x = 2352, x = 56$

8. When 48 is multiplied by a number the answer is 624. $48x = 624, x = 13$

Translate to an equation and solve.

9. Joe says he missed a perfect quiz paper by 5 problems. There were 8 problems on the quiz. How many did Joe get right? $8 - x = 5, x = 3$

10. A football player caught 3 passes for a total of 55 yards. The first two were for 23 and 8 yards. Find the third. $23 + 8 + x = 55, x = 24$

11. The New York Yankees won 37 more games than the Minnesota Twins. The Yankees won 101. How many did the Twins win? $x + 37 = 101, x = 64$

12. A game board has 64 squares. If you win 35 squares, how many does your opponent get? $35 + x = 64, x = 29$

13. Jeremy has $48 less than Marissa. Marissa has $115. How much does Jeremy have? $x + 48 = 115, x = 67$

14. There are 352,198 people in a city. 187,804 are at least 28 years old. How many have not reached age 28? $352,198 - x = 187,804, x = 164,394$

15. A dozen bagels cost $3.12. How much is each bagel? $12x = 3.12, x = \$0.26$

16. A movie theater took in $438.75 from 117 customers. What was the price of a ticket? $117x = 438.75, x = \$3.75$

17. A consultant charges $80 an hour. How many hours did the consultant work to make $53,400? $80x = 53,400, x = 667.5$

18. The area of Lake Superior is about four times the area of Lake Ontario. The area of Lake Superior is 78,114 km². What is the area of Lake Ontario? $4x = 78,114, x = 19,528.5$

19. It takes a 60-watt bulb about 16.6 hours to use one kilowatt-hour of electricity. That is about 2.5 times as long as it takes a 150-watt bulb to use one kilowatt-hour. How long does it take a 150-watt bulb to use one kilowatt-hour? $2.5x = 16.6, x = 6.64$

20. The area of Alaska is about 483 times the area of Rhode Island. The area of Alaska is 1,519,202 km². What is the area of Rhode Island? $483x = 1{,}519{,}202, x = 3145.3$ km²

21. The boiling point of ethyl alcohol is 78.3°C. That is 13.5°C higher than the boiling point of methyl alcohol. What is the boiling point of methyl alcohol? $x + 13.5 = 78.3, x = 64.8$°C

22. The height of the Eiffel Tower is 295 m. It is about 203 m higher than the Statue of Liberty. What is the height of the Statue of Liberty? $x + 203 = 295, x = 92$ m

23. The distance from the earth to the sun is about 150,000,000 km. That is about 391 times the distance from the earth to the moon. What is the distance from the earth to the moon? $391x = 150{,}000{,}000,$ $x = 383{,}631.7$ km

Extension

Translate to an equation and solve.

24. In baseball, "batting average" times "at bats" equals hits. Reggie has 125 at bats and 36 hits. Write an equation and find his batting average. $x \cdot 125 = 36$; .288

25. The equation for converting Celsius temperature to Farenheit is °F = 1.8°C + 32. Find °F if the temperature is 15°C. 59°F

26. In three-way light bulbs, the highest wattage is a sum of the two lower wattages. If the lowest is 30 watts and the highest is 150 watts, what is the middle wattage? $30 + x = 150$; 120 watts

27. A roll of film cost $3.14 and development cost $6.13. What was the cost for each of the 36 prints? $36x = 3.14 + 6.13$; 25.75¢

Challenge

Translate to an equation and solve.

28. Franklin Laundry dryers cost a dime for 7 minutes. How many dimes will you have to put in if your clothes dry in 45 minutes? 7 dimes

29. One inch = 2.54 cm. A meter is 100 cm. Find the number of inches in a meter. $2.54x = 100$; 39.37 in.

30. If sound travels at 1087 feet per second. How long does it take to hear the sound an airplane makes when it is 10,000 feet overhead? $1087x = 10{,}000$; 9.2 sec

31. Brenda gives Abbie $1 more than Abbie already had. Now Abbie has $13. How much did Brenda give her? $x + (x + 1) = 13$; $7

CAREERS/Computer Industry

The small electronic device known as the computer is changing the way people work throughout the world. When properly used, a computer can help a person answer questions or sort information much faster than has ever been possible before. It is not surprising that millions of jobs now involve the design, sales, or use of computers.

We are all aware of the computer's ability as a calculator. Computers do such complex things as guiding space vehicles. The key to the value of computers, though, is not that they can do things people cannot do. Most of the calculations done by computers could be done by people using paper and pencil. The key is speed. If we did not have computers, the space program would be a trial-and-error operation. By the time people solved equations telling engineers what to do to correct the course of a space vehicle, the vehicle would already have flown millions of miles in the wrong direction.

In business, computers are most often used to do very simple tasks, such as keeping count of items or dollars. Once again, the important thing is not what is done by the computer, but how fast it is done. For example, one company used to have a billing department of eight people. These people spent 6 working days—48 hours—preparing bills each month. The total number of person-hours involved in billing was 48 × 8, or 384. Today, one person working with a computer spends a total of 2 working days—16 hours—preparing bills each month. The computer saves the company 368 person-hours each month on the billing tasks.

Exercises

The following problems are similar to those that a person working in the computer industry might solve.

1. Ron works for Kemble Manufacturing Co. He is in charge of issuing checks to suppliers. Before he began using a computer to help him do this, he spent eight times as much time on this task as he now does. At present he spends 35 minutes each week issuing checks. How much time did he formerly spend? (See Section 1–1.)

2. Monica is a sales representative for Corinthian Computers. Her company's research shows that their model L2C-7, when set up to function as a word processor, reduces the time spent on typing tasks by $\frac{3}{7}$. Write an algebraic expression, using t for time, to express the time savings that can be achieved by the L2C-7 when it is used as a word processor. (See Section 1–4.) $\frac{3}{7}t$

3. Bob is the office manager for Carson Supply Co. He wants to know the rate at which a clerk can update towel inventory using Computer A. The clerk takes 20 minutes to get ready to begin the update, and 6 minutes to enter data from each invoice. Bob writes this as the expression $6x + 20$. Factor this expression. Then evaluate both expressions for $x = 7$. (See Section 1–5.)

1. 280 minutes per week
3. 2(3x + 10), 62, 62

Review the material in the chapter. Then see how you have done by trying these review exercises. If you miss an exercise, restudy the indicated lesson.

1–1   Evaluate.

1. $3a$ for $a = 5$. 15

2. $\frac{x}{y}$ for $x = 12$ and $y = 2$ 6

3. $\frac{2 \cdot p}{q}$ for $p = 20$ and $q = 8$ 5

4. $\frac{x - y}{3}$ for $x = 17$ and $y = 5$ 4

1–1   Write an algebraic expression for each of the following.

5. 8 less than z $z - 8$

6. three times x 3x

7. A number x is 1 more than a smaller number. Write an expression for the smaller number. $x - 1$

1–2   Use a commutative law to write an equivalent expression.

8. $4 + y$ **9.** ab **10.** $pq + 2$ 8. y + 4   9. ba   10. qp + 2, 2 + pq, or 2 + qp

1–2   Write an equivalent expression. Use the indicated name for 1.

11. $\frac{2}{5}$ Use $\frac{6}{6}$ for 1. $\frac{12}{30}$ **12.** $\frac{2x}{y}$ Use $\frac{z}{z}$ for 1. $\frac{2xz}{yz}$

1–2   Simplify.

13. $\frac{20}{48}$ $\frac{5}{12}$

14. $\frac{10ac}{18bc}$ $\frac{5a}{9b}$

1–3

15. What is the meaning of the expression $(2m)^3$? $2m \cdot 2m \cdot 2m$

16. Write $6z \cdot 6z$ in exponential notation. $(6z)^2$

17. Evaluate $n^3 + 1$ for $n = 2$. 9

1–4   Evaluate each expression.

18. $(x + 1)^2$ for $x = 4$ 25

19. $(y - 1)(y + 3)$ for $y = 5$ 32

1–4   Use an associative law to write an equivalent expression.

20. $(3 + x) + 1$ $3 + (x + 1)$

21. $m \cdot (4 \cdot n)$ $(m \cdot 4) \cdot n$

1–4 Use the commutative and associative laws to write three equivalent expressions. <small>Answers may vary.</small>

22. $(1 + m) + n$

23. $4 \cdot (x \cdot y)$

1–5 Multiply.

24. $6(3x + 5y)$ <small>18x + 30y</small>

25. $8(5x + 3y + 2)$ <small>40x + 24y + 16</small>

1–5 Factor.

26. $18x + 6y$ <small>6(3x + y)</small>

27. $36x + 16 + 4y$ <small>4(9x + 4 + y)</small>

1–5 Collect like terms.

28. $36y + 8a + 4y + 2a$ <small>40y + 10a</small> **29.** $54x + 3b + 9b + 6x$ <small>60x + 12b</small>

1–6 Solve.

30. $x + 11 = 50$ <small>39</small> **31.** $x + \dfrac{3}{8} = \dfrac{4}{8}$ <small>$\frac{1}{8}$</small> **32.** $7n = 126$ <small>18</small> **33.** $1.3z = 33.8$ <small>26</small>

1–7 Translate to an equation and solve.

34. What number added to 35 is 102? <small>x + 35 = 102, x = 67</small>

35. Nine times what number is 3033? <small>9x = 3033, x = 337</small>

36. An artist charges \$75 for each drawing. How many drawings did the artist complete to earn \$2400? <small>75x = 2400, x = 32</small>

CHAPTER 1   Test

1. Evaluate $\dfrac{3x}{y}$ for $x = 10$ and $y = 5$. <small>6</small>

2. Write an algebraic expression for 6 more than n. <small>n + 6</small>

Use a commutative law to write an equivalent expression.

3. pq <small>qp</small>

4. $z + 3$ <small>3 + z</small>

Simplify.

5. $\dfrac{16}{24}$ <small>$\frac{2}{3}$</small>

6. $\dfrac{9xy}{15yz}$ <small>$\frac{3x}{5z}$</small>

Evaluate.

7. $x^2 - 5$ for $x = 4$ <small>11</small>

8. $(y + 3)(y - 4)$ for $y = 6$ <small>18</small>

Use an associative law to write an equivalent expression.

9. $x \cdot (4 \cdot y)$ $(x \cdot 4) \cdot y$ **10.** $a + (b + 1)$ $(a + b) + 1$

Multiply.

11. $10(9x + 3y)$ $90x + 30y$ **12.** $7(9m + 2x + 1)$ $63m + 14x + 7$

Factor.

13. $15y + 5$ $5(3y + 1)$ **14.** $24x + 16 + 8y$ $8(3x + 2 + y)$

Collect like terms.

15. $21x + 96 + 5x + 6$ **16.** $18y + 30a + 9a + 4y$ 15. $26x + 102$ 16. $22y + 39a$

Solve.

17. $x + 9 = 11$ 2 **18.** $y + \frac{3}{10} = \frac{9}{10}$ $\frac{3}{5}$ **19.** $5t = 95$ 19 **20.** $0.3z = 1.5$ 5

Translate to an equation and solve.

21. What number added to 43 is 60? $x + 43 = 60, x = 17$
22. Four times what number is 56? $4x = 56, x = 14$

Challenge

23. Suppose we define a new operation $\odot$ on the set of whole numbers as follows: $a \odot b = a^b$. Find $2 \odot 3$ and $3 \odot 2$. Is $\odot$ commutative? That is, does $a \odot b = b \odot a$? No. $2^3 \neq 3^2$.

Ready for Integers and Rational Numbers?

1–5 Multiply.

1. $5(a + b + d)$ **2.** $11(w + 4)$ **3.** $7(3z + y + 2)$ $21z + 7y + 14$ 1. $5a + 5b + 5d$
                                                     2. $11w + 44$

1–5 Factor.

4. $45 + 9y$ $9(5 + y)$ **5.** $3a + 12b$ $3(a + 4b)$ **6.** $4x + 10 + 8y$ $2(2x + 5 + 4y)$

1–5 Collect like terms.

7. $5x + 3y + 2x$ **8.** $b^2 + 3a + 4b^2$ **9.** $5t + 2 + 3t + 7$ $8t + 9$ 7. $7x + 3y$
                                                     8. $3a + 5b^2$

1–6 Solve and check.

10. $b + 3 = 20$ 17 **11.** $y + 5 = 14$ 9 **12.** $4x = 32$ 8 **22.** $8a = 40$ 5

Ready for Integers and Rational Numbers? 37

2

CHAPTER TWO

Integers
and Rational Numbers

The problems we solved in Chapter 1 used numbers of arithmetic. These numbers can be represented on a number line.

In this chapter we will use the number line to learn about other sets of numbers. The numbers of arithmetic help us to describe many real world situations. However, we can increase our ability to describe such situations by using numbers called integers.

The Set of Integers

To create the set of integers we begin with the set of whole numbers. We call the natural numbers positive integers. For each positive integer we invent a new number called a negative integer. For instance, 3 is a positive integer; so we invent -3, read "negative three." We locate the negative integers on the number line by reflecting the positive integers across zero. Zero is neither positive nor negative.

The set of *integers* consists of the positive integers, negative integers, and zero.

EXAMPLES

Tell which integers correspond to each situation.

1. The temperature is 3 degrees below zero.
   The integer -3 corresponds to the situation.
   That number is the temperature.

2. Paul went down 21 points in a card game.
   The integer -21 corresponds to the change in Paul's score. It stands for the number of points he lost.

3. Death Valley is 280 feet below sea level. The integer -280 corresponds to the situation. That number is the elevation.

4. Flo's Popcorn Stand made a profit of $18 on Monday and lost $7 on Tuesday. The integers 18 and -7 correspond to the change in sales. The first number is the profit on Monday and -7 can be thought of as the profit on Tuesday.

TRY THIS Tell which integers correspond to each situation.

1. Julia has a debt of $12 and Lynn has $15 in her savings account. $-12, 15$

2. The halfback made a gain of 8 yards on first down. The quarterback was sacked for a 5-yard loss on second down. $8, -5$

3. At 3 seconds before liftoff ignition occurs. At 128 seconds after liftoff the first stage engine stops. $-3, 128$

Order on the Number Line

We use the symbol $<$ to mean is less than. For example, $6 < 8$ means "6 is less than 8." The sentence $3 < 5$ is true. The sentence $9 < 2$ is false. The symbol $>$ means is greater than. For example, $7 > 3$ means "7 is greater than 3." The sentence $12 > 2$ is true. The sentence $5 > 16$ is false.

On the number line numbers increase to the right. For any two numbers the one farther to the right is greater or the one to the left is less. This means that all negative numbers are less than 0 and all positive numbers are greater than 0.

EXAMPLES
Use either $<$ or $>$ to write true sentences.

5.   2   9   Since 9 is to the right of 2, 9 is greater than 2 or 2 is less than 9. The answer is $2 < 9$.

6. -7 3   Since -7 is to the left of 3, we have $-7 < 3$.

7.   6 -12 Since 6 is to the right of -12, then $6 > -12$.

8. -18 -5 Since -18 is to the left of -5, we have $-18 < -5$.

In a card game, if you are down 40 points, that is better than being down 80 points. This corresponds to saying $-40 > -80$. If you have a debt of $150, that is worse than having a debt of $100. This corresponds to $-150 < -100$.

TRY THIS Use < or > to write true sentences.

4. 14   7 $>$ **5.** 11 -2 $>$ **6.** -15 -5 $<$

Absolute Value

From the number line we see that numbers like 4 and -4 are both the same distance from zero. We call this distance the absolute value of the number.

> The *absolute value* of a number is its distance from 0 on a number line. We use the symbol $|n|$ to represent the absolute value of a number n.

> To find absolute value:
> 1. If a number is negative, make it positive.
> 2. If a number is positive or zero, leave it alone.

EXAMPLES
Find the absolute value.

9. $|-7|$ The distance of -7 from 0 is 7, so $|-7|$ is 7.

10. $|12|$ The distance of 12 from 0 is 12, so $|12|$ is 12.

11. $|0|$ The distance of 0 from 0 is 0.

TRY THIS Find the absolute value.

7. $|17|$ 17 **8.** $|-8|$ 8 **9.** $|-14|$ 14 **10.** $|21|$ 21

Exercises

Tell which integers correspond to each situation.

1. In one game Carlos won 5 marbles. In the next he lost 12 marbles. +5, −12

2. The temperature on Wednesday was 18° above zero. On Thursday it was 2° below zero. +18, −2

3. Ramona has a debt of $17 while Alicia has $12 in her wallet. −17, +12

4. Jane's business made $2500 one week and lost $560 the next. +2500, −560

5. The Dead Sea, between Jordan and Israel, is 1286 feet below sea level, whereas Mt. Everest is 29,028 feet above sea level. −1286, +29,028

6. In bowling, Evan's team was behind by 34 pins while Terry's team was ahead by 47 pins. −34, +47

7. On Monday, Vicky made a deposit of $750 in her savings account. On Friday, she withdrew $125. +750, −125

8. In U.S. foreign trade, the U.S. had an excess of 3 million dollars. +3,000,000

9. While playing a video game, Carroll intercepted a missile worth 20 points, lost a starship worth 150 points, and captured a base worth 300 points. +20, −150, +300

Write a true sentence using < or >.

10. 5   0 $>$ **11.** 9   0 $>$ **12.** -9 5 $<$ **13.** 8 -8 $>$

14. -6 6 $<$ **15.** 0 -7 $>$ **16.** -8 -5 $<$ **17.** -4 -3 $<$

18. -5 -11 $>$ **19.** -3 -4 $>$ **20.** -6 -5 $<$ **21.** -10 -14 $>$

Find the absolute value.

22. $|-3|$ 3   **23.** $|-7|$ 7   **24.** $|10|$ 10   **25.** $|11|$ 11

26. $|0|$ 0   **27.** $|-4|$ 4   **28.** $|-24|$ 24   **29.** $|325|$ 325

30. $|x|$ when $x = 5$ 5   **31.** $|b|$ when $b = -3$ 3

Extension

List the following sets of integers in order from least to greatest.

32. 13, -12, 5, -17 **33.** -23, 4, 0, -17
    $-17, -12, 5, 13$ $-23, -17, 0, 4$

Translate into mathematical language.

34. In pinochle a score of 120 is better than a score of -20. $+120 > -20$

35. A deposit of \$20 to a savings account is better than a withdrawl of \$25. $20 > -25$

36. In trade, a deficit of \$500,000 is worse than an excess of \$1,000,000. $-500,000 < 1,000,000$

37. In bowling it is better to be 60 pins ahead than to be 20 pins ahead. $+60 > +20$

38. On a test it is better to have 2 points taken off than 10 points taken off. $-2 > -10$

Challenge

39. Explain why in golf or dieting it is better to be -2 than $+3$ with respect to par or a certain weight.   In either case, a lower number is better than a greater one.

40. Solve $|x| = 7$.   **41.** Solve $|x| < 2$. (Choose integer replacements.)
    -7 or 7 $-1, 0, 1$

Write a true sentence using <, >, or =.

42. $|-3|$ 5 $<$ **43.** 2 $|-4|$ $<$ **44.** -2 $|-1|$ $<$ **45.** 0 $|0|$ $=$

46. $|-5|$ $|-2|$ $>$ **47.** $|4|$ $|-7|$ $<$ **48.** $|x|$ -1 $>$ **49.** $|-8|$ $|8|$ $=$

50. Does $|x + y| = |x| + |y|$? If not, give an example.
    No. $|-3 + 2| = 1$, $|-3| + |2| = 5$

List in order from least to greatest.

51. 7^1, -5, $|-6|$, 4, $|3|$, -100, 0, 1^7, $\frac{14}{4}$ $-100, -5, 0, 1^7, |3|, \frac{14}{4}, 4, |-6|, 7^1$

Naming Rational Numbers

We have studied the numbers of arithmetic and the integers. We now consider the rational numbers. The word rational comes from the word ratio. Every number of arithmetic can be named as a quotient, or ratio, of two whole numbers. We use this idea to define a rational number.

DEFINITION

Any number that can be expressed as the ratio of two integers is called a *rational number*. The denominator of the ratio may not be zero.

EXAMPLE 1
List five examples of rational numbers.

a. $\dfrac{-2}{-2} = 1$ b. $\dfrac{0}{100} = 0$ c. $\dfrac{19}{4} = 4\dfrac{3}{4}$

d. $\dfrac{-56}{100} = -0.56$ e. $\dfrac{-16}{2} = -8$

TRY THIS

1. List five examples of rational numbers. Answers may vary.

The absolute value of a rational number has the same meaning as for integers. For example, $\left|\dfrac{3}{2}\right| = \dfrac{3}{2}$ and $\left|\dfrac{-5}{4}\right| = \dfrac{5}{4}$.

Graphing Rational Numbers

There is a point of a number line for every rational number. The number is called the coordinate of the point. The point is the graph of the number. When we draw a point for a number, we say that we have graphed the number.

EXAMPLES

Graph each of these numbers.

2. $\frac{5}{2}$ The number $\frac{5}{2}$ can be named $2\frac{1}{2}$ or 2.5. Its graph is halfway between 2 and 3.

3. -3.2 The graph of -3.2 is $\frac{2}{10}$ of the way from -3 to -4.

4. $\frac{13}{8}$ The number $\frac{13}{8}$ can be named $1\frac{5}{8}$ or 1.625. The graph is about $\frac{6}{10}$ of the way from 1 to 2.

TRY THIS Graph each of these numbers.

2. $\frac{12}{5}$ **3.** -4.8 **4.** $\frac{-18}{5}$ **5.** 8.3

Order of the Rational Numbers

The relations $<$ (is less than) and $>$ (is greater than) are the same for rational numbers as they are for integers. Recall that numbers on the line increase from left to right.

EXAMPLES

Use either $<$ or $>$ to write a true sentence.

5.   1.38   1.83   The answer is $1.38 < 1.83$.

6. -3.45 1.32   The answer is $-3.45 < 1.32$ because -3.45 is to the left of 1.32.

7. -3.33 -4.44 The answer is $-3.33 > -4.44$.

8. $\frac{5}{8}$ $\frac{7}{11}$ We convert to decimal notation. $\frac{5}{8} = 0.625$, $\frac{7}{11} = 0.6363 \ldots$ Thus, $\frac{5}{8} < \frac{7}{11}$.

In Example 8 we can abbreviate $\frac{7}{11}$ by putting a bar over the repeating part.

$$\frac{7}{11} = 0.63\overline{63}$$

Note that decimal notation for a rational number either ends or repeats.

TRY THIS Use either < or > to write a true sentence.

6. 4.62   4.26 $>$ **7.** 3.11 -9.56 $>$

8. $\frac{6}{7}$ $\frac{13}{15}$ $<$ **9.** $-\frac{3}{5}$ $-\frac{5}{9}$ $<$

Showing a Number is Rational

We know that every rational number can be named as a ratio, or quotient, of two integers. Thus, to show that a number is rational, we only have to find one way of naming it as a ratio of two integers.

EXAMPLES

Show that each of the following numbers is a rational number.

9.   3   We look for two integers whose quotient is 3. There are many possibilities, such as, $\frac{3}{1}$, $\frac{6}{2}$, or $\frac{-30}{-10}$. Since 3 can be named as a ratio of two integers, it is rational.

10. -9.2 We know that 9.2 can be named $\frac{92}{10}$, so -9.2 can be named $-\frac{92}{10}$, $\frac{-92}{10}$, or $\frac{92}{-10}$. It can also be named in other ways as a ratio of two integers. The number is rational.

11. $-\frac{4}{5}$ If we divide 4 by 5 we get $\frac{4}{5}$. If we divide -4 by 5 or 4 by -5 we get a negative number, the additive inverse of $\frac{4}{5}$. Thus, $-\frac{4}{5}$ can be named $\frac{-4}{5}$ or $\frac{4}{-5}$ and is therefore rational.

Example 11 shows that in fractional notation with a negative number, we can write the minus sign in any of three places.

> For any whole numbers a and b, $b \neq 0$,
>
> $$-\frac{a}{b} = \frac{-a}{b} = \frac{a}{-b}.$$

TRY THIS Show that each number is rational.   Answers may vary.

10. 4.5   **11.** $-\frac{3}{2}$ **12.** -10

13. -14.3 **14.** 0   **15.** -0.01

10. $\frac{45}{10}$ 11. $\frac{-3}{2}$ 12. $\frac{-10}{1}$

13. $\frac{-143}{10}$ 14. $\frac{0}{1}$ 15. $\frac{-1}{100}$

The rational numbers include all of the numbers we have studied so far. All whole numbers are rational because any whole number n can be named $\frac{n}{1}$. All integers are also rational for the same reason. Here is a diagram showing the relationships between the various kinds of numbers.

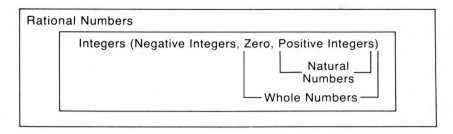

Some numbers such as $\sqrt{2}$ are not rational numbers. They are called irrational numbers. The set of rational numbers along with the irrational numbers are called the real numbers. In beginning algebra we are concerned mostly with rational numbers. From now on when we refer to numbers, we will mean rational numbers.

2–2	

Exercises

1. List 10 examples of rational numbers.

Graph each number on a line.

2. $\frac{10}{3}$ 3. $-\frac{17}{5}$ 4. -4.3 5. 6.45

Use either < or > to write a true sentence.

6. $2.14 \; > \; 1.24$ 7. $-3.3 \; < \; -2.2$

8. $-14.5 \; < \; 0.011$ 9. $17.2 \; > \; -1.67$

10. $-12.88 \; < -6.45$ 11. $-14.34 \; > -17.88$

12. $\frac{5}{12} \; < \frac{11}{25}$ 13. $-\frac{14}{17} \; < \; -\frac{27}{35}$

Show that each number is rational by writing it as a quotient of integers.

14. $14 \quad \frac{14}{1}$ 15. $-7 \quad \frac{-7}{1}$ 16. $0 \quad \frac{0}{\text{any integer but 0}}$ 17. $-3 \quad \frac{-3}{1}$

18. $4.2 \quad \frac{42}{10}$ 19. $-8.1 \quad \frac{-81}{10}$ 20. $3.444 \quad \frac{3444}{1000} \text{ or } \frac{861}{250}$ 21. $-5.333 \quad \frac{-5333}{1000}$

22. $-\frac{3}{5} \quad \frac{-3}{5}$ 23. $-\frac{5}{6} \quad \frac{-5}{6}$ 24. $0.2 \quad \frac{2}{10} \text{ or } \frac{1}{5}$ 25. $-0.68 \quad \frac{-68}{100} \text{ or } \frac{-17}{25}$

Extension

Let $x = 5$, $y = -3$ and $z = -4$. Evaluate these expressions and tell which rational number they represent.

26. $\dfrac{x - y}{2z}$ $\scriptstyle -1$ **27.** $\dfrac{2x + z}{|x| - |y|}$ $\scriptstyle 3$ **28.** $\dfrac{3x + y - z}{2x - y}$ $\scriptstyle \frac{16}{13}$ **29.** $\dfrac{|x| - |y|}{2z}$ $\scriptstyle \frac{-1}{4}$

Solve.

30. $|n| = \dfrac{13}{5}$ **31.** $|x| = \dfrac{11}{18}$ **32.** $|s| = -\left(\dfrac{-2}{15}\right)$ **33.** $|g| = \dfrac{-2.35}{6.7}$ $\scriptstyle \text{no value}$

34. What is a possible coordinate for point A? $\scriptstyle \sim -1.7$

35. What is a possible coordinate for point B? $\scriptstyle \sim 0.9$

36. Graph C is -2.71429.   **37.** Graph D is $\dfrac{302}{764}$.

$\scriptstyle 30.\ \frac{-13}{5}, \frac{13}{5}$

$\scriptstyle 31.\ \frac{-11}{18}, \frac{11}{18}$

$\scriptstyle 32.\ \frac{2}{15}\ \text{or}\ \frac{-2}{15}$

Challenge

38. Argue that for any rational numbers $\dfrac{a}{b}$ and $\dfrac{c}{d}$, $\dfrac{a}{b} < \dfrac{c}{d}$ if and only if $ad < cb$.

(Hint: Find common denominators.) Use this principle to compare $\dfrac{-5}{23}$ and $-\dfrac{4}{27}$. $\scriptstyle \frac{-4}{27} > \frac{-5}{23}$

39. If $0.3333\ldots$ is $\dfrac{1}{3}$ and $0.6666\ldots$ is $\dfrac{2}{3}$, what rational number is named by

   a. $0.9999\ldots$?   **b.** $0.1111\ldots$?
   $\scriptstyle 1$ $\scriptstyle \frac{1}{9}$

SUBSETS OF THE RATIONAL NUMBERS

We can use the diagram on page 47 and set notation to write subsets of the rational numbers. Consider these sets: Natural numbers or positive integers

$N = \{1, 2, 3, \ldots\}$

Whole numbers

$W = \{0, 1, 2, 3, \ldots\}$

Integers

$I = \{\ldots, -3, -2, -1, 0, 1, 2, 3, \ldots\}$

Consider these definitions: Each number in a set is called an element or member of the set. The symbol $\in$ is read "is an element of." We write: $-3 \in I$. Set A is a subset of set B if every element of set A is an element of set B. The symbol $\subset$ is read "is a subset of." We write: $A \subset B$.

The following are true statements.

$N \subset W$ The natural numbers are a subset of the whole numbers.

$W \subset I$ The whole numbers are a subset of the integers.

$I \subset R$ (rational numbers) The integers are a subset of the rational numbers.

1. Write at least five subset statements using the sets shown in the diagram on page 47.

2. The empty set or null set, symbolized $\varnothing$, is a subset of every set. Is $\varnothing$ a subset of the rational numbers?

2–3 Addition of Rational Numbers

Addition on a Number Line

Addition of whole numbers can be illustrated by moves on a number line. To add $2 + 5$, we start at 2, the first number. Then we move a distance of 5 to the right. We end up at 7, the sum.

We can also add any two rational numbers using moves on the line. When we add a negative number, however, we must move to the left. Recall that 0 plus any number is 0.

EXAMPLE 1
Add using a number line.

$-5.2 + 0$

$-5.2 + 0 = -5.2$

TRY THIS Add using a number line.

1. $0 + (-8)$ $_{-8}$ **2.** $0 + (-5)$ $_{-5}$ **3.** $0 + (-7.2)$ $_{-7.2}$ **4.** $-\frac{16}{5} + 0$ $_{-\frac{16}{5}}$

From Example 1 we can see that the additive property of zero holds for all rational numbers, not just for numbers of arithmetic. Zero is called the additive identity.

> **Additive Property of Zero**
>
> For any rational number a, $a + 0 = a$. (Adding 0 to any rational number gives the same rational number.)

Next, let's investigate the addition of two negative numbers.

EXAMPLES
Add using a number line.

2. $-5 + (-3)$

$$-5 + (-3) = -8$$

3. $-4 + (-2)$

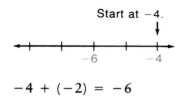

$$-4 + (-2) = -6$$

TRY THIS Add using a number line.
5. $-4 + (-5)$ ₋₉ **6.** $-2 + (-4)$ ₋₆ **7.** $-3 + (-2)$ ₋₅

From Examples 2 and 3 we can see how to add two negative numbers. We add their absolute values, but the sign of the answer is negative. Let's look at adding a positive number and a negative number.

EXAMPLES

4. $-7 + 7$

Start at -7.

Move to the right 7 units.

$$-7 + 7 = 0$$

5. $8 + (-3)$

Start at 8.

Move to the left 3 units.

5   8

$8 + (-3) = 5$

6. $-9 + 4$

Start at -9.

Move to the right 4 units.

-9 -5

$-9 + 4 = -5$

TRY THIS Add using a number line.

8. $8 + (-8)$ ₀ **9.** $-2 + 9$ ₇ **10.** $6 + (-5)$ ₁ **11.** $3 + (-7)$ ₋₄

Adding Without a Number Line

We can add numbers without using a number line. We state a rule for adding numbers based on our experience with number lines.

> **Rules for Addition**
>
> 1. To add two negative numbers: Add the absolute values. The answer is negative.
> 2. To add a positive and a negative number: Subtract the smaller absolute value from the larger absolute value.
>   a. If the positive addend has the greater absolute value, the answer is positive,
>   b. If the negative addend has the greater absolute value, the answer is negative.
>   c. If the addends have the same absolute value, the answer is zero.

Add without using a number line.

   7. $-12 + (-7)$ Two negatives. Think: Add the absolute values, getting 19. But the answer is negative, -19.

   8. $-1.4 + 8.5$ The absolute values are 1.4 and 8.5. The difference is 7.1. The positive addend has the larger absolute value, so the answer is positive, 7.1.

   9. $-36 + 21$ The absolute values are 36 and 21. The difference is 15. The negative addend has the larger absolute value, so the answer is negative, -15.

10. $1.5 + (-1.5)$ The sum is 0.

TRY THIS Add without using a number line.

12. $-17 + 17$ $_0$ **13.** $-13 + (-7)$ $_{-20}$ **14.** $-15 + (-10)$ $_{-25}$

15. $-0.17 + 0.7$ $_{53}$ **16.** $-12 + 25$ $_{13}$ **17.** $14 + (-21)$ $_{-7}$

18. $-23 + 0$ $_{-23}$ **19.** $16 + (-5)$ $_{11}$ **20.** $-6.4 + 8.7$ $_{2.3}$

21. $-4.5 + (-3.2)$ $_{-7.7}$ **22.** $-6.3 + 6.3$ $_0$

Suppose we wish to add as follows. How can we proceed?

$$13 + (-4) + 17 + (-5) + (-2)$$

The commutative and associative laws of addition hold for rational numbers as they do for other kinds of numbers. That means that we can change group and order as we please. For instance, we can group the positive numbers together and the negative numbers together and add them separately. Then we add the two results.

EXAMPLE 11
Add. $15 + (-2) + 7 + 14 + (-5) + (-12)$

   $15 + 7 + 14 = 36$ Adding the positive numbers and
   $-12 + (-5) + (-12) = -29$ the negative numbers separately
   $36 + (-29) = 7$ Adding the results.

TRY THIS Add.

23. $(-15) + (-37) + 25 + 42 + (-59) + (-14)$ $_{-58}$

24. $42 + (-81) + (-28) + 24 + 18 + (-31)$ $_{-56}$

25. $-2.5 + (-10) + 6 + (-7.5)$ $_{-14}$

Additive Inverses

We have seen that when pairs of numbers such as 6 and -6 or -7 and 7 are added, their sum is 0. Number pairs such as 6 and -6 are called opposites or additive inverses. Every rational number has an additive inverse.

DEFINITION

Two rational numbers whose sum is 0 are called *additive inverses* of each other.

EXAMPLES

Find the additive inverse of each number.

12. 34   The additive inverse of 34 is -34 since $34 + (-34) = 0$.

13. -2.96 The additive inverse of -2.96 is 2.96 since $-2.96 + 2.96 = 0$.

14. $\dfrac{-5}{4}$ The additive inverse of $\frac{-5}{4}$ is $\frac{5}{4}$ since $-\frac{5}{4} + \frac{5}{4} = 0$.

TRY THIS Find the additive inverse of each number.

26. -19 19 **27.** 54 -54 **28.** 0 0 **29.** -7.4 7.4 **30.** $-\dfrac{8}{3}$ $\frac{8}{3}$

A symbol such as -8 can be read negative 8. It can also be read the inverse of 8. But negative 8 is the inverse of 8, so we can read -8 either way. On the other hand, a symbol like $-x$ should be read the inverse of x rather than negative x since we do not know whether it represents a positive or negative number.

The *inverse* of any number n can be named $-n$ (the inverse of n). The *inverse of the inverse* of a number is the number itself, $-(-n) = n$.

EXAMPLES

15. Find $-x$ and $-(-x)$ when x is 16.

$$\text{If } x = 16$$
$$\text{then } -x = -16 \quad \text{Replacing } x \text{ by 16}$$
$$\text{and } -(-x) = -(16) \quad \text{Replacing } x \text{ by 16}$$
$$= 16.$$

16. Find $-x$ and $-(-x)$ when x is -3.

$$\text{If } x = -3$$
$$\text{then } -x = -(-3) \qquad \text{Replacing } x \text{ by } -3$$
$$= 3$$
$$\text{and } -(-x) = -(-(-3)) \qquad \text{Replacing } x \text{ by } -3$$
$$= -3.$$

TRY THIS Find $-x$ and $-(-x)$ when x is each of the following.

31. 14   **32.** 1   **33.** -19 **34.** -6 31. $-14, 14$ 32. $-1, 1$ 33. $19, -19$ 34. $6, -6$

Solving Problems with Integers

Some problems can be solved by adding integers.

EXAMPLE 17

Flo's popcorn stand made a profit of $18 on Monday. There was a loss of $7 on Tuesday. On Wednesday there was a loss of $5, and on Thursday there was a profit of $11. Find the total profit (or loss).

We can represent a loss with a negative integer. We use a positive integer to represent each profit.

$$18 + (-7) + (-5) + 11 = 17$$

The total is 17, so the total profit was $17.

EXAMPLE 18

Rico Perez, a halfback, carried the ball six times in the third quarter. Here are his gains and losses.

11-yd gain, 4-yd loss, 6-yd loss, 5-yd gain, 8-yd gain, 2-yd loss

We can represent a loss with a negative integer, and a gain as a positive integer.

$$11 + (-4) + (-6) + 5 + 8 + (-2) = 12$$

The total gain was 12 yards.

TRY THIS Solve.

35. A submarine is cruising at a depth of 30 meters. It climbs 12 meters, then dives 21 meters, and then climbs 13 meters. At what depth is the submarine then? 34 meters

Exercises

Add using a number line.

1. $-9 + 2$ $_{-7}$ **2.** $2 + (-5)$ $_{-3}$ **3.** $-10 + 6$ $_{-4}$ **4.** $8 + (-3)$ $_5$

5. $-8 + 8$ $_0$ **6.** $6 + (-6)$ $_0$ **7.** $-3 + (-5)$ $_{-8}$ **8.** $-4 + (-6)$

Add without using a number line.

9. $-7 + 0$ $_{-7}$ **10.** $-13 + 0$ $_{-13}$ **11.** $0 + (-27)$ $_{-27}$ **12.** $0 + (-35)$

13. $17 + (-17)$ $_0$ **14.** $-15 + 15$ $_0$ **15.** $-17 + (-25)$ $_{-42}$ **16.** $-24 + (-17)$

17. $-14 + (-29)$ $_{-43}$ **18.** $-38 + (-42)$ $_{-80}$ **19.** $-\frac{1}{4} + \left(-\frac{7}{4}\right)$ $_{-2}$ **20.** $-\frac{13}{8} + \left(-\frac{43}{8}\right)$

21. $17 + (-12)$ $_5$ **22.** $14 + (-25)$ $_{-11}$ **23.** $\frac{25}{7} + \left(-\frac{50}{7}\right)$ $\frac{-25}{7}$ **24.** $\frac{11}{19} + \left(-\frac{4}{19}\right)$ $\frac{7}{19}$

25. $-73 + 62$ $_{-11}$ **26.** $-88 + 94$ $_6$ **27.** $-\frac{7}{16} + \frac{7}{8}$ $\frac{7}{16}$ **28.** $-\frac{3}{28} + \frac{5}{42}$ $\frac{1}{84}$

29. $75 + (-14) + (-17) + (-5)$ $_{39}$ **30.** $28 + (-44) + 17 + 31 + (-94)$

31. $-44 + \left(-\frac{3}{8}\right) + 95 + \left(-\frac{5}{8}\right)$ $_{50}$ **32.** $24 + 3.1 + (-44) + (-8.2) + 63$

33. $98 + (-54) + 113 + (-998) + 44 + (-612) + (-18) + 334$ $_{-1093}$

34. $-455 + (-123) + 1026 + (-919) + 213 + 111 + (-874)$ $_{-1021}$

Find the additive inverse of each.

35. 24 $_{-24}$ **36.** -64 $_{64}$ **37.** -9 $_9$ **38.** $\frac{7}{2}$ $\frac{-7}{2}$ **39.** -26.9 $_{26.9}$ **40.** 48.2 $_{-48.2}$

Find $-x$ when x is

41. 9 $_{-9}$ **42.** -26 $_{26}$ **43.** $-\frac{14}{3}$ $\frac{14}{3}$ **44.** $\frac{1}{328}$ $\frac{-1}{328}$ **45.** 0.101 $_{-0.101}$ **46.** 0 $_0$

Find $-(-x)$ when x is

47. -65 $_{-65}$ **48.** 29 $_{29}$ **49.** $\frac{5}{3}$ $\frac{5}{3}$ **50.** -9.1 $_{-9.1}$

Solve these problems.

51. In a football game, the quarterback attempted passes with the following results.

    First try   13-yd gain
    Second try   incomplete
    Third try   12-yd loss (tackled behind the line)
    Fourth try   21-yd gain
    Fifth try   14-yd loss

    Find the total gain (or loss). $_{+8}$ yards

52. In a game of MONOPOLY, Alice started with $1475. After these transactions how much did Alice have? $1715

Purchased properties	1700
Collected rents	1640
Purchased houses	900
Passing Go (collected money)	1200

53. The table below shows the profits and losses of a company over a five-year period. Find the profit or loss after this period of time.

Year	Profit or loss
1979	+32,056
1980	− 2,925
1981	+81,429
1982	−19,365
1983	−13,875 77,320 profit

54. The barometric pressure at Omaha was 1012 millibars (mb). The pressure dropped 6 mb, then it rose 3 mb. After that it dropped 14 mb and then rose 4 mb. What was the pressure then? 999 mb

55. Francine received an allowance of $2.00, bought a pen for 59¢, gave 75¢ to Pat, made $4.50 babysitting, and spent $2.75 at a movie. How much did she have left? $2.41

Extension

56. When is $-x$ negative?   57. When is $-x$ positive?
   When x is positive   When x is negative

Tell whether the sum is positive, negative, or zero.

58. n and m are positive. $n + m$ is ____. Positive

59. n is positive, m is negative. $n + (-m)$ is ____. Positive

60. n is positive, m is negative. $-n + m$ is ____. Negative

61. $n = m$, n and m are negative. $-n + (-m)$ is ____. Positive

62. $n = m$, n and m are negative. $n + (-m)$ is ____. Zero

63. Describe three ways to read -8. Minus 8, the additive inverse of 8, or negative 8

Challenge

Solve.

64. $x + x = 0$ 0   65. $x + (-5) = x$ No value

66. $3y + (-2) = 7$ 3   67. $x + (-5) = 16$ 21

68. Does $x - y = x + (-y)$? Try different values for x and y. Yes

2–4 Subtraction of Rational Numbers

Subtraction on a Number Line

We can use the definition of subtraction and a number line to see
how to subtract rational numbers.

> **DEFINITION**
>
> The difference $m - n$ is the number which when added to n
> gives m.

EXAMPLE 1

Subtract. $10 - 12$

From the definition of subtraction, the number we add to 12 to get
10 will be the answer. On a number line we start at 12 and move to 10.

We moved 2 units in the negative direction. The answer is -2.
Then $10 - 12 = -2$. We can check by adding, $12 + (-2) = 10$.

EXAMPLE 2

Subtract. $-1 - (-5)$

We read this "negative 1 minus negative 5." From the definition of
subtraction, the number we add to -5 to get -1 will be the
answer. Start at -5 and move to -1.

We move 4 units in the positive direction. The answer is 4. Then
$-1 - (-5) = 4$. Check by adding, $-5 + 4 = -1$.

TRY THIS Subtract using a number line.

1. $-2 - 6$ ₋₈ **2.** $4 - 10$ ₋₆ **3.** $-9 - (-4)$ (negative 9 minus negative 4) ₋₅

Subtracting Without a Number Line

To subtract without using a number line look for a pattern in the following examples.

$$3 - 8 = -5 \qquad\qquad 3 + (-8) = -5$$
$$-7 - (-10) = 3 \qquad\qquad -7 + 10 = 3$$
$$-4.5 - (-2) = -2.5 \qquad -4.5 + 2 = -2.5$$

TRY THIS Do each subtraction or addition, then compare.

4. $-5 - 4$ ₋₉ **5.** $-5 + (-4)$ ₋₉ **6.** $-7 - (-2)$ ₋₅

7. $-7 + 2$ ₋₅ **8.** $-6.2 - 3.5$ _{-9.7} **9.** $-6.2 + (-3.5)$ _{-9.7}

From the preceding examples we see that we can subtract by adding an inverse.

> **Subtraction Rule**
>
> For any rational numbers m and n, $m - n = m + (-n)$. (To subtract we can add an inverse.)

EXAMPLES

Subtract by adding an inverse. Check your answers.

3. $2 - 6 = 2 + (-6)$ Finding the inverse and making the subtraction an addition
$\qquad\qquad = -4$ Adding

Check: $6 + (-4) = 2$

4. $-4 - (-9) = -4 + 9 = 5$
Check: $-9 + 5 = -4$

5. $-4.2 - (-3.6) = -4.2 + 3.6 = -0.6$
Check: $-3.6 + (-0.6) = -4.2$

6. $-\dfrac{1}{2} - \left(-\dfrac{3}{4}\right) = -\dfrac{1}{2} + \dfrac{3}{4} = \dfrac{1}{4}$

Check: $\left(-\dfrac{3}{4}\right) + \dfrac{1}{4} = -\dfrac{1}{2}$

TRY THIS Subtract by adding an inverse. Check your answers.

10. $4 - 9$ ₋₅   **11.** $6 - (-4)$ ₁₀   **12.** $-4 - 17$ ₋₂₁

13. $-3 - (-12)$ ₉   **14.** $-7.3 - (-2.1)$ _{-5.2}

When addition and subtraction occur several times we can use the subtraction rule to make them all additions.

EXAMPLES
Simplify.

7. $8 - (-4) - 2 - (-4) + 2$
   $8 + 4 + (-2) + 4 + 2$
   16

8. $8.2 - (-6.1) + 2.3 - (-4)$
   $8.2 + 6.1 + 2.3 + 4$
   20.6

9. $-4 - (-2x) + x - (-5)$
   $-4 + 2x + x + 5$
   $3x + 1$

TRY THIS Simplify.

15. $-6 - (-2) - (-4) - 12 + 3$ ₋₉ $_{-9}$

16. $3 - (-7.1) + 6.3 - (-5.2)$ $_{21.6}$

17. $-8 - (-3x) + 2x - (-13)$ $_{5x + 5}$

Working Problems

In arithmetic you have used subtraction to deal with ideas such as take away, how much more, distance between, and how much less. The same kinds of ideas can be dealt with in situations where rational numbers apply.

EXAMPLE 10
You owe your uncle $25. He decides to forgive or cancel $5 of that debt. How much do you then owe him?

You may already know the answer, but let us see how to use integers in this situation. Let the debt be -25. Then think of taking away a debt of $5. That corresponds to subtracting -5.

$$-25 - (-5) = -25 + 5$$
$$= -20$$

The answer is that you then owe $20.

EXAMPLE 11
The lowest point in Asia is the Dead Sea which is 400 meters below sea level. The lowest point in the United States is Death Valley which is 86 meters below sea level. How much higher is Death Valley than the Dead Sea?

Assign -86 as the higher altitude at Death Valley. Assign -400 as the lower altitude at the Dead Sea. Subtract the lower altitude from the higher.

$$-86 - (-400)$$
$$= -86 + 400$$
$$= 314$$

The difference in altitude is 314 meters.

EXAMPLE 12

You are in debt $126.50. How much money will you need to make your total savings x dollars?

To find "how much more" we can subtract.

$$x - (-126.50)$$
$$= x + 126.50$$

You will need $x + 126.50$ dollars.

TRY THIS

18. Your total savings are y dollars. To buy a motorcycle, you borrow $500. What are your total savings now? $y - 500$ dollars

---

2–4	

Exercises

Subtract using a number line.

1. $3 - 7$ -4
2. $4 - 9$ -5
3. $0 - 7$ -7
4. $0 - 10$ -10
5. $-8 - (-2)$ -6
6. $-6 - (-8)$ 2
7. $-10 - (-10)$ 0
8. $-8 - (-8)$ 0

Subtract by adding an inverse.

9. $7 - 7$ 0
10. $0.9 - 0.9$ 0
11. $7 - (-7)$ 14
12. $4 - (-4)$ 8
13. $8 - (-3)$ 11
14. $-7 - 4$ -11
15. $-6 - 8$ -14
16. $6 - (-10)$ 16
17. $-4 - (-9)$ 5
18. $-14 - 2$ -16
19. $2 - 9$ -7
20. $1 - 8$ -7
21. $-6 - (-5)$ -1
22. $-4 - (-13)$ 9
23. $8 - (-10)$ 18
24. $15 - (-6)$ 21
25. $0 - 5$ -5
26. $0 - 0.6$ -0.6
27. $-51 - (-2)$ -49
28. $-39 - (-41)$ 2
29. $-79 - 114$ -193
30. $-197 - 216$ -413
31. $0 - (-500)$ 500
32. $500 - (-1000)$ 1500
33. $-2.8 - 0$ -2.8
34. $6.04 - 1.1$ 4.94
35. $7 - 10.53$ -3.53
36. $8 - (-9.3)$ 17.3
37. $\frac{1}{6} - \frac{2}{3}$ $\frac{-1}{2}$
38. $\frac{-3}{8} - \left(\frac{-1}{2}\right)$ $\frac{1}{8}$
39. $\frac{12}{5} - \frac{12}{5}$ 0
40. $\frac{-4}{7} - \left(\frac{-10}{7}\right)$ $\frac{6}{7}$

41. $\frac{-7}{10} - \frac{10}{15}$ $\frac{-41}{30}$ **42.** $\frac{-4}{18} - \left(\frac{-2}{9}\right)$ 0 **43.** $\frac{1}{13} - \frac{1}{12}$ $\frac{-1}{156}$ **44.** $\frac{-1}{7} - \left(\frac{-1}{6}\right)$ $\frac{1}{42}$

Simplify.

45. $18 - (-15) - 3 - (-5) + 2$ 37

46. $22 - (-18) + 7 + (-42) - 27$ −22

47. $-31 + (-28) - (-14) - 17$ −62

48. $-43 - (-19) - (-21) + 25$ 22

49. $-34 - 28 + (-33) - 44$ −139

50. $39 + (-88) - 29 - (-83)$ −5

51. $-93 - (-84) - 41 - (-56)$ 6

52. $84 + (-99) + 44 - (-18) - 43$ 4

53. $-5 - (-3x) + 3x + 4x - (-12)$

54. $14 + (-5x) + 2x - (-32)$ −3x + 46

55. $13x - (-2x) + 45 - (-21)$ 15x + 66

56. $8x - (-2x) - 14 - (-5x) + 53$ 15x + 39

53. 10x + 7

Solve each problem.

57. Your total assets are $619.46. You borrow $950 for the purchase of a stereo system. What are your total assets now? −$330.54

58. You owe a friend $42. She decides to cancel $12 of the debt. How much do you owe now? $30

59. You are in debt $215.50. How much money will you need to make your total assets y dollars? y + $215.50

60. On a winter night the temperature dropped from $-5°C$ to $-12°C$. How many degrees did it drop? 7

61. The lowest point in Africa is Lake Assal which is 156 m below sea level. The lowest point in South America is the Valdes Peninsula which is 40 m below sea level. How much lower is Lake Assal than the Valdes Peninsula? 116 m

62. The deepest point in the Pacific Ocean is the Marianas Trench with a depth of 10,415 m. The deepest point in the Atlantic Ocean is the Puerto Rico Trench with a depth of 8,648 m. How much higher is the Puerto Rico Trench than the Marianas Trench? 1767 m

Extension

Tell whether each of the following statements is true or false for all integers m and n. If false, give a counterexample.

63. $n - 0 = 0 - n$. False. 3 − 0 ≠ 0 − 3

64. $0 - n = n$. False. 0 − 3 ≠ 3

65. If $m \neq n$, then $m - n \neq 0$. True

66. If $m = -n$, then $m + n = 0$. True

67. If $m + n = 0$, then m and n are additive inverses. True by definition

68. If $m - n = 0$, then $m = -n$. False, m = n. If 3 − 3 = 0, 3 ≠ −3.

Challenge

69. Does the expression $9 - 5$ mean 9 subtract 5 or 9 plus the inverse of 5? Discuss.

70. Do the commutative and associative laws hold for subtraction of integers?

71. Does $-[-(-5)] = 5$? What does $-\{-[-(-5)]\}$ equal? Can you determine a rule for any number of minus signs?

2–5 Multiplication of Rational Numbers

Multiplication

Multiplying rational numbers is much like multiplying numbers of arithmetic. The difference is that we must determine whether an answer is positive or negative. Look for a pattern in the following.

This number decreases by 1 each time. $\rightarrow$

This number decreases $\leftarrow$ by 5 each time.

$$4 \cdot 5 = 20$$
$$3 \cdot 5 = 15$$
$$2 \cdot 5 = 10$$
$$1 \cdot 5 = 5$$
$$0 \cdot 5 = 0$$
$$-1 \cdot 5 = -5$$
$$-2 \cdot 5 = -10$$
$$-3 \cdot 5 = -15$$

TRY THIS

1. Complete and look for a pattern.

$$3 \cdot 10 = 30$$
$$2 \cdot 10 = 20$$
$$1 \cdot 10 = 10$$
$$0 \cdot 10 = 0$$
$$-1 \cdot 10 = -10$$
$$-2 \cdot 10 = -20$$

From the pattern it looks as if the product of a positive number and a negative number should be negative. That is actually so, and we have the first part of the rule for multiplying rational numbers.

> To multiply a positive and a negative number, multiply their absolute values. The answer is negative.

EXAMPLES
Multiply.

1. $8(-5) = -40$ **2.** $-\dfrac{1}{3} \cdot \dfrac{5}{7} = -\dfrac{5}{21}$ **3.** $(-7.2)5 = -36.0$

Multiply.

2. $(-3)6$ $_{-18}$ **3.** $20(-5)$ $_{-100}$ **4.** $4.5(-20)$ $_{-90}$ **5.** $\left(-\dfrac{2}{3}\right)\left(\dfrac{9}{4}\right)$ $_{-\frac{3}{2}}$

How do we multiply two negative numbers? Again, we look for a pattern.

This number decreases by 1 each time.		This number increases by 5 each time.
$\rightarrow$ $4(-5) = -20$	$\leftarrow$	
$3(-5) = -15$		
$2(-5) = -10$		
$1(-5) = -5$		
$0(-5) = 0$		
$-1(-5) = 5$		
$-2(-5) = 10$		
$-3(-5) = 15$		

TRY THIS

6. Complete and look for a pattern.

$$2(-10) = -20$$
$$1(-10) = {\scriptstyle -10}$$
$$0(-10) = {\scriptstyle 0}$$
$$-1(-10) = {\scriptstyle 10}$$
$$-2(-10) = {\scriptstyle 20}$$

From the pattern it looks as if the product of two negative numbers should be positive. That is actually so, and we have the second part of the rule for multiplying rational numbers.

> To multiply two negative numbers, multiply their absolute values. The answer is positive.

We already know how to multiply two positive numbers of course. The only case we have not considered is multiplying by 0. As with other numbers, the product of any rational number and 0 is 0.

> **Multiplicative Property of Zero**
>
> For any rational number n, $n \cdot 0 = 0$. (The product of 0 and any rational number is 0.)

EXAMPLES

Multiply.

4. $-3(-4) = 12$ 5. $-1.6(-2) = 3.2$ 6. $-19 \cdot 0 = 0$ 7. $\left(-\frac{5}{6}\right)\left(-\frac{1}{9}\right) = \frac{5}{54}$

TRY THIS Multiply.

7. $(-5)(-4)$ 20 8. $(-8)(-9)$ 72 9. $(-4.2)(-3)$ 12.6 10. $\left(-\frac{3}{8}\right)\left(-\frac{1}{7}\right)$ $\frac{3}{56}$

Just as for numbers of arithmetic, the commutative and associative laws of multiplication hold for rational numbers. Thus we can choose the order and grouping we please.

EXAMPLES

Multiply.

8. $-8 \cdot 2(-3) = -16(-3)$ Multiplying the first two numbers
$\qquad\qquad = 48$ Multiplying the results

9. $-8 \cdot 2(-3) = 24 \cdot 2$ Multiplying the negatives
$\qquad\qquad = 48$

10. $-3(-2)(-5)(4) = 6(-5)(4)$ Multiplying the first two numbers
$\qquad\qquad\quad = (-30)4$
$\qquad\qquad\quad = -120$

11. $\left(-\frac{1}{2}\right)(8)\left(-\frac{2}{3}\right)(-6) = (-4)4$
$\qquad\qquad\qquad\qquad = -16$

TRY THIS Multiply.

11. $(4)(-7)(5)$ –140 12. $(-5)(-6)(-3)$ –90 13. $(-4)(5)(-3)(2)$ 120 14. $(-7)\left(-\frac{2}{3}\right)\left(-\frac{1}{7}\right)(9)$ –6

Moment Problems

Multiplying positive and negative numbers is fundamental to working with algebraic expressions. One simple type of real-world problem where we use these operations concerns the idea of a moment. To introduce the idea, think of a seesaw. George weighs 120 lb and Mary weighs 100 lb. To balance each other Mary must sit farther from the hinge of fulcrum than George. How much farther?

The product of George's weight and his distance from the fulcrum is called a moment. That moment is 120 lb · 5 ft or 600 ft-lb. The product of Mary's weight and distance is 100 lb · 6 ft or 600 ft-lb. The moments are the same, so there is a balance.

   Scientists have discovered a physical law, or principle of moments, that allows us to tell when there is a balance on a seesaw. That principle applies in many other physical situations, such as bridges and machines.

   Before we state the principle of moments, think of a number line on the seesaw with zero as the fulcrum.

George is now sitting at -5. We call that number his coordinate. Mary's coordinate is 6. Downward forces (weight) will be considered negative. Upward forces will be considered positive. George's weight is a downward force of 120 lb, so that force is -120 lb. Mary's weight is -100 lb.

   To find the moments we multiply each force by its coordinate.

> George's moment is $-120 \cdot (-5)$ or 600.
> Mary's moment is $-100 \cdot 6$ or -600.

If we add the moments we get 0, so there is a balance.

The Principle of Moments (A Scientific Law)

When several parallel forces act on an object, there will be a balance if the sum of the moments is 0.

The principle of moments holds for any number of forces.

EXAMPLE 12
George, weighing 120 lb, sits 6 ft from the fulcrum of a seesaw. Mary, weighing 100 lb, also sits 6 ft from the fulcrum. Helen, weighing 60 lb, sits on Mary's side 2 ft from the fulcrum. Does the seesaw balance?
We compute the moments and add them to see if we get 0.
George's moment is $-120(-6)$ or 720.
Mary's moment is $-100(6)$ or -600.
Helen's moment is $-60(2)$ or -120.
The sum of the moments is 0, so there is a balance.

TRY THIS

15. Bob, weighing 150 lb, sits 6 ft from the fulcrum of a seesaw. Fred weighing 100 lb, sits 6 ft from the fulcrum. Angie, weighing 50 lb, sits 4 ft from the fulcrum on Fred's side. Does the seesaw balance? No. $-800 + 900 \neq 0$ or $-900 + 800 \neq 0$

2–5	

Exercises

Multiply.

1. $-8 \cdot 2$ -16 **2.** $-2 \cdot 5$ -10 **3.** $-7 \cdot 6$ -42 **4.** $-9 \cdot 2$ -18

5. $8 \cdot (-3)$ -24 **6.** $9 \cdot (-5)$ -45 **7.** $-9 \cdot 8$ -72 **8.** $-10 \cdot 3$ -30

9. $-8 \cdot (-2)$ 16 **10.** $-2 \cdot (-5)$ 10 **11.** $-7 \cdot (-6)$ 42 **12.** $-9 \cdot (-2)$ 18

13. $15 \cdot (-8)$ -120 **14.** $-12 \cdot (-10)$ 120 **15.** $-14 \cdot 17$ -238 **16.** $-13 \cdot (-15)$ 195

17. $-25 \cdot (-48)$ 1200 **18.** $39 \cdot (-43)$ -1677 **19.** $-3.5 \cdot (-28)$ 98 **20.** $97 \cdot (-2.1)$ -203.7

21. $\frac{1}{5}\left(\frac{-2}{9}\right)$ $\frac{-2}{45}$ **22.** $-\frac{3}{5}\left(-\frac{2}{7}\right)$ $\frac{6}{35}$

23. $-7 \cdot (-21) \cdot 13$ 1911 **24.** $-14 \cdot (34) \cdot 12$ -5712

25. $-4 \cdot (-1.8) \cdot 7$ 50.4 **26.** $-8 \cdot (-1.3) \cdot (-5)$ -52

27. $-\frac{1}{9}\left(\frac{-2}{3}\right)\left(\frac{5}{7}\right)$ $\frac{10}{189}$ **28.** $-\frac{7}{2}\left(\frac{-5}{7}\right)\left(\frac{-2}{5}\right)$ -1

29. $4 \cdot (-4) \cdot (-5) \cdot (-12)$ -960 **30.** $-2 \cdot (-3) \cdot (-4) \cdot (-5)$ 120

31. $0.07 \cdot (-7) \cdot 6 \cdot (-6)$ 17.64 **32.** $80 \cdot (-0.8) \cdot (-90) \cdot (-0.09)$ -518.4

33. $\left(-\frac{5}{6}\right)\left(\frac{1}{8}\right)\left(-\frac{3}{7}\right)\left(-\frac{1}{7}\right)$ $\frac{5}{784}$ **34.** $\left(\frac{4}{5}\right)\left(\frac{-2}{3}\right)\left(-\frac{15}{7}\right)\left(\frac{1}{2}\right)$ $\frac{4}{7}$

35. $(-14) \cdot (-27) \cdot 0$ 0 **36.** $7 \cdot (-6) \cdot 5 \cdot (-4) \cdot 3 \cdot (-2) \cdot 1 \cdot 0$ 0

Solve.

37. On a seesaw, Theo who weighs 170 lb is sitting 7 feet to the left of the fulcrum. Sam, who weighs 150 lb is sitting 8 feet to the right of the fulcrum. Does the seesaw balance?

No. $170(-7) + 150(8) \neq 0$

38. Does the seesaw balance? Yes

39. Does the seesaw balance? Yes

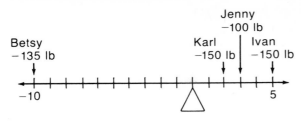

40. Penny and her friends are trying to build a diving board at a pond. They laid a board on a rock ledge which acts as the fulcrum. Then they put a 150-pound rock on the board with its center 3 feet from the fulcrum. They found another rock weighing 80 pounds and put it on the board with its center 1 foot from the fulcrum. Penny weighs 90 lb. If she walks slowly out on the board 5 feet from the fulcrum, will the board tip? No. $150(3) + 80(1) > 90(5)$

Extension
Simplify.

41. $-6[(-5) + (-7)]$ 72

42. $7[(-16) + 9]$ -49

43. $\dfrac{-3[(-8) + (-6)]}{-7}$ -6

44. $\dfrac{8[17 - (-3)]}{-4}$ -40

45. $-(3^5) \cdot -(2^3)$ 1944

46. $4(2^4) \cdot -(3^3) \cdot 6$ $-10,368$

47. $(-2)^5$ -32

48. $(-1)^{23}$ -1

In Exercises 49–52, evaluate when $x = -2$, $y = -4$, and $z = 5$. $-12,600$

49. $xy + z$ 13 **50.** $-4y + 3x + z$ 15 **51.** $-6(3x - 5y) + z$ -79 **52.** $(-9z)(-5x)(-7y)$

53. Consider $2 \cdot 3 \cdot 4 \cdot 5 = 120$. Make any one number negative and multiply. Make two negative, then three, then all four. Find a rule for the sign of the answer for any number of negative factors. If odd number of factors, negative; if even, positive

54. What must be true of m and n if $-mn$ is to be **a.** positive, **b.** zero, **c.** negative.

a) Either m or n is negative. b) Either m or n is zero.

c) Both m and n are positive or both are negative.

55. Is it true that for any rational numbers a and b, $ab = (-a)(-b)$? Discuss.

Yes. $(-a)(-b) = (-1)(a)(-1)(b) = (-1)^2(ab) = 1ab = ab$

56. Richie weighs 135 lb and John weighs 90 lb. John sits 9 feet to the right of the fulcrum. Where must Richie sit to balance? 6 ft. left

57. A 20-foot board is centered directly over a fulcrum. Two-pound weights are placed every foot on one side up to and including the end.
a. How much weight would you place on the other end to balance?
b. Where would you place a 20-pound weight to balance?

a. $2(10) + 2(9) + 2(8) + 2(7) + 2(6) + 2(5) + 2(4) + 2(3) + 2(2) + 2(1) - 10x = 0$, $10x = 110$, $x = 11$lbs,

b. $20w = 110$, $w = 5.5$, 5.5 ft from the center

2-6 Division of Rational Numbers

Division

To divide we can use the definition of division.

DEFINITION

The quotient $\frac{m}{n}$ (or $m \div n$) is the number, if there is one, which when multiplied by n gives m.

EXAMPLES
Divide, if possible. Check your answer.

1. $14 \div (-7)$ We look for a number which when multiplied by -7 gives 14. That number is -2. Thus, $14 \div (-7) = -2$. Check: $(-2)(-7) = 14$.

2. $\frac{-32}{-4}$ We look for a number which when multiplied by -4 gives -32. That number is 8. Thus, $\frac{-32}{-4} = 8$. Check: $8(-4) = -32$.

3. $-10 \div 7$ We look for a number which when multiplied by 7 gives -10. That number is $-\frac{10}{7}$. Check: $-\frac{10}{7} \cdot 7 = -10$.

4. $-17 \div 0$ We look for a number which when multiplied by 0 gives -17. There is no such number because the product of 0 and *any* number is 0.

When we divide a positive number by a negative or a negative number by a positive, the answer is negative. When we divide two negative numbers, the answer is positive.

TRY THIS Divide, if possible. Check your answer.

1. $15 \div (-3)$ -5 2. $-21 \div 7$ -3 3. $-44 \div (-11)$ 4 4. $13 \div (-5)$ $-\frac{13}{5}$
5. $9 \div (-4)$ $-\frac{9}{4}$ 6. $\frac{-35}{-7}$ 5 7. $-24 \div 27$ $-\frac{8}{9}$ 8. $\frac{-105}{0}$ Not possible

---

Example 4 shows why we cannot divide -17 by 0. We can use the same argument to show why we cannot divide any nonzero number b by 0. For $b \div 0$ we look for a number which, when multiplied by 0 gives b. There is no such nonzero number because the product of 0 and any number is 0.

On the other hand, if we divide 0 by 0, we look for a number r, such that $r \cdot 0 = 0$. But, $0 \cdot r = 0$ for any number r. Thus, it appears that $0 \div 0$ could be any number we choose. Since for any operation there must only be one answer, we agree that we shall not divide 0 by 0.

> We never divide any number by 0.

Reciprocals

We have seen that when pairs of numbers like $-\frac{1}{8}$ and -8 are multiplied, their product is 1. Such pairs of numbers are called reciprocals. Every rational number except 0 has a reciprocal.

DEFINITION

Two numbers are *reciprocals* if their product is 1.

For any nonzero rational number n, we can name its reciprocal $\frac{1}{n}$. If the rational number is named with fractional notation $\frac{a}{b}$, then its reciprocal can be named $\frac{b}{a}$. The reciprocal of a negative number is a negative number. Reciprocals are sometimes called multiplicative inverses

EXAMPLES
Find the reciprocal.

5. $\frac{7}{8}$ The reciprocal of $\frac{7}{8}$ is $\frac{8}{7}$ because $\frac{7}{8} \cdot \frac{8}{7} = 1$.

6. -5 The reciprocal of -5 is $\frac{1}{-5}$ because $-5\left(-\frac{1}{5}\right) = 1$.

7. 3.9 The reciprocal of 3.9 is $\frac{1}{3.9}$ because $3.9\left(\frac{1}{3.9}\right) = 1$.

8. $\frac{m}{n}$ The reciprocal of $\frac{m}{n}$ is $\frac{n}{m}$ because $\frac{m}{n} \cdot \frac{n}{m} = 1$.

9. $\frac{3}{6}$ $\frac{6}{3}$ **10.** -4 $\frac{1}{-4}$ **11.** -2.6 $\frac{1}{-2.6}$ **12.** $\frac{1}{2.3}$ 2.3 **13.** $\frac{x}{y}$, $y \neq 0$ $\frac{y}{x}$

Division and Reciprocals

We know we can subtract a rational number by adding its inverse. Similarly, we can divide a rational number by multiplying by a reciprocal.

> For any rational number a, and any nonzero rational number b, the division $\frac{a}{b}$ (or $a \div b$), is equivalent to the multiplication $a \cdot \frac{1}{b}$. (Dividing a number b is the same as multiplying by the reciprocal of b.)

EXAMPLES

Rewrite each division as multiplication.

9. $-4 \div 3$ $-4 \div 3$ is the same as $-4 \cdot \frac{1}{3}$

10. $\frac{6}{-7}$ $\frac{6}{-7} = 6\left(-\frac{1}{7}\right)$

11. $\frac{x+2}{5}$ $\frac{x+2}{5} = (x+2)\frac{1}{5}$ Parentheses are necessary here.

12. $\frac{-17}{\frac{1}{b}}$ $\frac{-17}{\frac{1}{b}} = -17 \cdot b$

13. $\frac{3}{5} \div \left(-\frac{9}{7}\right)$ $\frac{3}{5} \div \left(-\frac{9}{7}\right) = \frac{3}{5}\left(-\frac{7}{9}\right)$

TRY THIS Rewrite each division as multiplication.

14. $-6 \div \frac{1}{5}$ **15.** $\frac{-5}{7}$ **16.** $\frac{x^2-2}{3}$ **17.** $\frac{13}{\frac{-2}{3}}$

14. $-6(5)$ 15. $-5\left(\frac{1}{7}\right)$

16. $(x^2-2)\frac{1}{3}$ 17. $13\left(-\frac{3}{2}\right)$

18. $\frac{-15}{\frac{1}{x}}$ **19.** $-\frac{4}{7} \div \left(-\frac{3}{5}\right)$ **20.** $\frac{a}{b}$ **21.** $\frac{a}{\frac{1}{b}}$

18. $-15x$ 19. $\frac{-4}{7}\left(-\frac{5}{3}\right)$

20. $a\left(\frac{1}{b}\right)$ 21. ab

When actually doing division calculations, we sometimes multiply by a reciprocal and we sometimes divide directly. With fractional notation, it is usually better to multiply by a reciprocal. With decimal notation, it is usually better to divide directly.

EXAMPLES

Divide.

14. $\dfrac{4}{3} \div \left(-\dfrac{9}{7}\right) = \dfrac{4}{3}\left(-\dfrac{7}{9}\right)$

$\qquad = -\dfrac{4 \cdot 7}{3 \cdot 9} = -\dfrac{28}{27}$

15. $-27.9 \div (-3) = \dfrac{-27.9}{-3} = 9.3$

TRY THIS Divide.

22. $-\dfrac{3}{5} \div \left(-\dfrac{12}{11}\right)$ $\frac{11}{20}$ **23.** $-\dfrac{8}{5} \div \dfrac{2}{3}$ $\frac{-12}{5}$ **24.** $-64.8 \div 4$ $_{-16.2}$ **25.** $78.6 \div (-3)$ $_{-26.2}$

2–6	

Exercises

Find a solution if possible. Check each answer.

1: $36 \div (-6)$ $_{-6}$ **2.** $\dfrac{28}{-7}$ $_{-4}$ **3.** $\dfrac{26}{-2}$ $_{-13}$ **4.** $26 \div (-13)$ $_{-2}$

5. $\dfrac{-16}{8}$ $_{-2}$ **6.** $-22 \div (-2)$ $_{11}$ **7.** $\dfrac{-48}{-12}$ $_{4}$ **8.** $-63 \div (-9)$ $_{7}$

9. $\dfrac{-72}{9}$ $_{-8}$ **10.** $\dfrac{-50}{25}$ $_{-2}$ **11.** $-100 \div (-50$ $_{2}$ **12.** $\dfrac{-200}{8}$ $_{-25}$

13. $-108 \div 9$ $\frac{-108}{9}$ **14.** $\dfrac{-64}{-7}$ $\frac{64}{7}$ **15.** $\dfrac{200}{-25}$ $_{-8}$ **16.** $(-300) \div (-13)$ $\frac{300}{13}$

17. $\dfrac{75}{0}$ None **18.** $\dfrac{0}{-5}$ $_{0}$ **19.** $\dfrac{88}{-9}$ $\frac{-88}{9}$ **20.** $\dfrac{-145}{-5}$ $_{29}$

Find the reciprocal.

21. $\dfrac{15}{7}$ $\frac{7}{15}$ **22.** $\dfrac{3}{8}$ $\frac{8}{3}$ **23.** $\dfrac{47}{13}$ $\frac{13}{47}$ **24.** $-\dfrac{31}{12}$ $\frac{-12}{31}$

25. 13 $\frac{1}{13}$ **26.** -10 $\frac{-1}{10}$ **27.** 4.3 $\frac{1}{4.3}$ **28.** -8.5 $\frac{-1}{8.5}$

29. $\dfrac{1}{7.1}$ $_{7.1}$ **30.** $\dfrac{1}{-4.9}$ $_{-4.9}$ **31.** $\dfrac{p}{q}$, $p,q \neq 0$ $\frac{q}{p}$ **32.** $\dfrac{s}{t}$, $s,t \neq 0$ $\frac{t}{s}$

33. $\dfrac{1}{4y}$ $_{4y}$ **34.** $\dfrac{-1}{8a}$ $_{-8a}$ **35.** $\dfrac{2a}{3b}$ $\frac{3b}{2a}$ **36.** $\dfrac{-4y}{3x}$ $\frac{-3x}{4y}$

Rewrite each division as multiplication.

37. $3 \div 19$ $3\left(\frac{1}{19}\right)$ **38.** $4 \div (-9)$ $4\left(\frac{-1}{9}\right)$ **39.** $\dfrac{6}{-13}$ $6\left(\frac{-1}{13}\right)$ **40.** $-\dfrac{12}{41}$ $-12\left(\frac{1}{41}\right)$

41. $\dfrac{13.9}{-1.5}$ $\scriptstyle 13.9\left(\frac{-1}{1.5}\right)$ **42.** $-\dfrac{47.3}{\cdot 21.4}$ $\scriptstyle 47.3\left(\frac{-1}{21.4}\right)$ **43.** $\dfrac{x}{\frac{1}{y}}$ $\scriptstyle x \cdot y$ **44.** $\dfrac{13}{x}$ $\scriptstyle 13\left(\frac{1}{x}\right)$

45. $\dfrac{3x+4}{5}$ $\scriptstyle \frac{1}{5}(3x\ +\ 4)$ **46.** $\dfrac{4y-8}{-7}$ $\scriptstyle \frac{-1}{7}(4y\ -\ 8)$ **47.** $\dfrac{5a-b}{5a+b}$ **48.** $\dfrac{2x+x^2}{x-5}$

$\qquad\qquad\qquad\qquad\qquad\qquad$ 47. $\scriptstyle (5a\ -\ b)\left(\frac{1}{5a\ +\ b}\right)$ $\qquad$ 48. $\scriptstyle (2x\ +\ x^2)\left(\frac{1}{x\ -\ 5}\right)$

Divide.

49. $\dfrac{3}{4} \div \left(-\dfrac{2}{3}\right)$ $\scriptstyle \frac{-9}{8}$ **50.** $\dfrac{7}{8} \div \left(-\dfrac{1}{2}\right)$ $\scriptstyle \frac{-7}{4}$ **51.** $-\dfrac{5}{4} \div \left(-\dfrac{3}{4}\right)$ $\scriptstyle \frac{5}{3}$ **52.** $-\dfrac{5}{9} \div \left(-\dfrac{5}{6}\right)$ $\scriptstyle \frac{2}{3}$

53. $-\dfrac{2}{7} \div \left(-\dfrac{4}{9}\right)$ $\scriptstyle \frac{9}{14}$ **54.** $-\dfrac{3}{5} \div \left(-\dfrac{5}{8}\right)$ $\scriptstyle \frac{24}{25}$ **55.** $-\dfrac{3}{8} \div \left(-\dfrac{8}{3}\right)$ $\scriptstyle \frac{9}{64}$ **56.** $-\dfrac{5}{8} \div \left(-\dfrac{6}{5}\right)$ $\scriptstyle \frac{25}{48}$

57. $-6.6 \div 3.3$ $\scriptstyle -2$ $\qquad\qquad\qquad$ **58.** $-44.1 \div (-6.3)$ $\scriptstyle 7$

59. $\dfrac{-11}{-13}$ $\scriptstyle \frac{11}{13}$ **60.** $\dfrac{-1.9}{20}$ $\scriptstyle -0.95$ **61.** $\dfrac{48.6}{-3}$ $\scriptstyle -16.2$ **62.** $\dfrac{-17.8}{3.2}$ $\scriptstyle 5.5625$

Extension

Simplify.

63. $\dfrac{(-9)(-8)+(-3)}{25}$ $\scriptstyle \frac{69}{25}$ **64.** $\dfrac{-3(-9)+7}{-4}$ $\scriptstyle \frac{-17}{2}$ **65.** $\dfrac{(-2)^7}{(-4)^2}$ $\scriptstyle -8$ **66.** $\dfrac{(-3)^4}{-9}$ $\scriptstyle -9$

67. $5\dfrac{3}{7} \div 4\dfrac{2}{5}$ $\scriptstyle \frac{95}{77}$ **68.** $\dfrac{10}{7} \div .25$ $\scriptstyle \frac{40}{7}$ **69.** $2\dfrac{2}{3} \div \dfrac{40}{15}$ $\scriptstyle 1$

70. Use a calculator to find the reciprocal of -10.5. $\scriptstyle .095238095238\ldots$

Challenge

71. Is division of rational numbers commutative? That is, does $a \div b = b \div a$ for all rational numbers a and b? $\scriptstyle \text{No, } \frac{4}{2} \neq \frac{2}{4}.$

72. Is division of rational numbers associative? That is, does $(a \div b) \div c = a \div (b \div c)$ for all rational numbers a, b, and c? $\scriptstyle \text{No. } (a \div b) \div c = \frac{1}{c} \cdot \left(\frac{a}{b}\right)\ \ a \div (b \div c) = c \cdot \left(\frac{a}{b}\right)$

73. Is it possible for a number to be its own reciprocal? $\scriptstyle \text{Yes, this is true for 1 and also for } -1.$

74. Is it possible for the additive inverse of a number to be its reciprocal? $\scriptstyle \text{No. A reciprocal has the same sign as the number. (zero has no reciprocal)}$

75. What should happen if you enter a number on a calculator and press the reciprocal key twice? Why? $\scriptstyle \text{You get the original number. The reciprocal of the reciprocal is the original number.}$

76. We know that for any nonzero rational number $\dfrac{a}{b}$, its reciprocal is $\dfrac{b}{a}$. Show that $\dfrac{1}{\left(\frac{a}{b}\right)}$ also names the reciprocal. $\scriptstyle \frac{1}{\left(\frac{a}{b}\right)} \cdot \frac{\left(\frac{b}{a}\right)}{\left(\frac{b}{a}\right)} = \frac{\left(\frac{b}{a}\right)}{1} = \frac{b}{a}$

Using the Distributive Laws

Multiplying a Number by a Difference

For numbers of arithmetic we know that multiplication is distributive over addition. For rational numbers the distributive law also holds.

The Distributive Law of Multiplication Over Addition

For any rational numbers a, b, and c,

$$a(b + c) = ab + ac.$$

There is another distributive law that relates multiplication and subtraction. This law says that to multiply a factor by a difference we can either subtract and then multiply, or multiply and then subtract.

The Distributive Law of Multiplication Over Subtraction

For any rational numbers a, b, and c,

$$a(b - c) = ab - ac.$$

EXAMPLES

Multiply.

1. $9(x - 5) = 9x - 9(5)$ Using the distributive law
$$= 9x - 45$$

2. $\frac{4}{3}(s - t + w) = \frac{4}{3}s - \frac{4}{3}t + \frac{4}{3}w$

3. $-4(x - 2y + 3z) = -4 \cdot x - (-4)(2y) + (-4)(3z)$
$$= -4x - (-8y) + (-12z) = -4x + 8y - 12z$$

TRY THIS Multiply.

1. $8(y - 7)$ **2.** $\frac{5}{6}(x - y - 7z)$ **3.** $-5(x - 3y + 8z)$

1. $8y - 56$
2. $\frac{5}{6}x - \frac{5}{6}y - \frac{35}{6}z$
3. $-5x + 15y - 40z$

Factoring

Equations can be reversed. Thus, we can write the distributive law as

$$ab - ac = a(b - c).$$

This allows us to factor other expressions.

EXAMPLES
Factor.

4. $5x - 5y = 5(x - y)$

5. $8x - 16 = 8 \cdot x - 8 \cdot 2 = 8(x - 2)$

6. $ax - ay + az = a(x - y + z)$

7. $9x - 27y - 9 = 9(x) - 9(3y) - 9(1)$
$$= 9(x - 3y - 1)$$

8. $-3x + 6y - 9z = -3(x - 2y + 3z)$

9. $18z - 12x - 24 = 6(3z - 2x - 4)$

10. $\frac{1}{2}x + \frac{3}{2}y - \frac{1}{2} = \frac{1}{2}(x + 3y - 1)$

TRY THIS Factor.

4. $4x - 8$ **5.** $3x - 6y - 15$ **6.** $bx - by + bz$

7. $-2y + 8z - 2$ **8.** $12z - 16x - 4$

4. $4(x - 2)$
5. $3(x - 2y - 5)$
6. $b(x - y + z)$
7. $-2(y - 4z + 1)$
8. $4(3z - 4x - 1)$

Terms

We have seen that the terms of an expression are separated by plus signs. If there are subtraction signs, we use the idea of additive inverses to rewrite each term.

EXAMPLE 11
What are the terms of $3x - 4y + 2z$?

$$3x - 4y + 2z = 3x + (-4y) + 2z$$ Subtracting is the same as adding an inverse.

The terms are $3x$, $-4y$, and $2z$.

TRY THIS Give the terms of each expression.

9. $5a - 4b + 3$ **10.** $-5y - 3x + 5z$

9. $5a$, $-4b$, 3
10. $-5y$, $-3x$, $5z$

Collecting Like Terms

By using the distributive law of multiplication over subtraction, we can collect like terms without rewriting each term as an addition.

EXAMPLES
Collect like terms.

12. $2x + 3y - 5y - 2y = 2x - 5x + 3y - 2y$
$$= (2 - 5)x + (3 - 2)y$$
$$= -3x + y$$

13. $3x - x = (3 - 1)x = 2x$

14. $x - 0.24x = 1 \cdot x - 0.24x = (1 - 0.24)x = 0.76x$

15. $x - 6x = 1 \cdot x - 6x = (1 - 6)x = -5x$

TRY THIS Collect like terms.

11. $6x - 3x$ 3x   **12.** $7y - y$ 6y   **13.** $m - 0.41m$ 0.59m

14. $5x + 4y - 2x - y$ 3x + 3y   **15.** $3x - 7x - 11 + 8y - 4 - 13y$ $-4x - 5y - 14$

2–7	

Exercises
Multiply.

1. $7(4 - 3)$ 7

2. $15(8 - 6)$ 30

3. $-3(3 - 7)$ 12

4. $1.2(5 - 2.1)$ 4.68   **5.** $4.1(6.3 - 9.4)$ −12.71

6. $-\dfrac{8}{9}\left(\dfrac{2}{3} - \dfrac{5}{3}\right)$ $\dfrac{8}{9}$

7. $7(x - 2)$ 7x − 14   **8.** $5(x - 8)$ 5x − 40

9. $-7(y - 2)$ −7y + 14

10. $-9(y - 7)$ −9y + 63 **11.** $-9(-5x - 6y + 8)$

12. $-7(-2x - 5y + 9)$ 14x + 35y − 63

13. $-4(x - 3y - 2z)$ −4x + 12y + 8z

14. $8(2x - 5y - 8z)$ 16x − 40y − 64z

15. $3.1(-1.2x + 3.2y - 1.1)$
   −3.72x + 9.92y − 3.41

16. $-2.1(-4.2x - 4.3y - 2.2)$
   8.82x + 9.03y + 4.62

Factor.

17. $8x - 24$

18. $10x - 50$

19. $32 - 4y$

20. $24 - 6m$

21. $8x + 10y - 22$

22. $9a + 6b - 15$

23. $ax - 7a$

24. $by - 9b$

25. $ax - ay - az$ a(x − y + z)

26. $cx + cy - cz$ c(x + y − z)

17. 8(x − 3)
18. 10(x − 5)
19. 8(4 − y)
20. 6(4 − m)
21. 2(4x + 5y − 11)
22. 3(3a + 2b − 5)
23. a(x − 7)
24. b(y − 9)

Give the terms of each expression.

27. $4x + 3z$ 4x, 3z **28.** $8x - 1.4y$ 8x, −1.4y   **29.** $7x + 8y - 9z$ **30.** $8a + 10b - 18c$

31. $12x - 13.2y + \frac{5}{8}z - 4.5$ **32.** $-7.8a - 3.4y - 8.7z - 12.4$

Collect like terms.

33. $11x - 3x$ 8x **34.** $9t - 17t$ −8t **35.** $6n - n$ 5n   **36.** $y - 17y$ −16y

37. $9x + 2y - 5x$ 4x + 2y   **38.** $8y - 3z + 4y$ 12y − 3z

39. $11x + 2y - 4x - y$ 7x + y   **40.** $13a + 9b - 2a - 4b$ 11a + 5b

41. $2.7x + 2.3y - 1.9x - 1.8y$
0.8x + 0.5y   **42.** $6.7a + 4.3b - 4.1a - 2.9b$ 2.6a + 1.4b

43. $\frac{1}{5}x + \frac{4}{5}y + \frac{2}{5}x - \frac{1}{5}y$ $\frac{3}{5}x + \frac{3}{5}y$ **44.** $\frac{7}{8}x + \frac{5}{8}y + \frac{1}{8}x - \frac{3}{8}y$ $x + \frac{1}{4}y$

Extension

Write an algebraic expression. Simplify each expression, if possible.

45. Eight times the difference of x and y. 8(x − y)

46. Nine times the difference of y and z, increased by $3z$. 9(y − z) + 3z or 9y − 6z

47. Three times the sum of a and b, decreased by $7a$. 3(a + b) − 7a or 3b − 4a

48. The total cost if you buy x cassette tapes at \$2.95 on Monday and y cassettes at the same price on Wednesday. 2.95(x + y)

29. 7x, 8y, −9z
30. 8a, 10b, −18c
31. 12x, −13.2y, $\frac{5}{8}$z, −4.5
32. −7.8a, −3.4y, −8.7z, −12.4

49. The total intake of a store when branch A sells x microcomputers at \$2500 and branch B sells y microcomputers at the same price. 2500(x + y)

Challenge

50. If the temperature is C degrees Celsius, it is $\frac{9}{5}C + 32$ degrees Fahrenheit. What is the Fahrenheit temperature if it drops 5° Celsius? $\frac{9}{5}(C - 5) + 32$ or $\frac{9}{5}C + 23$

51. Jill has 5420 shares of a stock she bought at $41\frac{1}{8}$. The stock is now worth $37\frac{3}{4}$. Show two ways of determining how much she has lost. Solve. 5420(41$\frac{1}{8}$ − 37$\frac{3}{4}$) or 5420(41$\frac{1}{8}$) − 5420(37$\frac{3}{4}$) Her loss is \$18,292.50.

2–8 Inverse of a Sum and Simplifying

Inverse of a Sum

What happens when we multiply a rational number by -1?

EXAMPLES
Multiply.

1. $-1 \cdot 7$ $\qquad -1 \cdot 7 = -7$

2. $-1(-5)$ $\qquad -1(-5) = 5$

3. $-1 \cdot 0$ $\qquad -1 \cdot 0 = 0$

From these examples we can see that when we multiply a number by -1, we get the additive inverse of that number.

The Property of -1

For any rational number a, $-1 \cdot a = -a$. (Negative one times a is the additive inverse of a.)

The property of -1 enables us to find an expression for the additive inverse of a sum.

EXAMPLES
Rename each additive inverse without parentheses.

$$
\begin{aligned}
\textbf{4.} \quad -(3 + x) &= -1(3 + x) \quad \text{Using the property of } -1 \\
&= -1 \cdot 3 + (-1)x \quad \text{Using a distributive law} \\
&= -3 + (-x) \quad \text{Using the property of } -1 \\
&= -3 - x \quad \text{Using the subtraction rule}
\end{aligned}
$$

$$
\begin{aligned}
\textbf{5.} \quad -(3x + 2y + 4) &= -1(3x + 2y + 4) \quad \text{Using the property of } -1 \\
&= -1(3x) + (-1)(2y) + (-1)4 \quad \text{Using a distributive law} \\
&= -3x - 2y - 4 \quad \text{Using the property of } -1 \text{ and the subtraction rule}
\end{aligned}
$$

TRY THIS Rename each additive inverse without parentheses.

1. $-(x + 2)$ $\qquad$ **2.** $-(5x + 2y + 8)$ $\quad$ 1. $-x - 2$ $\quad$ 2. $-5x - 2y - 8$

Examples 4 and 5 illustrate an important property of rational numbers.

> **The Inverse of a Sum Property**
>
> For any rational numbers a and b,
>
> $-(a + b) = -a + (-b)$. (The inverse of a sum is the sum of the inverses.)

The inverse of a sum property holds for differences as well as sums, because any difference can be expressed as a sum. It also holds when there is a sum or difference of more than two terms. When we apply the inverse of a sum property we sometimes say that we "change the sign of every term."

EXAMPLES

Rename each additive inverse without parentheses.

6. $-(5 - y) = -5 + y$ Changing the sign of every term

7. $-(2a - 7b - 6) = -2a + 7b + 6$

TRY THIS Rename each additive inverse without parentheses. Try to do that in one step.

3. $-(6 - t)$ **4.** $-(-4a + 3t - 10)$ **5.** $-(18 - m - 2n + 4t)$

3. $-6 + t$
4. $4a - 3t + 10$
5. $-18 + m + 2n + 4t$

Removing Parentheses and Simplifying

When a sum is added as in $5x + (2x + 3)$ we can simply remove the parentheses and collect like terms. On the other hand, when a sum is subtracted, as in $3x - (4x + 2)$, we can subtract by adding an inverse, as usual. We then remove parentheses and collect like terms.

EXAMPLE 8

Remove parentheses and simplify.

$$
\begin{aligned}
3x - (4x + 2) &= 3x + (-(4x + 2)) &&\text{Adding the inverse of } (4x + 2) \\
&= 3x + (-4x - 2) &&\text{Using the inverse of a sum property} \\
&= 3x - 4x - 2 \\
&= -x - 2 &&\text{Collecting like terms}
\end{aligned}
$$

We can combine the first two steps of Example 8 and remove the parentheses by changing the sign of every term.

EXAMPLES

Remove parentheses and simplify.

9. $5y - (3y + 4) = 5y - 3y - 4$ Removing parentheses by changing the sign of every term
$$= 2y - 4$$

10. $3y - 2 - (2y - 4) = 3y - 2 - 2y + 4$
$$= y + 2$$

TRY THIS Remove parentheses and simplify.

6. $5x - (3x + 9)$ $2x - 9$ **7.** $5x - 2y - (2y - 3x - 4)$ $8x - 4y + 4$

Next, consider subtracting an expression consisting of several terms preceded by a number.

EXAMPLES

Remove parentheses and simplify.

11. $x - 3(x + y) = x + (-3(x + y))$ Adding the inverse of $3(x + y)$
$$= x + (-3x - 3y)$$ Multiplying $x + y$ by -3
$$= x - 3x - 3y$$ Removing parentheses
$$= -2x - 3y$$ Collecting like terms

12. $3y - 2(4y - 5) = 3y + (-2(4y - 5))$ Adding the inverse of $2(4y - 5)$
$$= 3y + (-8y + 10)$$
$$= 3y - 8y + 10$$
$$= -5y + 10$$

TRY THIS Remove parentheses and simplify.

8. $y - 9(x + y)$ **9.** $5a - 3(7a - 6)$ 8. $-9x - 8y$ 9. $-16a + 18$

Parentheses Within Parentheses

Sometimes parentheses occur within parentheses. When this happens we may use parentheses of different shapes, such as [], called "brackets," or {}, called "braces."

> When parentheses occur within parentheses, the computations in the innermost ones are to be done first.

EXAMPLES

Simplify.

13. $[3 - (7 + 3)]$
$= [3 - 10]$ Computing $7 + 3$
$= -7$

14. $\{8 - [9 - (12 + 5)]\}$
$= \{8 - [9 - 17]\}$ Computing $12 + 5$
$= \{8 - [-8]\}$ Computing $9 - 17$
$= 16$

15. $4(2 + 3) - \{7 - [4 - (8 + 5)]\}$
$= 4 \cdot 5 - \{7 - [4 - 13]\}$ Working with innermost parentheses first
$= 20 - \{7 - [-9]\}$ Computing $4 \cdot 5$ and $4 - 13$
$= 20 - 16$ Computing $7 - [-9]$
$= 4$

16. $[5(x + 2) - 3x] - [3(y + 2) - 7(y - 3)]$
$= [5x + 10 - 3x] - [3y + 6 - 7y + 21]$ Working with innermost parentheses first
$= [2x + 10] - [-4y + 27]$ Collecting like terms
$= 2x + 10 + 4y - 27$
$= 2x + 4y - 17$

TRY THIS Simplify.

10. $[9 - (6 + 4)]$ $_{-1}$
11. $3(4 + 2) - \{7 - [4 - (6 + 5)]\}$ $_4$
12. $[3(4 + 2) + 2x] - [4(y + 2) - 3(y - 2)]$ $_{2x\ -\ y\ +\ 4}$

When we evaluate expressions, parentheses are often used to show the order in which we perform calculations. We use the following rules which we have obeyed throughout Chapters 1 and 2.

Order of Operations

1. Compute within parentheses first.
2. Simplify powers in order from left to right.
3. Multiply and divide in order from left to right.
4. Add and subtract in order from left to right.

It is interesting to note that computers follow the same set of rules as we do in algebra.

Exercises

Rename each additive inverse without parentheses.

1. $-(2x + 7)$
2. $-(3x + 5)$
3. $-(5x - 8)$
4. $-(6x - 7)$
5. $-(4a - 3b + 7c)$
6. $-(5x - 2y - 3z)$
7. $-(6x - 8y + 5)$
8. $-(8x + 3y + 9)$
9. $-(3x - 5y - 6)$
10. $-(6a - 4b - 7)$
11. $-(-8x - 6y - 43)$
12. $-(-2a + 9b - 5c)$

1. $-2x - 7$
2. $3x + 5$
3. $-5x + 8$
4. $-6x + 7$

5. $-4a + 3b - 7c$
6. $-5x + 2y + 3z$
7. $-6x + 8y - 5$
8. $-8x - 3y - 9$

Remove parentheses and simplify.

13. $9x - (4x + 3)$ $5x - 3$
14. $7y - (2y + 9)$ $5y - 9$
15. $2a - (5a - 9)$ $-3a + 9$
16. $11n - (3n - 7)$ $8n + 7$
17. $2x + 7x - (4x + 6)$ $5x - 6$
18. $3a + 2a - (4a + 7)$ $a - 7$
19. $2x - 4y - 3(7x - 2y)$ $-19x + 2y$
20. $3a - 7b - 1(4a - 3b)$ $-a - 4b$
21. $15x - y - 5(3x - 2y + 5z)$ $9y - 25z$
22. $4a - b - 4(5a - 7b + 8c)$
$-16a + 27b - 32c$

9. $-3x + 5y + 6$
10. $-6a + 4b + 7$
11. $8x + 6y + 43$
12. $2a - 9b + 5c$

Simplify.

23. $[9 - 2(5 - 4)]$ 7
24. $[6 - 5(8 - 4)]$ -14
25. $8[7 - 6(4 - 2)]$ -40
26. $10[7 - 4(7 - 5)]$ -10
27. $[4(9 - 6) + 11] - [14 - (6 + 4)]$ 19
28. $[7(8 - 4) + 16] - [15 - (7 + 3)]$ 39
29. $[10(x + 3) - 4] + [2(x - 1) + 6]$ $12x + 30$
30. $[9(x + 5) - 7] + [4(x - 12) + 9]$ $13x - 1$
31. $[7(x + 5) - 19] - [4(x - 6) + 10]$ $3x + 30$
32. $[6(x + 4) - 12] - [5(x - 8) + 11]$ $x + 41$
33. $3\{[7(x - 2) + 4] - [2(2x - 5) + 6]\}$
$9x - 18$
34. $4\{[8(x - 3) + 9] - [4(3x - 7) + 2]\}$
$-16x + 44$

Extension

Find an equivalent expression for each by enclosing the last three terms in parentheses preceded by a minus sign.

35. $6y + 2x - 3a + c$
36. $x - y - a - b$
37. $6m + 3n - 5m + 4b$
38. If $-(a + b)$ is $-a + (-b)$ what should be the sum of $(a + b)$ and $-a + (-b)$? Show that your answer is correct.
$a + b + -a + (-b) = a + (-a) + b + (-b) = 0$

35. $6y - (-2x + 3a - c)$
36. $x - (y + a + b)$
37. $6m - (-3n + 5m - 4b)$

Challenge

Simplify.

39. $z - \{2z - [3z - (4z - 5z) - 6z] - 7z\} - 8z$ $-4z$
40. $\{x - [f - (f - x)] + [x - f]\} - 3x$ $-f$
41. $x - \{x - 1 - [x - 2 - [(x - 3) - \{x - 4 - [x - 5 - (x - 6)]\}])]\}$ $x - 3$
42. A bar or *vinculum* can be used as a grouping symbol. Simplify the following. $\{y - [y + (3 - y)] - \overline{y + 1}\} + 5y$ $5y - 4$

2-9 Equations and Percents

Many applied problems involve percents. We can use our knowledge of equations to solve such problems. First, let's recall some basic ideas about percents.

DEFINITION

A symbol $n\%$ means $n \times 0.01$ or $n \times \dfrac{1}{100}$

From this definition, we know that these are ways to write 73%.

73×0.01 or 0.73 $73 \times \dfrac{1}{100}$ or $\dfrac{73}{100}$

Similarly, 78.5% is 78.5×0.01 or 0.785. Since $0.93 = 93 \times 0.01$, we can say $0.93 = 93\%$.

EXAMPLES

1. What percent of 40 is 15?

Let y = the unknown number.

What percent of 40 is 15?

$$
\begin{aligned}
y \quad \% \quad \times 40 &= 15 \quad \text{Translating} \\
y \times 0.01 \times 40 &= 15 \quad \text{Replacing \% by } \times 0.01 \\
y \times 0.40 \quad\quad &= 15 \\
y &= \frac{15}{0.40} \quad \text{Dividing on both sides by 0.40} \\
y &= 37.5 \quad \text{So, 15 is 37.5\% of 40.}
\end{aligned}
$$

2. Three is sixteen percent of what number?

Let t = the unknown number.

Three is sixteen percent of what number?

$$
\begin{aligned}
3 &= 16 \quad \% \quad \times \quad t \quad\quad \text{Translating} \\
3 &= 16 \times 0.01 \times \quad t \quad\quad \text{Replacing \% by } \times 0.01 \\
3 &= 0.16t \\
\frac{3}{0.16} &= \frac{0.16t}{0.16t} \quad \text{Dividing on both sides by 0.16} \\
18.75 &= \quad t \quad\quad \text{So, 3 is 16\% of 18.75.}
\end{aligned}
$$

1. What percent of 25 is 16? _{64%}   2. 15 is what percent of 90? $16\frac{2}{3}\%$

3. 45 is 20 percent of what number? ₂₂₅ 4. 120% of what number is 60? ₅₀

EXAMPLE 3

Translate to an equation and solve.

The price of an automobile rose 16% to a new price of $10,393.60. What was the price before?

Let y = the former price.

Former price plus the increase in price is the new price.   Rewording

$$y \quad + \quad 16\% \times y \quad = \quad \$10{,}393.60 \qquad \text{Translating}$$

$$y + 0.16y = 10{,}393.60 \qquad \text{Converting 16\% to 0.16}$$

$$1.16y = 10{,}393.60 \qquad \text{Collecting like terms on the left}$$

$$y = \frac{10{,}393.60}{1.16} \qquad \text{Dividing on both sides by 1.16}$$

$$y = 8960$$

The number 8960 checks in the original problem. The former price was $8960.

TRY THIS Translate to an equation and solve.

5. A person's salary increased 12% to an amount of $20,608. What was the salary before?

Let x = the former price, Former price + increase = new price, x + 0.12x = 20,608, 1.12x = 20,608, x = 18,400, Check: 12% of 18,400 is 2208. 18,400 plus 2208 is 20,608.

2–9	

Exercises

Translate to an equation and solve.

1. What percent of 68 is 17? ₂₅   2. What percent of 75 is 36? ₄₈

3. What percent of 125 is 30? ₂₄   4. What percent of 300 is 57? ₁₉

5. 45 is 30% of what number? ₁₅₀   6. 20.4 is 24% of what number? ₈₅

7. 0.3 is 12% of what number? _{2.5}   8. 7 is 175% of what number? ₄

9. What number is 65% of 840? ₅₄₆ 10. What number is 1% of a million? _{10,000}

11. What percent of 80 is 100? ₁₂₅   12. What percent of 10 is 205? ₂₀₅₀

13. What is 2% of 40? 0.8   **14.** What is 40% of 2? 0.8
15. 2 is what percent of 40? 5   **16.** 40 is 2% of what number? 2000
17. On a test of 88 items, a student got 76 correct. What percent were correct? 86.4%
18. A baseball player had 13 hits in 25 times at bat. What percent were hits? 52%
19. A family spent $208 one month for food. This was 26% of its income. What was their monthly income? $800
20. The sales tax rate in New York City is 8%. How much would be charged on a purchase of $428.86? How much will the total cost of the purchase be? $34.31, $463.17
21. Water volume increases 9% when it freezes. If 400 cubic centimeters of water is frozen, how much will its volume increase? What will be the volume of the ice? 36, 436
22. An investment is made at 9% simple interest for 1 year. It grows to $8502. How much was originally invested? 7800
23. An investment is made at 8% simple interest for 1 year. It grows to $7776. How much was originally invested? 7200
24. Due to inflation the price of an item rose 8%, which was 12¢. What was the old price? the new price? 150, 162

Extension

Simplify.

25. 12% + 14% 26% **26.** 84% − 16% 68% **27.** 1 − 10% 90%
28. 1% − 10% −9% **29.** 12 × 100% 12   **30.** 42% − (1 − 58%) 0
31. 3(1 + 15%)   **32.** 7(1% + 13%) 98% **33.** $\frac{100\%}{40}$ 2.5%   31. 345% or 3.45

34. A group of 27 people make a certain amount of money at a sale. What percentage does each receive if they share the profit equally? $\frac{100\%}{27}$ = 3.7%
35. A meal came to $16.41 without tax. Calculate 6% sales tax and then calculate 15% tip based on the sum of the meal price and the tax. What is the total paid? (16.41)(1.06)(1.15) = $20.00
36. Rollie's Records charges $7.99 for an album. Warped Records charges $9.95 but you have a coupon for $2 off. 7% sales tax is charged on the *regular* prices. How much does the record cost at each store? Rollie's 7.99(1.07) = $8.47, Warped 7.95 + 7%(9.95) = $8.65
37. The weather report is "a 60% chance of showers during the day, 30% tonight, and 5% tomorrow morning." What are the chances it won't rain during the day? tonight? tomorrow morning? 40%, 70%, 95%

38. x is 160% of y. y is what % of x? $\frac{100}{160} = 0.625$, or 62.5%

39. The new price of a car is 25% higher than the old price of $8,800. The old price is what percent lower than the new price? 125% of 8800 = 11,000. $\frac{11,000 - 8800}{11,000} = \frac{2200}{11,000} = 20\%$

Challenge

40. A distributing company gives successive discounts to dealers and computes prices as follows:
    List price (price printed in the catalog) less successive discounts of 10%, 20%, and 10%. To find the actual price, take 10% off. Then take 20% off what is left and then 10% off that amount. A list price is $140. What is the actual price? 90% of 140 = 126, 80% of 126 = 100.80, 90% of 100.80 = $90.72

41. Which is better, a discount of 40% or successive discounts of 20% and 20%? 40%. Successive 20% discounts means you pay 80% of 80%, or 64%, which is only a 36% discount.

42. Which is better, successive discounts of 10%, 10% and 20% or 20%, 10% and 10%? Equal. Both are 35.2% discounts, since (.9)(.9)(.8) = (.8)(.9)(.9) = .648

43. a. "Everyone will get $\frac{4}{10}$% of the profits", says Big Louie. How many people must there be for all to share equally? $\frac{100\%}{\frac{4}{10}\%} = 250$

    b. It turned out that Louie was taking 10% of the profits. Everyone else received $\frac{4}{10}$% of the 90% that remained. How many people were there? $\frac{90\%}{\left(\frac{4}{10}\right)\%} = 225$ and Big Louie, or 226 people.

44. Show that a% of $b = b$% of a. $a \cdot \frac{1}{100} \cdot b = b \cdot \frac{1}{100} \cdot a = \frac{ab}{100}$

45. There must be less than 6 parts per billion (ppb) of chlorine in a swimming pool. What percent of total volume is this? .0000006%

46. a. Your boss says "I'll raise your $1,000 salary 50% this month but lower *that* salary 50% next month." Would you receive more money by taking the offer or by keeping your old salary for the two months? By taking the offer, you receive $2,250 rather than $2,000. Take the offer.

    b. Would you receive more money by continuing to alternate 50% increases and decreases indefinitely or by keeping your old salary? (Hint: calculate each for six months) Old salary $6,000 for 6 months, new method $5,203.12. After 2 years you would be down to $30 a month. Keep the old salary.

47. How many successive 10% discounts would be necessary to lower the price of an item to below 50% of its original price? Seven. $(0.9)^7 = 47.8\%$

2–10 Number Properties and Proofs

Number Properties in Algebra

In algebra we use variables to represent rational numbers. We add them, multiply them, and so on, in various algebraic expressions. To know what kinds of changes we can make in expressions, we depend on properties of numbers. For example, instead of $x + 2$ we might write $2 + x$. We know that the two expressions are equivalent by the commutative law of addition. Thus the equation $x + 2 = 2 + x$ is true for all rational numbers x.

EXAMPLES

What properties of numbers guarantee that these statements are true?

1. $xy = yx$ Commutative law of multiplication

2. $(xy)z = z(yx)$ Commutative and associative laws of multiplication

3. $3(x + y) = (y + x)3$ Commutative laws of addition and multiplication

4. $y[x + (-x)] = 0$ Property of additive inverses, $x + (-x) = 0$ and multiplicative property of 0, $y \cdot 0 = 0$

TRY THIS What properties of numbers guarantee that these statements are true?

1. $2 + 3x = 3x + 2$ 2. $z + [y + (-y)] = z$

3. $a + (b + c) = (b + a) + c$ 4. $2(x + 3) = 2x + 6$

1. Comm. for add.
2. Add. inverses, add. prop. of zero
3. Asso. law for add., comm. law for add.
4. Distributive law

Some of the number properties that we use can be proved. Others seem so obvious that we accept them without proof. Then we can use them to help prove other properties.

Axioms and Definitions

The properties that we accept without proof are called axioms. Which properties shall we use as axioms? There is no one correct answer to the question. We should try to choose the more obvious properties as axioms, but different mathematicians may make different choices.

The properties that we prove are called theorems. From a small set of axioms it may be possible to prove many theorems. Thus, a list of number properties can grow substantially.

Following is a list of properties that we shall accept as axioms. As we prove number properties we will use these axioms. Once we have proved a theorem we may use it in the proof of others. We may also use any of the definitions that we have stated.

Axioms For Rational Numbers

Commutative Laws of Addition and Multiplication.
For any numbers a and b, $a + b = b + a$ and $ab = ba$.

Associative Laws of Addition and Multiplication.
For any numbers a, b, and c, $a + (b + c) = (a + b) + c$ and $a(bc) = (ab)c$.

Distributive Law of Multiplication over Addition.
For any numbers a, b, and c, $a(b + c) = ab + ac$.

Additive Property of 0.
For any number a, $a + 0 = 0$

Property of Additive Inverses.
For each number a, there is an additive inverse, $-a$, for which $a + (-a) = 0$

Multiplicative Property of 1.
For any number a, $a \cdot 1 = a$

Property of Reciprocals.

For each nonzero number a, there is a reciprocal, $\frac{1}{a}$, for which $a \cdot \frac{1}{a} = 1$.

These axioms hold for rational numbers, but they also hold in some other number systems. Any number system with two operations defined in which these axioms hold is called a field. Hence the axioms are known as the field axioms.

EXAMPLES

Which axioms guarantee that these are true?

5. $x(y + 2) = xy + 2x$
   By the distributive law, $x(y + 2) = xy + x \cdot 2$. Then by the commutative law, $x \cdot 2 = 2x$, so $x(y + 2) = xy + 2x$.

6. $(a + 3)b = ab + 3b$

By the commutative law, $(a + 3)b = b(a + 3)$. Next, by the distributive law, $b(a + 3) = ba + b \cdot 3$. Then, by the commutative law, $ba = ab$ and $b \cdot 3 = 3b$, so $(a + 3)b = ab + 3b$.

TRY THIS Which axioms guarantee that these are true?

5. $a + (b + 0) = b + a$ **6.** $a[\frac{1}{a} + (-1)] = 0$

7. $a + a(-1) = a \cdot 0$ Hint: $a = a \cdot 1$.

5. Add. prop. of zero, comm. law for add.
6. Asso. law for add., reciprocals, add. inverses
7. Prop. of 1, distrib., add. inverses

Here are some important definitions that we have made. Remember that other definitions can be made and used whenever they are needed.

DEFINITIONS

Subtraction

The difference $a - b$ is that number c such that $c + b = a$.

Division

The quotient $\frac{a}{b}$, or $a \div b$, is that number c (if there is one) such that $c \cdot b = a$.

Equality

A sentence $a = b$ says that a and b are names for the same thing.

From the definition of equality we can easily see how to handle the $=$ symbol. For example, if $a = b$ is true, then so is $b = a$. Both sentences say that a and b are names of the same thing. We summarize the properties of the equality relation below.

Properties of Equality

Reflexive property	Symmetric property	Transitive property
$a = a$ is always true.	If $a = b$, then $b = a$.	If $a = b$ and $b = c$, then $a = c$.

EXAMPLES
Which property of equality justifies each statement?

7. $a(b + c) = ab + ac$, so
$ab + ac = a(b + c)$ Symmetric property

8. $2x^3 = 2x^3$ Reflexive property

9. If $5xy^2 = 5y^2x$ and $5y^2x = 5 \cdot y \cdot y \cdot x$,
then $5xy^2 = 5 \cdot y \cdot y \cdot x$.   Transitive property

TRY THIS Which properties of equality justify each statement?

8. $3a + 5b = 3a + 5b$ Reflexive

9. $(b + c)a = a(b + c)$ and $a(b + c) = ab + ac$. Therefore,
$(b + c)a = ab + ac$.   Transitive

10. If $a(b - c) = ab - ac$, then $ab - ac = a(b - c)$ Symmetric

Theorems and Proofs (Optional)

We now consider some number properties that can be proved. The first theorem is a restatement of the distributive law. To prove this theorem we write a sequence of statements. Each statement must be supported by a reason which can be an axiom or definition.

THEOREM
For any rational numbers a, b and c, $(b + c)a = ba + bc$.

1. $(b + c)a = a(b + c)$	1. Commutative law
2. $\qquad = ab + ac$	2. Distributive law
3. $\qquad = ba + ca$	3. Commutative law
4. $(b + c)a = ba + ca$	4. Transitive property of equality

Here is another theorem dealing with the distributive law. It involves three addends. We outline the proof.

THEOREM
For any numbers a, b, c and d, $a(b + c + d) = ab + ac + ad$

1. $a(b + c + d) = a[(b + c) + d]$	**1.** Associative law
2. $\qquad\qquad\quad = a(b + c) + ad$	**2.** Distributive law
3. $\qquad\qquad\quad = ab + ac + ad$	**3.** Distributive law
4. $a(b + c + d) = ab + ac + ad$	**4.** Transitive property of equality

TRY THIS

11. Complete the preceding proof by supplying the missing reasons.

The next theorem concerns a rule for multiplying by 0.

THEOREM

For any number a, $a \cdot 0 = 0$.

1. $a \cdot 0 = a \cdot 0 + 0$	**1.** Additive property of 0
2. $\qquad\quad = a \cdot 0 + a + (-a)$	**2.** Additive inverses
3. $\qquad\quad = a \cdot 0 + a \cdot 1 + (-a)$	**3.** Multiplicative property of 1
4. $\qquad\quad = a(0 + 1) + (-a)$	**4.** Distributive law
5. $\qquad\quad = a \cdot 1 + (-a)$	**5.** Additive property of 0
6. $\qquad\quad = a + (-a)$	**6.** Multiplicative prop. of 1
7. $\qquad\quad = 0$	**7.** Additive inverses
8. $a \cdot 0 = 0$	**8.** Transitive property of equality

TRY THIS Complete the preceding proof by supplying the missing reasons.

2–10	

Exercises

Tell which number properties guarantee the truth of these statements.

1. $a + b = b + a$

2. $(a + b) + c = c + (a + b)$

3. $x(y + 3) = xy + 3x$

4. $a(b + 4) = 4a + ab$

5. $y + [x + (-x)] = y$

6. $3x(x + 2) = 3x^2 + 6x$

7. $-(x - 3) = 3 - x$

8. $6x - 3y = 3(2x - y)$

1. Comm. of add.
2. Comm. of add.
3. Distrib.
4. Distrib.
5. Add. inv., add. prop. of zero
6. Distrib.
7. Add. inv.
8. Distrib.

Tell which axioms or properties of equality guarantee each statement.

9. $(a \cdot b)c = a(b \cdot c)$

10. $(a + b) \cdot 1 = a + b$

11. $17(2b + 1) = 17 + 34b$

12. $(2a + 3b) + 19 = 19 + (3b + 2a)$

13. $\dfrac{1}{x + y} \cdot (x + y) = 1$

14. $-(a + b) + (a + b) = 0$

15. $3x(y + z) = 3x(y + z)$

16. $\dfrac{1}{x} \cdot x = 1$. Thus $1 = \dfrac{1}{x} \cdot x$

17. $3(xy) = (xy)3$

18. $5(x + y) = 5x + 5y$ and $5x + 5y = 5y + 5x$ Therefore $5(x + y) = 5y + 5x$

Complete the following proofs by supplying the missing reasons.

19. Property of -1. For any number a, $-1 \cdot a = -a$

1. $-1 \cdot a = -1 \cdot a + 0$	1. Property of zero
2. $\qquad = -1 \cdot a + (a + (-a))$	2. Additive Inverses
3. $\qquad = (-1 \cdot a + a) + (-a)$	3. Asso. law of addition
4. $\qquad = (-1 \cdot a + 1 \cdot a) + (-a)$	4. Multiplicative property of 1
5. $\qquad = (-1 + 1) \cdot a + (-a)$	5. Distributive law
6. $\qquad = 0 \cdot a + (-a)$	6. Additive inverses
7. $\qquad = 0 + -a$	7. Mult. property of zero
8. $\qquad = -a$	8. Add. property of zero
9. $-1 \cdot a = -a$	9. Transitive property of equality

Extension

20. A property of rational numbers that is sometimes stated is the *closure property of addition*. We may say that the set of rational numbers is *closed* under addition since the sum of any two rational numbers is a rational number. Consider the set of even whole numbers $\{0, 2, 4, 6, 8, 10, \ldots\}$. Is the set of even whole numbers closed under addition? Yes

21. Is the set of odd whole numbers $\{1, 3, 5, 7, 9, \ldots\}$ closed under addition? No. $1 + 3 = 4$
    4 is not in the set of odd whole numbers.

22. We may say that the set of rational numbers is closed under multiplication since the product of any two rational numbers is a rational number. Consider the set of multiples of three $\{0, 3, 6, 9, 12. \ldots\}$. Is this set closed under multiplication? Yes

23. Determine whether the set $\{0, 1\}$ is closed under multiplication. Yes

9. Asso. of mult.
10. Mult. prop. of 1
11. Distrib.
12. Comm. of add.
13. Axiom of reciprocals
14. Add. inverse
15. Reflexive
16. Symmetric
17. Comm. of mult.
18. Transitive

Challenge

24. Prove that for any numbers a and b, $(-a)b = -ab$

25. Prove that $-(a - b) = b - a$. Hint: Use the definition of subtraction and the inverse of a sum property.

Automating the Market

Many supermarkets have a small computer system for checkout. The clerk passes the bar code on each item over a scanner which reads the code and rings up the price.

The key to this system is the bar code which is printed on almost every item in the store. It is called the Universal Product Code (UPC). The first five digits represent the manufacturer and the second five digits represent the particular product.

These codes are stored inside the computer with the current prices. The scanner reads the code and the computer "looks up" the price. It tells the cash register. The register tape is then printed with the name of each item, its category, and its price.

Comparative Shopping

Most of us are interested in spending our money wisely. One way of finding economical buys is to compare unit prices. The unit price is the price per unit. To find this cost, divide the total cost by the number of units. Many shoppers use a calculator for these computations.

A 16-ounce jar of grape jelly costs 99¢. A 24-ounce jar costs $1.29. Which jar of jelly has the lower unit price?

16-ounce jar: $0.99 ÷ 16 is approximately $0.06 per ounce.
24-ounce jar: $1.29 ÷ 24 is approximately $0.05 per ounce.

The 24-ounce jar has the lower unit price.

When comparing different brands, quality as well as price must be considered.

Brand X dishwashing liquid is 99¢ for 32 ounces. Its unit price is $0.99 ÷ 32, or approximately $0.03 per ounce.

Brand Y dishwashing liquid is $1.39 for 28 ounces. Its unit price is $1.39 ÷ 28, or approximately $0.05 per ounce.

Brand X seems to be the better buy, but after using it we may discover that it takes twice as much of brand X to wash the same dishes brand Y will wash. Therefore, we would need 56 ounces of brand X to wash as many dishes as the 28-ounce size of brand Y.

Brand X: 56 ounces costs $0.03 × 56, or $1.68.
Brand Y: 28 ounces costs $0.05 × 28, or $1.40.

Therefore, brand Y is actually the better buy.

Exercises

1. List two advantages and two disadvantages of the computer-ized check-out system in use in some supermarkets. Answers may vary.

Determine which has the lower unit price. Round to the nearest tenth of a cent.

2. Laundry detergent at $6.99 for 10 pounds, or $3.29 for 5 pounds. $0.699, $0.658, the 5-pound box

3. Sugarfree gum at $.99 for eight packs, or $1.19 for ten packs. $0.124, $0.119, the ten-pack size

4. Toothpaste at $1.49 for eight ounces, or $1.09 for six ounces. $0.186, $0.182, the six-ounce tube

5. Oranges at 6 for $0.89 or 8 for $1.09. $0.148, $0.136, the 8 oranges

6. Tuna at $0.68 for 6 ounces or $0.92 for 8 ounces. $0.113, $0.115, the 6-ounce size

7. Flour at $1.95 for 5 pounds or $0.89 for 2 pounds. $0.39, $0.445, the 5-pound size

8. Tomato sauce at $0.39 for 16 ounces or at $0.56 for 24 ounces. $0.024, $0.023, the 24-ounce size

9. Peanut butter at $0.63 for 10 ounces or at $1.19 for 20 ounces. $0.063, $0.060, the 20-ounce size

10. Olives at $0.79 for 5 ounces or at $1.19 for 7 ounces. $0.158, $0.17, the 5-ounce size

11. Syrup at $0.65 for 10 ounces or at $1.39 for 20 ounces. $0.065, $0.070, the 10-ounce size

12. Rice at $1.39 for 8 ounces or at $1.59 for 10 ounces. $0.174, $0.159, the 10-ounce size

13. Shampoo at $2.49 for 8 ounces or at $3.15 for 12 ounces. $0.311, $0.263, the 12-ounce size

14. Cheese at $1.15 for 6 ounces or at $1.55 for 8 ounces. $0.192, $0.194, the 6-ounce size

15. Grapefruit juice at $0.59 for 12 ounces or at $0.90 for 20 ounces. $0.049, $0.045, the 20-ounce size

CHAPTER 2   Review

Review the material in the chapter. Then see how you have done by trying these review exercises. If you miss an exercise, restudy the indicated lesson.

2–1

1. Tell what integers correspond to this situation: Mike has a debt of $45 and Joe has $72 in his savings account. $-45, 72$

2–1   Use < or > to write a true sentence.

2. -3 10

3. -1 -6 >

2–1   Find the absolute value.

4. $|-38|$ 38

5. $|91|$ 91

−2 Graph each number on a number line.

6. −2.5

7. $\frac{4}{3}$

2–2 Use < or > to write a true sentence.

8. $\frac{5}{8}$ $\frac{1}{2}$ >

9. $-\frac{2}{3}$ $-\frac{1}{10}$ <

2–3 Add.

10. $4 + (-7)$ -3

11. $-3.9 + 7.4$ 3.5

12. $6 + (-9) + (-8) + 7$ -4

13. $-3.8 + 5.1 + (-12) + (-4.3) + 10$ -5

2–3 Find the additive inverse of each.

14. 3.8 -3.8

15. $-\frac{3}{4}$ $\frac{3}{4}$

2–3

16. Find $-x$ when x is -34. 34

17. Find $-(-x)$ when x is 5. 5

2–3

18. On first, second, and third down a football team had these gains and losses: 5-yd gain, 12-yd loss, and 15-yd gain. Find the total gain (or loss). 8-yd gain

2–4 Subtract.

19. $-3 - (-7)$ 4

20. $-\frac{9}{10} - \frac{1}{2}$ $-\frac{7}{5}$

21. $-3.8 - 4.1$ -7.9

2–4 Simplify.

22. $13 - 4 + 8 - (-2)$ 19

23. $20 - 17 - 12 + 13 - (-4)$ 8

24. $-5 - 3x + 8 - (-9x)$ 3 + 6x

25. $4y - 19 - (-7y) + 3$ 11y − 16

2–4

26. Your total assets are $170. You borrow $300. What are your total assets now? −$130

2–5 Multiply.

27. $-9 \cdot (-6)$ 54

28. $-2.7(3.4)$ -9.18

29. $\frac{2}{3} \cdot \left(-\frac{3}{7}\right)$ $-\frac{2}{7}$

30. $3 \cdot (-7) \cdot (-2) \cdot (-5)$ -210

2–6 Find the reciprocal.

31. $\frac{3}{8}$ $\frac{8}{3}$

32. -7 $-\frac{1}{7}$

33. $\frac{x}{2y}$ $\frac{2y}{x}$

2–6   Divide.

34. $35 \div (-5)$ -7   **35.** $-5.1 \div 1.7$ -3   **36.** $-\frac{3}{5} \div \left(-\frac{4}{5}\right)$ $\frac{3}{4}$

2–7   Multiply.

37. $5(3x - 7)$ **38.** $-2(4x - 5)$ **39.** $10(0.4x + 1.5)$ **40.** $-8(3 - 6x)$

$15x - 35$ $-8x + 10$ $-24 + 4x$

37. 15x − 35   41. 2(c − 7)
38. − 8x + 10   42. 3(x − 3)
39. 4x + 15   43. 5(x + 2)
40. − 24 + 48x   44. 3(4 − x)

2–7   Factor.

41. $2x - 14$ **42.** $6x - 9$ **43.** $5x + 10$ **44.** $12 - 3x$

$2(x-7)$ $3(2x-9)$ $5(x+L)$ $4(3-x)$

2–7   Collect like terms.

$7A + 3b$

45. $11a + 2b - 4a - 5b$ 7a − 3b **46.** $7x - 3y - 9x + 8y$ -2x + 5y

$-2x + 5y$

47. $6x + 3y - x - 4y$ 5x − y   **48.** $-3a + 9b + 2a - b$ -a + 8b

$5x - 1y$ $-a + 8b$ $2x + 12$

2–8   Simplify.

$-3a + 9$ $4x + 12 - 2x$

49. $2a - (5a - 9)$ 3a + 9   **50.** $4(x + 3) - 2x$ 2x + 12

51. $3(b + 7) - 5b$ -2b + 21   **52.** $4y + (9 - 8y)$ -4y + 9

53. $3[11 - 3(4 - 1)]$ 6   **54.** $2[6(y - 4) + 7]$ 12y − 34

2–9   Translate to an equation and solve.

55. 25 is 10% of what number? 250 **56.** 40% of 75 is what number? 30

2–10   Tell which axioms or properties guarantee each statement.

57. $x(4 + y) = 4x + xy$ **58.** $-9y + 9y = 0$ Additive inverse

Distributive law

CHAPTER 2   Test

Use < or > to write a true sentence.

1. -4 0 <   **2.** -3 -8 >

Find the absolute value.

3. $|-7|$ 7   **4.** $|53|$ 53

Use < or > to write a true sentence.

5. $\frac{3}{5}$ $\frac{1}{3}$ >   **6.** $-\frac{1}{8}$ $\frac{1}{2}$ <

Add.

7. $3.1 + (-4.7)$ -1.6   **8.** $-8 + 4 + (-7) + 3$ -8

Find the additive inverse of each.

9. $\frac{2}{3}$ $-\frac{2}{3}$

10. -1.4 1.4

Solve.

11. Wendy had \$43 in her savings account. She withdrew \$25. Then she made a deposit of \$30. How much was in her savings account? $48

Subtract.

12. $2 - (-8)$ 10

13. $3.2 - 5.7$ −2.5

Simplify.

14. $6 + 7 - 4 - (-3)$ 12

Multiply.

15. $4 \cdot (-12)$ −48

16. $\frac{-1}{2} \cdot \frac{-3}{8}$ $\frac{3}{16}$

Find the reciprocal.

17. -2 $-\frac{1}{2}$

18. $\frac{4}{7}$ $\frac{7}{4}$

Divide.

19. $-45 \div 5$ −9

20. $\frac{-3}{5} \div \frac{(-4)}{5}$ $\frac{3}{4}$

Multiply.

21. $3(6 - x)$ 18 − 3x

22. $-5(y - 1)$ −5y + 5

Factor.

23. $2x - 14$ 2(x − 7)

24. $7x + 21$ 7(x + 3)

Simplify.

25. $5x - (3x - 7)$ 2x + 7 **26.** $3[5(y - 3) + 9]$ 15y − 18

27. Translate to an equation and solve.

20 is what percent of 80? 25%

Challenge

28. If $0.090909\ldots = \frac{1}{11}$ and $0.181818\ldots = \frac{2}{11}$, what rational number is named by

a. $0.272727\ldots$ $\frac{3}{11}$ **b.** $0.909090\ldots$ $\frac{10}{11}$

Ready for Solving Equations and Problems?

2–3   Add.

1. $-3 + (-8)$ -11 **2.** $-9 + (-4)$ -13 **3.** $-3 + 7$ 4

4. $-6 + 2$ -4 **5.** $8 + (-3) + (-11)$ -6 **6.** $-3.1 + 6.8$ 3.7

7. $-\frac{2}{3} + \left(-\frac{1}{4}\right)$ $-\frac{11}{12}$ **8.** $-0.8 + (-1.6)$ -2.4 **9.** $\frac{4}{7} + \left(-\frac{2}{5}\right)$ $\frac{6}{35}$

2–4   Subtract.

10. $9 - (-13)$ 22 **11.** $-7.2 - (-10.1)$ 2.9 **12.** $\frac{2}{3} - \frac{9}{10}$ $-\frac{7}{30}$

2–5   Multiply.

13. $9 \cdot (-4)$ -36 **14.** $-6 \cdot 8$ -48 **15.** $-\frac{2}{3} \cdot \frac{5}{8}$ $-\frac{5}{12}$

16. $\frac{3}{2} \cdot \left(-\frac{4}{7}\right)$ $-\frac{6}{7}$ **17.** $-11(-3)$ 33 **18.** $-7(-5)$ 35

19. $-\frac{6}{7}\left(-\frac{1}{3}\right)$ $\frac{2}{7}$ **20.** $-0.6(-4.7)$ 2.82 **21.** $0.068(-10)$ -0.68

2–6   Divide.

22. $\frac{3}{4} \div \left(-\frac{1}{8}\right)$ -6 **23.** $-\frac{7}{9} \div \left(-\frac{2}{3}\right)$ $\frac{7}{6}$

24. $-9.5 \div 1.9$ -5 **25.** $(-9.37) \div (-0.1)$ 93.7

2–7   Factor.

26. $9y - 45$ $9(y - 5)$ **27.** $bw + bx - by$ $b(w + x - y)$

28. $3y + 15 - 21x$ **29.** $6w - 12x + 10$ $2(3w - 6x + 5)$
$3(y + 5 - 7x)$

2–7   Multiply.

30. $3(x - 5)$ $3x - 15$ **31.** $8(4 + w)$ $32 + 8w$

2–7   Collect like terms.

32. $9y - 3y$ $6y$ **33.** $x - 8x$ $-7x$

2–8   Remove parentheses and simplify.

34. $5x - (6 + 3x)$ $2x - 6$
35. $7w - 3 - (4w - 8)$ $3w + 5$
36. $[3(5 - 2) + 18] - [12 - (3 + 4)]$ 22
37. $[2(4x + 7) - 3] + [5(3 + x) + 2x]$ $15x + 26$

3

CHAPTER THREE

Solving Equations and Problems

3-1 The Addition Principle

Using the Addition Principle

In Chapter 1 we learned that solving equations is an important part of algebra. In this chapter we shall learn other ways to solve equations. First recall the following.

> The replacements that make an equation true are called *solutions*. To *solve* an equation means to find all of its solutions.

There are many ways to solve equations. One way is based on an idea called the addition principle.

> **The Addition Principle**
> If an equation $a = b$ is true, then $a + c = b + c$ is true for any number c.

This principle makes sense if we think of an equation $a = b$. We know that a and b stand for the same number. Suppose this is true and then add a number c to the number a. We get the same answer if we add c to b, because a and b are the same number.

When using the addition principle, we sometimes say that we "add the same number on both sides of an equation."

EXAMPLE 1
Solve.

$$x + 5 = -7$$
$$x + 5 + (-5) = -7 + (-5)$$ Using the addition principle, adding -5 on both sides
$$x + 0 = -12$$
$$x = -12$$ Simplifying

Check:
$$
\begin{array}{c|c}
x + 5 = -7 \\
\hline
-12 + 5 & -7 \\
-7 & -7
\end{array}
$$

The solution is -12.

In Example 1, to get x alone, we added the inverse of 5. This "got rid of" the 5 on the left. The idea behind using the addition principle is to change an equation into a simpler equation whose solution is obvious. In Example 1 we started with $x + 5 = -7$ and, using the addition principle, changed it to $x = -12$. We can see that the solution of $x = -12$ is the number -12. Equations with the same solution, such as $x + 5 = -7$ and $x = -12$, are called equivalent equations.

EXAMPLE 2
Solve.

$$-6 = y - 8$$
$$-6 + 8 = y - 8 + 8 \quad \text{Adding 8 on both sides to get rid}$$
$$2 = y \qquad\qquad \text{of } -8 \text{ on the right}$$

Check:
$$\begin{array}{c|c} -6 = y - 8 \\ \hline -6 & 2 - 8 \\ & -6 \end{array}$$

The solution is 2.

TRY THIS Solve using the addition principle.

1. $x + 7 = 2$ $_{-5}$ **2.** $y + 8 = -3$ $_{-11}$ **3.** $5 = -4 + y$ $_9$
4. $n - 9 = -3$ $_6$ **5.** $y - 4.5 = 8.7$ $_{13.2}$ **6.** $-7 = 3 + x$ $_{-10}$

The addition principle also allows us to subtract on both sides of an equation. This is so because subtracting is the same as adding an inverse. In Example 1 we could have subtracted 5 on both sides.

Solving Problems

Recall from Chapter 1 that some problems can be solved if we begin by translating to equations.

EXAMPLE 3
Translate to an equation and solve.

In a basketball game Paula scored 18 points. This was 4 points higher than her average. What is her average?

Let $x = $ Paula's average.

$$\underbrace{\text{Paula's average}}\ \text{plus}\ \underbrace{\text{4 points}}\ \text{is}\ \underbrace{\text{18 points.}}\quad\text{Rewording}$$
$$\qquad x \qquad\quad + \qquad 4 \quad = \qquad 18 \qquad\qquad \text{Translating}$$

Now solve the equation.

$$x + 4 = 18$$
$$x + 4 + (-4) = 18 + (-4)$$
$$x + 0 = 14$$
$$x = 14$$

Is 14 points the answer to the original problem? If Paula's average is 14 points and she scored 4 more than her average, then she must have scored 18 points. This checks with the original problem.

Note that we have used these steps in solving the problem.

Steps for Problem Solving
1. Choose a variable for the unknown number.
2. Translate to an equation.
3. Solve the equation.
4. Check the answer in the original problem.

TRY THIS Translate to an equation and solve.

7. The weekly rent on an ocean-front apartment was increased by $32. The new rental cost is $475. What was the previous rent?

Let x = amount of old rental cost, Amount of old rental cost increased by $32 = $475, $x + 32 = 475$, $x = 443$, Check: $443 plus $32 increase is $475.

$$r + 32 = 475$$
$$r = 475 - 32$$
$$r = 443$$

3–1

Exercises

Solve using the addition principle.

1. $x + 2 = 6$ 4
2. $x + 5 = 8$ 3
3. $x + 15 = 26$ 11
4. $y + 9 = 43$ 34
5. $x + 6 = -8$ −14
6. $t + 9 = -12$ −21
7. $x + 16 = -2$ −18
8. $y + 25 = -6$ −31
9. $x - 9 = 6$ 15
10. $x - 8 = 5$ 13
11. $x - 7 = -21$ −14
12. $x - 3 = -14$ −11
13. $5 + t = 7$ 2
14. $8 + y = 12$ 4
15. $-7 + y = 13$ 20
16. $-9 + z = 15$ 24
17. $-3 + t = -9$ −6
18. $-6 + y = -21$ −15

19. $r + \frac{1}{3} = \frac{8}{3}$ $\frac{7}{3}$
20. $t + \frac{3}{8} = \frac{5}{8}$ $\frac{1}{4}$
21. $m + \frac{5}{6} = -\frac{11}{12}$ $-\frac{21}{12}$

22. $x + \frac{2}{3} = -\frac{5}{6}$ $-\frac{3}{2}$
23. $x - \frac{5}{6} = \frac{7}{8}$ $\frac{41}{24}$
24. $y - \frac{3}{4} = \frac{5}{6}$ $\frac{19}{12}$

25. $-\frac{1}{5} + z = -\frac{1}{4}$ $\frac{-1}{20}$ **26.** $-\frac{1}{8} + y = -\frac{3}{4}$ $\frac{-5}{8}$ **27.** $x + 2.3 = 7.4$ 5.1

28. $y + 4.6 = 9.3$ 4.7   **29.** $x - 4.8 = 7.6$ 12.4   **30.** $y - 8.3 = 9.5$ 17.8

Solve these problems by translating to equations.

31. Six more than a number is 57. Find the number. 51

32. A number decreased by 18 is -53. Find the number. -35

33. After six weeks at the exercise club, Marcie could leg lift 70 lbs. This was 12 pounds more than when she started. How much could she leg lift when she started? 58

34. In Churchill, Manitoba, the average daily low temperature in January is $-31°C$. This is 50 degrees less than the average daily low temperature in Key West, Florida. What is the average daily low temperature in Key West in January? 19°C

35. In 1980, a TV magazine had a circulation of 18,870,730. This was 15,918,215 more than a newspaper circulation. What was the newspaper circulation? 2,952,515

Extension

Solve each equation for x.

36. $8 - 25 = 8 + x - 21$ -4 **37.** $16 + x - 22 = -16$ -10

38. $x + x = x$ 0   **39.** $x + 3 = 3 + x$ Any value

40. $x + 7 = b + 10$ $b + 3$ **41.** $1 - c = a + x$ $x = 1 - c - a$

Translate and solve.

42. At the end of the month, the computer inventory indicated that there were 319 blank video cassettes in stock. This was after sales of 142 and a restock of 75. How many cassettes were in stock at the beginning of the month? 386

Challenge

43. Solve $|y| + 6 = 19$ 13 or -13

44. Suppose k is a solution of some equation. Can $-k$ ever be a solution of this equation? Yes, for $x^2 = 9$, both 3 and -3 are solutions.

45. Tell why it is not necessary to state a subtraction principle for equation solving. Subtraction is addition of inverses.

46. Solve $x - 1 + 2x - 2 + 3x - 3 = 30 + 4x$ 18

47. Solve $-\frac{3}{2} + x = \frac{-5}{17} - \frac{3}{2}$ $\frac{-5}{17}$

48. If $x - 4720 = 1634$, find $x + 4720$. 11,074

3–2 The Multiplication Principle

Using the Multiplication Principle

Another way to solve some equations is based on the multiplication principle.

> **The Multiplication Principle**
> If an equation $a = b$ is true, then $a \cdot c = b \cdot c$ is true for any number c.

This principle makes sense if we think of an equation $a = b$. We know $a = b$ means that a and b stand for the same number. It follows that if we multiply a by some number c we get the same answer as multiplying b by c, since a and b are the same number.

When using the multiplication principle we sometimes say that we "multiply on both sides by the same number."

EXAMPLE 1
Solve.

$$3x = 12$$
$$3x \cdot \frac{1}{3} = 12 \cdot \frac{1}{3} \quad \text{Using the multiplication principle, multiplying by } \tfrac{1}{3} \text{ on both sides}$$
$$1 \cdot x = 4$$
$$x = 4$$

Check:
$$\begin{array}{c|c} 3x & 12 \\ \hline 3 \cdot 4 & 12 \\ 12 & \end{array}$$

The solution is 4.

In Example 1, to get x alone, we multiplied by the reciprocal of 3. When we multiplied we got $1 \cdot x$, which simplified to x. This enabled us to "get rid of" the 3 on the left.

TRY THIS Solve using the multiplication principle.

1. $5x = 25$ 5   **2.** $4x = -7$ $-\tfrac{7}{4}$ **3.** $-3y = -42$ 14

EXAMPLE 2
Solve.

$$-x = 9$$
$$-1 \cdot x = 9 \quad \text{Using the property of } -1$$
$$-1 \cdot -1 \cdot x = 9 \cdot -1 \quad \text{Multiplying on both sides by } -1, \text{ the reciprocal of itself}$$
$$1 \cdot x = -9$$
$$x = -9$$

Check:

$$\begin{array}{c|c} -x = 9 \\ \hline -(-9) & 9 \\ 9 & \end{array}$$

The solution is -9.

EXAMPLE 3
Solve.

$$\frac{-y}{9} = 14$$

$$9 \cdot \frac{-y}{9} = 9 \cdot 14 \quad \text{Think of } \frac{-y}{9} \text{ as } \frac{1}{9} \cdot -y; \text{ multiply by 9 on both sides.}$$
$$-y = 126$$
$$y = -126$$

Check:

$$\begin{array}{c|c} \frac{-y}{9} = 14 \\ \hline \frac{-(-126)}{9} & 14 \\ \frac{126}{9} & \\ 14 & \end{array}$$

The solution is 14.

EXAMPLE 4
Solve.

$$\frac{3}{8} = -\frac{5}{4}x$$

$$-\frac{4}{5} \cdot \frac{3}{8} = -\frac{4}{5}\left(-\frac{5}{4}x\right) \quad \text{Multiplying on both sides by } -\frac{4}{5}, \text{ the reciprocal of } -\frac{5}{4}.$$

$$-\frac{3}{10} = x \quad \text{Simplifying}$$

Check:

$$\begin{array}{c|c} \frac{3}{8} = -\frac{5}{4}x \\ \hline \frac{3}{8} & -\frac{5}{4}\left(-\frac{3}{10}\right) \\ & \frac{3}{8} \end{array}$$

The solution is $-\frac{3}{10}$.

TRY THIS Solve using the multiplication principle.

4. $-x = 6$ $_{-6}$ **5.** $-\dfrac{x}{5} = 10$ $_{-50}$ **6.** $4 = -\dfrac{1}{3}y$ $_{-12}$ **7.** $\dfrac{5}{6} = -\dfrac{2}{3}x$ $_{-\frac{5}{4}}$

The multiplication principle also allows us to divide by a nonzero number on both sides of an equation if we wish. This is because dividing by a number is the same as multiplying by its reciprocal.

$12x = 6.72$

Solving Problems

Sometimes when we translate a problem to an equation we can use the multiplication principle to help solve problems.

EXAMPLE 5

Translate to an equation and solve.

A wildlife expert estimates that in a certain year the number of female fawns born will be about 43% of the number of adult female deer. Suppose there are 1290 female fawns born. About how many adult female deer were there?

Let y = the number of adult female deer.

$$
\begin{array}{cccc}
43\% \text{ of} & \text{the number of adult female deer} & = & 1290 \\
\downarrow \ \ \downarrow & \underbrace{} & \downarrow & \downarrow \\
0.43 \ \cdot & y & = & 1290
\end{array}
$$

Now, solve the equation.

$$0.43y = 1290$$

$$\dfrac{0.43y}{0.43} = \dfrac{1290}{0.43} \qquad \text{Dividing on both sides by 0.43 is the same as multiplying by } \dfrac{1}{0.43}$$

$$1 \cdot y = 3000$$

$$y = 3000$$

Since 43% of 3000 is 1290, there were about 3000 female deer.

TRY THIS Translate to an equation and solve.

8. Penny bought a 12-bottle case of juice on sale for $6.72. Find the price of a bottle.

8. Let x = cost of 1 bottle, Cost of 1 bottle times 12 bottles = $6.72, $x \cdot 12$ = 6.72, $12x$ = 6.72, x = 0.56, Check: $0.56 × 12 = $6.72

Exercises

Solve using the multiplication principle. Don't forget to check.

1. $6x = 36$ ₆
2. $3x = 39$ ₁₃
3. $5x = 45$ ₉
4. $9x = 72$ ₈
5. $84 = 7x$ ₁₂
6. $56 = 8x$ ₇
7. $-x = 40$ ₋₄₀
8. $100 = -x$ ₋₁₀₀
9. $-x = -1$ ₁
10. $-68 = -r$ ₆₈
11. $7x = -49$ ₋₇
12. $9x = -36$ ₋₄
13. $-12x = 72$ ₋₆
14. $-15x = 105$ ₋₇
15. $-21x = -126$ ₆
16. $-13x = -104$ ₈

17. $\frac{t}{7} = -9$ ₋₆₃
18. $\frac{y}{-8} = 11$ ₋₈₈
19. $\frac{3}{4}x = 27$ ₃₆
20. $\frac{4}{5}x = 16$ ₂₀

21. $\frac{-t}{3} = 7$ ₋₂₁
22. $\frac{-x}{6} = 9$ ₋₅₄
23. $-\frac{m}{3} = \frac{1}{5}$ $\frac{-3}{5}$
24. $\frac{1}{9} = -\frac{z}{7}$ $\frac{-7}{9}$

25. $-\frac{3}{5}r = -\frac{9}{10}$ $\frac{3}{2}$
26. $-\frac{2}{5}y = -\frac{4}{15}$ $\frac{2}{3}$
27. $-\frac{3}{2}r = -\frac{27}{4}$ $\frac{9}{2}$
28. $\frac{5}{7}x = -\frac{10}{14}$ ₋₁

29. $6.3x = 44.1$ ₇
30. $2.7y = 54$ ₂₀
31. $-3.1y = 21.7$ ₋₇
32. $-3.3y = 6.6$ ₋₂

33. $38.7m = 309.6$ ₈
34. $29.4x = 235.2$ ₈
35. $-\frac{2}{3}y = -10.6$ ₁₅.₉
36. $-\frac{9}{7}y = 12.06$ ₋₉.₃₈

Translate to an equation and solve.

37. Eighteen times a number is -1008. Find the number. ₋₅₆
38. Some number multiplied by negative eight is 744. Find the number. ₋₉₃
39. Dave and Shirley King paid $340 for an eight-performance symphony concert series. What is the price of each performance? $42.50
40. In 1980, the population of Las Vegas, the largest city in Nevada, was 164,275. That was about 30 times the population of Ely, Nevada's 9th largest city. What was the population of Ely? 5476
41. Apollo 10 reached a speed of 24,790 miles per hour. That is 37 times the speed of the first supersonic flight in 1947. What was the speed of the 1947 flight? 670 mi/h
42. A case of a dozen video cassette tapes cost $191.40. Find the cost of a single tape. $15.95
43. A wildlife expert estimates that in a certain year, the number of male fawns born will be about 39% of the number of adult female deer. Suppose there are 1131 male fawns born. About how many adult female deer were there? 2900

44. The population of London, England is about 7,028,000. This is about 94% of the population of New York City. What is the population of New York?

45. Roger Staubach completed 1685 passes in his pro football career. This is about 57% of the number he attempted. How many did he attempt? ~2956

46. A bottle factory had 59 breaks during a business day. The expected breakage rate is 1.3%. About how many bottles were produced? 4538

Extension

Translate to an equation and solve.

47. One third of a number is 89.　**48.** One eleventh of a number is 74.

49. Two fifths of a number is 95.　**50.** Three tenths of a number is 57.

51. Eleven thirteenths of a number is 242. 286

52. A hundredth of a number is 1000. 100,000

47. 267
48. 814
49. 237.5
50. 190

Solve each equation for x.

53. $ax = 5a$ ₅　**54.** $3x = \dfrac{b}{a}$ $(a \neq 0)$ $\frac{b}{3a}$　**55.** $cx = a^2 + 1$ $\frac{a^2 + 1}{c}$

56. $abx = 1$ $\frac{1}{ab}$　**57.** $0 \cdot x = 0$ Any value　**58.** $0 \cdot x = 9$ No value

Challenge

59. Solve $8|x| = 24$ $x = 3$ or -3

60. Determine whether you can square both sides of an equation and always get an equivalent equation. Yes. If $x = y$, then $x^2 = y^2$.

61. Tell why it is not necessary to state a division principle for equation solving. Division is multiplication of reciprocals.

DISCOVERY/Al-jabr

The word *algebra* comes from the arabic word *al-jabr,* which means the reuniting of broken parts. The word was used around 825 A.D. by an Arabic mathematician. He applied al-jabr to a rule for re-uniting terms in an equation.

Here is a an example using modern terms.

$$5x + 3y = 7y$$
$$5x = 3y - 7y$$

In the second equation, the y-terms are together, or re-united. The mathematician who first used the word al-jabr was Mohammed ibn Musa al-Khowarizimi, from

whose name we get the word "algorithm." He was one of many Arab scholars who contributed to mathematics in the Middle Ages. His writings were not translated into Latin for 300 years. From this translation the word algebra became known and used in Europe.

3-3 Using the Principles Together

Applying Both Principles

For some equations we might apply both principles.

EXAMPLE 1
Solve.

$$3x + 4 = 13$$
$$3x + 4 + (-4) = 13 + (-4) \quad \text{Using the addition principle, adding } -4 \text{ on both sides}$$
$$3x = 9$$
$$\frac{1}{3} \cdot 3x = \frac{1}{3} \cdot 9 \quad \text{Using the multiplication principle}$$
$$x = 3$$

Check:
$$\begin{array}{c|c} 3x + 4 = 13 & \\ \hline 3(3) + 4 & 13 \\ 9 + 4 & \\ 13 & \end{array}$$

The solution is 3.

In Example 1, we used the addition principle first. This is usually best, although there might be equations for which we would use the multiplication principle first.

EXAMPLE 2
Solve.

$$-5x + 6 = 16$$
$$-5x + 6 + (-6) = 16 + (-6) \quad \text{Adding } -6 \text{ on both sides}$$
$$-5x = 10$$
$$-\frac{1}{5} \cdot (-5x) = -\frac{1}{5} \cdot 10 \quad \text{Multiplying on both sides by } -\frac{1}{5}$$
$$x = -2$$

Check:
$$\begin{array}{c|c} -5x + 6 = 16 & \\ \hline -5(-2) + 6 & 16 \\ 10 + 6 & \\ 16 & \end{array}$$

The solution is -2.

EXAMPLE 3

Solve.

$$45 - 2x = 13$$
$$-45 + 45 - 2x = -45 + 13 \quad \text{Adding } -45 \text{ on both sides}$$
$$-2x = -32$$
$$\left(-\frac{1}{2}\right) - 2x = \left(-\frac{1}{2}\right)(-32) \quad \text{Multiplying on both sides by } -\frac{1}{2}$$
$$x = 16$$

The number 16 checks and is a solution.

TRY THIS Solve.

3. $-18 - 3x = -57$ ₁₃   **4.** $-4 - 8x = -4x$ ₋₁

Collecting Like Terms in Solving Equations

If there are like terms on one side of an equation, we collect them before using the principles.

EXAMPLE 4

Solve.

$$6x + 2x = 15$$
$$8x = 15 \qquad \text{Collecting like terms}$$
$$\frac{1}{8} \cdot 8x = \frac{1}{8} \cdot 15 \quad \text{Multiplying on both sides by } \frac{1}{8}$$
$$x = \frac{15}{8}$$

The number $\frac{15}{8}$ checks, so the solution is $\frac{15}{8}$.

TRY THIS Solve.

5. $4x + 3x = 21$ ₃   **6.** $9x - 4x = 20$ ₄

If there are like terms on opposite sides of an equation, we get them on the same side using the addition principle. Then we collect them.

EXAMPLE 5
Solve.

$$
\begin{aligned}
2x - 2 &= -3x + 3 \\
2x - 2 + 2 &= -3x + 3 + 2 \quad \text{Adding 2 on both sides to get constant terms on one side} \\
2x &= -3x + 5 \\
2x + 3x &= -3x + 3x + 5 \quad \text{Adding } 3x \text{ on both sides to get terms with a variable} \\
&\qquad\qquad\qquad\qquad \text{on the other side} \\
5x &= 5 \quad \text{Collecting like terms and simplifying} \\
\tfrac{1}{5} \cdot 5x &= \tfrac{1}{5} \cdot 5 \quad \text{Multiplying on both sides by } \tfrac{1}{5} \\
x &= 1
\end{aligned}
$$

Check:

$$
\begin{array}{c|c}
\multicolumn{2}{c}{2x - 2 = -3x + 3} \\
\hline
2 \cdot 1 - 2 & -3 \cdot 1 + 3 \\
2 - 2 & -3 + 3 \\
0 & 0
\end{array}
$$

The solution is 1.

In Example 5 the addition principle was used to get all terms with the variable on one side and all other terms on the other side. Then like terms were collected and we proceeded as before. If there are like terms on one side at the outset, they should be collected first.

EXAMPLE 6
Solve.

$$
\begin{aligned}
6x + 5 - 7x &= 10 - 4x + 3 \\
-x + 5 &= 13 - 4x \quad \text{Collecting like terms} \\
-x + 4x + 5 + (-5) &= 13 + (-5) - 4x + 4x \quad \text{Adding } 4x \text{ and } -5 \text{ on both sides} \\
3x &= 8 \quad \text{Collecting like terms} \\
\tfrac{1}{3} \cdot 3x &= \tfrac{1}{3} \cdot 8 \quad \text{Multiplying on both sides by } \tfrac{1}{3} \\
x &= \tfrac{8}{3}
\end{aligned}
$$

The number $\frac{8}{3}$ checks, so it is the solution.

TRY THIS Solve.

7. $7y + 5 = 2y + 10$ ₁

8. $5 - 2y = 3y - 5$ ₂

9. $7x - 17 + 2x = 2 - 8x + 15$ ₂

10. $3x - 15 = 5x + 3 - 4x$ ₉

Solving Problems

We know we can solve problems by translating to equations. We may get an equation in which it is necessary to use both principles or collect like terms. Keep these steps in mind.

---

1. Choose a variable for the unknown number.
2. Translate to an equation.
3. Solve the equation.
4. Check the answer in the original problem.

EXAMPLE 7

If 6 is added to twice a certain number the result is 20. What is the number? Let x = the number.

6 added to twice a certain number is 20.   Rewording

$$6 \quad + \qquad\qquad 2x \qquad = 20 \qquad \text{Translating}$$

Now we solve.
$$6 + 2x = 20$$
$$2x = 14$$
$$x = 7$$

Check: Twice 7 is 14. Adding 6 to 14 gives 20. This checks.

TRY THIS Translate to an equation and solve.

11. If 5 is subtracted from three times a certain number, the result is 10. What is the number?

11. Let x = a number, 3 times a number minus 5 is 10, $3 \cdot x - 5 = 10$, $3x - 5 = 10$, $3x = 15$, $x = 5$.

3-3	

Exercises

Solve and check.

1. $5x + 6 = 31$ ₅   2. $3x + 6 = 30$ ₈   3. $8x + 4 = 68$ ₈

4. $7z + 9 = 72$ ₉   5. $4x - 6 = 34$ ₁₀   6. $6x - 3 = 15$ ₃

7. $3x - 9 = 33$ ₁₄   8. $5x - 7 = 48$ ₁₁   9. $7x + 2 = -54$ ₋₈

10. $5x + 4 = -41$ ₋₉   11. $6y + 3 = -45$ ₋₈   12. $9t + 8 = -91$ ₋₁₁

13. $-4x + 7 = 35$ ₋₇   14. $-5x - 7 = 108$ ₋₂₃ 15. $-7x - 24 = -129$ ₁₅

16. $-6z - 18 = -132$ ₁₉ 17. $-4x + 71 = -1$ ₂₄   18. $-8y + 83 = -85$ ₂₁

Solve and check.

19. $5x + 7x = 72$ ₆   **20.** $4x + 5x = 45$ ₅

21. $8x + 7x = 60$ ₄   **22.** $3x + 9x = 96$ ₈

23. $4x + 3x = 42$ ₆   **24.** $6x + 19x = 100$ ₄

25. $4y - 2y = 10$ ₅   **26.** $8y - 5y = 48$ ₁₆

27. $-6y - 3y = 27$ ₋₃   **28.** $-4y - 8y = 48$ ₋₄

29. $-7y - 8y = -15$ ₁   **30.** $-10y - 3y = -39$ ₃

31. $10.2y - 7.3y = -58$ ₋₂₀   **32.** $6.8y - 2.4y = -88$ ₋₂₀

33. $x + \frac{1}{3}x = 8$ ₆   **34.** $x + \frac{1}{4}x = 10$ ₈

35. $8y - 35 = 3y$ ₇   **36.** $4x - 6 = 6x$ ₋₃

37. $4x - 7 = 3x$ ₇   **38.** $9x - 6 = 3x$ ₁

39. $8x - 1 = 23 - 4x$ ₂   **40.** $5y - 2 = 28 - y$ ₅

41. $2x - 1 = 4 + x$ ₅   **42.** $5x - 2 = 6 + x$ ₂

43. $6x + 3 = 2x + 11$ ₂   **44.** $5y + 3 = 2y + 15$ ₄

45. $5 - 2x = 3x - 7x + 25$ ₁₀   **46.** $10 - 3x = 2x - 8x + 40$ ₁₀

47. $4 + 3x - 6 = 3x + 2 - x$ ₄   **48.** $5 + 4x - 7 = 4x + 3 - x$ ₅

Translate to an equation and solve.

49. A 6 m board is cut into two pieces, one twice as long as the other. How long are the pieces? _{4m, 2m}

50. An 8 m board is cut into two pieces One piece is 2 m longer than the other. How long are the pieces? _{5m, 3m}

51. When 18 is subtracted from six times a certain number, the result is 96. What is the number? ₁₉

52. When 28 is subtracted from five times a certain number, the result is 232. What is the number? ₅₂

53. If you double a number and then add 16, you get $\frac{2}{5}$ of the original number. What is the original number? ₋₁₀

54. If you double a number and then add 85, you get $\frac{3}{4}$ of the original number. What is the original number? ₋₆₈

55. If you add two fifths of a number to the number itself, you get 56. What is the number? ₄₀

56. If you add one third of a number to the number itself, you get 48. What is the number? ₃₆

57. A 480 m wire is cut into three pieces. The second piece is three times as long as the first. The third piece is four times as long as the second. How long is each piece? _{30 m, 90 m, 360 m}

Extension

Solve.

58. $0.26 + y = 0.98 + 3y$ $\quad -0.36$ **59.** $0 = y - (-14) - (-3y)$ $\quad 3.5$

60. $\frac{5 + 2m}{3} = \frac{25}{12} + \frac{5m + 3}{4}$ $\quad -2$ **61.** $0.05x - 1.82 = 0.708x - 0.504$ $\quad -2$

62. Solve the equation $4x - 8 = 32$ by using the multiplication principle first. Then solve it using the addition principle first.

63. Bowling at Chan's 10 Pin cost Steve and Zorina $9.00. This included shoe rental of 75¢ a pair. How much was each game if Steve bowled 3 games and Zorina bowled 2 games?

64. Rafael spent $2011 to drive his car last year. He drove 7400 miles. He paid $972 for insurance and $114 for his registration fee. If the only other cost was for gas, how much did gas cost per mile?

62. $\frac{1}{4}(4x) - \frac{1}{4}(8) = \frac{1}{4}(32)$
$x - 2 = 8$
$x = 10$
$4x - 8 = 32$
$4x = 40$
$x = 10$

63. $x = $ cost of game,
$3x + 2x + 2(0.75) = 9$,
$1.50

64. $x = $ cost of gas per mile,
$972 + 114 + 7400x = 2011$, $0.125

Challenge

Solve the first equation for x and substitute this value into the second equation. Then solve for y.

65. $9x - 5 = 22$
$4x + 2y = 2$ $\quad x = 3, y = -5$

66. $9x + 2 = -1$
$4x - y = \frac{11}{3}$ $\quad x = \frac{-1}{3}, y = -5$

67. $0.2x + 0.12 = 0.146$
$0.17x + 0.03y = 0.01238$
$\quad x = 0.13, y = -0.324$

68. Solve for y
$\frac{y - 2}{3} = \frac{2 - y}{5}$ $\quad 2$

69. The total length of the Nile and Amazon rivers is 13,108 km. If the Amazon were 234 km longer, it would be as long as the Nile. Find the length of each river.

70. In 1979, tennis players John McEnroe and Martina Navratilova earned a total of $1,752,786. If McEnroe had earned $257,690 less, he would have earned the same amount as Navratilova. How much did each person earn?

71. Ronald can do a job alone in 3 days. His assistant can do the same job alone in 6 days. How long will it take Ronald and his assistant to do the same job together? (Hint: Determine how much work each can do in one day.)

72. One cashier works at a rate of 3 minutes per customer and a second express cashier workes at a rate of 2 customers per minute.
  a. How many customers are served in an hour?
  b. At what rate are customers being served?

69. Amazon 6437, Nile 6671

70. McEnroe $1,005,238,
Navratilova $747,548

71. They can do $\frac{1}{3} + \frac{1}{6} = \frac{1}{2}$
the job in one day, or the entire job in 2 days.

72. a. $\frac{60}{3} + 60 \times 2 = 140$
b. $2\frac{1}{3}$ per minute or $\frac{3}{7}$ min. per customer

More on Solving Equations

Equations Containing Parentheses

Some equations containing parentheses can be solved by first using the distributive law.

EXAMPLE 1
Solve.

$$4x = 2(12 - x)$$
$$4x = 24 - 2x \qquad \text{Using the distributive law}$$
$$4x + 2x = 24 - 2x + 2x \qquad \text{Adding } 2x \text{ on both sides to get}$$
$$6x = 24 \qquad \qquad \text{all } x\text{-terms on one side}$$
$$x = 4$$

Check:

$4x$	$= 2(12 - x)$
$4(4)$	$2(12 - 4)$
16	$2 \cdot 8$
	16

The solution is 4.

TRY THIS Solve.

1. $2(2y + 3) = 14$ ₂   **2.** $5(3x - 2) = 35$ ₃

If parentheses occur on both sides of the equation, we use the distributive property and then solve.

EXAMPLE 2
Solve.

$$3(x - 2) - 1 = 2 - 5(x + 5)$$
$$3x - 6 - 1 = 2 - 5x - 25 \qquad \text{Using the distributive law}$$
$$3x - 7 = -5x - 23 \qquad \text{Simplifying}$$
$$3x + 5x - 7 + 7 = -5x + 5x - 23 + 7 \qquad \text{Adding } 5x \text{ and 7 to both sides, to}$$
$$8x = -16 \qquad\qquad\qquad \text{get all } x\text{-terms on one side and all}$$
$$x = -2 \qquad\qquad\qquad\quad \text{other terms on the other side and}$$
$$\text{then simplifying}$$

Check:

$3(x - 2) - 1$	$= 2 - 5(x + 5)$
$3(-2 - 2) - 1$	$2 - 5(-2 + 5)$
$3(-4) - 1$	$2 - 5(3)$
$-12 - 1$	$2 - 15$
-13	-13

The solution is -2.

Solve.

3. $3(7 + 2x) = 30 + 7(x - 1)$ ₋₂ **4.** $4(3 + 5y) - 4 = 3 + 2(y - 2)$ ₋½

Using the Multiplication Principle First

In Section 3–3 we stated that there might be equations for which we would use the multiplication principle first. If we wish to clear an equation of fractions or decimals to make it easier to solve, then we can use the multiplication principle first.

EXAMPLE 3
Solve.

$$\frac{2}{3}x + \frac{1}{2}x = \frac{5}{6} + 2x$$ The number 6 is the least common denominator. We insert parentheses and multiply on both sides by 6.

$$6\left(\frac{2}{3}x + \frac{1}{2}x\right) = 6\left(\frac{5}{6} + 2x\right)$$ Using the multiplication principle

$$6 \cdot \frac{2}{3}x + 6 \cdot \frac{1}{2}x = 6 \cdot \frac{5}{6} + 6 \cdot 2x$$ Using the distributive property; be sure to multiply ALL the terms by 6. Simplifying; note that the equation is cleared of fractions.

$$4x + 3x = 5 + 12x$$
$$7x = 5 + 12x$$
$$7x - 12x = 5 + 12x - 12x$$
$$-5x = 5$$
$$x = -1$$ The number -1 checks and is the solution.

To clear an equation of fractions we multiply on both sides by the least common denominator of the fractions.

TRY THIS Solve and check. Clear of fractions first.

5. $\frac{7}{8}x + \frac{3}{4} = \frac{1}{2}x + \frac{3}{2}$ ₂

EXAMPLE 4
Solve

$$16.3 - 7.2y = -8.18$$ Multiplying by 100, which has two 0's, will clear the decimals.
$$100(16.3 - 7.2y) = 100(-8.18)$$ Using the multiplication principle
$$100(16.3) - 100(7.2y) = 100(-8.18)$$ Using a distributive law
$$1630 - 720y = -818$$ Note that the equation is cleared of decimals.
$$-720y = -818 - 1630$$
$$-720y = -2448$$
$$y = \frac{-2448}{-720}$$
$$y = 3.4$$ The number 3.4 checks and is the solution.

To clear an equation of decimals we multiply on both sides by an appropriate power of 10.

TRY THIS Solve and check. Clear of decimals first.

6. $41.68 = 4.7 - 8.6y$ $_{-4.3}$

Solving Problems

When we translate some problems to equations, the equations may contain parentheses. If so, we use the distributive property and solve as before.

Some problems involve consecutive integers. Consecutive integers are next to each other, such as 3 and 4. The larger is 1 plus the smaller. Consecutive even integers are integers such as 6 and 8. The larger is 2 plus the smaller. Consecutive odd integers are integers such as 5 and 7. The larger is 2 plus the smaller.

EXAMPLE 5

The sum of an integer and twice the next consecutive integer is 29. What are the integers? (Consecutive integers are next to each other, such as 3 and 4. The larger is 1 plus the smaller.)

Let $x =$ the first integer. Then $x + 1 =$ the second integer.

$$\underbrace{\text{First integer}}_{x} + \underbrace{\text{twice second integer}}_{2 \quad (x + 1)} = 29. \quad \text{Rewording}$$
$$= 29 \quad \text{Translating}$$

$$x + 2(x + 1) = 29 \quad \text{Parentheses are necessary here.}$$
$$x + 2x + 2 = 29 \quad \text{Using the distributive property}$$
$$3x + 2 = 29$$
$$3x = 27$$
$$x = 9$$
$$x + 1 = 10$$

Check: Our answers are 9 and 10. The sum of 9 and twice 10 is 29. So, the answers check in the original problem.

TRY THIS Translate to an equation and solve.

7. The sum of an even integer and twice the next even integer is 40. (Consecutive even integers are next to each other, such as 6 and 8. The larger is always 2 plus the smaller.) What are the integers?

7. Let $x =$ even integer. Then $x + 2 =$ next even integer, An even integer + twice next even integer $= 40$, $x + 2(x + 2) = 40$, $x + 2(x + 2) = 40$, $x + 2x + 4 = 40$, $3x = 36$, $x = 12$, $x + 2 = 14$, Check: The sum of 12 and twice 14 is 40.

EXAMPLE 6

Translate to an equation and solve.

One third of a number plus one fourth of a number is four more than one half of the number.

Let x = the number.

$\frac{1}{3}$ of the number plus $\frac{1}{4}$ of the number is 4 more than $\frac{1}{2}$ of the number

$\frac{1}{3}\cdot \qquad x \qquad + \frac{1}{4}\cdot \qquad x \qquad = 4 \quad + \quad \frac{1}{2}\cdot \qquad x$

$$\frac{1}{3}x + \frac{1}{4}x = 4 + \frac{1}{2}x$$

$$12\left(\frac{1}{3}x + \frac{1}{4}x\right) = 12\left(4 + \frac{1}{2}x\right)$$

$$4x + 3x = 48 + 6x$$
$$7x = 48 + 6x$$
$$x = 48$$

Check: $\frac{1}{3}$ of 48 is 16, $\frac{1}{4}$ of 48 is 12, and $\frac{1}{2}$ of 48 is 24. 16 plus 12 is 4 more than 24. The number 48 checks in the original equation.

TRY THIS Translate to an equation and solve.

8. The sum of one sixth of a number and one fourth of the number is three less than one half the number.

8. Let x = the number (no.), $\frac{1}{6}$ of the no. $+\frac{1}{4}$ of the no. $=\frac{1}{2}$ of the no. -3, $\frac{1}{6}\cdot x + \frac{1}{4}\cdot x = \frac{1}{2}\cdot x - 3$, $12(\frac{1}{6}x + \frac{1}{4}x) = 12(\frac{1}{2}x - 3)$, $2x + 3x = 6x - 36$, $x = 36$

| **3–4** | |

Exercises

Solve and check.

1. $3(2y - 3) = 27$ ₆
2. $4(2y - 3) = 28$ ₅
3. $40 = 5(3x + 2)$ ₂
4. $9 = 3(5x - 2)$ ₁
5. $2(3 + 4m) - 9 = 45$ ₆
6. $3(5 + 3m) - 8 = 88$ ₉
7. $5r - (2r + 8) = 16$ ₈
8. $6b - (3b + 8) = 16$ ₈
9. $3g - 3 = 3(7 - g)$ ₄
10. $3d - 10 = 5(d - 4)$ ₅
11. $6 - 2(3x - 1) = 2$ ₁
12. $10 - 3(2x - 1) = 1$ ₂
13. $5(d + 4) = 7(d - 2)$ ₁₇
14. $9(t + 2) = 3(t - 2)$ ₋₄
15. $5(x + 2) = 3(x - 2)$ ₋₈
16. $5(y + 4) = 3(y - 2)$ ₋₁₃
17. $8(3t - 2) = 4(7t - 1)$ ₋₃
18. $7(5x - 2) = 6(6x - 1)$ ₋₈

19. $3(r - 6) + 2 = 4(r + 2) - 21$ $_{-3}$

20. $5(t + 3) + 9 = 3(t - 2) + 6$ $_{-12}$

21. $19 - (2x + 3) = 2(x + 3) + x$ $_2$

22. $13 - (2c + 2) = 2(c + 2) + 3c$ $_1$

23. $\frac{1}{4}(8y + 4) - 17 = -\frac{1}{2}(4y - 8)$ $_5$

24. $\frac{1}{3}(6x + 24) - 20 = -\frac{1}{4}(12x - 72)$ $_6$

Solve and check. Clear of fractions or decimals first.

25. $\frac{7}{2}x + \frac{1}{2}x = 3x + \frac{3}{2} + \frac{5}{2}x$ $_{-1}$

26. $\frac{7}{8}x - \frac{1}{4} + \frac{3}{4}x = \frac{1}{16} + x$ $_{\frac{1}{2}}$

27. $\frac{2}{3} + \frac{1}{4}t = \frac{1}{3}$ $_{-\frac{4}{3}}$

28. $-\frac{3}{2} + x = -\frac{5}{6} - \frac{4}{3}$ $_{-\frac{2}{3}}$

29. $\frac{2}{3} + 3y = 5y - \frac{2}{15}$ $_{\frac{2}{5}}$

30. $\frac{1}{2} + 4m = 3m - \frac{5}{2}$ $_{-3}$

31. $\frac{5}{3} + \frac{2}{3}x = \frac{25}{12} + \frac{5}{4}x + \frac{3}{4}$ $_{-2}$

32. $1 - \frac{2}{3}y = \frac{9}{5} - \frac{y}{5} + \frac{3}{5}$ $_{-3}$

33. $2.1x + 45.2 = 3.2 - 8.4x$ $_{-4}$

34. $0.96y - 0.79 = 0.21y + 0.46$ $_{\frac{5}{3}\text{ or }1.67}$

35. $1.03 - 0.62x = 0.71 - 0.22x$ $_{0.8}$

36. $1.7t + 8 - 1.62t = 0.4t - 0.32 + 8$ $_1$

37. $0.42 - 0.03y = 3.33 - y$ $_3$

38. $0.7n - 15 + n = 2n - 8 - 0.4n$ $_{70}$

39. $\frac{2}{7}x + \frac{1}{2}x = \frac{3}{4}x + 1$ $_{28}$

40. $\frac{5}{16}y + \frac{3}{8}y = 2 + \frac{1}{4}y$ $_{\frac{32}{7}}$

41. $\frac{4}{5}x - \frac{3}{4}x = \frac{3}{10}x - 1$ $_4$

42. $\frac{8}{5}y - \frac{2}{3}y = 23 - \frac{1}{15}y$ $_{23}$

Translate to an equation and solve.

43. The sum of two consecutive odd integers is 76. What are the integers? $_{37,\,39}$

44. The sum of two consecutive odd integers is 84. What are the integers? $_{41,\,43}$

45. The sum of two consecutive even integers is 114. What are the integers? $_{56,\,58}$

46. The sum of two consecutive even integers is 106. What are the integers? $_{52,\,54}$

47. The sum of three consecutive integers is 108. What are the integers? $_{35,\,36,\,37}$

48. The sum of three consecutive integers is 126. What are the integers? $_{41,\,42,\,43}$

49. The sum of three consecutive odd integers is 189. What are the integers? $_{61,\,63,\,65}$

50. The sum of three consecutive odd integers is 255. What are the integers? $_{83,\,85,\,87}$

51. The perimeter of a rectangle is 150 cm. The length is 15 cm greater than the width. Find the dimensions. $_{30,\,45}$

52. One angle of a triangle is twice as large as another. The measure of the third angle is 20° greater than that of the smallest angle. How large are the angles? (Remember that the measures of the angles of a triangle add up to 180°.) $_{40,\,80,\,60}$

53. The perimeter of a rectangle is 310 m. The length is 25 m greater than the width. Find the width and length of the rectangle. _{65, 90}

54. The perimeter of a rectangle is 304 cm. The length is 40 cm greater than the width. Find the width and length of the rectangle. _{56, 96}

55. The perimeter of a rectangle is 152 m. The width is 22 m less than the length. Find the width and the length. _{27, 49}

56. The perimeter of a rectangle is 280 m. The width is 26 m less than the length. Find the width and the length. _{57, 83}

57. One angle of a triangle is four times as large as another. The third angle is 45° less than the sum of the other two angles. Find the measure of the smallest angle. _{22.5°}

58. One angle of a triangle is three times as large as another. The third angle is 25° less than the sum of the other two angles. Find the measure of the smallest angle. _{25.625°}

59. One angle of a triangle is three times as large as another. The measure of the third angle is 40° greater than that of the smallest angle. How large are the angles? _{28, 84, 68}

60. One angle of a triangle is 32 times as large as another. The measure of the third angle is 10° greater than that of the smallest angle. How large are the angles? _{5, 160, 15}

Extension

Exercises 61–63 appeared in the famous Rhind papyrus written about 1650 B.C. by Ahmes, the Egyptian scribe.

61. When a number and one fifth of it are added, they sum to 21. Find the number. _{17.5}

62. When a number and one fourth of it are added, they sum to 15. Find the number. ₁₂

63. When a number, one third of the number, and one quarter of it are added, they become 2. Find the number. $\frac{24}{19}$

Solve and check.

64. $7\frac{1}{2}x - \frac{1}{2}x = 3\frac{3}{4}x + 39$ ₁₂

65. $\frac{1}{5}t - 0.4 + \frac{2}{5}t = 0.6 - \frac{1}{10}t$ _{10/7}

66. $\frac{1}{4}(8y + 4) - 17 = -\frac{1}{2}(4y - 8)$ ₅

67. $\frac{1}{3}(6x + 24) - 20 = -\frac{1}{4}(12x - 72)$ ₆

68. $30,000 + 20,000x = 55,000$ $\frac{5}{4}$

69. $25,000(4 + 3x) = 125,000$ $\frac{1}{3}$

Challenge

70. Apples are collected in a basket for six people. One third, one fourth, one eighth and one fifth are given to four people respectively. The fifth person gets ten apples with one apple remaining for the sixth person. Find the original number of apples in the basket. ₁₂₀

We know that many problems can be solved if we begin by translating to an equation. Let's review the steps that we have been using.

1. Choose a variable for the unknown.
2. Translate to an equation.
3. Solve the equation.
4. Check the answer in the original problem.

EXAMPLE 1
Translate to an equation and solve.

Money is invested in a savings account at 11% simple interest. After a year there is $9990 in the account. How much was originally invested?

Let x = the original investment.

$$\underbrace{\text{Original investment}}_{x} \text{ plus interest is } \$9990.$$
$$x \quad + \quad 11\% \, x \quad = \quad 9990$$

$$1x + 0.11x = 9990$$
$$1.11x = 9990$$
$$x = \frac{9990}{1.11}$$
$$x = 9000$$

Check: 11% of 9000 is 990. Adding this to 9000, we get 9990. This checks, so the original investment was $9000.

---

1. Always read the problem carefully.
2. Make a list of the information in the problem.
3. Decide which information is needed to solve the problem.

TRY THIS Translate to an equation and solve.

1. Money is borrowed at 10.5% simple interest. After one year $8287.50 pays off the loan. How much was originally borrowed?

Let x = original amount, original amount + interest = $8287.50, $x + 0.105x =$ 8287.50, $1.105x = 8287.50$, $x = 7500$

EXAMPLE 2

Translate to an equation and solve.

Acme Rent-a-Car rents an intermediate-size car at a daily rate of $19.95 plus 28¢ per mile. A businessperson on a 7-day trip is not to exceed a daily car rental budget of $60. What mileage will allow the businessperson to stay within budget?

Let m = the number of miles driven. (The length of the trip is not needed.)

$19.95 plus 28¢ times number of miles driven is $60.

$$19.95 + 0.28 \cdot m = 60$$

$$19.95 + 0.28m = 60$$
$$0.28m = 40.05 \qquad \text{Adding} -19.95 \text{ on both sides}$$
$$m = \frac{40.05}{0.28}$$
$$m = 143.04 \qquad \text{Rounded to the nearest hundredth}$$

This checks in the original problem. In this case it is an approximation.

TRY THIS Translate to an equation and solve.

2. Acme also rents compact cars which average 35 miles per gallon at a daily rate of $19.95 plus 18¢ per mile. What mileage will allow the businessperson to stay within a budget of $50?

Let m = no. of miles, $19.95 + 0.18 times no. of miles = $50, $19.95 + 0.18 \cdot m = 50$, $0.18m = 30.05$, $m = 166.94$

EXAMPLE 3

Translate to an equation and solve.

After a 20% reduction, an item is on sale for $9600. What was the marked price (the price before reduction)?

Let x = the marked price.

Marked price minus reduction is $9600.

$$x - 20\%x = 9600$$

$$1x - 0.2x = 9600$$
$$(1 - 0.2)x = 9600$$
$$0.8x = 9600$$
$$x = \frac{9600}{0.8}$$
$$x = 12,000$$

Check: 20% of $12,000 is $2400. Subtracting this amount from $12,000 we get $9600. This checks, so the marked price is $12,000.

Translate to an equation and solve.

3. After a 30% reduction, an item is on sale for $8050. What was the marked price (the price before reduction)?

Let x = marked price, Marked price − reduction = $8050, $x − 0.3x = 8050$, $0.7x = 8050$, $x = 11,500$, Check: 30% of $11,500 is $3450. $11,500 minus $3450 is $8050.

3–5

Exercises

Translate to an equation and solve.

1. Money is invested in a savings account at 12% simple interest. After one year there is $6272 in the account. How much was originally invested? $5,600

2. Money to purchase a 4-cylinder car is borrowed at 10% simple interest. After one year $7194 pays off the loan. How much was originally borrowed? $6,540

3. Badger Rent-a-Car rents an intermediate-size car at a daily rate of $21.95 plus 19¢ per mile. A businessperson is not to exceed a daily car rental budget of $70. What mileage will allow the businessperson to stay within budget? 252.9 mi

4. Badger rents compact cars at $18.95 plus 17¢ per mile. What mileage will allow the businessperson to stay within the budget of $70? 300.3 mi

5. After a 40% reduction, a shirt which is $\frac{1}{2}$ cotton and $\frac{1}{2}$ polyester is on sale at $9.60. What was the marked price (the price before reduction)? $16

6. After a 34% reduction, a blouse is on sale at $9.24. What was the marked price? $14

7. The population of the world in 1980 was 4.4 billion. This was a 23% increase over the population in 1970. What was the former population? 3.6 billion

8. The population of the United States in 1980 was 224 million. This was a 48% increase over the population in 1950. What was the former population to the nearest million? 151 million

9. The sum of the interior angles of any polygon of n-sides is $180(n - 2)$. How many sides must a polygon have if the sum of the interior angles is 1440°? 10

10. How many sides must a polygon have if the sum of the interior angles is 2520°? 16

Extension

11. Abraham Lincoln's 1863 Gettysburg Address refers to the year 1776 as "Four score and seven years ago." Write an equation and solve for a score. $4s + 7 = 1863 - 1776, s = 20$

12. One number is 25% of another. The larger number is 12 more than the smaller. What are the numbers? $25\%x = x - 12, x = 16, 25\%x = 4$

13. If the daily rental for a car is \$18.90 and a person must drive 190 miles and stay within a \$55.00 budget, what is the highest price per mile the person can afford? 19¢

14. Jana scored 78 on a test that had 4 seven-point fill-ins and 24 three-point multiple choice questions. She had one fill-in wrong. How many multiple choice did she get right? 19

15. The width of a rectangle is $\frac{3}{4}$ the length. The perimeter of the rectangle becomes 50 cm when the length and width are each increased by 2 cm. Find the length and width. 12 cm, 9 cm

16. A phone company charges \$13.72/month + 50¢/call + 8¢/minute. How much did it cost Helga one month to make 35 calls that totaled 172 minutes? \$44.98

Challenge

17. In a basketball league, the Falcons won 15 out of their first 20 games. How many more games will they have to play where they win only half the time in order to win 60% of the total games? 30

18. In one city, a sales tax of 9% was added to the price of gasoline as registered on the pump. Suppose a driver asked for \$10 worth of regular. The attendant filled the tank until the pump read \$9.10 and charged the driver \$10. Something was wrong. Use algebra to correct the error. $1.09p = 10.00, p = \$9.17$, not \$9.10

19. The buyer of a piano priced at \$2000 is given the choice of paying cash at the time of purchase or \$2150 at the end of one year. What rate of interest is the buyer being charged if payment is made at the end of one year? 7.5%

20. If you receive 7% interest on savings, but 30% tax is charged on savings and interest, how much do you have left from an initial \$1000 deposit? $.7[1000 \cdot 1.07] = \$749$

21. Frank, a storekeeper, goes to the bank to get \$10 worth of change. He requests twice as many quarters as half dollars, twice as many dimes as quarters, three times as many nickels as dimes and no pennies or dollars. How many of each coin did Frank get? 5 half dollars, 10 quarters, 20 dimes, 60 nickels

3—6 Formulas

A formula is a kind of recipe for doing certain calculations. Formulas are often given as equations. A familiar formula from electricity is

$$E = IR.$$

Suppose we know the voltage E and the current I. We wish to calculate the resistance R. We can get R alone on one side, or "solve" the formula for R.

EXAMPLE 1
Solve $E = IR$, for R

$$\frac{1}{I} \cdot E = \frac{1}{I} \cdot IR \quad \text{Multiplying on both sides by } \frac{1}{I}$$

$$\frac{E}{I} = R$$

Multiplying by $\frac{1}{I}$ is the same as dividing by I. The formula now says we can find R by dividing E by I.

TRY THIS

1. Solve $E = IR$, for I. $I = \frac{E}{R}$

Remember, formulas are equations. Use the same principles in solving that you use for any other equation. To see how the principles apply to formulas compare the following three solving problems.

A Solve.

$$5x + 2 = 12$$
$$5x = 12 - 2$$
$$x = \frac{10}{5}$$

B Solve.

$$5x + 2 = 12$$
$$5x = 12 - 2$$
$$x = \frac{12 - 2}{5}$$

C Solve for x.

$$ax + b = c$$
$$ax = c - b$$
$$x = \frac{c - b}{a}$$

In A we solved as we did before. In B we did not carry out the calculations. In C we could not carry out the calculations because we had unknown numbers.

EXAMPLE 2

A formula for the circumference C of a circle with radius r is

$$C = 2\pi r.$$

Solve for r.

$$\frac{1}{2\pi} \cdot C = \frac{1}{2\pi} \cdot 2\pi r \quad \text{Multiplying by } \frac{1}{2\pi} \text{ on both sides}$$

$$\frac{C}{2\pi} = \frac{2\pi}{2\pi} \cdot r$$

$$\frac{C}{2\pi} = r$$

TRY THIS

2. A formula for the circumference C of a circle with diameter d is

$$C = \pi d.$$

Solve for d. $d = \frac{C}{\pi}$

To solve a formula for a given letter, identify the letter, and
1. Multiply on both sides to clear fractions or decimals.
2. Collect like terms on each side, if necessary.
3. Get all terms with the letter to be solved for on one side and all other terms on the other side of the equation.
4. Collect like terms again, if necessary.
5. Solve for the letter in question.

EXAMPLE 3

A formula for the average A of three numbers a, b, and c is

$$A = \frac{a + b + c}{3}.$$

Solve for a.

$$A = \frac{a + b + c}{3}$$

$$3A = a + b + c \quad \text{Multiplying on both sides by 3}$$

$$3A - b - c = a$$

3. A formula for the average A of four numbers a, b, c, and d is

$$A = \frac{a + b + c + d}{4}.$$

Solve for c. $c = 4A - a - b - d$

EXAMPLE 4

A formula for computing the earned run average A of a pitcher who has given up R earned runs in I innings of pitching is

$$A = \frac{9R}{I}.$$

Solve for I.

$$A = \frac{9R}{I}$$

$$AI = 9R \qquad \text{Multiplying on both sides by } I$$

$$I = \frac{9R}{A} \qquad \text{Multiplying on both sides by } \frac{1}{A}$$

TRY THIS

4. A formula for a football player's rushing average r with a total of y yards rushed in n carries of the ball is $r = \frac{y}{n}$.

   Solve for n. $n = \frac{y}{r}$

3–6	

Exercises

Solve.

1. $A = bh$, for b. (an area formula) $\frac{A}{h}$

2. $A = bh$, for h. $\frac{A}{b}$

3. $d = rt$, for r. (a distance formula) $\frac{d}{t}$

4. $d = rt$, for t. $\frac{d}{r}$

5. $I = Prt$, for P. (an interest formula) $\frac{I}{rt}$

6. $I = Prt$, for t. $\frac{I}{Pr}$

7. $F = ma$, for a. (a physics formula) $\frac{F}{m}$

8. $F = ma$, for m. $\frac{F}{a}$

9. $P = 2l + 2w$, for w. (a perimeter formula)

10. $P = 2l + 2w$, for l $\frac{P - 2w}{2}$

11. $A = \pi r^2$, for r^2. (an area formula) $\frac{A}{\pi}$ $\frac{P - 2l}{2}$

12. $A = \pi r^2$, for π. $\frac{A}{r^2}$

13. $A = \frac{1}{2}bh$, for b. (an area formula) $\frac{2A}{h}$

14. $A = \frac{1}{2}bh$, for h. $\frac{2A}{b}$

15. $E = mc^2$, for m. (a relativity formula) $\frac{E}{c^2}$ **16.** $E = mc^2$, for c^2. $\frac{E}{m}$

17. $A = \dfrac{a + b + c}{3}$, for b. $3A - a - c$ **18.** $A = \dfrac{a + b + c}{3}$, for c. $3A - a - b$

19. $v = \dfrac{3k}{t}$, for t. $\frac{3K}{V}$ **20.** $P = \dfrac{ab}{c}$, for c. $\frac{ab}{P}$

A formula to find the horsepower H of an N-cylinder engine is
$$H = \frac{D^2N}{2.5}.$$

21. Solve for D^2. $\frac{2.5H}{N}$ **22.** Solve for N. $\frac{2.5H}{D^2}$

A formula for the area of a sector of a circle is $A = \dfrac{\pi r^2 S}{360}$, where r is the radius and S is the angle measure of the sector.

23. Solve for S. $\frac{360A}{\pi r^2}$ **24.** Solve for r^2. $\frac{360A}{\pi S}$

25. The formula $F = \frac{9}{5}C + 32$ can be used to convert from Celsius temperature C to Farenheit temperature F. Solve for C. $\frac{5}{9}(F - 32)$

Extension
Solve.

26. $ax + b = c$, for b $c - ax$ **27.** $ax + b = c$, for a $\frac{c - b}{a}$

28. $ax + b = 0$, for x $\frac{-b}{a}$ **29.** $A = \dfrac{1}{R}$, for R $\frac{1}{A}$

30. $\dfrac{s}{t} = \dfrac{t}{v}$, for s $\frac{t^2}{v}$ **31.** $\dfrac{a}{b} = \dfrac{c}{d}$, for $\dfrac{a}{c}$ $\frac{b}{d}$

32. The formula $R = -0.00625t + 3.85$ can be used to estimate the world record in the 1500m run t years after 1930. Solve for t. $\frac{R - 3.85}{-0.00625}$, $-160R + 616$

Challenge
Solve.

33. $g = 40n + 20k$, for k $\frac{9}{20} - 2n$ **34.** $r = 2h - \frac{1}{4}f$, for f $8h - 4r$

35. $y = a - ab$, for a $\frac{y}{1 - b}$ **36.** $x = a + b - 2ab$, for a $\frac{x - b}{1 - 2b}$

37. $d = \dfrac{1}{e + f}$, for f $\frac{1}{d} - e$ **38.** $x = \dfrac{\left(\dfrac{y}{z}\right)}{\left(\dfrac{z}{t}\right)}$, for y $\frac{xz^2}{t}$

39. $m = ax^2 + bx + c$, for b $\frac{m - ax^2 - c}{x}$ **40.** If $a^2 = b^2$, does $a = b$? No, a may be $-b$.

41. If $P = 2a + 2b$, when P doubles, do a and b both double? Yes

The ratio of two quantities is their quotient. For instance, the ratio of the age of a 27-year old parent to that of a 3-year old child is

$$\frac{27 \text{ years}}{3 \text{ years}}, \text{ or } 9$$

An equation which says that two ratios are equal is called a proportion. These are proportions.

$$\frac{2}{3} = \frac{6}{9} \qquad \frac{5}{7} = \frac{25}{35} \qquad \frac{x}{24} = \frac{2}{3} \qquad \frac{9}{y} = \frac{32}{81}$$

Since proportions are equations we can use equation solving principles to solve them.

EXAMPLE 1

Solve the proportion $\frac{x}{63} = \frac{2}{9}$.

First clear of fractions. The least common denominator is 63. We multiply on both sides by 63.

$$63 \cdot \frac{x}{63} = 63 \cdot \frac{2}{9}$$
$$x = 14$$

EXAMPLE 2

Solve the proportion $\frac{65}{10} = \frac{13}{x}$.

To clear of fractions we multiply by $10x$.

$$10x \cdot \frac{65}{10} = 10x \cdot \frac{13}{x}$$
$$65x = 130$$
$$x = 2$$

TRY THIS Solve each proportion.

1. $\frac{3}{5} = \frac{12}{y}$ 20   2. $\frac{1}{2} = \frac{x}{5}$ $\frac{5}{2}$ 3. $\frac{m}{4} = \frac{7}{6}$ $\frac{14}{3}$

Solving Problems

Some problems can be solved by first translating to a proportion.

EXAMPLE 3

The property tax on a house is $8 per $1000 assessed evaluation. What is the tax on a $65,000 house?

Think: $8 is to $1000 as x dollars is to $65,000. This translates to the following proportion.

$$\frac{8}{1000} = \frac{x}{65,000}$$

$$65,000 \cdot \frac{8}{1000} = 65,000 \cdot \frac{x}{65,000} \qquad \text{clearing of fractions}$$

$$520 = x$$

The tax is $520.

TRY THIS Translate to a proportion and solve.

4. The scale on a map says that 0.5 cm represents 25 kilometers. On the map the measurement between two cities is 5 cm. How far apart are the two cities? 250 km

---

3–7	

Exercises

Solve these proportions.

1. $\frac{y}{3} = \frac{9}{27}$ 1

2. $\frac{7}{8} = \frac{m}{4}$ $\frac{7}{2}$

3. $\frac{9}{x} = \frac{2}{3}$ $\frac{27}{2}$

4. $\frac{25}{75} = \frac{1}{x}$ 3

5. $\frac{2}{y} = \frac{5}{9}$ $\frac{18}{5}$

6. $\frac{16}{m} = \frac{1}{4}$ 64

7. $\frac{8}{5} = \frac{40}{y}$ 25

8. $\frac{12}{15} = \frac{t}{5}$ 4

9. $\frac{y}{4} = \frac{5}{8}$ $\frac{5}{2}$

10. $\frac{3}{8} = \frac{12}{x}$ 32

11. $\frac{5}{x} = \frac{9}{11}$ $\frac{55}{9}$

12. $\frac{2}{7} = \frac{5}{y}$ $\frac{35}{2}$

Translate to a proportion, and solve.

13. A car travels 150 kilometers on 12 liters of gasoline. How many liters of gasoline are needed to travel 500 kilometers? 40

14. A baseball pitcher strikes out an average of 3.6 batters per 9 innings. At this rate how many would the pitcher strike out in 315 innings? 126

15. A watch loses 2 minutes every 15 hours. How much time will it lose in 2 hours? $\frac{4}{15}$ min

Extension

16. On a map, 1 inch represents 3.27 km. It is 24.5 inches between two cities on the map. How far apart are the cities? 80.1 km

17. An automobile engine crankshaft revolves 3000 times per
   · minute. How long does it take to revolve 50 times? $\frac{1}{60}$ min, or 1 sec

18. A scale model of a ship is in ratio 1:250. How tall is the model if the actual ship is 87 feet tall? 0.348 ft or 4.18 in.

19. Frosted Fruity Cereal is 45% sugar. Cafco Cola is 4% sugar. How much cola has the same amount of sugar as one ounce of cereal? $\frac{45}{4} = \frac{x}{1}$, $x = 11\frac{3}{4}$ oz

20. A refrigerator goes on a defrost cycle one hour for every 14 hours of operation. How long does it defrost in a week? $\frac{1}{14} = \frac{x}{24.7}$, $x = 12$ hr

Challenge

21. How many weeks are in a 30-day month? How many are in a 31-day month? How many are in a 365-day year? A 366-day year? $4\frac{2}{7}$, $4\frac{3}{7}$, $52\frac{1}{7}$, $52\frac{2}{7}$

22. Jill tries to guess the number of marbles in an 8-gallon jar and win a moped. She knows there are 128 ounces in a gallon, and she finds that 46 marbles fill a 6-ounce jar. How many should she guess? 7851

PRIME FACTORS

A *prime* number is a whole number greater than 1 whose only positive factors are 1 and itself. Any whole number greater than 1 can be written as a product of primes. These are called the number's *prime factors*.

1. $2 \times 3 \times 5 \times 7$
2. $2 \times 3^3 \times 7$
3. $3 \times 5^2 \times 11$
4. $2^3 \times 5^2$
5. $2^{11} \times 3$

Factor 60 into its prime factors.

$$60 = 2 \times 30$$
$$= 2 \times 2 \times 15$$
$$= 2 \times 2 \times 3 \times 5$$

$2 \times 2 \times 3 \times 5$ is called the *prime factorization* of 60. There is only one way to factor 60 into its prime factors. We can write it as $2^2 \times 3 \times 5$.

Find the prime factorization of of 897.

$$897 = 3 \times 299$$
To factor 299, try increasingly larger primes. It is not divisible by 2, 3, 5, 7, or 11. It is, however, divisible by 13.

$$897 = 3 \times 13 \times 23$$

Find the prime factorizations for the following.

1. 210   2. 378   3. 825
4. 1000   5. 6144

3–8   Proofs in Solving Equations (Optional)

In Section 2–10 we used number properties or axioms to prove theorems. In this section we use principles or axioms to prove equations.

If–then Statements

If–then statements are important in mathematics and elsewhere. Here are some examples.

If $x = 1$, then $x + 1 = 2$.
If $x < 5$, then $x < 10$.
If an animal is a cat, then it has four legs.
· If a figure is a square, then it has four sides.

In a statement
  If A then B,
A is a sentence that follows *if* and B is a sentence that follows *then*. The sentence A is called the antecedent and the sentence B is called the consequent.

   To prove an if–then statement, we *suppose* or *assume* that the antecedent A is true. Then we try to show that it leads to B. That allows us to conclude that the statement *If A then B* is true. Solving equations provides a good example of proving if–then statements.

EXAMPLE 1
Prove the following statement.

    If $5x + 4 = 24$, then $x = 4$.

We first assume that $5x + 4 = 24$ is true. We call such an assumption a hypothesis. Then we use equation solving principles to arrive at $x = 4$. We use a column proof to list each statement and the principle or axiom which allows us to make this statement.

1. $5x + 4 = 24$	1. Hypothesis (assumed true)
2. $5x = 20$	2. Using the addition principle
3. $x = 4$	3. Using the multiplication principle
4. If $5x + 4 = 24$, then $x = 4$.	4. Statements 1-3

Here is a proof written in paragraph form called a narrative proof.

Suppose that $5x + 4 = 24$ is true. Then, by the addition principle, adding -4 on both sides, it follows that $5x = 20$. By the multiplication principle, multiplying on both sides by $\frac{1}{5}$, we then obtain $x = 4$. Therefore, if $5x + 4 = 24$, then $x = 4$, which was to be shown.

TRY THIS Prove the following statement. Write both a column proof and a narrative proof.

1. If $3x + 5 = 20$, then $x = 5$.

Converses

From a statement *If A then B,* we can make a new statement by interchanging the antecedent and consequent. We get

If *B* then *A.*

The two statements are called converses of each other.

EXAMPLES

Write the converse of each statement.

2. If $x = 2$, then $x + 3 = 5$.   The converse is: If $x + 3 = 5$, then $x = 2$.

3. If $x < 5$, then $x < 10$.   The converse is: If $x < 10$, then $x < 5$.

4. If an animal is a cat, then it has four legs.   The converse is: If an animal has four legs, then it is a cat.

TRY THIS Write the converse of each statement.

2. If $3x + 7 = 37$, then $x = 10$. If $x = 10$, then $3x + 7 = 37$.

3. If $x > 15$, then $x > 12$. If $x > 12$, then $x > 15$.

What does an if–then statement tell us? Consider the statement.

If $x < 5$, then $x < 10$.

This statement is true. It tells us that any replacement for x that makes the antecedent true, also must make the consequent true. It does *not* tell us what happens if the antecedent is false. Let's try some substitutions.

	Antecedent	Consequent
x	$x < 5$	$x < 10$
3	$3 < 5$ true	$3 < 10$ true
6	$6 < 5$ false	$6 < 10$ true
15	$15 < 5$ false	$15 < 10$ false

Now let's look at the converse: If $x < 10$, then $x < 5$.

This converse is false.

	Antecedent	Consequent
x	$x < 10$	$x < 5$
20	$20 < 10$ false	$20 < 5$ false
7	$7 < 10$ true	$7 < 5$ false
3	$3 < 10$ true	$3 < 5$ true

For the replacement 7, we have a true antecedent and a false consequent. That can happen only when the if–then statement is *false*. Some true if–then statements have true converses. Some have false converses. We have just seen an example in which the converse is not true. Consider another statement:

$$\text{If } 5x + 4 = 24, \text{ then } x = 4.$$

We know this statement is true, because we proved it in Example 1. Therefore, any number that makes $5x + 4 = 24$ true must also make $x = 4$ true. Let's prove the converse.

EXAMPLE 5
Prove: If $x = 4$, then $5x + 4 = 24$. We reverse the steps of Example 1.

1. $x = 4$	1. Hypothesis
2. $5x = 20$	2. Using the multiplication principle
3. $5x + 4 = 24$	3. Using the addition principle
4. If $x = 4$, then $5x + 4 = 24$.	4. Statements 1-3

Any number that makes $x = 4$ true must also make $5x + 24$ true.

TRY THIS

4. In Try This 1, you proved that If $3x + 5 = 20$, then $x = 5$. Prove the converse by reversing the steps.

Solving Equations

In Example 1 we proved If $5x + 4 = 24$, then $x = 4$. Thus, we know that any number making $5x + 4 = 24$ true must also make $x = 4$ true. There is only one number that makes $x = 4$ true, the number 4. Do we know that 4 is a solution of the equation $5x + 4 = 24$? To be sure of that we could prove the converse, as we did in Example 5. Then we would know that any number making $x = 4$ true will also make $5x + 4$ true, and so 4 is a solution of the equation $5x + 4 = 24$.

EXAMPLE 6

Solve $4x + 5 = 29$ by proving the statement and its converse.

a. We prove: If $4x + 5 = 29$, then $x = ?$

1. $4x + 5 = 29$	1. Hypothesis
2. $4x = 24$	2. Using the addition principle
3. $x = 6$	3. Using the multiplication principle
4. If $4x + 5 = 29$, then $x = 6$	4. Statements 1-3

b. We prove: If $x = 6$, then $4x + 5 = 29$.

1. $x = 6$	1. Hypothesis
2. $4x = 24$	2. Using the multiplication principle
3. $4x + 5 = 29$	3. Using the addition principle
4. If $x = 6$, then $4x + 5 = 29$	4. Statements 1-3

There is just one solution, the number 6.

EXAMPLE 7

Solve the equation $7x - 1 = 34$ by proving the statement and then substituting.

a. We prove: If $7x - 1 = 34$, then $x = ?$

1. $7x - 1 = 34$	1. Hypothesis
2. $7x = 35$	2. Using the addition principle
3. $x = 5$	3. Using the multiplication principle
4. If $7x - 1 = 34$, then $x = 5$.	4. Statements 1-3

b. We check by substituting.

$$
\begin{array}{c|c}
7x - 1 = 34 & \\
\hline
7(5) - 1 & 34 \\
34 &
\end{array}
$$

There is just one solution, the number 5.

5. Solve $6y - 12 = 30$ by proving a statement and its converse.

6. Solve $8x + 17 = 81$ by proving a statement and substituting.

3–8	

Exercises

Prove these statements. Write both column and narrative proofs.

1. If $8x - 12 = 68$, then $x = 10$.   **2.** If $3x + 5 = 32$, then $x = 9$.

3. If $\frac{x}{2} + 3 = 15$, then $x = 24$.   **4.** If $0.5x + 0.25 = 1.75$, then $x = 3$.

Write the converse of each statement.

5. If $x + 3 = 9$, then $x = 6$.   **6.** If $y < 5$, then $y < 23$.

<small>5. If $x = 6$, then $x + 3 = 9$.</small>
<small>6. If $y < 23$, then $y < 5$.</small>

7. If it is snowing, then schools are closed. <small>If schools are closed, then it is snowing.</small>

8. If the sky is blue, then there is no rain. <small>If there is no rain, then the sky is blue.</small>

9.–12. Prove the converse of each statement in Exercises 1–4.

Solve each equation by proving the statement and its converse.

13. $3x + 5 = 14$ <small>($x = 3$)</small>   **14.** $4x + 8 = 19$ <small>($x = \frac{11}{4}$)</small>

15. $2m - 5 = 17$ <small>($m = 11$)</small>   **16.** $3y - 4 = 22$ <small>($y = \frac{26}{3}$)</small>

17. $\frac{x}{2} - 4 = 8$ <small>($x = 16$)</small>   **18.** $\frac{a}{3} + 6 = 9$ <small>($a = 9$)</small>

19. $2(y - 1) - 7 = 5$ <small>($y = 7$)</small>   **20.** $5(x - 2) + 8 = 3$ <small>($x = 1$)</small>

Solve each equation by proving a statement and substituting.

21. $14 + 5m = -76$ <small>($m = -18$)</small>   **22.** $8 + 5(y + 3) = 53$ <small>($y = 6$)</small>

23. $2(x - 3) - x = -2$ <small>($x = 4$)</small>   **24.** $3(y + 4) - 2y = -5$ <small>($y = -17$)</small>

Extension

Find values for which the converse is false.

25. If $a = b$, then $|a| = |b|$.   **26.** If $a = b$, then $a^2 = b^2$.

27. If $a > 0$, then $a + 3 > 0$.   **28.** If $st \neq 0$, then $t \neq 0$.

<small>25. a is $-b$
26. a is $-b$

27. Any a between -3 and 0
28. $s = 0, t \neq 0$.</small>

Challenge

29. Prove: If $x = 1$, then $x \cdot x = x$. Then show that the converse is not true, by finding a number that makes $x \cdot x = x$ true, but makes $x = 1$ false.

<small>$x = 1$, Hypothesis, $x \cdot x = 1 \cdot x$, Mult. prin., $x \cdot x = x$, Prop. of 1; If $x = 0$, $x \cdot x = x$ is true but $0 = 1$ is false.</small>

CAREERS/Space Travel

With the successful first flight of the space shuttle *Columbia* in April of 1981, space travel entered a new era. Previously, flights into space required millions of dollars' worth of equipment, since each rocket could be used only once. The space shuttle proved that designing a vehicle to travel into space again and again was a workable idea.

The success of the space shuttle could not have been achieved without the careful use of mathematical formulas. Mathematics is the language of space travel. Numbers in algebraic equations tell astronauts and ground personnel about the speed and direction of the moving spacecraft. Numerical readings from instruments tell of the astronaut's health during the voyage. Temperature readings are carefully watched by flight engineers; the spacecraft must protect the astronauts from the extreme cold of outer space as well as from the tremendous heat generated by friction during re-entry into the atmosphere.

There is little room for error in any activity associated with space travel. Even workers in nontechnical jobs must know the meaning of the numbers involved in each task for which they have responsibility. A worker who does not pay attention to gauges while filing fuel tanks with liquid oxygen and liquid hydrogen endangers many lives.

Exercises

The problems that follow are similar to problems that people involved in the aerospace industry may be called upon to solve.

1. In rocket launchings, the letter T is used to represent the scheduled time for liftoff. Thus, $T - 7$ seconds means 7 seconds before liftoff; $T + 2$ seconds means 2 seconds after liftoff. The following list gives time, in terms of T, that certain tasks are to be accomplished by the ground crew. The numbers represent time in seconds. Place these in order from earliest to latest tasks. (See Section 2–1.)

$T + 12, T - 20, T - 2,$
$T + 5, T + 2, T - 4$

$T - 20, T - 4, T - 2,$
$T + 2, T + 5, T + 12$

2. The president of an aerospace company is reviewing monthly budget figures for a major project. (Each month's budget is kept separate from all other months.) Here are the data for 6 months: January, $16 million over budget; February, $2 million over; March, $11.5 million under budget; April, $4 million under; May, $6.5 million over; June, $9 million under. Find the total amount that the aerospace company is over or under budget after these six months. (See Section 2–3.)

3. As long as interior temperatures remain 10°C below the maximum level which equipment has been designed to withstand, engineers do not worry about failure of space equipment. Use an algebraic expression to express the Fahrenheit equivalent of this safe temperature. (If the temperature is C degrees Celsius, it is $\frac{9}{5}C + 32$ degrees Fahrenheit.) (See Section 2–7.) 50°F

2. 0; The company is neither over or under budget

Review the material in the chapter. Then see how you have done by trying these review exercises. If you miss an exercise, restudy the indicated lesson.

3–1   Solve using the addition principle.

1. $x + 5 = -17$ -22 2. $x - 11 = 14$ 25 3. $n - 7 = -6$ 1

3–1   Solve by translating to an equation.

4. A color TV sold for $629 in May. This was $38 more than the January cost. Find the January cost. $591

3–2   Solve using the multiplication principle.

5. $-8x = -56$ 7 6. $15x = -35$ $-\frac{7}{3}$ 7. $-\frac{x}{4} = 48$ -192

3–2   Translate to an equation and solve.

8. Selma gets a $4 commission for each appliance that she sells. One week she got $108 in commissions. How many appliances did she sell? 27

3–3   Solve.

9. $5t + 9 = 3t - 1$ -5 10. $7x - 6 = 25x$ $-\frac{1}{3}$

11. $\frac{1}{4}x - \frac{5}{8} = \frac{3}{8}$ 4 12. $14y = 23y - 17 - 10$ 3

3–3   Translate to an equation and solve.

13. An 8-m board is cut into two pieces. One piece is 2 m longer than the other. How long are the pieces? 3 m, 5 m

14. If 14 is added to three times a certain number, the result is 41. Find the number 9

3–4   Solve.

15. $4(x + 3) = 36$ 6 16. $3(5x - 7) = -66$ -3

17. $8(x - 2) = 5(x + 4)$ 12 18. $-5x + 3(x + 8) = 16$ 4

3–4   Translate to an equation and solve.

19. The sum of two consecutive odd integers is 116. Find the integers. 57, 59

20. The perimeter of a rectangle is 56 cm. The width is 6 cm less than the length. Find the width and the length. Width is 11 cm; length is 17 cm.

3–5

21. After a 30% reduction, an item is on sale for $154. What was the marked price (the price before reducing)? $220

22. Karen's salary is $30,000. That is a 15% increase over her previous salary. What was her previous salary (to the nearest dollar)? $26,087

3–6   Solve the given formula for the given variable.

23. $V = \frac{1}{3}Bh$ for h.   **24.** $V = Bh$ for B.   **25.** $V = \frac{1}{3}Ar$ for A.

23. $h = \frac{3V}{B}$

24. $B = \frac{V}{h}$

25. $A = \frac{3V}{r}$

3–7   Translate to a proportion and solve.

26. The winner of an election for class president won by a vote of 3 to 2, with 324 votes. How many votes did the loser get? 216

27. A student traveled 234 kilometers in 14 days. At this rate, how far would the student travel in 42 days? 702 km

---

CHAPTER 3   Test

Solve.

1. $x + 7 = 15$ 8   **2.** $t - 9 = 17$ 26

3. $3x = -18$ −6   **4.** $-7x = -28$ 4

5. $3t + 7 = 2t - 5$ −12   **6.** $\frac{1}{2}x - \frac{3}{5} = \frac{2}{5}$ 2

7. $3(x + 2) = 27$ 7   **8.** $-3x + 6(x + 4) = 9$ −5

Translate to an equation and solve.

9. The perimeter of a rectangle is 36 cm. The length is 4 cm greater than the width. Find the width and length. 7 cm, 11 cm

10. Money is invested in a savings account at 12% simple interest. After one year there is $840 in the account. How much was originally invested? $750

Solve the formulas for the given letter.

11. Solve $A = 2\pi rh$ for r.   **12.** Solve $b = \frac{2A}{h}$ for A.   11. $r = \frac{A}{2\pi h}$ 12. $A = \frac{1}{2}bh$

13. A sample of 184 light bulbs contained 6 defective bulbs. At this rate how many would you expect in 1288 bulbs? ₄₂

Challenge

14. A movie theater had a certain number of tickets to give away. Five people got the tickets. The first got $\frac{1}{3}$ of the tickets, the second got $\frac{1}{4}$ of the tickets, and the third got $\frac{1}{5}$ of the tickets. The fourth person got eight tickets and there were five tickets left for the fifth person. Find the total number of tickets given away. $\frac{1}{3}n + \frac{1}{4}n + \frac{1}{5}n + 8 + 5 = n, n = 60$

CHAPTERS 1–3   Cumulative Review

1–1   Evaluate.

1. $\dfrac{y-x}{4}$ for $y = 12$ and $x = 6$. ₁.₅ **2.** $\dfrac{3x}{y}$ for $x = 5$ and $y = 4$. ₃.₇₅

1–1   Write an algebraic expression for each of the following.

3. four less than twice w ₂w ₋ ₄   **4.** three times the sum of x and y ₃(x + y)

1–2   Simplify.

5. $\dfrac{9xy}{12yz}$ $\frac{3x}{4z}$ **6.** $\dfrac{108x}{72xy}$ $\frac{3}{2y}$

1–3

7. Evaluate $x^3 - 3$ for $x = 3$. ₂₄

1–4

8. Evaluate $(x - 2)(x + 1)$ for $x = 6$. ₂₈

9. Use the commutative and associative laws to write an equivalent expression: $2(x + y) + 3$. Ex. 3 + (y + x)2

1–5   Multiply.

10. $5(3x + 5y + 2z)$ **11.** $8(2w + 4x + 3y)$ 10. 15x + 25y + 10z
11. 16w + 32 + 24y

1–5   Factor.

12. $56x + 16y$ 8(7x + 2y)   **13.** $64 + 18x + 24y$ 2(32 + 9x + 12y)

1–5   Collect like terms.

14. $9b + 18y + 6b + 4y$ **15.** $3y + 4z + 6z + 6y$ 14. 15b + 22y
15. 18y + 10z

1–6   Solve.

16. $x + 1.75 = 6.25$ 4.5   **17.** $y + \frac{3}{4} = \frac{5}{2}$ 1.75

2–1   Use $<$ or $>$ to write a true sentence.

18. $-4 \quad\quad -6$ >   **19.** $-5 \quad\quad 2$ <

2–3   Add.

19. $-6.7 + 2.3 - 4.8$ **20.** $-\frac{1}{6} + \frac{4}{3} - \frac{7}{6}$ 19. −9.2
20. 0

2–4   Simplify.

21. $-2 - 4x - 6x + 5$ **22.** $6 - (-7x) - 5 - 6x$ **23.** $7 - 2x - (-5x) - 8$
21. 3 − 10x
22. 1 + x
23. −1 + 3x

2–5   Multiply.

24. $-\frac{5}{8}\left(-\frac{4}{3}\right)$ $\frac{5}{6}$ **25.** $(-7)(5)(-6)(-0.5)$ −105

2–6   Divide.

26. $\frac{-10.8}{36}$ **27.** $-\frac{4}{5} \div \frac{25}{-8}$ **28.** $\frac{8.1}{-90}$ 26. −0.3   27. $\frac{32}{125}$ 28. −0.09

2–7   Multiply.

29. $4(-3x - 2)$ **30.** $-6(2y - 4x)$ **31.** $-5(-x - 1)$ 29. −12x − 8
30. −12y + 24x
31. 5x + 5

2–7   Factor.

32. $16y - 56$ **33.** $-2x - 8$ **34.** $5a - 15b + 25$ 32. 8(2y − 7)
33. 2(−x − 4) or −2(x + 4)
34. 5(a − 3b + 5)

2–7   Collect like terms.

35. $-4d - 6a + 3a - 5d + 1$ **36.** $3.2x + 2.9y - 5.8x - 8.1y$ 35. −9d − 3a + 1
36. −2.6x − 5.2y

2–8   Simplify.

37. $-3x - (-x + y)$ **38.** $-3(x - 2) - 4x$ **39.** $10 - 2(5 - 4x)$ 37. −2x − y
38. −7x + 6
39. 8x

2–9   Translate to an equation and solve.

40. What percent of 60 is 18? 30% **41.** Two is four percent of what number? 50

3–1 to 3–7   Solve.

42. $-2.6 + x = 8.3$ 10.9 **43.** $4\frac{1}{2} + y = 8\frac{1}{3}$ $3\frac{5}{6}$
44. $-\frac{3}{4}x = 36$ −48   **45.** $-2.2y = -26.4$ 12   **46.** $5.8x = -35.96$ −6.2

47. $-4x + 3 = 15$ **48.** $-3x + 5 = -8x - 7$ **49.** $4y - 4 + y = 6y + 20 - 4y$

50. $-3(x - 2) = -15$ **51.** $\frac{1}{3}x - \frac{5}{6} = \frac{1}{2} + 2x$ **52.** $-3.7x + 6.2 = -7.3x - 5.8$

53. Money is invested in a savings account at 12% simple interest. After one year there is $1680 in the account. How much was originally invested?

54. A car uses 32 liters of gas to travel 450 kilometers. How many liters would be required to drive 800 kilometers (to the nearest tenth)?

Ready for Polynomials?

1–5, 2–7 Multiply.

1. $3(s + t + w)$ **2.** $-7(x + 4)$ 1. $3s + 3t + 3w$
2. $-7x - 28$

1–5 Collect like terms.

3. $2x + 8y + 7x + 5y$ **4.** $x + 0.73x$ 3. $9x + 13y$
4. $1.73x$

2–3 Add.

5. $6 + (-9)$ -3 **6.** $-2 + (-8)$ -10

2–3 Find the additive inverse of each number.

7. 4 -4 **8.** -9 9

2–3

9. Simplify: $-(-6)$. 6

2–4 Solve.

10. $-3 - 9$ -12 **11.** $7 - (-5)$ 12

2–5 Multiply.

12. $(-6)(-5)$ 30 **13.** $-\frac{1}{2} \cdot \frac{5}{8}$ $-\frac{5}{16}$

2–8

14. Rename the additive inverse without parentheses: $-(4x - 7y + 2)$. $-4x + 7y - 2$

2–8

15. Remove parentheses and simplify: $5y - 8 - (9y - 6)$. $-4y - 2$

4

Polynomials

Multiplying Using Exponents

We know that an expression like a^3 means $a \cdot a \cdot a$. We also know that $a^1 = a$ and $a^0 = 1$ when $a \neq 0$. Now consider an expression like $a^3 \cdot a^2$.

$$a^3 \cdot a^2 \text{ means } (a \cdot a \cdot a)(a \cdot a)$$

Since an exponent tells how many times we use a base as a factor, then $(a \cdot a \cdot a)(a \cdot a) = a^5$. Notice that the exponent in a^5 is the sum of those in $a^3 \cdot a^2$. Likewise $b^4 \cdot b^3 = (b \cdot b \cdot b \cdot b)(b \cdot b \cdot b) = b^7$. Again, the exponent in b^7 is the sum of those in $b^4 \cdot b^3$. Adding the exponents gives the correct result.

For any number a and any whole numbers m and n,
$a^m \cdot a^n = a^{m+n}$.

> (When multiplying with exponential notation, we can add the exponents if the bases are the same.)

EXAMPLES
Multiply and simplify.

1. $8^4 \cdot 8^3 = 8^{4+3}$
   $= 8^7$

2. $x^2 \cdot x^9 = x^{2+9}$
   $= x^{11}$

3. $(2x)^5 \cdot (2x)^{10} \cdot (2x)^3 = (2x)^{5+10+3}$
   $= (2x)^{18}$

4. $y^1 \cdot y^0 \cdot y^{12} = y^{13}$

TRY THIS Multiply and simplify.

1. $y^2 \cdot y^3$ $\quad _{y^5}$
2. $(4y)^3 \cdot (4y)^4$ $\quad _{(4y)^7}$
3. $a^0 \cdot a^{13} \cdot a^2$ $\quad _{a^{15}}$

Dividing Using Exponents

What happens when we divide using exponential notation? Look at these examples.

EXAMPLES

5. $\dfrac{4^5}{4^2} = \dfrac{4 \cdot 4 \cdot 4 \cdot 4 \cdot 4}{4 \cdot 4}$

$= 4 \cdot 4 \cdot 4 \cdot \dfrac{4 \cdot 4}{4 \cdot 4}$

$= 4 \cdot 4 \cdot 4$

$= 4^3$

Note that the exponent in 4^3 is the difference of those in $4^5 \div 4^2$. That is, $5 - 2 = 3$.

6. $\dfrac{9^3}{9^6} = \dfrac{9 \cdot 9 \cdot 9}{9 \cdot 9 \cdot 9 \cdot 9 \cdot 9 \cdot 9}$

$= \dfrac{9 \cdot 9 \cdot 9}{9 \cdot 9 \cdot 9} \cdot \dfrac{1}{9 \cdot 9 \cdot 9}$

$= \dfrac{1}{9^3}$

Once again, the exponent is the difference, namely $6 - 3$.

7. $\dfrac{5^3}{5^3} = \dfrac{5 \cdot 5 \cdot 5}{5 \cdot 5 \cdot 5} = 1$

Here the exponent is $3 - 3$ or 0 and 5^0 is 1. These examples suggest the following rule in which we subtract exponents.

For any nonzero number a and any whole numbers m and n,

$\dfrac{a^m}{a^n} = a^{m-n}$ if $m > n$; $\dfrac{a^m}{a^n} = \dfrac{1}{a^{n-m}}$ if $n > m$; $\dfrac{a^m}{a^n} = 1$ if $m = n$.

EXAMPLES
Divide and simplify.

8. $\dfrac{6^5}{6^3} = 6^{5-3}$

$= 6^2$

9. $\dfrac{19^5}{19^8} = \dfrac{1}{19^{8-5}}$

$= \dfrac{1}{19^3}$

10. $\dfrac{t^3}{t^{12}} = \dfrac{1}{t^{12-3}}$

$= \dfrac{1}{t^9}$

11. $\dfrac{m^9}{m^9} = m^{9-9}$

$= m^0$

$= 1$

TRY THIS Divide and simplify.

4. $\dfrac{7^{13}}{7^4}$ 7^9 **5.** $\dfrac{x^8}{x^{16}}$ $\frac{1}{x^8}$ **6.** $\dfrac{r^9}{r^9}$ 1 **7.** $\dfrac{y^2}{y^6}$ $\frac{1}{y^4}$

Raising a Power to a Power

Next, consider an expression like $(3^2)^4$. In this case, we are raising the second power of 3 to the fourth power.

$$
\begin{aligned}
(3^2)^4 &= (3^2)(3^2)(3^2)(3^2) \\
&= (3 \cdot 3)(3 \cdot 3)(3 \cdot 3)(3 \cdot 3) \\
&= 3^8
\end{aligned}
$$

Notice that in this case we could have multiplied the exponents.

$$(3^2)^4 = 3^{2 \cdot 4} = 3^8$$

Likewise, $(y^8)^3 = (y^8)(y^8)(y^8) = y^{24}$. Once again we could have multiplied the exponents.

$$(y^8)^3 = y^{8 \cdot 3} = y^{24}$$

> For any number a and any whole numbers m and n, $(a^m)^n = a^{mn}$. (To raise a power to a power we multiply the exponents.)

EXAMPLES

Simplify.

12. $(3^5)^4 = 3^{5 \cdot 4} = 3^{20}$ **13.** $(y^5)^7 = y^{5 \cdot 7} = y^{35}$

TRY THIS Simplify.

8. $(5^9)^6$ 5^{54} **9.** $(n^8)^3$ n^{24}

Sometimes there may be several factors inside the parentheses.

> For any numbers a and b and any whole number n, $(ab)^n = a^n \cdot b^n$. (To find a power of a product we find the power of each factor and multiply the exponents.)

EXAMPLES

Simplify.

14. $(3x^2)^3 = (3x^2)(3x^2)(3x^2)$
$= 3 \cdot 3 \cdot 3 \cdot x^2 \cdot x^2 \cdot x^2$
$= 3^3 \cdot (x^2)^3$
$= 27x^6$

15. $(5x^3y^5z^2)^4 = 5^4 \cdot x^{12} \cdot y^{20} \cdot z^8$
$= 625x^{12}y^{20}z^8$

16. $(-5x^4y^3)^3 = (-5)^3(x^4)^3(y^3)^3$
$= -125x^{12}y^9$ Multiplying the exponents

17. $[(-x)^{25}]^2 = (-x)^{50}$
$= (-1 \cdot x)^{50}$ Using the property of -1
$= (-1)^{50}x^{50}$ An even number of negative
$= 1 \cdot x^{50}$ factors gives a positive product.
$= x^{50}$

TRY THIS   Simplify.

10. $(4y^3)^4$ **11.** $(3x^4y^7z^6)^5$ **12.** $(-7x^9y^6)^2$ **13.** $[(-y)^{15}]^3$

10. $256y^{12}$
11. $243x^{20}y^{35}z^{30}$
12. $49x^{18}y^{12}$
13. $-y^{45}$

4–1

Exercises

Multiply and simplify.

1. $2^4 \cdot 2^3$ 2^7 **2.** $3^5 \cdot 3^2$ 3^7 **3.** $8^5 \cdot 8^9$ 8^{14} **4.** $n^3 \cdot n^{20}$ n^{23}

5. $x^4 \cdot x^3$ x^7 **6.** $y^7 \cdot y^9$ y^{16} **7.** $9^{17} \cdot 9^{21}$ 9^{38} **8.** $t^0 \cdot t^{16}$ t^{16}

9. $(3y)^4(3y)^8$ $(3y)^{12}$ **10.** $(2t)^8(2t)^{17}$ $(2t)^{25}$ **11.** $(7y)^1(7y)^{16}$ $(7y)^{17}$ **12.** $(8x)^0(8x)^1$ $8x$

Divide and simplify.

13. $\dfrac{7^5}{7^2}$ 7^3 **14.** $\dfrac{4^7}{4^3}$ 4^4 **15.** $\dfrac{8^{12}}{8^6}$ 8^6 **16.** $\dfrac{9^{14}}{9^2}$ 9^{12} **17.** $\dfrac{y^9}{y^5}$ y^4

18. $\dfrac{x^{12}}{x^{11}}$ x **19.** $\dfrac{16^2}{16^8}$ $\dfrac{1}{16^6}$ **20.** $\dfrac{5^4}{5^{10}}$ $\dfrac{1}{5^6}$ **21.** $\dfrac{m^6}{m^{12}}$ $\dfrac{1}{m^6}$ **22.** $\dfrac{p^4}{p^5}$ $\dfrac{1}{p}$

23. $\dfrac{(8x)^6}{(8x)^{10}}$ $\dfrac{1}{(8x)^4}$ **24.** $\dfrac{(9t)^4}{(9t)^{11}}$ $\dfrac{1}{(9t)^7}$ **25.** $\dfrac{18^9}{18^9}$ $18^0 = 1$ **26.** $\dfrac{(6y)^7}{(6y)^7}$ $(6y)^0 = 1$ **27.** $\dfrac{(7x)^0}{(7x)^0}$ 1

Simplify.

28. $(2^5)^2$ 2^{10} **29.** $(3^4)^3$ 3^{12} **30.** $(5^2)^3$ 5^6 **31.** $(6^8)^9$ 6^{72} **32.** $(y^5)^9$ y^{45}

33. $(x^3)^{20}$ x^{60} **34.** $(m^{18})^4$ m^{72} **35.** $(n^5)^{21}$ n^{105} **36.** $(3y^4)^3$ $27y^{12}$ **37.** $(5a^5)^2$ $25a^{10}$

38. $(2x^8y^3z^7)^5$ **39.** $(3x^5y^9z^3)^4$ **40.** $(-2x^8y^6)^3$ **41.** $[(-x)^{40}]^5$ **42.** $[(-y)^{18}]^3$

38. $32x^{40}y^{15}z^{35}$
39. $81x^{20}y^{36}z^{12}$
40. $-8x^{24}y^{18}$
41. x^{200}
42. y^{54}

Extension

43. Write $4^3 \cdot 8 \cdot 16$ as a power of 2. $(2^2)^3 \cdot 2^3 \cdot 2^4 = 2^{13}$

44. Write $2^8 \cdot 16^3 \cdot 64$ as a power of 4. 4^{13}

45. Are $(5y)^0$ and $5y^0$ equivalent expressions? No, $(5y)^0 = 1$ and $5(y)^0 = 5$.

46. Simplify $(y^{2x})(y^{3x})$. y^{5x}

Simplify.

47. $\dfrac{(5^{12})^2}{5^{25}}$ $\frac{1}{5}$ **48.** $\dfrac{a^{20+20}}{(a^{20})^2}$ 1   **49.** $\dfrac{(3^5)^4}{3^5 \cdot 3^4}$ 3^{11}

50. $\dfrac{(7^5)^{14}}{(7^{14})^5}$ 1   **51.** $\dfrac{a^{22}}{(a^2)^{11}}$ 1   **52.** $\dfrac{49^{18}}{7^{35}}$ (Hint: Study Problem 51.) 7

Challenge

53. Simplify. $\dfrac{\left(\frac{1}{2}\right)^4}{\left(\frac{1}{2}\right)^5}$ **54.** Simplify. $\dfrac{(0.4)^5}{((0.4)^3)^2}$ 53. $\frac{1}{\frac{1}{2}}$ or 2   54. $\frac{1}{0.4}$ or 2.5

55. How might you define 3^{-2} so that your definition is consistent with our rules for operating with exponents? $3^{0-2} = \frac{3^0}{3^2} = \frac{1}{3^2}$

56. Is $(a + b)^m = a^m + b^m$ true for all numbers? (Hint: Substitute and evaluate.) No, $(2 + 3)^4 \neq 2^4 + 3^4$.

57. Does $(a^b)^c = a^{(b^c)}$? Try different values. Remember to work inside parentheses first. No, $(a^b)^c = a^{(b \cdot c)}, b \cdot c \neq b^c$.

58. $\dfrac{w^{50}}{w^x} = w^x$ Find x. $2x = 50$ $x = 25$ **59.** $\dfrac{(9x)^{12}}{(9x)^{14}} = \dfrac{1}{ax^2}$ Find a. 9^2 or 81

DISCOVERY/Charles Babbage and Ada Lovelace

Charles Babbage was an inventor who may have been born 100 years too early. Babbage is often called the father of the computer, although he lived in the 1800's. He spent much of his life designing calculating machines. One machine had input and output mechanisms and could store 1000 50-digit numbers. Although he spent the equivalent of $100,000 on his machines, he could never perfect a working model. Manufacturing techniques at that time could not provide the close-fitting gears he needed.

Ada Byron Lovelace worked with Babbage and set down the first examples of how a calculating machine could be programmed. She wrote of the possibility that machines could someday compose music. The modern programming language ADA is named for her.

4–2 Polynomials and Their Terms

Identifying Terms

Algebraic expressions like these are called polynomials.

$$-2 \qquad 5y + 3 \qquad 3x^2 + 2x - 5 \qquad -5a^3 + \frac{1}{2}a \qquad -6x$$

In this chapter we will learn how to add, subtract, and multiply polynomials. In a polynomial, each part to be added or subtracted is called a monomial. A monomial is a numeral or constant, a variable to a power, or a product of a numeral and a variable to a power. These expressions are monomials.

$$4x^3 \qquad -7a \qquad x \qquad \frac{1}{2}y^5 \qquad -8$$

These expressions are not monomials.

$$\frac{1}{y} \qquad \sqrt{x} \qquad \frac{1}{x^2} \qquad \frac{2}{3a}$$

DEFINITION

A *polynomial* is a sum of monomials.

In a polynomial, subtractions can be rewritten as additions. When a polynomial has only additions, the monomials are called terms.

EXAMPLE 1
Identify the terms of the polynomial.

$$4x^6 + 3x^2 + 12 + 8x^3 + 5x^4$$

The terms are: $4x^6$, $3x^2$, 12, $8x^3$, and $5x^4$.

EXAMPLE 2
If there are subtractions you can *think* of the subtractions as additions. Identify the terms of the polynomial $4x^5 - 2x^6 - 4x - 9$.

Think of the polynomial as $4x^5 + (-2x^6) + (-4x) + (-9)$.

The terms are: $4x^5$, $-2x^6$, $-4x$, -9.

TRY THIS Identify the terms of each polynomial.

1. $5y^6 + 8y^4 + 9y^5 + 12 + 6y$ **2.** $-6x^3 + 5x^5 - 2x^3 - 103$

1. $5y^6$, $8y^4$, $9y^5$, 12, $6y$
2. $-6x^3$, $5x^5$, $-2x^3$, -103

Make sure that you do not confuse terms (things added) with factors (things multiplied). We know that a polynomial with one term is a monomial. Polynomials with exactly two terms are called binomials. Terms with exactly three terms are called trinomials.

EXAMPLE 3

Monomials	Binomials	Trinomials
$4x^2$	$2x + 4$	$3x^3 + 4x + 7$
9	$3x^5 + 6x$	$6x^7 - 7x^2 + 4$
$-23x^{19}$	$-9x^7 - 6$	$4x^2 - 6x - \frac{1}{2}$

TRY THIS Tell whether each polynomial is a monomial, binomial, trinomial, or none of these.

3. $5x^4$ **4.** $4x^3 - 3x^2 + 8x + 8$ **5.** $2y^4 + 9$ **6.** $8y^3 + 3y - 7$

3. monomial
4. none
5. binomial
6. trinomial

Collecting Like Terms

Terms with the same variable and the same exponent are called like terms. We can often simplify polynomials by collecting like terms.

EXAMPLES

Collect like terms.

4. $2x^3 - 6x^3 = (2 - 6)x^3 = -4x^3$ Using the distributive law

5. $5x^2 + 4x^4 + 2x^2 - 2x^4 = (5 + 2)x^2 + (4 - 2)x^4$
$$= 7x^2 + 2x^4$$

Recall that we may multiply a term by 1 to make it easier to collect terms.

6. $3x^4 - 6x^3 - x^4 = 3x^4 - 6x^3 - 1x^4$
$$= (3 - 1)x^4 - 6x^3$$
$$= 2x^4 - 6x^3$$

Sometimes when collecting like terms we get zero.

7. $2x^4 - 2x^4 + 3x^2 + 5 = (2 - 2)x^4 + 3x^2 + 5$
$$= 0x^4 + 3x^2 + 5$$
$$= 0 + 3x^2 + 5$$
$$= 3x^2 + 5$$

TRY THIS Collect like terms.

7. $2x - 4x^3 - 24 - 6x^3$

8. $7x^2 - x - x^2 - 7$

9. $8x^2 - x^2 + x^3 - 1 - 4x^2$

10. $\frac{1}{2}x^5 - \frac{3}{4}x^5 + 4x^2 - 2x^2$

7. $-10x^3 + 2x - 24$
8. $6x^2 - x - 7$
9. $x^3 + 3x^2 - 1$
10. $-\frac{1}{4}x^5 + 2x^2$

Degrees

The degree of a term with one variable is its exponent. The degree of a polynomial is its greatest exponent.

EXAMPLE 8

Identify the degree of each term of $8x^4 + 3x + 7$. Tell the degree of the polynomial.

The degree of $8x^4$ is 4.
The degree of $3x$ is 1.   Recall $x = x^1$.
The degree of 7 is 0.   Think of 7 as $7x^0$.
The degree of $8x^4 + 3x + 7$ is 4.

TRY THIS Identify the degree of each term and the degree of each polynomial.

11. $-6x^4 + 8x^2 - 2x + 9$

12. $9y^5 - 7y^3 + 3y + 17$

11. 4, 2, 1, 0; 4
12. 5, 3, 1, 0; 5

Coefficients

The coefficient of a term is the constant by which the variable is multiplied.

EXAMPLE 9

Identify the coefficient of each term of

$$3x^4 - 4x^3 + 7x^2 + x - 8.$$

The coefficient of $3x^4$ is 3.
The coefficient of $-4x^3$ is -4.
The coefficient of $7x^2$ is 7.
The coefficient of x is 1.
The coefficient of -8 is -8.

The term with the highest degree is called the leading term. The coefficient of the leading term is called the leading coefficient.

150 CHAPTER 4 POLYNOMIALS

13. Identify the coefficient of each term of

$$5x^9 - 6x^3 + x^2 - x - 4.$$ 5, −6, 1, −1, −4

4-2	

Exercises

Identify the terms of each polynomial.

1. $5x^3 - 6x - 3$
$5x^3, -6x, -3$

2. $-4x^9 + 6x - 1$
$-4x^9, 6x, -1$

3. $-2 - 3y + 7y^2 - 3y^3$
$-2, -3y, 7y^2, -3y^3$

Tell which polynomials are monomials, binomials, trinomials, or none of these.

4. $-x$

5. $x^2 - 1$

6. $3x^{100} + 2x - 2^5$

7. $x^7 - x^8 + x^9 - 10$

8. x^0

9. $\frac{1}{8} + x^3$

4. monomial
5. binomial
6. trinomial
7. none
8. monomial
9. binomial

Collect like terms.

10. $2x - 5x$ $-3x$

11. $x - 9x$ $-8x$

12. $2x^2 + 8x^2$ $10x^2$

13. $3x^2 - 4x^2$ $-x^2$

14. $x^3 - 5x - 2x^3$ $-x^3 - 5x$

15. $5x^3 + 6x^3 + 4$ $11x^3 + 4$

16. $6x^4 - 3x^4 + 7$ $3x^4 + 7$

17. $6x^4 - 2x^4 + 5$ $4x^4 + 5$

18. $5x^3 - 3 - 2x^3$ $3x^3 - 3$

19. $-3x^4 - 6x^4 + 5$ $-9x^4 + 5$

20. $3a^4 - 2a + 2a + a^4$ $4a^4$

21. $2x^2 - 6x + 3x + 4x^2$ $6x^2 - 3x$

22. $\frac{1}{4}x^5 - 5 + \frac{1}{2}x^5 - 2x$ $\frac{3}{4}x^5 - 2x - 5$

23. $\frac{1}{3}x^3 + 2x - \frac{1}{6}x^3 + 4$ $\frac{1}{6}x^3 + 2x + 4$

24. $6x^2 + 2x^4 - 2x^2 - x^4 - 4x^2$ x^4

25. $8x^2 + 2x^3 - 3x^3 - 4x^2 - 4x^2$ $-x^3$

Identify the degree of each term and the degree of the polynomial.

26. $2x - 4$ 1, 0; 1

27. $-3x + 6$ 1, 0; 1

28. $3x^2 - 5x + 2$ 2, 1, 0; 2

29. $5x^2 + 3x + 3$ 2, 1, 0; 2

30. $-7x^3 + 6x^2 + 3x + 7$ 3, 2, 1, 0; 3

31. $5x^4 + x^2 - x + 2$ 4, 2, 1, 0; 4

32. $x^2 - 3x + x^6 - 9x^4$ 2, 1, 6, 4; 6

33. $8x - 3x^2 + 9 - 8x^3$ 1, 2, 0, 3; 3

Identify the coefficient of each term.

34. $-3x + 6$ −3, 6

35. $2x - 4$ 2, −4

36. $5x^2 + 3x + 3$ 5, 3, 3

37. $3x^2 - 5x + 2$ 3, −5, 2

38. $-7x^3 + 6x^2 + 3x + 7$ $-7, 6, 3, 7$ **39.** $5x^4 + x^2 - x + 2$ $5, 1, -1, 2$

40. $-5x^4 + 6x^3 - 3x^2 + 8x - 2$ **41.** $7x^3 - 4x^2 - 4x + 5$ $7, -4, -4, 5$
$-5, 6, -3, 8$

Extension

42. Construct a polynomial in x of degree 5 with four terms, and coefficients that are integers. Any ax^5 plus 3 terms of degree < 5

43. Construct a trinomial in y of degree 4 with coefficients that are rational numbers. Answers may vary, ex. $\frac{1}{2}y^4 + \frac{2}{3}y - 2$.

44. What is the degree of $(5m^5)^2$? 10

45. Construct three like terms of degree 4. Three ax^4 terms

Combine like terms.

46. $3x^2 + 2x - 2 + 3x^0$ $3x^2 + 2x + 1$

47. $\frac{9}{2}x^8 + \frac{1}{9}x^2 + \frac{1}{2}x^9 + \frac{9}{2}x^1 + \frac{9}{2}x^9 + \frac{8}{9}x^2 + \frac{1}{2}x - \frac{1}{2}x^8$ $5x^9 + 4x^8 + x^2 + 5x$

48. $(3x^2)^3 + 4x^2 \cdot 4x^4 - x^4(2x)^2 + ((2x)^2)^3 - 100x^2(x^2)^2$ $3x^6$

49. Tell why the following algebraic expressions are not polynomials

$\frac{1}{x}$ $\quad$ $7 + \frac{5}{y}$ $\quad$ $x^2 - 5x + \sqrt{x}$ $\quad$ $(y^2 + 3) \div y$

not a monomial $\quad$ $\frac{5}{y}$ not a monomial $\quad$ $\sqrt{x}$ not a monomial $\quad$ $\frac{y^2 + 3}{y} = y + \frac{3}{y}, \frac{3}{y}$ not a monomial

Challenge

50. Write a polynomial for the perimeter of these figures. Simplify your polynomials by collecting like terms.

14y + 17

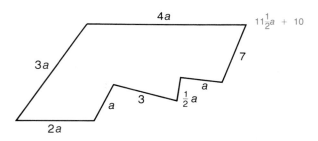

$11\frac{1}{2}a + 10$

51. The sum of a number and 2 is multiplied by the number and then 3 is subtracted from the result. Express the final result as a polynomial. $n(n + 2) - 3 = n^2 + 2n - 3$

52. A polynomial in x has degree 3. The coefficient of x^2 is 3 less than the coefficient of x^3. The coefficient of x is 3 times the coefficient of x^2. The remaining coefficient is 2 more than the coefficient of x^3. The sum of the coefficients is -4. Find the polynomial.
$ax^3 + (a - 3)x^2 + 3(a - 3)x + (a + 2), a + a - 3 + 3(a - 3) + a + 2 = -4, a = 1, x^3 - 2x^2 - 6x + 3$ is the polynomial.

More on Polynomials

Descending Order

This polynomial is arranged in descending order.

$$8x^4 - 2x^3 + 5x^2 - x + 3$$

The order is determined by exponents of the terms. The term with the greatest exponent is first. The term with the next greatest exponent is second, and so on. The associative and commutative laws allow us to arrange the terms of a polynomial in descending order.

EXAMPLES

Arrange each polynomial in descending order.

1. $4x^5 + 4x^7 + x^2 + 2x^3 = 4x^7 + 4x^5 + 2x^3 + x^2$

2. $3 + 4x^5 - 4x^2 + 5x + 3x^3 = 4x^5 + 3x^3 - 4x^2 + 5x + 3$

We usually arrange polynomials in descending order. The opposite order is called ascending.

TRY THIS Arrange each polynomial in descending order.

1. $x + 3x^5 + 4x^3 + 5x^2 + 6x^7 - 2x^4$ $\quad$ $6x^7 + 3x^5 - 2x^4 + 4x^3 + 5x^2 + x$

2. $4x^2 - 3 + 7x^5 + 2x^3 - 5x^4$ $\quad$ $7x^5 - 5x^4 + 2x^3 + 4x^2 - 3$

3. $-14 + 7t^2 - 10t^3 - 14t^7$ $\quad$ $-14t^7 - 10t^3 + 7t^2 - 14$

EXAMPLE 3

Sometimes we may need to collect like terms before arranging in descending order.

$$2x^2 - 4x^3 + 3 - x^2 - 2x^3$$
$$= x^2 - 6x^3 + 3 \quad \text{Collecting like terms}$$
$$= -6x^3 + x^2 + 3 \quad \text{Descending order}$$

TRY THIS Collect like terms and then arrange in descending order.

4. $3x^2 - 2x + 3 - 5x^2 - 1 - x$ $\quad$ $-2x^2 - 3x + 2$

5. $-4 + \dfrac{1}{2} + 14x^4 - 7x - 2 - 4x^4$ $\quad$ $10x^4 - 7x - 5.5$

Missing Terms

If a coefficient is 0, we usually do not write the term. We say that we have a missing term. In $8x^5 - 2x^3 + 5x^2 + 7x + 8$, there is no term with x^4. We say that the x^4, or the fourth degree term, is missing. We could write missing terms with zero coefficients or leave spaces.

EXAMPLE 4
Identify the missing term of

$$3x^2 + 9 = 3x^2 + 0x + 9 = 3x^2 \quad\quad + 9.$$

The first degree term is missing. When writing polynomials it is shorter not to write missing terms or to leave space.

TRY THIS Identify the missing terms in each polynomial.

6. $2x^3 + 4x^2 - 2$ 7. $-3x^4$
8. $x^3 + 1$ 9. $y^4 - y^2 + 3y + 0.25$

6. first degree term
7. third, second, first degree, and constant term.
8. second, first degree term
9. third degree term

Evaluating Polynomials

When we replace the variable in a polynomial by a number and simplify, the polynomial then represents a number. Finding that number is called evaluating the polynomial

EXAMPLES
Evaluate each polynomial for $x = 2$.

5. $3x + 5$ $3 \cdot 2 + 5 = 6 + 5 = 11$
6. $2x^2 + 7x + 3$ $2 \cdot 2^2 + 7 \cdot 2 + 3 = 8 + 14 + 3 = 25$

TRY THIS Evaluate each polynomial for $x = 3$.
10. $-4x - 7$ ₋₁₉ 11. $-5x^2 + 7x + 10$ ₋₁₄

Evaluate each polynomial for $x = -4$.
12. $5x + 7$ ₋₁₃   13. $2x^2 + 5x - 4$ $2 \cdot (-4)^2 + 5(-4) - 4 = 32 - 20 - 4 = 8$

EXAMPLE 7
The cost, in cents per mile, of operating an automobile at speed s, in mi/hr, is approximated by the polynomial

$$0.005s^2 - 0.35s + 28.$$

Evaluate the polynomial for $s = 50$ to find the cost of operating an automobile at 50 mi/hr.

$$0.005(50)^2 - 0.35(50) + 28 = 0.005(2500) - 17.5 + 28$$
$$= 12.5 - 17.5 + 28 = 23$$

The cost is 23¢ per mile.

TRY THIS

14. Evaluate the polynomial in Example 7 for $s = 55$ to find the cost of operating an automobile at 55 mi/h.

0.005(55)^2 - 0.35(55) + 28 = 0.005(3025) - 19.25 + 28 = 15.125 - 19.25 + 28 = 23.875
The cost is 23.875¢ per mile.

4–3

Exercises

Arrange each polynomial in descending order.

1. $x^5 + x + 6x^3 + 1 + 2x^2$

2. $3 + 2x^2 - 5x^6 - 2x^3 + 3x$

3. $5x^3 + 15x^9 + x - x^2 + 7x^8$

4. $9x - 5 + 6x^3 - 5x^4 + x^5$

5. $8y^3 - 7y^2 + 9y^6 - 5y^8 - y^7$

6. $p^8 - 4 + p + p^2 - 7p^4$

1. $x^5 + 6x^3 + 2x^2 + x + 1$ 3. $15x^9 + 7x^8 + 5x^3 - x^2 + x$ 5. $-5y^8 - y^7 + 9y^6 + 8y^3 - 7y^2$
2. $-5x^6 - 2x^3 + 2x^2 + 3x + 3$, 4. $x^5 - 5x^4 + 6x^3 + 9x - 5$, 6. $p^8 - 7p^4 + p^2 + p - 4$

Collect like terms and then arrange in descending order.

7. $3x^4 - 5x^6 - 2x^4 + 6x^6$

8. $-1 + 5x^3 - 3 - 7x^3 + x^4 + 5$

9. $-2x + 4x^3 - 7x + 9x^3 + 8$

10. $-6x^2 + x - 5x + 7x^2 + 1$

11. $3x + 3x + 3x - x^2 - 4x^2$

12. $-2x - 2x - 2x + x^3 - 5x^3$

13. $-x + \frac{3}{4} + 15x^4 - x - \frac{1}{2} - 3x^4$

14. $2x - \frac{5}{6} + 4x^3 + x + \frac{1}{3} - 2x$

7. $x^6 + x^4$
8. $x^4 - 2x^3 + 1$
9. $13x^3 - 9x + 8$
10. $x^2 - 4x + 1$
11. $-5x^2 + 9x$
12. $-4x^3 - 6x$
13. $12x^4 - 2x + \frac{1}{4}$
14. $4x^3 + x - \frac{1}{2}$

Identify the missing terms in each polynomial.

15. $x^3 - 27$ 16. $x^5 + x$ 17. $x^4 - x$

18. $5x^4 - 7x + 2$ 19. $2x^3 - 5x^2 + x - 3$ 20. $-6x^3$

Evaluate each polynomial for $x = 4$.

21. $-5x + 2$ $_{-18}$ 22. $-3x + 1$ $_{-11}$ 23. $2x^2 - 5x + 7$ $_{19}$

24. $3x^2 + x - 7$ $_{45}$ 25. $x^3 - 5x^2 + x$ $_{-12}$ 26. $7 - x + 3x^2$ $_{51}$

15. 2nd, 1st degree terms
16. 4th, 3rd, 2nd degree, constant
17. 3rd, 2nd degree, constant
18. 3rd, 2nd degree
19. no missing terms
20. 2nd, 1st degree, constant

Evaluate each polynomial for $x = -1$.

27. $3x + 5$ $_2$ 28. $6 - 2x$ $_8$

29. $x^2 - 2x + 1$ $_4$ 30. $5x - 6 + x^2$ $_{-10}$

31. $-3x^3 + 7x^2 - 3x - 2$ $_{11}$ 32. $-2x^3 - 5x^2 + 4x + 3$ $_{-4}$

4–3 More on Polynomials **155**

The daily number of accidents involving drivers of age x is approximated by the polynomial $0.4x^2 - 40x + 1039$.

33. Evaluate the polynomial for $x = 18$ to find the number of daily accidents involving 18-year-old drivers. 448.6

34. Evaluate the polynomial for $x = 20$ to find the number of daily accidents involving 20-year-old drivers. 399

Extension

35. A 4-ft by 4-ft sandbox is placed on a square lawn x ft on a side. Express the area left over as a polynomial. $x^2 - 16$

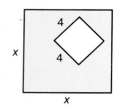

36. Express the shaded area in the figure below as a polynomial. $\pi r^2 - 9\pi$

37. Evaluate $s^2 - 50s + 675$ and $-s^2 + 50s - 575$ for $s = 18$, for $s = 25$ and for $s = 32$. 99,1; 50,50; 99,1

38. If an object is thrown upward at a speed of 160 feet per second, the height it reaches in t seconds is $160t - 16t^2$. Find its height after 2 seconds, 6 seconds, and 9 seconds. 256, 384, 144

39. The amount of water in a tub while it drains is $25(4 - t)^2$, $t =$ time in min. How much water is in the tub before it begins draining? After 1 minute? After 3 minutes? 384, 225, 25

Challenge

40. For a polynomial of degree 2 of the form $ax^2 + bx + c$ where a, b, and c are coefficients, the extreme (highest or lowest) value of the polynomial is the value of x when $2ax = -b$. Find the age with the lowest daily accidents for the polynomial $0.4x^2 - 40x + 1039$. (Refer to Exercise 33.)

$2(0.4x) = -(-40)$
$0.8x = 40$
$x = 50$

Addition of Polynomials

Addition

To add polynomials we can write a plus sign between the polynomials and collect like terms. We usually arrange a polynomial in descending order.

EXAMPLE 1

Add $-3x^3 - 2x - 4$ and $4x^3 - 3x^2 + 2$.

$$-3x^3 - 2x - 4 + 4x^3 - 3x^2 + 2$$
$$= (-3 + 4)x^3 - 3x^2 - 2x + (-4 + 2) \quad \text{Collecting like terms}$$
$$= x^3 - 3x^2 - 2x - 2$$

TRY THIS Add.

1. $3x^2 + 2x - 2$ and $-2x^2 + 5x + 5$ $\quad$ $x^2 + 7x + 3$
2. $31x^4 + x^2 + 2x - 1$ and $-7x^4 + 5x^3 - 2x + 2$ $\quad$ $24x^4 + 5x^3 + x^1 + 1$

EXAMPLE 2

After some practice you can add mentally.
Add $3x^2 - 2x + 2$ and $5x^3 - 2x^2 + 3x - 4$.

$$3x^2 - 2x + 2 + 5x^3 - 2x^2 + 3x - 4$$
$$= 5x^3 + (3 - 2)x^2 + (-2 + 3)x + (2 - 4) \quad \text{You might do this step mentally.}$$
$$= 5x^3 + x^2 + x - 2 \quad \text{Then you would write only this.}$$

TRY THIS Add mentally. Try to just write the answer.

3. $(4x^2 - 5x + 3) + (-2x^2 - 2x - 4)$ $\quad$ $2x^2 - 7x - 1$
4. $(3x^3 - 4x^2 - 5x - 3) + (5x^3 + 2x^2 - 3x - \frac{1}{2})$ $\quad$ $8x^3 - 2x^2 - 8x - 3.5$

EXAMPLE 3

We can also add polynomials by writing like terms in columns.
Add $9x^5 - 2x^3 + 6x^2 + 3$ and $5x^4 - 7x^2 + 6$ and $3x^6 - 5x^5 + x^2 + 5$.

$$
\begin{array}{rl}
9x^5 \qquad\quad -2x^3 + 6x^2 + 3 & \text{Arrange with like terms in columns.} \\
5x^4 \qquad\quad -7x^2 + 6 & \text{We leave spaces for missing terms.} \\
\underline{3x^6 - 5x^5 \qquad\qquad\quad + x^2 + 5} \\
3x^6 + 4x^5 + 5x^4 - 2x^3 \qquad\quad + 14
\end{array}
$$

TRY THIS Add.

5.
$$
\begin{array}{r}
-2x^3 - 5x^2 - 2x - 4 \\
x^4 \qquad\quad - 6x^2 + 7x - 10 \\
-9x^4 + 6x^3 + x^2 \qquad\quad - 2 \\
\hline
-8x^4 + 4x^3 - 10x^2 + 5x - 16
\end{array}
$$

6. $-3x^3 - 5x + 2$ and
$x^3 + x^2 + 5$ and
$x^2 - 2x - 4$

$-2x^3 + 2x^2 - 7x + 3$

Solving Problems

Suppose we want to find the sum of the areas of these rectangles.

EXAMPLE 4

We can proceed as follows.

$$
\underbrace{\text{area of A}}\ \text{plus}\ \underbrace{\text{area of B}}\ \text{plus}\ \underbrace{\text{area of C}}\ \text{plus}\ \underbrace{\text{area of D}}
$$

$$
\qquad 4 \cdot 3 \qquad + \qquad 5 \cdot 3 \qquad + \qquad 3 \cdot 3 \qquad + \qquad 2 \cdot 5
$$

$$
= 12 + 15 + 9 + 10
$$
$$
= 46
$$

EXAMPLE 5
Now suppose certain sides were unknown, but represented by a variable x.

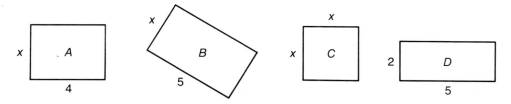

The sum of the areas is found as follows.

$$
\underbrace{\text{area of A}}\ \text{plus}\ \underbrace{\text{area of B}}\ \text{plus}\ \underbrace{\text{area of C}}\ \text{plus}\ \underbrace{\text{area of D}}
$$

$$
\qquad 4x \qquad + \qquad 5x \qquad + \qquad x \cdot x \qquad + \qquad 2 \cdot 5
$$

$$
= 4x + 5x + x^2 + 10
$$
$$
= x^2 + 9x + 10
$$

If we replace x by 3, we have the same areas as Example 4.

$$x^2 + 9x + 10 = 3^2 + 9 \cdot 3 + 10 = 9 + 27 + 10 = 46 \ .$$

The polynomial, $x^2 + 9x + 10$, is a formula for the sum of the areas of the rectangles with certain sides of length x. Thus, we can substitute any length for x, say 8, 4, or 78.6, and find the sum of the areas.

TRY THIS

7. Find the sum of the areas of these rectangles. $8 \cdot 16 + 8 \cdot 8 + 8 \cdot 4 = 224$

8. Find the sum of the areas of these rectangles. $x \cdot 2x + x \cdot x + x \cdot \frac{1}{2}x = 2x^2 + x^2 + \frac{1}{2}x^2 = 3\frac{1}{2}x^2$

9. Find the sum of the areas in Try This 7 by substituting 8 for x in the polynomial of Try This 8. $3\frac{1}{2}(8)^2 = 3\frac{1}{2} \cdot 64 = 224$

4–4

Exercises

Add.

1. $3x + 2$ and $-4x + 3$ $-x + 5$ 2. $5x^2 + 6x + 1$ and $-7x + 2$ $5x^2 - x + 3$

3. $-6x + 2$ and $x^2 + x - 3$ 4. $6x^4 + 3x^3 - 1$ and $4x^2 - 3x + 3$
   $x^2 - 5x - 1$ $6x^4 + 3x^3 + 4x^2 - 3x + 2$

5. $3x^5 + 6x^2 - 1$ and $7x^2 + 6x - 2$ $3x^5 + 13x^2 + 6x - 3$

6. $7x^3 + 3x^2 + 6x$ and $-3x^2 - 6$ $7x^3 + 6x - 6$

7. $-4x^4 + 6x^2 - 3x - 5$ and $6x^3 + 5x + 9$ $-4x^4 + 6x^3 + 6x^2 + 2x + 4$

8. $5x^3 + 6x^2 - 3x + 1$ and $5x^4 - 6x^3 + 2x - 5$ $5x^4 - x^3 + 6x^2 - x - 4$

9. $(7x^3 + 6x^2 + 4x + 1) + (-7x^3 + 6x^2 - 4x + 5)$ $12x^2 + 6$

10. $(3x^4 - 5x^2 - 6x + 5) + (-4x^3 + 6x^2 + 7x - 1)$ $3x^4 - 4x^3 + x^2 + x + 4$

11. $5x^4 - 6x^3 - 7x^2 + x - 1$ and $4x^3 - 6x + 1$ $5x^4 - 2x^3 - 7x^2 - 5x$

12. $8x^5 - 6x^3 + 6x + 5$ and $-4x^4 + 3x^3 - 7x$ $8x^5 - 4x^4 - 3x^3 - x + 5$

13. $9x^8 - 7x^4 + 2x^2 + 5$ and $8x^7 + 4x^4 - 2x$ $9x^8 + 8x^7 - 3x^4 + 2x^2 - 2x + 5$

14. $4x^5 - 6x^3 - 9x + 1$ and $6x^3 + 9x^2 + 9x$ $4x^5 + 9x^2 + 1$

15. $\frac{1}{4}x^4 + \frac{2}{3}x^3 + \frac{5}{8}x^2 + 7$ and $-\frac{3}{4}x^4 + \frac{3}{8}x^2 - 7$ $-\frac{1}{2}x^4 + \frac{2}{3}x^3 + x^2$

16. $\left(\frac{1}{3}x^9 + \frac{1}{5}x^5 - \frac{1}{2}x^2 + 7\right) + \left(-\frac{1}{5}x^9 + \frac{1}{4}x^4 - \frac{3}{5}x^5 + \frac{3}{4}x^2 + \frac{1}{2}\right)$ $\frac{2}{15}x^9 - \frac{2}{5}x^5 + \frac{1}{4}x^4 + \frac{1}{4}x^2 + \frac{15}{2}$

17. $0.02x^5 - 0.2x^3 + x + 0.08$ and $-0.01x^5 + x^4 - 0.8x - 0.02$
    $0.01x^5 + x^4 - 0.2x^3 + 0.2x + 0.06$

18. $(0.03x^6 + 0.05x^3 + 0.22x + 0.05) + \left(\frac{7}{100}x^6 - \frac{3}{100}x^3 + 0.5\right)$ $0.1x^6 + 0.02x^3 + 0.22x + 0.55$

19. $-3x^4 + 6x^2 + 2x - 1$
    $\underline{\quad\quad - 3x^2 + 2x + 1}$
    $-3x^4 + 3x^2 + 4x$

20. $-4x^3 + 8x^2 + 3x - 2$
    $\underline{\quad\quad - 4x^2 + 3x + 2}$
    $-4x^3 + 4x^2 + 6x$

21. $3x^5 \quad\quad - 6x^3 \quad\quad + 3x$
    $\underline{\quad - 3x^4 + 3x^3 + x^2\quad}$
    $3x^5 - 3x^4 - 3x^3 + x^2 + 3x$

22. $4x^5 \quad\quad - 5x^3 \quad\quad + 2x$
    $\underline{\quad - 4x^4 + 2x^3 + 2x^2\quad}$
    $4x^5 - 4x^4 - 3x^3 + 2x^2 + 2x$

23. $\quad\quad - 3x^2 + x$
    $5x^3 - 6x^2 \quad\quad + 1$
    $\underline{\quad\quad\quad\quad 3x - 8}$
    $5x^3 - 9x^2 + 4x - 7$

24. $\quad\quad - 4x^2 + 2x$
    $3x^3 - 5x^2 \quad\quad + 3$
    $\underline{\quad\quad\quad\quad 5x - 5}$
    $3x^3 - 9x^2 + 7x - 2$

25. $-\frac{1}{2}x^4 - \frac{3}{4}x^3 + \quad\quad + 6x$

    $\frac{1}{2}x^3 + x^2 + \frac{1}{4}x$

    $\underline{\frac{3}{4}x^4 \quad\quad + \frac{1}{2}x^2 + \frac{1}{2}x + \frac{1}{4}}$
    $\frac{1}{4}x^4 - \frac{1}{4}x^3 + \frac{3}{2}x^2 + 6\frac{3}{4}x + \frac{1}{4}$

26. $-\frac{1}{4}x^4 - \frac{1}{2}x^3 - \quad\quad + 2x$

    $\frac{3}{4}x^3 - x^2 + \frac{1}{2}x$

    $\underline{\frac{1}{2}x^4 \quad\quad + \frac{1}{2}x^2 + \frac{1}{2}x + \frac{1}{2}}$
    $\frac{1}{4}x^4 + \frac{1}{4}x^3 - \frac{1}{2}x^2 + 3x + \frac{1}{2}$

27. $\quad\quad\quad - 4x^2$
    $4x^4 - 3x^3 + 6x^2 + 5x$
    $\quad\quad 6x^3 - 8x^2 \quad\quad + 1$
    $-5x^4$
    $\underline{\quad\quad\quad\quad 6x^2 - 3x}$
    $-x^4 + 3x^3 - 6x^2 + 2x + 1$

28. $\quad\quad\quad 3x^2$
    $5x^4 - 2x^3 + 4x^2 + 5x$
    $\quad\quad 5x^3 - 5x^2 \quad\quad + 2$
    $-7x^4$
    $\underline{\quad\quad\quad\quad 3x^2 - 2x}$
    $-2x^4 + 3x^3 + 5x^2 + 3x + 2$

29. $3x^4 - 6x^2 + 7x$
    $\quad\quad 3x^2 - 3x + 1$
    $-2x^4 + 7x^2 + 3x$
    $\underline{\quad\quad\quad\quad 5x - 2}$
    $x^4 + 4x^2 + 12x - 1$

30. $5x^4 - 8x^2 + 4x$
    $\quad\quad 5x^2 - 2x + 3$
    $-3x^4 + 3x^2 + 5x$
    $\underline{\quad\quad\quad\quad 3x - 5}$
    $2x^4 + 10x - 2$

31.
$$3x^5 - 6x^4 + 3x^3 \qquad\quad - 1$$
$$6x^4 - 4x^3 + 6x^2$$
$$3x^5 \qquad\quad + 2x^3$$
$$- 6x^4 \qquad\quad - 7x^2$$
$$\underline{-5x^5 \qquad\quad + 3x^3 \qquad\quad + 2}$$
$$x^5 - 6x^4 + 4x^3 - x^2 + 1$$

32.
$$4x^5 - 3x^4 + 2x^3 \qquad\quad - 2$$
$$6x^4 + 5x^3 + 3x^2$$
$$5x^5 \qquad\quad + 4x^3$$
$$- 6x^4 \qquad\quad - 5x^2$$
$$\underline{-3x^5 \qquad\quad + 2x^3 \qquad\quad + 5}$$
$$6x^5 - 3x^4 + 13x^3 - 2x^2 + 3$$

33.
$$- x^3 + 6x^2 + 3x + 5$$
$$x^4 + 2x^3 - 3x^2 \qquad\quad + 2$$
$$-7x^4 \qquad\quad - 5x + 3$$
$$6x^4 \qquad\quad + 4x^2 - 4x - 1$$
$$\underline{- x^3 - 7x^2 + 6x - 9}$$
$$0$$

34.
$$- 2x^3 + 3x^2 + 5x + 3$$
$$x^4 \qquad\quad - 5x^2 - 2x + 1$$
$$-5x^4 \qquad\quad - 7x + 4$$
$$4x^4 + 3x^3 + 6x^2 \qquad\quad - 2$$
$$\underline{- x^3 - 4x^2 + 5x - 5}$$
$$x + 1$$

35,
$$- 3x^4 + 6x^3 - 6x^2 + 5x + 1$$
$$5x^5 \qquad\quad - 3x^3 \qquad\quad - 5x$$
$$4x^4 + 7x^3 \qquad\quad + 3x + 1$$
$$\underline{-2x^5 \qquad\quad + 7x^2 \qquad\quad - 8}$$
$$3x^5 + x^4 + 10x^3 + x^2 + 3x - 6$$

36.
$$0.15x^4 + 0.10x^3 - 0.9x^2$$
$$- 0.01x^3 + 0.01x^2 + x$$
$$1.25x^4 \qquad\quad + 0.11x^2 \qquad\quad + 0.01$$
$$0.27x^3 \qquad\quad + 0.99$$
$$\underline{-0.35x^4 \qquad\quad + 15x^2 \qquad\quad - 0.03}$$
$$1.05x^4 + 0.36x^3 + 15.03x^2 + x + 0.97$$

Solve.

37. a. Express the sum of the areas of these rectangles as a
polynomial. $3x^2 + x^2 + x^2 + 4x = 5x^2 + 4x$

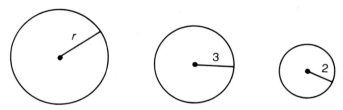

b. Find the sum of the areas when $x = 3$ and $x = 8$. 57,352

38. a. Express the sum of the areas of these circles as a polynomial (area $= \pi r^2$).

$\pi r^2 + 9\pi + 4\pi = r^2\pi + 13\pi$

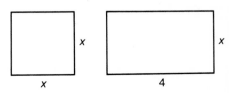

b. Find the sum of the areas when $r = 5$ and $r = 11.3$. 38π, 140.69π

Extension

39. Three brothers have ages that are consecutive multiples of five. The sum of their ages two years ago was 69. Find their ages now. $x + (x + 5) + (x + 10) - 3(2) = 69$, $x = 20$, $x + 5 = 25$, $x + 10 = 30$

40. Find four consecutive multiples of four when the sum of the first two is the fourth. $x + (x + 4) = z + 12$, $x = 8$, others are 12, 16, 20.

Find the area of each figure by adding the 4 areas inside the figure.

41. $25 + 65 + 45 + 117 = 252$

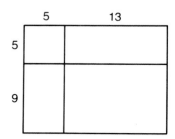

42. $9r + 99 + r^2 + 11r = r^2 + 20r + 99$

43. $20 + 5(m - 4) + 4(m - 5)$
$+ (m - 4)(m - 5) = m^2$

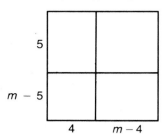

44. Find $(x + 3)^2$ using the 4 areas of the square below. $x^2 + 3x + 3x + 9 = x^2 + 6x + 9$

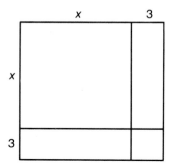

Challenge

45. Addition of real numbers is commutative. That is, $a + b = b + a$, where a and b are any real numbers. Show that addition of binomials such as $(ax + b)$ and $(cx + d)$ is commutative.

45.
$$\begin{aligned} ax &+ b \\ + \ cx &+ d \\ \hline (a + c)x &+ (b + d) \end{aligned}$$

$$\begin{aligned} cx &+ d \\ + \ ax &+ b \\ \hline (c + a)x &+ (d + b) \end{aligned}$$

Both equal $ax + cx + b + d$

46. Show that addition of trinomials such as $(ax^2 + bx + c)$ and $(dx^2 + ex + f)$ is commutative. See 45 above.

47. Show that addition of polynomials is commutative. Use
$a_n x^n + a_{n-1} x^{n-1} + \ldots + a_1 x + a_0$ and
$b_n x^n + b_{n-1} x^{n-1} + \ldots + b_1 x + b_0$ See 45 above.

Additive Inverses

We know that two numbers are additive inverses if their sum is zero. The same definition is true of polynomials.

> **DEFINITION**
>
> Two polynomials are *additive inverses* of each other if their sum is 0.

To help find the additive inverse of a polynomial look for a pattern in the following examples.

a. $-6x^2 + 6x^2 = 0$
b. $(5t^3 + 2) + (-5t^3 - 2) = 0$
c. $(7x^3 - 6x^2 - x - 4) + (-7x^3 + 6x^2 + x + 4) = 0$

The additive inverse of a polynomial is found by replacing each coefficient by its additive inverse.

EXAMPLE 1
Find the additive inverse of $4x^5 - 7x - 8$.

The additive inverse is $-4x^5 + 7x + 8$. Note that we simply changed the sign of each coefficient.

TRY THIS Find the additive inverse of each polynomial.
1. $12x^4 - 3x^2 + 4x$ **2.** $-13x^6 + 2x^4 - 3x^2 + x - \dfrac{5}{13}$

1. $-12x^4 + 3x^2 - 4x$
2. $13x^6 - 2x^4 + 3x^2 - x + \dfrac{5}{13}$

Symbols for Additive Inverses

The additive inverse of the polynomial $8x^2 - 4x + 3$ is the polynomial obtained by replacing each coefficient with its additive inverse. Thus, the inverse of $8x^2 - 4x + 3$ is $-8x^2 + 4x - 3$.

We can also represent the additive inverse of $8x^2 - 4x + 3$ as $-(8x^2 - 4x + 3)$. Thus,

$$-(8x^2 - 4x + 3) = -8x^2 + 4x - 3.$$

EXAMPLE 2

Simplify.

$$-\left(-7x^4 - \frac{5}{9}x^3 + 8x^2 - x + 67\right)$$
$$= 7x^4 + \frac{5}{9}x^3 - 8x^2 + x - 67 \quad \text{Replacing each coefficient by its inverse}$$

TRY THIS Simplify.

3. $-(4x^3 - 6x + 3)$ 4. $-(-5x^4 - 3x^2 + 7x - 5)$ 3. $-4x^3 + 6x - 3$
4. $5x^4 + 3x^2 - 7x + 5$

Subtraction

Recall that we can subtract a rational number by adding its additive inverse: $a - b = a + (-b)$. This rule also applies to polynomials.

EXAMPLE 3

Subtract.

$$(9x^5 + x^3 - 2x^2 + 4) - (2x^5 + x^4 - 4x^3 - 3x^2)$$
$$= (9x^5 + x^3 - 2x^2 + 4) + [-(2x^5 + x^4 - 4x^3 - 3x^2)] \quad \text{Adding an inverse}$$
$$= (9x^5 + x^3 - 2x^2 + 4) + (-2x^5 - x^4 + 4x^3 + 3x^2)$$
$$= 7x^5 - x^4 + 5x^3 + x^2 + 4 \quad \text{Collecting like terms}$$

TRY THIS Subtract.

5. $(5x^2 + 4) - (2x^2 - 1)$ $3x^2 + 5$

6. $(-7x^3 + 2x + 4) - (-2x^3 - 4)$ $-5x^3 + 2x + 8$

7. $(-3x^2 + 5x - 4) - (-4x^3 + 11x^2 - 2x - 6)$ $4x^3 - 14x^2 + 7x + 2$

EXAMPLE 4

Subtract. After some practice you will be able to subtract mentally.

$$(9x^5 + x^3 - 2x) - (-2x^5 + 5x^3 + 6)$$
$$= (9x^5 + 2x^5) + (x^3 - 5x^3) - 2x - 6 \quad \text{Subtract the like terms mentally.}$$
$$= 11x^5 - 4x^3 - 2x - 6 \quad \text{Write only this.}$$

TRY THIS Subtract mentally. Try to write just the answer.

8. $(-6x^4 + 3x^2 + 6) - (2x^4 + 5x^3 - 5x^2 + 7)$ $-8x^4 - 5x^3 + 8x^2 - 1$

9. $\left(\frac{3}{2}x^3 - \frac{1}{2}x^2 + 0.3\right) - \left(\frac{1}{2}x^3 + \frac{1}{2}x^2 + \frac{4}{3}x + 1.3\right)$ $x^3 - x^2 - \frac{4}{3}x - 1$

EXAMPLE 5

Use columns to subtract. $(5x^2 - 3x + 6) - (9x^2 - 5x - 3)$.

a. $\begin{array}{r} 5x^2 - 3x + 6 \\ - \quad 9x^2 - 5x - 3 \end{array}$ Writing similar terms in columns

b. $\begin{array}{r} 5x^2 - 3x + 6 \\ + \; -9x^2 + 5x + 3 \end{array}$ Changing signs to add

c. $\begin{array}{r} 5x^2 - 3x + 6 \\ -9x^2 + 5x + 3 \\ \hline -4x^2 + 2x + 9 \end{array}$ Adding

If you can do so without error, skip step (b). Just write the answer.

EXAMPLE 6

Subtract.

$$\begin{array}{r} x^3 + x^2 + 2x - 12 \\ 2x^3 + x^2 - 3x \\ \hline -x^3 \quad\quad + 5x - 12 \end{array}$$

TRY THIS

10. Subtract the second polynomial from the first. Use columns.

$4x^3 + 2x^2 - 2x - 3, \; 2x^3 - 3x^2 + 2$ $_{2x^3 \; + \; 5x^2 \; - \; 2x \; - \; 5}$

11. Subtract.

$$\begin{array}{r} 2x^3 + \; x^2 - 6x + 2 \\ x^5 + 4x^3 - 2x^2 - 4x \\ \hline \end{array}$$ $_{-x^5 \; - \; 2x^3 \; + \; 3x^2 \; - \; 2x \; + \; 2}$

4–5

Exercises

Find the additive inverse of each polynomial.

1. $-5x$ $_{5x}$

2. $x^2 - 3x$ $_{-x^2 \; + \; 3x}$

3. $-x^2 + 10x - 2$ $_{x^2 \; - \; 10x \; + \; 2}$

4. $-4x^3 - x^2 - x$ $_{4x^3 \; + \; x^2 \; + \; x}$

5. $12x^4 - 3x^3 + 3$ $_{-12x^4 \; + \; 3x^3 \; - \; 3}$

6. $4x^3 - 6x^2 - 8x + 1$ $_{-4x^3 \; + \; 6x^2 \; + \; 8x \; - \; 1}$

Simplify.

7. $-(3x - 7)$ $_{-3x \; + \; 7}$

8. $-(-2x + 4)$ $_{2x \; - \; 4}$

11. $4x^4 + 6x^2 - \frac{3}{4}x + 8$

9. $-(4x^2 - 3x + 2)$ $_{-4x^2 \; + \; 3x \; - \; 2}$

10. $-(-6a^3 + 2a^2 - 9a + 1)$ $_{6a^3 \; - \; 2a^2 \; + \; 9a \; - \; 1}$

11. $-(-4x^4 - 6x^2 + \frac{3}{4}x - 8)$

12. $-(-5x^4 + 4x^3 - x^2 + 0.9)$ $_{5x^4 \; - \; 4x^3 \; + \; x^2 \; - \; 0.9}$

Subtract.

13. $(5x^2 + 6) - (3x^2 - 8)$ $2x^2 + 14$

14. $(7x^3 - 2x^2 + 6) - (7x^2 + 2x - 4)$ $7x^3 - 9x^2 - 2x + 10$

15. $(6x^5 - 3x^4 + x + 1) - (8x^5 + 3x^4 - 1)$ $-2x^5 - 6x^4 + x + 2$

16. $\left(\frac{1}{2}x^2 - \frac{3}{2}x + 2\right) - \left(\frac{3}{2}x^2 + \frac{1}{2}x - 2\right)$ $-x^2 - 2x + 4$

17. $(6x^2 + 2x) - (-3x^2 - 7x + 8)$ $9x^2 + 9x - 8$

18. $7x^3 - (-3x^2 - 2x + 1)$ $7x^3 + 3x^2 + 2x - 1$

19. $\left(\frac{5}{8}x^3 - \frac{1}{4}x - \frac{1}{3}\right) - \left(-\frac{1}{8}x^3 + \frac{1}{4}x - \frac{1}{3}\right)$ $\frac{3}{4}x^3 - \frac{1}{2}x$

20. $\left(\frac{1}{5}x^3 + 2x^2 - 0.1\right) - \left(-\frac{2}{5}x^3 - 2x^2 - 0.01\right)$ $\frac{3}{5}x^3 + 4x^2 - 0.09$

21. $(0.08x^3 - 0.02x^2 + 0.01x) - (0.02x^3 - 0.03x^2 - 1)$ $0.06x^3 - 0.05x^2 + 0.01x + 1$

22. $(0.8x^4 + 0.2x - 1) - \left(\frac{7}{10}x^4 - \frac{1}{5}x - 0.1\right)$ $0.1x^4 - 0.9$

Subtract.

23. $x^2 + 5x + 6$
   $\underline{x^2 + 2x}$
   $3x + 6$

24. $x^3 \qquad + 1$
   $\underline{x^3 + \ \ x^2}$
   $-x^2 + 1$

25. $x^4 \qquad \ \ - 3x^2 + x + 1$
   $\underline{x^4 - 4x^3}$
   $4x^3 - 3x^2 + x + 1$

26. $3x^2 - 6x + 1$
   $\underline{6x^2 + 8x - 3}$
   $-3x^2 - 14x + 4$

27. $\ \ 5x^4 + \quad 6x^3 - 9x^2$
   $\underline{-6x^4 \quad -6x^3 \qquad \ + 8x}$
   $11x^4 \ + \quad 12x^3 \ - \quad 9x^2 \ - \quad 8x$

28. $5x^4 \qquad + 6x^2 - 3x + 6$
   $\underline{\qquad 6x^3 + 7x^2 - 8x - 9}$
   $5x^4 - 6x^3 \ - \quad x^2 \ + \quad 5x \ + \quad 15$

29. $\qquad \ \ 3x^4 \ + 6x^2 + 8x - 1$
   $\underline{4x^5 - 6x^4 \quad - 8x - 7}$
   $-4x^5 + \quad 9x^4 \ + \quad 6x^2 \ + \quad 16x \ + \quad 6$

30. $\ \ 6x^5 \qquad \ \ + 3x^2 - 7x + 2$
   $\underline{10x^5 + 6x^3 - 5x^2 - 2x + 4}$
   $-4x^5 \ - \quad 6x^3 \ + \quad 8x^2 \ - \quad 5x \ - \quad 2$

31.
$$x^5 \qquad\qquad\quad\; - 1$$
$$\underline{x^5 - x^4 + x^3 - x^2 + x - 1}$$
$$x^4 - x^3 + x^2 - x$$

32.
$$x^5 + x^4 - x^3 + x^2 - x + 2$$
$$\underline{x^5 - x^4 + x^3 - x^2 - x + 2}$$
$$2x^4 - 2x^3 + 2x^2$$

Extension

Simplify.

33. $(y + 4) + (y - 5) - (y + 8)$ $y - 9$

34. $(7y^2 - 5y + 6) - (3y^2 + 8y - 12) + (8y^2 - 10y + 3)$ $12y^2 - 23y + 21$

35. $(4a^2 - 3a) + (7a^2 - 9a - 13) - (6a - 9)$ $11a^2 - 18a - 4$

36. $(3x^2 - 4x + 6) - (-2x^2 + 4) + (-5x - 3)$ $5x^2 - 9x - 1$

37. $(-8y^2 - 4) - (3y + 6) - (2y^2 - y)$ $-10y^2 - 2y - 10$

38. $(5x^3 - 4x^2 + 6) - (2x^3 + x^2 - x) + (x^3 - x)$ $4x^3 - 5x + 6$

39. $(-y^4 - 7y^3 + y^2) + (-2y^4 + 5y - 2) - (-6y^3 + y^2)$ $-3y^4 - y^3 + 5y - 2$

40. $(-4 + x^2 + 2x^3) - (-6 - x + 3x^3) - (-x^2 - 5x^3)$ $2 + x + 2x^2 + 4x^3$

Find the shaded area by subtraction.

41.

42.

$$Z^2 - (24z - 3) \cdot (24 \times 3) - 3(z - 24)$$
$$Z^2 + 24z + 3 - 72 - 3z + 72$$
$$Z^2 - 21$$

$$\begin{array}{r}24 \\ 3 \\ \hline 72 \end{array} \qquad \begin{array}{r}49 \\ 21 \end{array}$$

$$Z^2 - 32 - 33$$
$$= 24(z - 3)$$
$$- 24 \times 3$$
$$= 3(z - 24)$$

$$Z^2 - 24(z - 3) - 3(24 - z)$$

Challenge

43. Find $(y - 2)^2$ by subtraction. $y^2 - 2(y - 2) - 2(y - 2) - (2 \cdot 2)$ $= y^2 - 4y + 4$

41. $m^2 - (7 \cdot 4) = m^2 - 28$
42. $z^2 - 24(z - 3) - (24 \cdot 3) - 3(z - 24)$ $= z^2 - 27z + 72$

44. Does replacing each variable x of $5x^3 - 3x^2 + 2x$ with its additive inverse result in the additive inverse of the polynomial? No, $-3(-x)^2 = -3x^2$.

45. What is the additive identity for addition of polynomials? Show that subtraction of binomials is not commutative. Is it associative? Justify your answer.

45. a) A zero polynomial, or 0
b) For each term, the coefficients are real numbers; subtraction of real numbers is not commutative, so $a_n x^n - b_n x^n = (a_n - b_n)x^n$ which $\neq (b_n - a_n)x^n$.
c) No, $a_n - (b_n - c_n) = a_n - b_n + c_n (a_n - b_n) - c_n = a_n - b_n - c_n$

4—6 Multiplication of Monomials and Binomials

Multiplying Monomials

To multiply two monomials, we multiply the coefficients and then use properties of exponents.

EXAMPLES

Multiply.

1. $(3x)(4x) = (3 \cdot 4)(x \cdot x)$ Using the commutative and associative laws
$$= 12x^2$$

2. $(3x)(-x) = (3x)(-1x)$
$$= (3)(-1)(x \cdot x)$$
$$= -3x^2$$

3. $(-7x^5)(4x^3) = (-7 \cdot 4)(x^5 \cdot x^3)$
$$= -28x^{5+3}$$ Adding exponents
$$= -28x^8$$

After some practice you can mentally multiply the coefficients and add the exponents. Write only the answer.

TRY THIS Multiply.

1. $3x$ and -5 **2.** $-x$ and x **3.** $-x$ and $-x$ **4.** $-x^2$ and x^3 $-y^5$

5. $3x^5$ and $4x^2$ **6.** $4x^5$ and $-2x^6$ **7.** $-7y^4$ and $-y$ **8.** $7x^5$ and 0

Multiplying a Polynomial by a Monomial

EXAMPLES

Multiplications are based on the distributive laws.

4. Multiply $2x$ and $5x + 3$.

$$(2x)(5x + 3) = (2x)(5x) + (2x)(3)$$ Using a distributive law
$$= 10x^2 + 6x$$ Multiplying the monomials

5. Multiply $8y$ and $3y^4 - 2y^3 - 5y + 16$.

$$(8y)(3y^4 - 2y^3 - 5y + 16) = (8y)(3y^4) + (8y)(-2y^3) + (8y)(-5y) + (8y)(16)$$
$$= 24y^5 - 16y^4 - 40y^2 + 128y$$

9. $4x$ and $2x + 4$

10. $3x^2$ and $-5x^3 + 2x - 7$

11. $5t$ and $8t^4 - 3t^3 + 4t^2 - 9t - 11$

There is a quick way to multiply a monomial and any polynomial. Use the distributive law mentally. Just write the answer.

EXAMPLE 6

We multiply every term inside the parentheses by the monomial.

$$5x(2x^2 - 3x + 4) = 10x^3 - 15x^2 + 20x$$

TRY THIS Multiply. Try to just write the answer.

12. $4x(2x^2 - 3x + 4)$

13. $2y^3(5y^3 - 4y^2 - 5y + 8)$

Multiplying Two Binomials

To multiply two binomials we use the distributive laws more than once.

EXAMPLE 7

Multiply $x + 5$ and $x + 4$.

$$(x + 5)(x + 4) = \underset{①}{(x + 5)x} + \underset{②}{(x + 5)4} \quad \text{Using a distributive law}$$

We now use a distributive law with parts ① and ②.

① $(x + 5)x = x \cdot x + 5 \cdot x$ Using a distributive law
           $= x^2 + 5x$ Multiplying the monomials

② $(x + 5)4 = x \cdot 4 + 5 \cdot 4$ Using a distributive law
           $= 4x + 20$ Multiplying the monomials

$x^2 + 4x + 5y + 20$

Now we replace parts ① and ② in the original expression with their answers and collect like terms.

$$(x + 5)(x + 4) = x^2 + 5x + 4x + 20$$
$$= x^2 + 9x + 20$$

TRY THIS Multiply.

14. $x - 8$ and $x + 5$ 15. $(x - 5)(x - 4)$

We can also use columns to multiply. We multiply each term on the top row by each term on the bottom. Then we add.

EXAMPLE 8

Multiply $4x - 3$ and $x - 2$.

$$
\begin{array}{r}
4x - 3 \\
\underline{x - 2} \\
4x^2 - 3x \qquad \text{Multiplying the top row by } x \\
\underline{ - 8x + 6} \qquad \text{Multiplying the top row by } -2 \\
4x^2 - 11x + 6 \qquad \text{Adding}
\end{array}
$$

TRY THIS Multiply.

16. $(5x + 3)(x - 4)$ 17. $(2y - 3)(3y - 5)$

16. $5x^2 - 17x - 12$
17. $6y^2 - 19y + 15$

4–6

Exercises

Multiply.

1. $6x^2$ and 7
2. $5x^2$ and -2
3. $-x^3$ and $-x$
4. $-x^4$ and x^2
5. $-x^5$ and x^3
6. $-x^6$ and $-x$
7. $3x^4$ and $2x^2$
8. $5x^3$ and $4x^5$
9. $7t^5$ and $4t^3$
10. $10a^2$ and $3a^2$
11. $-0.1x^6$ and $0.2x^4$
12. $0.3x^3$ and $-0.4x^6$
13. $-\frac{1}{5}x^3$ and $-\frac{1}{3}x$
14. $-\frac{1}{4}x^4$ and $\frac{1}{5}x^8$
15. $-4x^2$ and 0

Multiply.

16. $3x$ and $-x + 5$
17. $2x$ and $4x - 6$
18. $4x^2$ and $3x + 6$
19. $5x^2$ and $-2x + 1$
20. $-6x^2$ and $x^2 + x$
21. $-4x^2$ and $x^2 - x$
22. $3y^2$ and $6y^4 + 8y^3$
23. $4y^4$ and $y^3 - 6y^2$
24. $3x^4$ and $14x^{50} + 20x^{11} + 6x^{57} + 60x^{15}$
25. $5x^6$ and $4x^{32} - 10x^{19} + 5x^8$
26. $-4a^7$ and $20a^{19} + 6a^{15} - 5a^{12} + 14a$
27. $-6y^8$ and $11y^{100} - 7y^{50} + 11y^{41} - 60y^4 + 9$

Multiply.

28. $(x + 6)(x + 3)$ 29. $(x + 5)(x + 2)$

30. $(x + 5)(x - 2)$ **31.** $(x + 6)(x - 2)$
32. $(x - 4)(x - 3)$ **33.** $(x - 7)(x - 3)$
34. $(x + 3)(x - 3)$ **35.** $(x + 6)(x - 6)$
36. $(x - 5)(2x - 5)$ **37.** $(x + 3)(2x + 6)$
38. $(2x + 5)(2x + 5)$ **39.** $(3x - 4)(3x - 4)$
40. $(3y - 4)(3y + 4)$ **41.** $(2y + 1)(2y - 1)$
42. $\left(x - \frac{5}{2}\right)\left(x + \frac{2}{5}\right)$ **43.** $\left(x + \frac{4}{3}\right)\left(x + \frac{3}{2}\right)$

Extension
44. $(a + b)^2$ **45.** $(a - b)^2$
46. $(2x + 3)^2$ **47.** $(5y + 6)^2$

Find the area of the shaded regions.

48.

14y − 5

6y

49.

21t + 8

3t − 4

4t

2t

50. A box with a square bottom is to be made from a 12 inch square piece of cardboard. Squares with side x are cut out of the corners and the sides are folded up. Express the volume and the surface area of the box as polynomials.

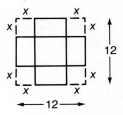

Challenge
Compute.

51. a. $(x + 3)(x + 6) + (x + 3)(x + 6)$
  b. $(x + 4)(x + 5) - (x + 4)(x + 5)$
    a. $2x^2 + 18x + 36$ b. 0

52. a. $(x - 2)(x - 7) + (x - 2)(x - 7)$
  b. $(x - 6)(x - 2) - (x - 6)(x - 2)$
    a. $2x^2 - 18x + 28$ b. 0

53. a. $(x + 5)(x - 3) + (x + 5)(x - 3)$
  b. $(x + 9)(x - 4) - (x + 9)(x - 4)$
    a. $2x^2 + 4x - 30$ b. 0

54. a. $(x + 7)(x - 8) + (x - 7)(x + 8)$
  b. $(x + 2)(x - 5) - (x - 2)(x + 5)$
    a. $2x^2 - 112$ b. $-6x$

Use the results of Exercises 51 − 54 to do Exercises 55 − 57.

55. If a and b are positive, how many terms are there in
$(x - a)(x - b) + (x - a)(x - b)$? 3

56. If a and b are positive, how many terms are there in
$(x + a)(x - b) + (x - a)(x + b)$? 2

57. If a and b are positive, how many terms are there in
$(x + a)(x - b) - (x + a)(x - b)$? 0

Multiplying a Trinomial and a Binomial

To multiply a trinomial and a binomial we can use the distributive laws more than once.

EXAMPLE 1
Multiply.

$$(x^2 + 2x - 3)(x^2 + 4) = \underbrace{(x^2 + 2x - 3)(x^2)}_{①} + \underbrace{(x^2 + 2x - 3)(4)}_{②}$$

Consider parts ① and ②.

$$① \ (x^2 + 2x - 3)x^2 = x^2(x^2) + 2x(x^2) - 3(x^2)$$
$$= x^4 + 2x^3 - 3x^2$$
$$② \ (x^2 + 2x - 3)4 \ = x^2(4) + 2x(4) + (-3)(4)$$
$$= 4x^2 + 8x - 12$$

We replace parts ① and ② in the original expression with their answers and collect like terms.

$$(x^2 + 2x - 3)(x^2 + 4) = (x^4 + 2x^3 - 3x^2) + (4x^2 + 8x - 12)$$
$$= x^4 + 2x^3 + x^2 + 8x - 12$$

We can also use columns to multiply a trinomial by a binomial.

EXAMPLE 2
Multiply $4x^2 - 2x + 3$ and $x^2 + 2$.

$$\begin{array}{r} 4x^2 - 2x + 3 \\ x^2 + 2 \\ \hline 4x^4 - 2x^3 + 3x^2 \\ 8x^2 - 4x + 6 \\ \hline 4x^3 - 2x^3 + 11x^2 - 4x + 6 \end{array}$$

Note that when we multiplied 2 times $4x^2$ we wrote $8x^2$ in the x^2 column.

TRY THIS Multiply.

1. $(x^2 + 3x - 4)(x^2 + 5)$
   $x^4 + 3x^3 + x^2 + 15x - 20$

2. $(2x^3 - 2x^2 + 5x)(3x^2 - 7)$
   $6x^5 - 6x^4 + x^3 + 14x^2 - 35x$

Multiplying Any Polynomials

Perhaps you have observed the following.

> To multiply two polynomials, multiply each term of one polynomial by every term of the other. Then add the results.

We usually use columns for long multiplications. We multiply each term at the top by every term at the bottom. Then we add.

EXAMPLE 3
Multiply $2x^2 + 3x - 4$ and $2x^2 - x + 3$.

$$
\begin{array}{l}
2x^2 + 3x - 4 \\
2x^2 - x + 3 \\
\hline
4x^4 + 6x^3 - 8x^2 \qquad\qquad \text{Multiplying by } 2x^2 \\
 - 2x^3 - 3x^2 + 4x \qquad \text{Multiplying by } -x \\
 6x^2 + 9x \cdot - 12 \quad \text{Multiplying by } 3 \\
\hline
4x^4 + 4x^3 - 5x^2 + 13x - 12
\end{array}
$$

EXAMPLE 4
Multiply $5x^3 - 3x + 4$ and $-2x^2 - 3$.

$$
\begin{array}{l}
5x^3 - 3x + 4 \\
-2x^2 - 3 \\
\hline
-10x^5 + 6x^3 - 8x^2 \qquad\qquad \text{Multiplying by } -2x^2 \\
 - 15x^3 + 9x - 12 \quad \text{Multiplying by } -3 \\
\hline
-10x^5 - 9x^3 - 8x^2 + 9x - 12
\end{array}
$$

When we multiplied $-2x^2$ times $-3x$, the power decreased from x^5 to x^3, so we left a space for the missing x^4 term. When we multiplied -3 times $-3x$, the power decreased from x^3 to x, so we left a space for the missing x^2 term. In column multiplication we leave spaces for missing terms. (Recall that a missing term is a term with a 0 coefficient.)

TRY THIS   Multiply.

3. $(3x^2 - 2x + 4)(x^2 + 5x + 1)$

4. $(-5x^2 + 4x + 2)(-4x^2 + x - 8)$

5. $(4x^3 - 6x - 5)(2x^2 + x - 2)$

6. $(3x^4 - 4x^2 - 5)(x^3 - x^2 + 2)$

3. $3x^4 + 13x^3 - 3x^2 + 18x + 4$
4. $20x^4 - 21x^3 + 36x^2 - 30x - 16$
5. $8x^5 + 4x^4 - 20x^3 - 16x^2 + 7x + 10$
6. $3x^7 - 3x^6 - 4x^5 + 10x^4 - 5x^3 - 3x^2 - 10$

Exercises

Multiply.

1. $(x^2 + x + 1)(x - 1)$

2. $(x^2 - x + 2)(x + 2)$

3. $(2x^2 + 6x + 1)(2x + 1)$

4. $(4x^2 - 2x - 1)(3x - 1)$

5. $(3y^2 - 6y + 2)(y^2 - 3)$

6. $(y^2 + 6y + 1)(3y^2 - 3)$

7. $(x^3 + x^2 - x)(x^3 + x^2)$

8. $(x^3 - x^2 + x)(x^3 - x^2)$

9. $(-5x^3 - 7x^2 + 1)(2x^2 - x)$

10. $(-4x^3 + 5x^2 - 2)(5x^2 + 1)$

11. $(x^2 + x + 1)(x^2 - x - 1)$

12. $(x^2 - x + 1)(x^2 - x + 1)$

13. $(2x^2 + 3x - 4)(2x^2 + x - 2)$

14. $(2x^2 - x - 3)(2x^2 - 5x - 2)$

15. $(2t^2 - t - 4)(3t^2 + 2t - 1)$

16. $(3a^2 - 5a + 2)(2a^2 - 3a + 4)$

17. $(2x^2 + x - 2)(-2x^2 + 4x - 5)$

18. $(3x^2 - 8x + 1)(-2x^2 - 4x + 2)$

19. $(x^5 - x^3 + x)(x^4 + x^2 - 1)$

20. $(3x^6 + 3x^4 + 3x^2)(x^5 - x^3 + x)$

21. $(x^3 + x^2 + x + 1)(x - 1)$

22. $(x^3 - x^2 + x - 2)(x - 2)$

23. $(x^3 + x^2 - x - 3)(x - 3)$

24. $(x^3 - x^2 - x + 4)(x + 4)$

20. $3x^{11} + 3x^7 + 3x^3$
21. $x^4 - 1$, 22. $x^4 - 3x^3 + 3x^2 - 4x + 4$

23. $x^4 - 2x^3 - 4x^2 + 9$
24. $x^4 + 3x^3 - 5x^2 + 16$

1. $x^3 - 1$
2. $x^3 + x^2 + 4$
3. $4x^3 + 14x^2 + 8x + 1$
4. $12x^3 - 10x^2 - x + 1$
5. $3y^4 - 6y^3 - 7y^2 + 18y - 6$
6. $3y^4 + 18y^3 - 18y - 3$
7. $x^6 + 2x^5 - x^3$
8. $x^6 - 2x^5 + 2x^4 - x^3$
9. $-10x^5 - 9x^4 + 7x^3 + 2x^2 - x$
10. $-20x^5 + 25x^4 - 4x^3 - 5x^2 - 2$
11. $x^4 - x^2 - 2x - 1$
12. $x^4 - 2x^3 + 3x^2 - 2x + 1$
13. $4x^4 + 8x^3 - 9x^2 - 10x + 8$
14. $4x^4 - 12x^3 - 5x^2 + 17x + 6$
15. $6t^4 + t^3 - 16t^2 - 7t + 4$
16. $6a^4 - 19a^3 + 31a^2 - 26a + 8$
17. $-4x^4 + 6x^3 - 2x^2 - 13x + 10$
18. $-6x^4 + 4x^3 + 36x^2 - 20x + 2$
19. $x^9 - x^5 + 2x^3 - x$

Extension

25. Find $(x + y)^3$ $x^3 + 3x^2y + 3xy^2 + y^3$

26. Find $(x + y)^4$ $x^4 + 4x^3y + 6x^2y^2 + 4xy^3 + y^4$

27. Study the pattern of your answers for Exercise 25 and 26. Without multiplying find $(x + y)^5$.

Coefficients are from Pascal's triangle.
$x^5 + 5x^4y + 10x^3y^2 + 10x^2y^3 + 5xy^4 + y^5$

Challenge

Multiply. Look for patterns.

28. a. $(x^2 + x + 1)(x - 1)$
    b. $(x^2 + x + 1)(x + 1)$
 c. $(x^2 - x + 1)(x - 1)$
    d. $(x^2 - x + 1)(x + 1)$
 e. $(-x^2 + x - 1)(x - 1)$
    f. $(-x^2 + x - 1)(x + 1)$
 g. $(x^3 + x^2 + x + 1)(x - 1)$
    h. $(x^3 + x^2 + x + 1)(x + 1)$
 i. $(x^3 - x^2 + x - 1)(x - 1)$
    j. $(x^3 - x^2 + x + 1)(x + 1)$
 k. $(-x^3 + x^2 - x + 1)(x - 1)$
    l. $(-x^3 + x^2 - x + 1)(x + 1)$

29. What polynomial times $(x - 1)$ equals $x^5 - 1$? $x^4 + x^3 + x^2 + x + 1$

30. What polynomial times $(x + 1)$ equals $x^5 + 1$? $x^4 - x^3 + x^2 - x + 1$

31. What polynomial times $(x - 1)$ equals $x^6 - 1$? $x^5 + x^4 + x^3 + x^2 + x + 1$

32. Find $(x^2 + xy + y^2)^2$ $x^4 + 2x^3y + 3x^2y^2 + 2xy^3 + y^4$

33. Find a trinomial $ax^2 + bx + c$ and a binomial $dx + e$ so that when they are multiplied, the coefficient of the x term is 1.

$dc + be = 1 x.$
$(ax^2 + 5x + 7)(3x - 4)$ or
$\left(ax^2 + \frac{1}{2}x + \frac{3}{2}\right)\left(\frac{1}{2}x + \frac{1}{2}\right)$

Special Products of Polynomials

Products of Two Binomials

To multiply two binomials, we multiply each term of one by every term of the other. We can do it like this.

$$(A + B)(C + D) = AC + AD + BC + BD$$

1. Multiply First terms: AC
2. Multiply Outside terms: AD
3. Multiply Inside terms: BC
4. Multiply Last terms: BD

$\downarrow$

FOIL   This will help you remember the rule.

EXAMPLE 1
Multiply.

$$\overset{\text{F}}{(x + 8)(x^2 + 5)} = x^3 + \overset{\text{O}}{5x} + \overset{\text{I}}{8x^2} + \overset{\text{L}}{40}$$

EXAMPLES
Multiply and collect like terms.

2. $(x + 6)(x - 6) = x^2 - 6x + 6x - 36$ Using FOIL
   $ = x^2 - 36$ Collecting like terms

3. $(x + 3)(x - 2) = x^2 - 2x + 3x - 6$
   $ = x^2 + x - 6$

4. $(x^3 + 5)(x^3 - 5) = x^6 - 5x^3 + 5x^3 - 25$
   $ = x^6 - 25$

5. $(4x^2 + 5)(3x^2 - 2) = 12x^4 - 8x^2 + 15x^2 - 10$
   $ = 12x^4 + 7x^2 - 10$

TRY THIS Multiply. Try to just write the answer.

1. $(x + 3)(x + 4)$ 2. $(x + 3)(x - 5)$
3. $(2x + 1)(x + 4)$ 4. $(2x^2 - 3)(x - 2)$
5. $(6x^2 + 5)(2x^3 + 1)$ 6. $(y^3 + 7)(y^3 - 7)$
7. $(2x^5 + x^2)(-x^3 + x)$

1. $x^2 + 7x + 12$
2. $x^2 - 2x - 15$
3. $2x^2 + 9x + 4$
4. $2x^3 - 4x^2 - 3x + 6$
5. $12x^5 + 10x^3 + 6x^2 + 5$
6. $y^6 - 49$
7. $-2x^8 + 2x^6 - x^5 + x^3$

EXAMPLES
Multiply.

6. $\left(x - \dfrac{2}{3}\right)\left(x + \dfrac{2}{3}\right) = x^2 + \dfrac{2}{3}x - \dfrac{2}{3}x - \dfrac{4}{9}$

$$= x^2 - \dfrac{4}{9}$$

7. $(x^2 - 0.3)(x^2 - 0.3) = x^4 - 0.3x^2 - 0.3x^2 + 0.09$
$$= x^4 - 0.6x^2 + 0.09$$

8. $(5x^4 + 2x^3)(3x^2 - 7x) = 15x^6 - 35x^5 + 6x^5 - 14x^4$
$$= 15x^6 - 29x^5 - 14x^4$$

If the original polynomials are in descending order, it is natural to write the product in descending order, but this is not a must.

EXAMPLE 9
Multiply. In this example the original polynomials are in ascending order and the product is in ascending order.

$$(3 - 4x)(7 - 5x^3) = 21 - 15x^3 - 28x + 20x^4$$
$$= 21 - 28x - 15x^3 + 20x^4$$

TRY THIS Multiply.

8. $\left(x + \dfrac{4}{5}\right)\left(x - \dfrac{4}{5}\right)$ $\;x^2 - \frac{16}{25}$ **9.** $(x^2 + 0.5)(x^2 + 0.5)$ $\;x^4 + x^2 + 0.25$

10. $(2 + 3x^2)(4 - 5x^2)$ **11.** $(6x^3 - 3x^2)(5x^2 + 2x)$ $\;30x^5 - 3x^4 - 6x^3$
$\quad 8 + 2x^2 - 15x^4$

Multiplying the Sum and the Difference of Two Expressions

Look for a pattern.

a. $(x + 2)(x - 2) = x^2 - 2x + 2x - 4$
$$= x^2 - 4$$

b. $(3x - 5)(3x + 5) = 9x^2 + 15x - 15x - 25$
$$= 9x^2 - 25$$

c. $(3 + x)(3 - x) = 9 - 3x + 3x - x^2$
$$= 9 - x^2$$

d. $(1 + 4x)(1 - 4x) = 1 - 4x + 4x - 16x^2$
$$= 1 - 16x^2$$

Perhaps you observed the following.

> The product of the sum and difference of two expressions is the square of the first expression minus the square of the second.
>
> $$(A + B)(A - B) = A^2 - B^2$$

EXAMPLES
Multiply.

$(A + B)(A - B) = A^2 - B^2$ Carry out the rule. Say the words as you go.

The square of the first expression, x^2, minus

10. $(x + 4)(x - 4) = x^2 - 4^2$ the square of the second, 4^2.

$\quad\quad\quad\quad\quad\quad = x^2 - 16$ Simplifying

11. $(2w + 5)(2w - 5) = (2w)^2 - 5^2$

$\quad\quad\quad\quad\quad\quad\quad = 4w^2 - 25$

12. $(3x^2 - 7)(3x^2 + 7) = (3x^2)^2 - 7^2$

$\quad\quad\quad\quad\quad\quad\quad\quad = 9x^4 - 49$

13. $(-4x - 10)(-4x + 10) = (-4x)^2 - 10^2$

$\quad\quad\quad\quad\quad\quad\quad\quad\quad = 16x^2 - 100$

TRY THIS Multiply.

12. $(x + 2)(x - 2)$ $x^2 - 4$ 13. $(x + 7)(x - 7)$ $x^2 - 49$

14. $(3t + 5)(3t - 5)$ 15. $(2x^3 + 1)(2x^3 - 1)$ $4x^6 - 1$

$\quad\quad\quad\quad\quad\quad 9t^2 - 25$

4-8

Exercises
Multiply.

1. $(x + 1)(x^2 + 3)$

2. $(x^2 - 3)(x - 1)$

3. $(x^3 + 2)(x + 1)$

4. $(x^4 + 2)(x + 12)$

5. $(x + 2)(x - 3)$

6. $(x + 2)(x + 2)$

7. $(3x + 2)(3x + 3)$

8. $(4x + 1)(2x + 2)$

9. $(5x - 6)(x + 2)$

10. $(x - 8)(x + 8)$

1. $x^3 + x^2 + 3x + 3$
2. $x^3 - x^2 - 3x + 3$
3. $x^4 + x^3 + 2x + 2$
4. $x^5 + 12x^4 + 2x + 24$
5. $x^2 - x - 6$
6. $x^2 + 4x + 4$
7. $9x^2 + 15x + 6$
8. $8x^2 + 10x + 2$
9. $5x^2 + 4x - 12$
10. $x^2 - 64$

11. $(3x - 1)(3x + 1)$

13. $(4x - 2)(x - 1)$

15. $\left(x - \dfrac{1}{4}\right)\left(x + \dfrac{1}{4}\right)$

17. $(x - 0.1)(x + 0.1)$

19. $(2x^2 + 6)(x + 1)$

21. $(-2x + 1)(x - 6)$

23. $(x + 7)(x + 7)$

25. $(1 + 2x)(1 - 3x)$

27. $(x^2 + 3)(x^3 - 1)$

29. $(x^2 - 2)(x - 1)$

31. $(3x^2 - 2)(x^4 - 2)$

33. $(3x^5 + 2)(2x^2 + 6)$

35. $(8x^3 + 1)(x^3 + 8)$

37. $(4x^2 + 3)(x - 3)$

39. $(4x^4 + x^2)(x^2 + x)$

12. $(2x + 3)(2x + 3)$

14. $(2x - 1)(3x + 1)$

16. $\left(x + \dfrac{3}{4}\right)\left(x + \dfrac{3}{4}\right)$

18. $(3x^2 + 1)(x + 1)$

20. $(2x^2 + 3)(2x - 1)$

22. $(3x + 4)(2x - 4)$

24. $(2x + 5)(2x + 5)$

26. $(-3x - 2)(x + 1)$

28. $(x^4 - 3)(2x + 1)$

30. $(x^3 + 2)(x - 3)$

32. $(x^{10} + 3)(x^{10} - 3)$

34. $(1 - 2x)(1 + 3x^2)$

36. $(4 - 2x)(5 - 2x^2)$

38. $(7x - 2)(2x - 7)$

40. $(5x^6 + 3x^3)(2x^6 + 2x^3)$

11. $9x^2 - 1$
12. $4x^2 + 12x + 9$
13. $4x^2 - 6x + 2$
14. $6x^2 - x - 1$
15. $x^2 - \dfrac{1}{16}$
16. $x^2 + \dfrac{3}{2}x + \dfrac{9}{16}$
17. $x^2 - 0.01$
18. $3x^3 + 3x^2 + x + 1$
19. $2x^3 + 2x^2 + 6x + 6$
20. $4x^3 - 2x^2 + 6x - 3$
21. $-2x^2 - 11x + 6$
22. $6x^2 - 4x - 16$
23. $x^2 + 14x + 49$
24. $4x^2 + 20x + 25$
25. $1 - x - 6x^2$
26. $-3x^2 - 5x - 2$
27. $x^5 + 3x^3 - x^2 - 3$
28. $2x^5 + x^4 - 6x - 3$
29. $x^3 - x^2 - 2x + 2$
30. $x^4 - 3x^3 + 2x - 6$
31. $3x^6 - 6x^2 - 2x^4 + 4$
32. $x^{20} - 9$
33. $6x^7 + 18x^5 + 4x^2 + 12$
34. $1 - 2x + 3x^2 - 6x^3$
35. $8x^6 + 65x^3 + 8$
36. $20 - 10x - 8x^2 + 4x^3$
37. $4x^3 - 12x^2 + 3x - 9$
38. $14x^2 - 53x + 14$
39. $4x^6 + 4x^5 + x^4 + x^3$
40. $10x^{12} + 16x^9 + 6x^6$

Multiply.

41. $(x + 4)(x - 4)$

43. $(2x + 1)(2x - 1)$

45. $(5m - 2)(5m + 2)$

47. $(2x^2 + 3)(2x^2 - 3)$

49. $(3x^4 - 4)(3x^4 + 4)$

51. $(x^6 - x^2)(x^6 + x^2)$

53. $(x^4 + 3x)(x^4 - 3x)$

55. $(x^{12} - 3)(x^{12} + 3)$

57. $(2x^8 + 3)(2x^8 - 3)$

42. $(x + 1)(x - 1)$

44. $(x^2 + 1)(x^2 - 1)$

46. $(3x^4 + 2)(3x^4 - 2)$

48. $(6x^5 - 5)(6x^5 + 5)$

50. $(t^2 - 0.2)(t^2 + 0.2)$

52. $(2x^3 - 0.3)(2x^3 + 0.3)$

54. $\left(\dfrac{3}{4} + 2x^3\right)\left(\dfrac{3}{4} - 2x^3\right)$

56. $(12 - 3x^2)(12 + 3x^2)$

58. $\left(x - \dfrac{2}{3}\right)\left(x + \dfrac{2}{3}\right)$

41. $x^2 - 16$
43. $4x^2 - 1$
45. $25m^2 - 4$
47. $4x^4 - 9$
49. $9x^8 - 16$
51. $x^{12} - x^4$
53. $x^8 - 9x^2$
55. $x^{24} - 9$
57. $4x^{16} - 9$

42. $x^2 - 1$
44. $x^4 - 1$
46. $9x^8 - 4$
48. $36x^{10} - 25$
50. $t^4 - 0.04$
52. $4x^6 - 0.09$
54. $\dfrac{9}{16} - 4x^6$
56. $144 - 9x^4$
58. $x^2 - \dfrac{4}{9}$

Extension

Solve as the difference of two squares.

59. 18×22 [Use $(20 - 2)(20 + 2)$.] $\quad 20^2 - 2^2$ or 396

60. 93×107 $\quad (100 - 7)(100 + 7) = 100^2 - 7^2 = 9951$

Multiply.

61. $4y(y + 5)(2y + 8)$ $\quad 8y^3 + 72y^2 + 160y$

62. $8x(2x - 3)(5x + 9)$ $\quad 80x^3 + 24x^2 - 216x$

Solve for x.

63. $(x + 2)(x - 5) = (x + 1)(x - 3)$ $\quad$ -7

64. $(2x + 5)(x - 4) = (x + 5)(2x - 4)$ $\quad$ 0

65. $(x + 1)(x + 2) = (x + 3)(x + 4)$ $\quad$ $-2\frac{1}{2}$

66. $(x + 4)^2 = (x + 8)(x - 8)$ $\quad$ -10

67. $x^2 = (x + 10)^2$ $\quad$ -5

68. $x^2 = (x - 12)^2$ $\quad$ 6

Challenge

Multiply.

69. $[(a + 5) + 1][(a + 5) - 1]$ $\quad$ $a^2 + 10a + 24$

70. $[3a - (2a - 3)][3a + (2a - 3)]$ $\quad$ $5a^2 + 12a - 9$

71. $[(2x - 1)(2x + 1)](4x^2 + 1)$ $\quad$ $16x^4 - 1$

72. $[(x + 1) - x^2][(x - 2) + 2x^2]$ $\quad$ $-2x^4 + x^3 + 5x^2 - x - 2$

Solve for x.

73. $(4x - 1)^2 - (3x + 2)^2 = (7x + 4)(x - 1)$ $\quad$ $\frac{1}{17}$

74. The product of the sum and difference of two expressions is $25a^2 - 49$. What are the two expressions? $\quad$ $(5a + 7)(5a - 7)$

75. The height of a box is one more than its length, and the length is one more than its width.
    a. Find the volume of the box in terms of the width w. $\quad$ $w(w + 1)(w + 2) = w^3 + 3w^2 + 2w$
    b. Find the volume in terms of the length l. $\quad$ $l(l - 1)(l + 1) = l^3 - l$
    c. Find the volume in terms of the height h. $\quad$ $h(h - 1)(h - 2) = h^3 - 3h^2 + 2h$

76. Find the shaded areas by two different methods.

$Q^2 - 14Q - 5(Q - 14)$ or
$(Q - 14)(Q - 5) = Q^2 - 19Q + 70$

$F^2 - (F - 17)(F - 7)$ or
$17F + 7(F - 17) = 24F - 119$

$(y - 1)(y + 1)$ or
$y^2 - y + 1(y - 1)$
$= y^2 - 1$

77. A cab company charges 70¢ for the first $\frac{1}{7}$ mile and 10¢ each additional $\frac{1}{7}$ mile per trip. A person takes x number of 4-mile trips every month for 11 months, and 6 trips in August before going on vacation. How much did a year of taxi service cost?

Each trip is $0.70 + 39(7)(.10) = 3.40$, $3.40(11x + 6) = 37.40x + 20.40$

More Special Products

Squaring Binomials

Multiplying a binomial by itself is called squaring the binomial.
Look for a pattern.

a. $(x + 2)(x + 2) = x^2 + 2x + 2x + 4$
$= x^2 + 4x + 4$

b. $(3x + 5)(3x + 5) = 9x^2 + 15x + 15x + 25$
$= 9x^2 + 30x + 25$

c. $(x - 2)(x - 2) = x^2 - 2x - 2x + 4$
$= x^2 - 4x + 4$

d. $(3x - 5)(3x - 5) = 9x^2 - 15x - 15x + 25$
$= 9x^2 - 30x + 25$

There is a quick way to square a binomial.

> The square of a binomial is the square of the first term, plus or
> minus twice the product of the two terms, plus the square of the
> last term.
>
> $$(A + B)^2 = A^2 + 2AB + B^2$$
> $$(A - B)^2 = A^2 - 2AB + B^2$$

EXAMPLES
Multiply.

$(A + B)^2 = A^2 + 2 \ A \quad B + B^2$

1. $(x + 3)^2 = x^2 + 2 \cdot x \cdot 3 + 3^2$
$= x^2 + 6x + 9$

2. $(t - 5)^2 = t^2 - 2 \cdot t \cdot 5 + 5^2$
$= t^2 - 10t + 25$

3. $(2x + 7)^2 = (2x)^2 + 2 \cdot 2x \cdot 7 + 7^2$
$= 4x^2 + 28x + 49$

4. $(3x^2 - 5x)^2 = (3x^2)^2 - 2 \cdot 3x^2 \cdot 5x + (5x)^2$
$= 9x^4 - 30x^3 + 25x^2$

1. $(x + 2)(x + 2)$ 2. $(y - 9)(y - 9)$ 3. $(4x - 5)^2$

4. $(a - 4)^2$ 5. $(5x^2 + 4)(5x^2 + 4)$ 6. $(4x^2 - 3x)^2$

1. $x^2 + 4x + 4$
2. $y^2 - 18x + 81$
3. $16x^2 - 40x + 25$
4. $a^2 - 8a + 16$
5. $25x^4 + 40x^2 + 16$
6. $16x^4 - 24x^3 + 9x^2$

Multiplication of Various Types

Now that we have considered how to quickly multiply certain types of polynomials, let us try several types mixed together so we can learn to sort them out. When you multiply, first see what kind of multiplication pattern you have. Then use the best method. The methods you have used so far are as follows.

1. $(A + B)(A + B) = (A + B)^2 = A^2 + 2AB + B^2$

2. $(A - B)(A - B) = (A - B)^2 = A^2 - 2AB + B^2$

3. $(A + B)(A - B) = A^2 - B^2$

4. FOIL

5. The product of a monomial and any polynomial
   Multiply each term of the polynomial by the monomial.

6. The product of any polynomials
   Multiply each term of one polynomial by every term of the other.

Note that FOIL will work for any of the first three rules, but it is faster to learn to use them as they are given.

EXAMPLES
Multiply.

5. $(x + 3)(x - 3) = x^2 - 9$ Using method 3 (the product of the sum and difference of two equations)

6. $(t + 7)(t - 5) = t^2 + 2t - 35$ Using method 4 (the product of two binomials)

7. $(x + 7)(x + 7) = x^2 + 14x + 49$ Using method 1 (the square of a binomial sum)

8. $2x^3(9x^2 + x - 7) = 18x^5 + 2x^4 - 14x^3$ Using method 5 (the product of a monomial and a trinomial)

9. $(3x^2 - 7x)^2 = 9x^4 - 42x^3 + 49x^2$ Using method 2 (the square of a binomial difference

10. $\left(3x + \dfrac{1}{4}\right)^2 = 9x^2 + 2(3x)\dfrac{1}{4} + \dfrac{1}{16}$

$\qquad = 9x^2 + \dfrac{3}{2}x + \dfrac{1}{16}$

Using method 1 (the square of a binomial sum)

11. $(x^2 - 3x + 2)(2x - 4)$

$\qquad = 2x^3 - 6x^2 + 4x - 4x^2 + 12x - 8$

$\qquad = 2x^3 - 10x^2 + 16x - 8$

Using method 6 (the product of any polynomials)

7. $x^2 + 11x + 30$
8. $x^2 - 16$
9. $-8x^5 + 20x^4 + 40x^2$
10. $81x^4 + 18x^2 + 1$
11. $4x^2 + 6x - 40$
12. $3x^3 - 14x^2 - x + 6$

TRY THIS Multiply.

7. $(x + 5)(x + 6)$ **8.** $(x - 4)(x + 4)$ **9.** $4x^2(-2x^3 + 5x^2 + 10)$

10. $(9x^2 + 1)^2$ **11.** $(2x - 5)(2x + 8)$ **12.** $(x^2 - 4x - 3)(3x - 2)$

4—9

Exercises
7. $9x^4 + 6x^2 + 1$ 11. $9x^2 + \frac{9}{2}x + \frac{9}{16}$
8. $25x^4 - 10x^2 + 1$ 12. $4x^2 - \frac{4}{5}x + \frac{1}{25}$

Multiply.

1. $(x + 2)^2$ $x^2 + 4x + 4$ **2.** $(x + 3)^2$ $x^3 + 6x + 9$ **3.** $(x - 3)^2$ $x^2 - 6x + 9$

4. $(x - 2)^2$ $x^2 - 4x + 4$ **5.** $(2x - 1)^2$ $4x^2 - 4x + 1$ **6.** $(3x + 1)^2$ $9x^2 + 6x + 1$

7. $(3x^2 + 1)(3x^2 + 1)$ **8.** $(5x^2 - 1)(5x^2 - 1)$ **9.** $\left(x - \dfrac{1}{2}\right)^2$ $x^2 - x + \frac{1}{4}$

10. $\left(x - \dfrac{1}{4}\right)^2$ $x^2 - \frac{1}{2}x + \frac{1}{16}$ **11.** $\left(3x + \dfrac{3}{4}\right)\left(3x + \dfrac{3}{4}\right)$ **12.** $\left(2x - \dfrac{1}{5}\right)\left(2x - \dfrac{1}{5}\right)$

13. $(3 - t)^2$ $t^2 - 6t + 9$ **14.** $(5 - w)^2$ $w^2 - 10w + 25$ **15.** $(x^3 + 1)^2$ $x^6 + 2x^3 + 1$

16. $(x^3 + 2)^2$ $x^6 + 4x^3 + 4$ **17.** $(8x + x^2)^2$ $64x^2 - 16x^3 + x^4$ **18.** $(5x + 6x^2)^2$ $25x^2 + 60x^3 + 36x^4$

Multiply.

19. $(x - 8)(x - 8)$ **20.** $(x + 7)(x + 7)$

21. $(x - 8)(x + 8)$ **22.** $(x + 7)(x - 7)$

23. $(x - 8)(x + 5)$ **24.** $(x + 7)(x - 4)$

25. $4x(x^2 + 6x - 3)$ **26.** $8x(-x^2 - 4x + 3)$

27. $\left(2x^2 - \dfrac{1}{2}\right)\left(2x^2 - \dfrac{1}{2}\right)$ **28.** $(1 - x^2)(1 - x^2)$

29. $(6a^3 - 1)(6a^3 + 1)$ **30.** $(2b^2 - 7)(3b^2 + 9)$

31. $(2 - 3x)(2 + 3x)$ **32.** $(4 + 5x)(4 - 5x)$

33. $(6x^4 + 4)^2$ **34.** $(8 - 6x^4)^2$

35. $-6x^2(x^3 + 8x - 9)$ **36.** $-5x^2(x^3 - 2x + 4)$

19. $x^2 - 16x + 64$
20. $x^2 + 14x + 49$
21. $x^2 - 64$
22. $x^2 - 49$
23. $x^2 - 3x + 40$
24. $x^2 + 3x - 28$
25. $4x^3 + 24x^2 - 12x$
26. $-8x^3 - 32x^2 + 24x$
27. $4x^4 - 2x^2 + \frac{1}{4}$
28. $x^4 - 2x^2 + 1$
29. $36a^6 - 1$
30. $6b^4 - 3b^2 - 63$
31. $-9x^2 + 4$
32. $-25x^2 + 16$
33. $36x^8 + 48x^4 + 16$
34. $36x^8 - 96x^4 + 64$
35. $-6x^5 - 48x^3 + 54x^2$
36. $-5x^5 + 10x^3 - 20x^2$

37. $(6q^3 - 1)(2q^2 + 1)$

38. $(7p^2 + 4)(5p^2 - 8)$

39. $\left(\frac{3}{4}x + 1\right)\left(\frac{3}{4}x + 2\right)$

40. $\left(\frac{1}{5}x^2 + 9\right)\left(\frac{3}{5}x^2 - 7\right)$

41. $(x^2 + 2x + 3)(4x + 5)$

42. $(x^2 + 2x)(3x^2 + 4x + 5)$

43. $(x^3 - 4x^2)(3x^2 - 2x + 5)$

44. $(x^3 - 4x^2 + 5)(3x^2 - 2x)$

37. $12q^5 + 6q^3 - 2q^2 - 1$
38. $35p^4 - 36p^2 - 32$
39. $\frac{9}{16}x^2 + \frac{9}{4}x + 2$
40. $\frac{3}{25}x^4 + 4x^2 - 63$
41. $4x^3 + 13x^2 + 22x + 15$
42. $3x^4 + 10x^3 + 13x^2 + 10x$
43. $3x^5 - 14x^4 + 13x^3 - 20x^2$
44. $3x^5 - 14x^4 + 8x^3 + 15x^2 - 10x$

Extension

45. a. Find the area of the 4 small rectangles. ac, ad, bc, bd

b. What is the sum of the areas? $ac + ad + bc + bd$

c. Find the area of the rectangle.
Compare your result with your answer to part b. $ac + ad + bc + bd$, equal

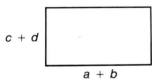

46. Consider the rectangle shown. The area of the shaded region is $(a + b)(a - b)$.

a. Find the area of the large rectangle. $a^2 + ab$

b. Find the area of the two small unshaded rectangles. $ab + b^2$

c. Find the difference of the areas in part a and part b. $a^2 + ab - (b^2 + ab) = a^2 - b^2$

d. Find the area of the shaded region and compare this result with part c. $a(a - b) + b(a - b) = a^2 - b^2$, equal

47. Find three consecutive integers, the sum of whose squares is 65 more than three times the square of the smallest. $a^2 + (a + 1)^2 + (a + 2)^2 = 3a^2 + 65$ $a = 10, a + 1 = 11, a + 2 = 12$

Challenge

48. a. What is the relationship between $x - y$ and $y - x$? Additive inverses.

b. Find $(x - y)^2$ and $(y - x)^2$. Both $= x^2 - 2xy + y^2$

c. Explain your results. $a^2 = (-a)^2$ for any a

49. Find $(10x + 5)^2$. Use your result to show how to mentally square any two digit number ending in 5. $100(x^2 + x) + 25$ Add the first digit to its square, multiple by 100, add 25.

Credit cards are a convenient way to pay when you are not carrying cash. Banks, credit card companies, and stores offer credit cards to qualified buyers.

Credit card purchases are totaled and a statement is sent to you each month. Note the types of information included in the statement.

NATIONAL EXPRESS

ACCOUNT NUMBER	BILLING DATE	PAYMENT DUE DATE
0000 0000 0000	2-19-85	3-12-85

DATE	REFERENCE	DESCRIPTION	CHARGES	CREDITS
01-20-85	0320068	JOE'S RESTAURANT RYE N.Y.	25.52	
01-23-85	0240035	COMPUTECH INC AVON N.J.	35.75	
01-30-85	0422002	TIMBER LUMBER CO. N.Y. N.Y.	49.25	
02-05-85	0500073	PAYMENT···THANK YOU		100.39
02-15-85	0660224	THE TOY BOX TROY N.Y.	11.48	

PREVIOUS BALANCE	PAYMENTS	PURCHASES	FINANCE CHARGES	NEW BALANCE	MINIMUM PAYMENT
100.39	100.39	122.00	0	122.00	10.00

FINANCE CHARGE 1$\frac{1}{2}$% PER MONTH
ANNUAL PERCENTAGE RATE IS 18%

If you pay the balance of $122.00 by the due date, no interest is charged. If you pay less, or only the minimum payment of $10.00, a finance charge of 1$\frac{1}{2}$% of the unpaid balance is included on your next monthly statement.

Monthly interest = Unpaid balance × monthly rate

$$= \$112.00 \times 1\tfrac{1}{2}\%$$
$$= \$112.00 \times 0.015$$
$$= \$1.68$$

Amount owed = Unpaid balance + monthly interest
$$= \$112.00 + \$1.68$$
$$= \$113.68$$

The next statement will include $113.68 in the new balance.

Suppose you had a balance of $122.00. You made the minimum payment of $10, and you also made some new credit card purchases totaling $73.18. Then the amount owed on your next monthly statement includes the new purchases.

Amount owed = Unpaid balance + monthly interest + new purchases
$$= \$112.00 + 1.68 + \$73.18$$
$$= \$186.86$$

Exercises

For each unpaid balance, calculate the finance charge and the total amount owed after one month. Round to the nearest cent.

1. $99.00   2. $56.50   3. $150.00   4. $72.00

1. $1.49, $100.49
2. $0.85, $57.35
3. $2.25, $152.25
4. $1.08, $73.08

For each of the following, find the unpaid balance and the finance charge on the unpaid balance.

5. Last month Lee Sung charged these purchases: gasoline $78.50, supermarket $253.40, and department store $198.30. When the statement arrived, she paid $100.00. $430.20, $6.46

6. Last month Tom bought a portable radio/tape player for $110.00 plus $5.50 sales tax. At that time, he paid $50.00 and charged the rest. When the statement arrived, Tom paid $25.00. $40.50, $0.61

For each of the following, find the unpaid balance, the finance charge on the unpaid balance, and the amount owed on the next monthly statement.

7. Bob LaRue owed $167.20 on his monthly statement. He paid $50.00. Then he made new purchases totaling $38.49. $117.20, $1.76, $157.49

8. The Gilberts owed $243.08 on their monthly statement. They paid $75.00 then they made new purchases totaling $51.74. $168.08, $2.52, $222.34

Review the material in the chapter. Then see how you have done by trying these review exercises. If you miss an exercise, restudy the indicated lesson.

4–1 Multiply.

1. $7^2 \cdot 7^4$ 7^6 **2.** $y^7 \cdot y^3 \cdot y$ y^{11} **3.** $(3x)^5(3x)^9$ $(3x)^{14}$

4–1 Divide.

4. $\dfrac{4^5}{4^2}$ 4^3 **5.** $\dfrac{6^2}{6^7}$ $\dfrac{1}{6^5}$ **6.** $\dfrac{a^5}{a^8}$ $\dfrac{1}{a^3}$

4–1 Simplify.

7. $(y^4)^3$ y^{12} **8.** $(x^3)^4$ x^{12} **9.** $(3t^4)^2$ $9t^8$ **10.** $(-2xy^2)^3$ $-8x^3y^6$

4–2 Identify the terms of each polynomial.

11. $3x^2 + 6x + \dfrac{1}{2}$
$3x^2, 6x, \frac{1}{2}$

12. $-4y^5 + 7y^2 - 3y - 2$
$-4y^5, 7y^2, -3y, -2$

4–2 Tell whether each polynomial is a monomial, binomial, trinomial, or none of these.

13. $4x^3 - x^3 + 2$ Trinomial **14.** $4 - 9t^3 - 7t^4 + 10t^2$ None **15.** $7y^2$ Monomial

4–2 Collect like terms.

16. $5x^3 - x^3 + 4$ **17.** $\dfrac{3}{4}x^3 + 4x^2 - x^3 + 7$ 16. $4x^3 + 4$ 17. $-\frac{1}{4}x^3 + 4x^2 + 7$
18. $-2x^4 + 16 + 2x^4 + 9 - 3x^5$ $-3x^5 + 25$

4–2 Identify the degree of each term and the degree of the polynomial.

19. $x^3 + 4x - 6$
3, 1, 0; 3

20. $x^5 + 3x^4 + 5x^3 + 2x^2 + 1$
5, 4, 3, 2, 0; 5

4–2 Identify the coefficient of each term.

21. $6x^2 + 17$
6, 17

22. $4x^3 + 6x^2 + 5x + 20$
4, 6, 5, 20

4–3 Collect like terms and then arrange in descending order.

23. $3x^2 - 2x + 3 - 5x^2 - 1 - x$
$-2x^3 - 3x + 2$

24. $-x + \dfrac{1}{2} + 14x^4 - 7x - 1 - 4x^4$
$10x^4 - 8x - \frac{1}{2}$

4–3

25. Identify the missing terms in $x^3 + x$. 2nd degree, constant

4–3 Evaluate each polynomial for $x = 5$.

26. $7x - 10$ $_{25}$

27. $x^2 - 3x + 6$ $_{16}$

4–4 Add.

28. $(3x^4 - x^3 + x - 4) + (x^5 + 7x^3 - 3x^2 - 5) + (-5x^4 + 6x^2 - x)$
$+ (2x^5 + 2x^4 - 5x^3 - 8x^2 + x - 7)$ $_{3x^5 + x^3 - 5x^2 + x - 16}$

29. $(3x^5 - 4x^4 + x^3 - 3) + (3x^4 - 5x^3 + 3x^2) + (4x^5 + 4x^3) + (-5x^5 - 5x^2)$
$+ (-5x^4 + 2x^3 + 5)$ $_{2x^5 - 6x^4 + 2x^3 - 2x^2 + 2}$

30. $-\frac{3}{4}x^4 + \frac{1}{2}x^3 \qquad\qquad + \frac{7}{8}$

$\qquad\qquad - \frac{1}{4}x^3 - x^2 - \frac{7}{4}x$

$\quad \frac{3}{2}x^4 \qquad\qquad + \frac{2}{3}x^2 \qquad\qquad - \frac{1}{2}$

$\overline{\quad \frac{3}{4}x^4 \quad + \quad \frac{1}{4}x^3 \quad - \quad \frac{1}{3}x^2 \quad - \quad \frac{7}{4}x \quad + \quad \frac{3}{8}}$

31. The length of a rectangle is 4m greater than the width. Express the area as a polynomial. $_{w^2 + 4w \text{ or } l^2 - 4l}$

4–5 Subtract.

32. $(5x^2 - 4x + 1) - (3x^2 + 7)$ $_{2x^2 - 4x - 6}$

33. $(3x^5 - 4x^4 + 2x^2 + 3) - (2x^5 - 4x^4 + 3x^3 + 4x^2 - 5)$ $_{x^5 - 3x^3 - 2x^2 + 8}$

34. $2x^5 \qquad\quad - x^3 \qquad\quad + x + 3$

$\quad\; 3x^5 - x^4 + 4x^3 + 2x^2 - x + 3$

$\overline{\quad x^5 \quad + \; x^4 \; - \; 5x^3 \; - \; 2x^2 \; + \; 2x}$

4–6 Multiply.

35. $3x$ and $-4x^2$ **36.** $5x^4(3x^3 - 8x^2 + 10x + 2)$ **37.** $(x + 4)(x - 7)$

38. $\left(x + \frac{2}{3}\right)\left(x + \frac{1}{2}\right)$ **39.** $(x - 0.3)(x - 0.75)$ **40.** $(1.5x + 6.5)(0.2x + 1.3)$

4–7

41. $(4x^2 - 5x + 1)(3x - 2)$ **42.** $(4x^3 - 2x + 3)(x^2 + 2)$ **43.** $(x^4 - 2x + 3)(x^3 + x - 1)$

4–8

44. $(2x^2 + 3)(x^2 - 7)$ **45.** $(3x^2 + 4)(3x^2 - 4)$ **46.** $(4x^7 + 3)(4x^7 - 3)$

4–9

47. $(x - 9)^2$ **48.** $(7x + 1)^2$

49. $(3x^2 - 2x)^2$

50. $(x^3 - 2x + 3)(4x^2 - 5x)$

35. $-12x^3$
36. $15x^7 - 40x^6 + 5x^5 + 10x^4$
37. $x^2 - 3x - 28$
38. $x^2 + \frac{7}{6}x + \frac{1}{3}$
39. $x^2 - 1.05x + 0.225$
40. $0.3x^2 + 3.25x + 8.45$
41. $12x^3 - 23x^2 + 13x - 2$
42. $4x^5 + 6x^3 + 3x^2 - 4x + 6$
43. $x^7 + x^5 - 3x^4 + 3x^3$
$\quad - 2x^2 + 5x - 3$
44. $2x^4 - 11x^2 - 21$
45. $9x^4 - 16$
46. $16x^{14} - 9$
47. $x^2 - 18x + 81$
48. $49x^2 + 14x + 1$
49. $9x^4 - 12x^3 + 4x^2$
50. $4x^5 - 13x^3 + 22x^2 - 15x$

Multiply.

1. $6^2 \cdot 6^3$ 6^5 2. $x^6 \cdot x^2$ x^8 3. $(4a)^3(4a)^8$ $(4a)^{11}$

Divide.

4. $\dfrac{3^5}{3^2}$ 3^3 5. $\dfrac{x^3}{x^8}$ $\dfrac{1}{x^5}$ 6. $\dfrac{a^{13}}{a^9}$ a^4

Simplify.

7. $(x^3)^2$ x^6 8. $(-3y^2)^3$ $-27y^6$ 9. $(2a^3b)^4$ $16a^{12}b^4$

Collect like terms.

10. $4a^2 - 6 + a^2$ 11. $y^2 - 3y - y + 2y^2$ 10. $5a^2 - 6$ 11. $3y^2 - 4y$

Identify the degree of each term and the degree of the polynomial.

12. $x^4 - 5x^3 + x^2 + x - 3$ 4, 3, 2, 1, 0, 4

Collect like terms and then arrange in descending order.

13. $3 - x^2 + 2x + 5x^2 - 6x$ $4x^2 - 4x + 3$

Evaluate the polynomial for $x = -2$.

14. $x^2 + 5x - 1$ -7

Add.

15. $(3x^5 + 5x^3 - 5x^2 - 3) + (x^5 + x^4 - 3x^3 - 3x^2 + 2x - 4)$ $4x^5 + x^4 + 2x^3 - 8x^2 + 2x - 7$
16. $(5x^4 + 7x^3 - 8) + (3x^4 - 5x^3 + 6x^2)$ $8x^4 + 2x^3 + 6x^2 - 8$

Subtract.

17. $(12x^2 - 3x - 8) - (4x^2 + 5)$ $8x^2 - 3x - 13$
18. $(2x^4 + x^3 - 8x^2 - 6x - 3) - (6x^4 - 8x^2 + 2x)$ $-4x^4 + x^3 - 8x - 3$

Multiply.

19. $-3x^2(4x^2 - 3x - 5)$ $-12x^4 + 9x^3 + 15x^2$ 20. $(2x + 1)(3x^2 - 5x - 3)$ $6x^3 - 7x^2 - 11x - 3$
21. $(3b + 5)(b - 3)$ $3b^2 - 4b - 15$ 22. $(x + 10)(x - 10)$ $x^2 - 100$ 23. $(5t + 2)^2$ $25t^2 + 20t + 4$

Challenge

24. The height of a box is one less than its length, and the length is 2 more than its width. Find the volume in terms of the length. $l(l - 2)(l - 1) = l^3 - 3l^2 + 2l$

1–5 Factor.

1. $6x + 6y$ **2.** $24w + 24z$ **3.** $4y + 28 + 12z$ **4.** $3w + 6z + 18$
$6(x + y)$ $24(w + z)$ $4(y + 7 + 3z)$ $3(w + 2z + 6)$

2–7

5. $8x - 32$ **6.** $22 - 11y$ **7.** $3x + 18y - 6$ **8.** $4a + 16b - 6c$
$8(x - 4)$ $11(2 - y)$ $3(x + 6y - 2)$ $2(2a + 8b - 3c)$

3–1 Solve.

9. $x + 4 = -11$ -15 **10.** $w - 8 = -2$ 6

3–2

11. $3x = 21$ 7 **12.** $-7x = -35$ 5

3–3

13. $4x + 9 = 17$ 2 **14.** $\frac{1}{2}y + \frac{2}{3} = -\frac{5}{6}$ -3

3–6

15. The perimeter of a rectangle is 280 cm. The length is 20 cm less than the width. Find the dimensions.   Width is 80 cm; length is 60 cm.

4–6 Multiply.

16. $(-6x^8)(2x^5) \cdot$ **17.** $9x(4x + 7)$
$-12x^{13}$ $36x^2 + 63x$

4–7

18. $(3x + 8)(x - 7)$ **19.** $(x + 3)(5x - 7)$
$3x^2 - 13x - 56$ $5x^2 + 8x - 21$

4–6

20. $8x(2x^2 - 6x + 1)$ $16x^3 - 48x^2 + 8x$

4–8

21. $(x + 6)(x - 4)$ **22.** $(y - 8)(y + 3)$ 21. $x^2 - 2x - 24$ 22. $y^2 - 5y - 24$
23. $(7w + 6)(4w - 1)$ $28w^2 + 17w - 6$

4–9

24. $(t - 9)^2$ **25.** $(5x + 3)^2$
$t^2 - 18t + 81$ $25x^2 + 30x + 9$

5

CHAPTER FIVE

Polynomials and Factoring

5-1 Factoring Polynomials

Factoring is the reverse of multiplication. To factor an expression means to write an equivalent expression that is a product of expressions.

Factoring Monomials

To factor a monomial we find two monomials whose product is that monomial. Compare.

Multiplying
$(4x)(5x) = 20x^2$
$(2x)(10x) = 20x^2$
$(-4x)(-5x) = 20x^2$
$(x)(20x) = 20x^2$

Factoring
$20x^2 = (4x)(5x)$
$20x^2 = (2x)(10x)$
$20x^2 = (-4x)(-5x)$
$20x^2 = (x)(20x)$

There are still many other ways to factor $20x^2$. Each is called a factorization of $20x^2$.

EXAMPLE 1
Find factorizations of $15x^3$.

Factors of $15x^3$ are: $1, -1, 3, -3, 5, -5, 15, -15, x, x^2, x^3$.
Possible factorizations are:

$(15x)(1x^2)$
$(5x)(3x^2)$
$(3x)(5x^2)$
$(1x)(15x^2)$

Since $(-1)(-1) = 1$, we could also have the following.

$(-15x)(-1x^2)$
$(-5x)(-3x^2)$
$(-3x)(-5x^2)$
$(-1x)(-15x^2)$

There are still other ways to factor $15x^3$.

TRY THIS Find three factorizations of each monomial.

1. $8x^4$ **2.** $6x^5$ **3.** $12x^2$ Answers may vary.

1. $(4x^2)(2x^2)$, $(4x)(2x^3)$, $(8x)(x^3)$
2. $(2x)(3x^4)$, $(x^2)(6x^3)$, $(2x^3)(3x^2)$
3. $(6x)(2x)$, $(-6x, -2x)$, $(4x)(3x)$

Factoring When Terms Have a Common Factor

To multiply a monomial and a polynomial with more than one term, we use the distributive law and multiply each term by the monomial. To factor, we do the reverse.

Compare

Multiply	**Factor**
$5(x + 3) = (5)x + (5)3$	$5x + 15 = (5)x + (5)3$
$\qquad = 5x + 15$	$\qquad = 5(x + 3)$
$3x(x^2 + 2x - 4)$	$3x^3 + 6x^2 - 12x$
$= (3x)x^2 + (3x)2x + (3x)(-4)$	$= (3x)x^2 + (3x)2x + (3x)(-4)$
$= 3x^3 + 6x^2 - 12x$	$= 3x(x^2 + 2x - 4)$

We use the factor with the greatest possible coefficient and the greatest exponent as a common factor. We say we have "factored out" the common factor.

EXAMPLES
Factor.

2. $3x^2 + 6 = (3)x^2 + (3)2 = 3(x^2 + 2)$ Factoring out the common factor, 3

3. $5x^4 + 20x^3 = (5x^3)x + (5x^3)4 = 5x^3(x + 4)$ Factoring out the common factor, $5x^3$

4. $16x^3 + 20x^2 = (4x^2)4x + (4x^2)5 = 4x^2(4x + 5)$ Factoring out the common factor, $4x^2$

5. $15x^5 - 12x^4 + 27x^3 - 3x^2$
$= (3x^2)5x^3 - (3x^2)4x^2 + (3x^2)9x - (3x^2)1$ Factoring each term
$= 3x^2(5x^3 - 4x^2 + 9x - 1)$ Factoring out the common factor, $3x^2$

6. $\frac{3}{5}x^4 - \frac{4}{5}x^2 = \left(\frac{1}{5}x^2\right)3x^2 - \left(\frac{1}{5}x^2\right)4 = \frac{1}{5}(3x^2 - 4)$ Factoring out the common factor $\frac{1}{5}x^2$

7. $9x^4 + 12x^2 - 2$ No common monomial factor

If you can find the common factor without factoring each term, you should just write the answer.

TRY THIS Factor.

4. $x^2 + 3x$ **5.** $3x^6 - 5x^3 + 2x^2$

6. $9x^4 - 15x^3 + 3x^2$

7. $\frac{3}{4}x^3 + \frac{5}{4}x^2 + \frac{7}{4}x - \frac{1}{4}$

8. $35x^7 - 49x^6 + 14x^5 - 63x^3$

4. $x(x + 3)$
5. $x^2(3x^4 - 5x + 2)$
6. $3x^2(3x^2 - 5x + 1)$
7. $\frac{1}{4}(3x^3 + 5x^2 + 7x - 1)$
8. $7x^3(5x^4 - 7x^3 + 2x^2 - 9)$

Exercises

Find three factorizations for each monomial.   Answers may vary.

1. $6x^3$

2. $9x^4$

3. $-9x^5$

4. $-12x^6$

5. $24x^4$

6. $15x^5$

Factor.

7. $x^2 - 4x$

8. $x^2 + 8x$

9. $2x^2 + 6x$

10. $3x^2 - 3x$

11. $x^3 + 6x^2$

12. $4x^4 + x^2$

13. $8x^4 - 24x^2$

14. $5x^5 + 10x^3$

15. $2x^2 + 2x - 8$

16. $6x^2 + 3x - 15$

17. $17x^5 + 34x^3 + 51x$

18. $16x^6 - 32x^5 - 48x$

19. $6x^4 - 10x^3 + 3x^2$

20. $5x^5 + 10x^2 - 8x$

21. $x^5 + x^4 + x^3 - x^2$

22. $x^9 - x^7 + x^4 + x^3$

23. $2x^7 - 2x^6 - 64x^5 + 4x^3$

24. $10x^3 + 25x^2 + 15x - 20$

25. $1.6x^4 - 2.4x^3 + 3.2x^2 + 6.4x$

26. $2.5x^6 - 0.5x^4 + 5x^3 + 10x^2$

27. $\frac{5}{3}x^6 + \frac{4}{3}x^5 + \frac{1}{3}x^4 + \frac{1}{3}x^3$

28. $\frac{5}{7}x^7 + \frac{3}{7}x^5 - \frac{6}{7}x^3 - \frac{1}{7}x$

Extension

Two polynomials are relatively prime if they have no common factors other than constants. Tell which pairs are relatively prime.

29. $5x, x^2$ No

30. $3x, ax - 3$ Yes

31. $x + x^2, 3x^3$ No

32. $y - 6, y$ Yes

33. $7a, a$ No

34. $2p^2 + 2, 2p$ Yes

35. $t^2 - 4t, t^2 - 4$ Yes

36. $4x^5 + 8x^3 - 6x, 8x^3 + 12x^2 + 24x - 16$ Yes

37. $b^3 + 3b^2, b^3 - a^2$ Yes

38. $ax^2 + a^2x, ax - 2a$ No

Challenge

Find the common factor.

39. $6t^3 + 30t^2, 9t^3 + 27t^2 + 9t$ $3t$

40. $12t^4 - 15t^3 + 6t + 18, 16t^4 + 24t^3 - 48t^2 - 32t$ no common factor

41. $192t^6 - 480t^4, 144t^8 + 72t^2$ $24t^2$

42. $\frac{1}{2}x^3 + \frac{3}{8}x^2 - \frac{3}{4}x, \frac{5}{8}x^5 - \frac{5}{4}x^3 - \frac{3}{2}x^2$ $\frac{1}{8}x$

43. $27x^5 - 81x^2 + 9x, 8x^4 - 16x + 4$ no common factor

5–2 Differences of Two Squares

Recognizing Differences of Two Squares

For a binomial to be a difference of two squares, two conditions
must be true.

a. There must be two expressions, both squares. Examples are $4x^2$,
$9x^4$, 16, y^2.

b. There must be a minus sign between the two expressions.

EXAMPLE 1

Is $9x^2 - 36$ a difference of two squares?

a. The first expression is a square. $9x^2 = (3x)^2$
The second expression is a square. $36 = 6^2$

b. There is a minus sign between them.

So, we have a difference of two squares.

TRY THIS Which of the following are differences of two squares?

1. $x^2 - 25$ Yes **2.** $x^2 - 24$ No **3.** $x^2 + 36$ No

4. $4x^2 - 15$ No **5.** $16x^4 - 49$ Yes **6.** $9x^6 - 1$ Yes

Factoring Differences of Two Squares

One special product concerns multiplying the sum and difference of
the same expression.

$$(A + B)(A - B) = A^2 - B^2$$

We can reverse this equation to factor a difference of two squares.

$$A^2 - B^2 = (A + B)(A - B)$$

EXAMPLE 2

Factor.

$$x^2 - 4 = x^2 - 2^2 = (x + 2)(x - 2)$$
$$A^2 - B^2 = (A + B)(A - B)$$

TRY THIS Factor.

7. $x^2 - 9$ **8.** $y^2 - 64$ 7. $(x + 3)(x - 3)$
8. $(y + 8)(y - 8)$

Always look first for the greatest common monomial factor. Write it as the first factor. Then continue factoring.

EXAMPLES
Factor.

3. $49x^4 - 9x^6 = x^4(49 - 9x^2)$ Factoring out the common factor
$= x^4(7 - 3x)(7 + 3x)$ Factoring a difference of two squares

4. $18x^2 - 50x^6 = 2x^2(9 - 25x^4)$
$= 2x^2[3^2 - (5x^2)^2]$ Writing as a difference of two squares
$= 2x^2(3 - 5x^2)(3 + 5x^2)$

TRY THIS Factor.

9. $32y^2 - 8y^6$ 10. $64x^4 - 25x^6$ 11. $5 - 20y^6$

9. $8y^2(2 + y^2)(2 - y^2)$
10. $x^4(8 + 5x)(8 - 5x)$
11. $5(1 + 2y^3)(1 - 2y^3)$

Factoring Completely

Factor until factoring is no longer possible. This is called factoring completely.

EXAMPLE 5
Factor.

$1 - 16x^{12} = (1 - 4x^6)(1 + 4x^6)$ Factoring a difference of two squares
$= (1 + 2x^3)(1 - 2x^3)(1 + 4x^6)$ Factoring the first factor as a difference of two squares

> **Factoring Hints**
>
> 1. Always look first for a common factor.
> 2. Always factor completely, even though such directions are not given.
> 3. Check by multiplying to see if you get the original polynomial.
> 4. Never try to factor a sum of squares.

TRY THIS Factor and check by multiplying.

12. $81x^4 - 1$ 13. $49x^4 - 25x^{10}$

12. $(9x^2 + 1)(9x^2 - 1) = (9x^2 + 1)(3x + 1)(3x - 1)$
13. $x^4(49 - 25x^6) = x^4(7 + 5x^3)(7 - 5x^3)$

5-2

Exercises

Which of the following are differences of squares? *1, 2, 7, 8*

1. $x^2 - 4$ 2. $x^2 - 36$ 3. $x^2 + 36$

4. $x^2 + 4$ 5. $x^2 - 35$ 6. $x^2 - 50$

7. $16x^2 - 25$ 8. $36x^2 - 1$ 9. $49x^2 - 2$

Factor. Remember to look first for a common factor.

10. $x^2 - 4$ 11. $x^2 - 36$ 12. $x^2 - 9$ 13. $x^2 - 1$

14. $16a^2 - 9$ 15. $25x^2 - 4$ 16. $4x^2 - 25$ 17. $9a^2 - 16$

18. $8x^2 - 98$ 19. $24x^2 - 54$ 20. $36x - 49x^3$ 21. $16x - 81x^3$

22. $16x^2 - 25x^4$ 23. $x^{16} - 9x^2$ 24. $49a^4 - 81$ 25. $25a^4 - 9$

26. $a^{12} - 4a^2$ 27. $121a^8 - 100$ 28. $81y^6 - 25$ 29. $100y^6 - 49$

Factor.

30. $x^4 - 1$ 31. $x^4 - 16$ 32. $4x^4 - 64$ 33. $5x^4 - 80$

34. $1 - y^8$ 35. $x^8 - 1$ 36. $x^{12} - 16$ 37. $x^8 - 81$

38. $\frac{1}{16} - y^2$ 39. $\frac{1}{25} - x^2$ 40. $25 - \frac{1}{49}x^2$ 41. $4 - \frac{1}{9}y^2$

42. $16 - t^4$ 43. $1 - a^4$

Extension

Factor.

44. $4x^4 - 4x^2$ 45. $3x^5 - 12x^3$ 46. $3x^2 - \frac{1}{3}$ 47. $18x^3 - \frac{8}{25}x$

48. $x^2 - 2.25$ 49. $x^3 - \frac{x}{1.69}$ 50. $3.24x^2 - 0.81$ 51. $0.64x^2 - 1.21$

52. $1.28x^2 - 2$ 53. $(x + 3)^2 - 9$ 54. $(y - 5)^2 - 36$ 55. $(3a + 4)^2 - 49$

56. $(2y - 7)^2 - 1$ 57. $y^8 - 256$ 58. $x^{16} - 1$ 59. $x^2 - \left(\frac{1}{x}\right)^2$

Challenge

A polynomial is called *irreducible* if it cannot be factored except for removing a common constant factor. If the coefficient of the leading term is 1, the irreducible polynomial is called *prime*. Which of these polynomials are irreducible? Which are prime?

60. $3x^3 + 9x$ 61. $4x^2 + 2y$ 62. $4x^2 + 16y^2$

63. $x^2 + y$ 64. $16x^3 - 9x$ 65. $-25y^2 - 49$

10. $(x + 2)(x - 2)$
11. $(x + 6)(x - 6)$
12. $(x + 3)(x - 3)$
13. $(x + 1)(x - 1)$
14. $(4a + 3)(4a - 3)$
15. $(5x + 2)(5x - 2)$
16. $(2x + 5)(2x - 5)$
17. $(3a + 4)(3a - 4)$
18. $2(2x + 7)(2x - 7)$
19. $6(2x + 3)(2x - 3)$
20. $x(6 + 7x)(6 - 7x)$

21. $x(4 + 9x)(4 - 9x)$
22. $x^2(4x + 5)(4x - 5)$
23. $x^2(x^7 + 3)(x^7 - 3)$
24. $(7a^2 + 9)(7a^2 - 9)$
25. $(5a^2 + 3)(5a^2 - 3)$
26. $a^2(a^5 + 2)(a^5 - 2)$
27. $(11a^4 + 10)(11a^4 - 10)$
28. $(9y^3 + 5)(9y^3 - 5)$
29. $(10y^3 + 7)(10y^3 - 7)$

60. factors to $3x(x^2 + 3)$
61. irred.
62. irred.
63. prime irred.
64. factors to $x(4x + 3)(4x - 3)$
65. prime irred.

Recognizing Squares of Binomials

From the study of special products we know that the square of a binomial is a trinomial. Such trinomials are often called trinomial squares.

$$(A + B)^2 = A^2 + 2AB + B^2$$
$$(A - B)^2 = A^2 - 2AB + B^2$$

Use the following to help recognize a square of a binomial.
1. Two of the terms must be squares, A^2 and B^2. Examples are 4, x^2, $25x^4$, $16x^2$
2. There must be no minus sign before A^2 or B^2.
3. If we multiply A and B and double the result, we get the remaining term $2AB$, or its additive inverse, $-2AB$.

EXAMPLES
1. Is $x^2 + 6x + 9$ the square of a binomial?
   A. x^2 and 9 are squares.
   B. There is no minus sign before x^2 or 9.
   C. If we multiply x and 3, and double, we get the remaining term: $2 \cdot 3 \cdot x$, or $6x$.

   Thus, $x^2 + 6x + 9$ is the square of a binomial.

2. Is $x^2 + 6x + 11$ the square of a binomial? The answer is *no*, because only one term is a square.

3. Is $16x^2 - 56x + 49$ a trinomial square?
   A. $16x^2$ and 49 are squares.
   B. There is no minus sign before $16x^2$ or 49.
   C. If we multiply $4x$ and 7, and double, we get the additive inverse of the remaining term. $2 \cdot 4x \cdot 7 = 56x$

Thus, $16x^2 - 56x + 49$ is a trinomial square.

TRY THIS Which of the following are squares of binomials?
1. $x^2 + 8x + 16$ Yes   2. $x^2 - 10x + 25$ Yes   3. $x^2 - 12x + 4$ No
4. $4x^2 + 20x + 25$ Yes 5. $9x^2 - 14x + 16$ No 6. $16x^2 + 40x + 25$ Yes
7. $x^2 + 6x - 9$ Yes   8. $25x^2 - 30x - 9$ Yes

Factoring Trinomial Squares

To factor a trinomial square we reverse the equation for squaring a binomial.

$$A^2 + 2AB + B^2 = (A + B)^2$$
$$A^2 - 2AB + B^2 = (A - B)^2$$

EXAMPLES

Factor.

4. $x^2 + 6x + 9 = x^2 + 2 \cdot x \cdot 3 + 3^2 = (x + 3)^2$ The sign of the middle term is positive.
$$A^2 + 2 \cdot A \cdot B + B^2 = (A + B)^2$$

5. $x^2 - 14x + 49 = x^2 - 2 \cdot x \cdot 7 + 7^2 = (x - 7)^2$ The sign of the middle term is negative.
$$A^2 - 2 \cdot A \cdot B + B^2 = (A - B)^2$$

6. $16x^2 - 40x + 25 = (4x - 5)^2$

7. $27x^2 + 72x + 48 = 3(9x^2 + 24x + 16)$
$$= 3(3x + 4)^2$$

TRY THIS Factor.

9. $x^2 + 2x + 1$ **10.** $x^2 - 2x + 1$ **11.** $x^2 + 4x + 4$

12. $25x^2 - 70x + 49$ **13.** $16x^2 - 56x + 49$ **14.** $48x^2 + 120x + 75$

5–3	

Exercises

Which of the following are squares of binomials? 1 and 2 only

1. $x^2 - 14x + 49$ **2.** $x^2 - 16x + 64$ **3.** $x^2 + 16x - 64$

4. $x^2 - 14x - 49$ **5.** $x^2 - 3x + 9$ **6.** $x^2 + 2x + 4$

7. $8x^2 + 40x + 25$ **8.** $9x^2 - 36x + 24$ **9.** $36x^2 - 24x + 16$

Factor. Remember to look first for a common factor.

10. $x^2 - 14x + 49$ **11.** $x^2 - 16x + 64$

12. $x^2 + 16x + 64$ **13.** $x^2 + 14x + 49$

14. $x^2 - 2x + 1$ **15.** $x^2 + 2x + 1$

16. $x^2 + 4x + 4$ **17.** $x^2 - 4x + 4$

18. $y^2 - 6y + 9$ **19.** $y^2 + 6y + 9$

20. $2x^2 - 4x + 2$ **21.** $2x^2 - 40x + 200$

10. $(x - 7)^2$
11. $(x - 8)^2$
12. $(x + 8)^2$
13. $(x + 7)^2$
14. $(x - 1)^2$
15. $(x + 1)^2$
16. $(x + 2)^2$
17. $(x - 2)^2$
18. $(y - 3)^2$
19. $(y + 3)^2$
20. $2(x - 1)^2$
21. $2(x - 10)^2$

22. $x^3 - 18x^2 + 81x$

23. $x^3 + 24x^2 + 144x$

24. $20x^2 + 100x + 125$

25. $12x^2 + 36x + 27$

26. $49 - 42x + 9x^2$

27. $64 - 112x + 49x^2$

28. $5y^4 + 10y^2 + 5$

29. $a^4 + 14a^2 + 49$

30. $y^6 + 26y^3 + 169$

31. $y^6 - 16y^3 + 64$

32. $16x^{10} - 8x^5 + 1$

33. $9x^{10} + 12y^5 + 4$

34. $4x^4 + 4x^2 + 1$

35. $1 - 2a^3 + a^6$

36. $\frac{1}{81}x^6 - \frac{8}{27} + \frac{16}{9}$

37. $\frac{1}{9}a^2 + \frac{1}{3}a + \frac{1}{4}$

22. $x(x - 9)^2$
23. $x(x + 12)^2$
24. $5(2x + 5)^2$
25. $3(2x + 3)^2$
26. $(7 - 3x)^2$
27. $(8 - 7x)^2$
28. $5(y^2 + 1)^2$
29. $(a^2 + 7)^2$
30. $(y^3 + 13)^2$
31. $(y^3 - 8)^2$
32. $(4x^5 - 1)^2$
33. $(3x^5 + 2)^2$
34. $(2x^2 + 1)^2$
35. $(a^3 - 1)^2$
36. $\left(\frac{1}{9}x^3 + \frac{4}{3}\right)^2$
37. $\left(\frac{1}{3}a + \frac{1}{2}\right)^2$

Extension

Factor, if possible.

38. $49x^2 - 216$

39. $27x^3 - 13x$

40. $x^2 + 22x + 121$

41. $4x^2 + 9$

42. $x^2 - 5x + 25$

43. $18x^3 + 12x^2 + 2x$

44. $63x - 28$

45. $162x^2 - 82$

46. $x^4 - 9$

47. $8.1x^2 - 6.4$

48. $x^8 - 2^8$

49. $3^4 - x^4$

48. $(x^4 + 16)(x^2 + 4)(x + 2)(x - 2)$
49. $(9 + x)(3 + x)(3 - x)$

38. No
39. $x(27x^2 - 13)$
40. $(x + 11)^2$
41. No
42. No
43. $2x(3x + 1)^2$
44. $7(9x - 4)$
45. $2(81x^2 - 41)$
46. $(x^2 + 3)(x^2 - 3)$
47. No

Factor.

50. $(y + 3)^2 + 2(y + 3) + 1$ $(y + 4)^2$ **51.** $(a + 4)^2 - 2(a + 4) + 1$ $(a + 3)^2$

52. $4(a + 5)^2 + 20(a + 5) + 25$ **53.** $49(x + 1)^2 - 42(x + 1) + 9$ $(7x + 4)^2$

54. $(x + 7)^2 - 4x - 24$ $(x + 5)^2$ **55.** $(a + 4)^2 - 6a - 15$ $(a + 1)^2$

$(2a + 15)^2$

56. Is $(y + 2)^2(y - 2)^2$ a factorization of $y^4 - 8y^2 + 16$? Prove your answer. Yes. $(y + 2)^2(y - 2)^2 = [(y + 2)(y - 2)]^2 = (y^2 - 4)^2 = y^4 - 8y^2 + 16$

57. Is $(x + 3)^2(x - 3)^2$ a factorization of $x^4 + 18x^2 + 81$? Prove your answer. No. $(x + 3)^2(x - 3)^2 = [(x + 3)(x - 3)]^2 = (x^2 - 9)^2 = x^4 - 18x^2 + 81$

Challenge

Factor.

58. $9x^{18} + 48x^9 + 64$ **59.** $x^{2n} + 10x^n + 25$

58. $(3x^9 + 8)^2$
59. $(x^n + 5)^2$

Factor as the square of a binomial, then as a difference of two squares. 60. $(a + 1)^2 - 3^2 = (a + 4)(a - 2)$ 61. $(y + 3)^2 - (x + 4)^2 = (y + x + 7)(y - x - 1)$

60. $a^2 + 2a + 1 - 9$ **61.** $y^2 + 6y + 9 - x^2 - 8x - 16$

Find c so that the polynomial will be the square of a binomial.

62. $cy^2 + 6y + 1$ 9   **63.** $cy^2 - 24y + 9$ 16

64. Show that the difference of the squares of two consecutive integers is the sum of the integers. (Hint: Use x for the smaller number.) $(x + 1)^2 - x^3 = 2x + 1$

65. If $x^2 + a^2x + a^2$ factors into $(x + a)^2$, find the value of a.
$x^2 + a^2x + a^2 = x^2 + 2ax + a^2, a^2x = 2ax, a = 2$

Constant Term Positive

Recall the FOIL method of multiplying two binomials.

$$
\begin{array}{cccc}
 & \text{F} & \text{O} & \text{I} & \text{L} \\
(x + 2)(x + 5) = & x^2 + & 5x + & 2x + & 10
\end{array}
$$

$$= x^2 \quad + 7x \quad + 10$$

The product is a trinomial. In the example, the term of highest degree, called the leading term, has a coefficient of 1. The constant term is positive. To factor $x^2 + 7x + 10$, we think of FOIL in reverse. We multiplied x times x to get the first term of the trinomial. So the first term of each binomial factor is x.

$$(x + \underline{\quad})(x + \underline{\quad})$$

To get the middle term and the last term of the trinomial we used two numbers whose product is 10 and whose sum is 7. Those numbers are 2 and 5. We write them as follows.

$$(x + 2)(x + 5)$$

EXAMPLE 1
Factor $x^2 + 5x + 6$.
Think of FOIL in reverse. The first term of each factor is x.

$$(x + \underline{\quad})(x + \underline{\quad})$$

Then we look for two numbers whose product is 6 and whose sum is 5.

Pairs of numbers	Sum of numbers
1, 6	7
2, 3	5

The numbers we want are 2 and 3. The factorization is $(x + 2)(x + 3)$. We can check by multiplying to see whether we get the original trinomial.

TRY THIS Factor.

1. $x^2 + 7x + 12$ **2.** $x^2 + 13x + 36$ 1. $(x + 4)(x + 3)$
                                                      2. $(x + 9)(x + 4)$

Consider this multiplication.

$$(x - 3)(x - 4) = \overset{\text{F}}{x^2} \overset{\text{O}}{- 4x} \overset{\text{I}}{- 3x} \overset{\text{L}}{+ 12}$$

$$= x^2 \quad - 7x \quad + 12$$

When the constant term of a trinomial is positive, we look for two numbers with the same sign. The sign is that of the middle term.

$$(x^2 - 7x + 12) = (x - 3)(x - 4)$$

EXAMPLE 2
Factor $x^2 - 8x + 12$.

Since the coefficient of the middle term is negative, we look for two negative numbers. Their product must be 12 and their sum must be -8.

Pairs of numbers	Sum of numbers
$-1, -12$	-13
$-2, -6$	-8
$-3, -4$	-7

The numbers we want are -2 and -6. The factorization is $(x - 2)(x - 6)$.

TRY THIS Factor.

3. $x^2 - 8x + 15$ **4.** $x^2 - 9x + 20$ 3. $(x - 5)(x - 3)$
                                                            4. $(x - 5)(x - 4)$

Constant Term Negative

Sometimes when we use FOIL, the product has a negative constant term. Consider these multiplications.

$$(x - 5)(x + 2) = \overset{\text{F}}{x^2} \overset{\text{O}}{+ 2x} \overset{\text{I}}{- 5x} \overset{\text{L}}{- 10}$$

$$= x^2 \quad - 3x \quad - 10$$

$$(x + 5)(x - 2) = \overset{\text{F}}{x^2} \overset{\text{O}}{- 2x} \overset{\text{I}}{+ 5x} \overset{\text{L}}{- 10}$$

$$= x^2 \quad + 3x \quad - 10$$

When the constant term is negative, the middle term may be positive or negative. In these cases, we still look for two numbers whose product is -10. One of them must be positive and the other negative. Their sum must still be the coefficient of the middle term.

EXAMPLES

Factor.

3. $x^2 - 8x - 20$

Since the constant term is negative, we look for a positive and a negative number. The product must be -20 and the sum must be -8.

Pairs of numbers	Sum of numbers
$-1, 20$	19
$1, -20$	-19
$-2, 10$	8
$2, -10$	-8
$-5, 4$	-1
$5, -4$	1

The numbers we want are 2 and -10. The factorization is $(x + 2)(x - 10)$.

4. $x^2 + 5x - 24$

We look for a positive and a negative number. The product must be -24 and the sum must be 5.

Pairs of numbers	Sum of numbers
$1, -24$	-23
$-1, 24$	23
$2, -12$	-10
$-2, 12$	10
$3, -8$	-5
$-3, 8$	5
$4, -6$	-2
$-4, 6$	2

The numbers we want are 8 and -3. The factorization is $(x + 8)(x - 3)$.

5. $x^2 - x - 110$

We look for a positive and negative number. The product must be -110 and the sum must be -1.

The numbers we want are 10 and -11. The factorization is $(x + 10)(x - 11)$.

TRY THIS Factor.

5. $x^2 + 4x - 12$ **6.** $x^2 - 4x - 12$ **7.** $x^2 + 5x - 14$ **8.** $x^2 - x - 30$

5-4

Exercises

Factor.

1. $x^2 + 8x + 15$
2. $x^2 + 5x + 6$
3. $x^2 + 7x + 12$
4. $x^2 + 9x + 8$
5. $x^2 - 6x + 9$
6. $y^2 + 11y + 28$
7. $x^2 + 9x + 14$
8. $a^2 + 11a + 30$
9. $b^2 + 5b + 4$
10. $x^2 - \frac{2}{5}x + \frac{1}{25}$
11. $x^2 + \frac{2}{3}x + \frac{1}{9}$
12. $z^2 - 8z + 7$
13. $d^2 - 7d + 10$
14. $x^2 - 8x + 15$
15. $y^2 - 11y + 10$

Factor.

16. $x^2 - 2x - 15$
17. $x^2 + x - 42$
18. $x^2 + 2x - 15$
19. $x^2 - 7x - 18$
20. $y^2 - 3y - 28$
21. $x^2 - 6x - 16$
22. $y^2 - x - 42$
23. $y^2 - 4y - 45$
24. $x^2 - 7x - 60$
25. $x^2 - 2x - 99$
26. $x^2 + 6x - 72$
27. $c^2 + c - 56$
28. $b^2 + 5b - 24$
29. $a^2 + 2a - 35$
30. $2 - x - x^2$

Extension

Factor.

31. $x^2 + 20x + 100$
32. $x^2 + 20x + 99$
33. $x^2 - 21x - 100$
34. $x^2 - 20x + 96$
35. $x^2 - 21x - 72$
36. $4x^2 + 40x + 100$
37. $x^2 - 25x + 144$
38. $y^2 - 21y + 108$
39. $a^2 + a - 132$
40. $a^2 + 9a - 90$
41. $120 - 23x + x^2$
42. $96 + 22d + d^2$
43. $108 - 3x - x^2$
44. $112 + 9y - y^2$

Challenge

45. Find all integers m for which $y^2 + my + 50$ can be factored. $15, 27, 51$
46. Find all integers b for which $a^2 + ba - 50$ can be factored. $-49, -23, -5, 5, 23, 49$

Factor.

47. $x^2 - \frac{1}{2}x - \frac{3}{16}$
48. $x^2 - \frac{1}{4}x - \frac{1}{8}$
49. $x^2 + \frac{30}{7}x - \frac{25}{7}$
50. $\frac{1}{3}x^3 + \frac{1}{3}x^2 - 2x$

47. $(x + \frac{1}{4})(x - \frac{3}{4})$
48. $(x + \frac{1}{4})(x - \frac{3}{4})$
49. $(x + 5)(x - \frac{5}{7})$
50. $\frac{1}{3}x(x + 3)(x - 2)$

5. $(x + 6)(x - 2)$
6. $(x - 6)(x + 2)$
7. $(x + 7)(x - 2)$
8. $(x - 6)(x + 5)$

1. $(x + 5)(x + 3)$
2. $(x + 3)(x + 2)$
3. $(x + 4)(x + 3)$
4. $(x + 8)(x + 1)$
5. $(x - 3)^2$
6. $(y + 7)(y + 4)$
7. $(x + 7)(x + 2)$
8. $(a + 6)(a + 5)$
9. $(b + 4)(b + 1)$
10. $\left(x - \frac{1}{5}\right)^2$
11. $\left(x + \frac{1}{3}\right)^2$
12. $(z - 7)(z - 1)$
13. $(d - 5)(d - 2)$
14. $(x - 5)(x - 3)$
15. $(y - 10)(y - 1)$
16. $(x + 3)(x - 5)$
17. $(x + 7)(x - 6)$
18. $(x + 5)(x - 3)$
19. $(x + 2)(x - 9)$
20. $(x - 4)(x - 7)$
21. $(x + 2)(x - 8)$
22. $(x + 6)(x - 7)$
23. $(y + 5)(y - 9)$
24. $(x + 5)(x - 7)$
25. $(x + 9)(x - 11)$
26. $(x + 12)(x - 6)$
27. $(c + 8)(c - 7)$
28. $(b + 8)(b - 3)$
29. $(a + 7)(a - 5)$
30. $(2 + x)(1 - x)$

31. $(x + 10)^2$
32. $(x + 11)(x + 9)$
33. $(x - 25)(x + 4)$
34. $(x - 12)(x - 8)$
35. $(x - 24)(x - 3)$
36. $4(x + 5)^2$
37. $(x - 16)(x - 9)$
38. $(y - 12)(y - 9)$
39. $(a + 12)(a - 11)$
40. $(a + 15)(a - 6)$
41. $(x - 15)(x - 8)$
42. $(d + 16)(d + 6)$
43. $(12 + x)(9 - x)$
44. $(7 + y)(16 - y)$

Factoring Trinomials

Suppose the leading coefficient of a trinomial is not 1. Consider this multiplication.

$$(2x + 5)(3x + 4) \overset{\text{F} \quad \text{O} \quad \text{I} \quad \text{L}}{=} 6x^2 + 8x + 15x + 20$$

$$= 6x^2 \quad + 23x \quad + 20$$

To factor a trinomial of the type $ax^2 + bx + c$, we look for two binomials of the pattern $(\_\_x + \_\_)(\_\_x + \_\_)$, so that

$$(\_\_x + \_\_)(\_\_x + \_\_) = ax^2 + bx + c.$$

1. The numbers in the first blanks of each binomial have product a.

    $(2x + \_\_)(3x + \_\_)$ or $6x^2$

2. The numbers in the last blanks of each binomial have product c.

    $(\_\_x + 5)(\_\_x + 4)$ or 20

3. The outside product and the inside product add up to b.

    $2 \cdot 4 + 5 \cdot 3$ or $23x$

$$6x^2 + 23x + 20 = (2x + 5)(3x + 4)$$

EXAMPLE 1

Factor $3x^2 + 5x + 2$.

We first look for a factor common to all terms. There is none. Next, we look for two numbers whose product is 3. They are

$$1, 3 \qquad -1, -3$$

Now we look for numbers whose product is 2. These are

$$1, 2 \qquad -1, -2$$

Here are some of the possibilities for factorizations.

$$(x + 1)(3x + 2) \qquad (x + 2)(3x + 1)$$
$$(x - 1)(3x - 2) \qquad (x - 2)(3x - 1)$$

When we multiply, the first term will be $3x^2$ and the last term will be 2 in each case. Only the first multiplication gives a middle term of $5x$. The factorization is $(x + 1)(3x + 2)$.

TRY THIS Factor.

1. $6x^2 + 7x + 2$ **2.** $8x^2 + 10x - 3$ **3.** $6x^2 - 41x - 7$

1. $(3x + 2)(2x + 1)$
2. $(4x - 1)(2x + 3)$
3. $(6x + 1)(x - 7)$

EXAMPLE 2

Factor $8x^2 + 8x - 6$.

a. First look for a factor common to all three terms. The number 2 is a common factor, so we factor it out.

$$2(4x^2 + 4x - 3)$$

b. Now we factor the trinomial. We look for pairs of numbers whose product is 4. We have these possibilities.

$$(4x + \underline{})(x + \underline{}) \text{ and } (2x + \underline{})(2x + \underline{})$$

Next we look for pairs of numbers whose product is -3. They are $3, -1$ and $-3, 1$. Since the sign of the last term of the trinomial is negative, then the second term of each binomial must have unlike signs. We have these possibilities for factorizations.

$$(4x + 3)(x - 1) \quad (4x - 3)(x + 1) \quad (2x + 3)(2x - 1)$$
$$(4x - 1)(x + 3) \quad (4x + 1)(x - 3) \quad (2x - 3)(2x + 1)$$

Each of these possibilities gives a first term of $4x^2$ and a last term of -3. We need to check which multiplication gives a middle term of $4x$. The factorization is $(2x + 3)(2x - 1)$.

c. But don't forget the common factor. We must write it to get a factorization of the original polynomial.

$$8x^2 + 8x - 6 = 2(2x + 3)(2x - 1)$$

When you factor trinomials of the type $ax^2 + bx + c$ always look first for a common factor.

TRY THIS

4. $2x^2 + 4x - 6$ 5. $4x^2 + 2x - 6$ 6. $6x^2 + 15x - 9$

4. $2(x - 1)(x + 3)$
5. $2(2x + 3)(x - 1)$
6. $3(2x - 1)(x + 3)$

5–5

Exercises

1. $(2x + 1)(x - 4)$ 4. $(3x + 5)(x - 3)$
2. $(3x - 4)(x + 1)$ 5. $(2x + 7)(3x + 1)$
3. $(5x - 9)(x + 2)$ 6. $(2x + 3)(3x + 2)$

Factor.

1. $2x^2 - 7x - 4$ **2.** $3x^2 - x - 4$ **3.** $5x^2 + x - 18$

4. $3x^2 - 4x - 15$ **5.** $6x^2 + 23x + 7$ **6.** $6x^2 + 13x + 6$

7. $3x^2 + 4x + 1$
8. $7x^2 + 15x + 2$
9. $4x^2 + 4x - 15$

10. $9x^2 + 6x - 8$
11. $2x^2 - x - 1$
12. $15x^2 - 19x - 10$

13. $9x^2 + 18x - 16$
14. $2x^2 + 5x + 2$
15. $3x^2 - 5x - 2$

16. $18x^2 - 3x - 10$
17. $12x^2 + 31x + 20$
18. $15x^2 + 19x - 10$

19. $14x^2 + 19x - 3$
20. $35x^2 + 34x + 8$
21. $9x^2 + 18x + 8$

22. $6 - 13x + 6x^2$
23. $49 - 42x + 9x^2$
24. $15x^2 - 19x + 6$

25. $24x^2 + 47x - 2$
26. $16a^2 + 78a + 27$
27. $35x^2 - 57x - 44$

28. $9a^2 + 12a - 5$
29. $20 + 6x - 2x^2$
30. $15 + x - 2x^2$

31. $12x^2 + 28x - 24$
32. $6x^2 + 33x + 15$
33. $30x^2 - 24x - 54$

34. $20x^2 - 25x + 5$
35. $6x^2 + 4x - 10$
36. $18x^2 - 21x - 9$

37. $3x^2 + 4x + 1$
38. $6x^2 + 13x + 6$
39. $12x^2 + 28x - 24$

40. $6x^2 + 33x + 15$
41. $2x^2 - x - 1$
42. $15x^2 - 19x + 6$

43. $9x^2 + 18x - 16$
44. $14x^2 + 35x + 14$
45. $15x^2 - 25x - 10$

46. $18x^2 - 3x - 10$
47. $12x^2 + 31x + 20$
48. $15x^2 + 19x - 10$

49. $14x^2 + 19x - 3$
50. $35x^2 + 34x + 8$
51. $56x^2 - 15x + 1$

7. $(3x + 1)(x + 1)$
8. $(7x + 1)(x + 2)$
9. $(2x + 5)(2x - 3)$
10. $(3x - 2)(3x + 4)$
11. $(2x + 1)(x - 1)$
12. $(3x + 5)(5x - 2)$
13. $(3x + 8)(3x - 2)$
14. $(2x + 1)(x + 2)$
15. $(3x + 1)(x - 2)$
16. $(6x - 5)(3x + 2)$
17. $(3x + 4)(4x + 5)$
18. $(3x + 5)(5x - 2)$
19. $(7x - 1)(2x + 3)$
20. $(7x + 4)(5x + 2)$
21. $(3x + 4)(3x + 2)$
22. $(2 - 3x)(3 - 2x)$
23. $(7 - 3x)^2$
24. $(3x - 2)(5x - 3)$
25. $(x + 2)(24x - 1)$
26. $(8a + 3)(2a + 9)$
27. $(7x + 4)(5x - 11)$
28. $(3a - 1)(3a + 5)$
29. $2(5 - x)(2 + x)$
30. $(5 + 2x)(3 - x)$
31. $4(3x - 2)(x + 3)$
32. $3(2x + 1)(x + 5)$
33. $6(5x - 9)(x + 1)$
34. $5(4x - 1)(x - 1)$
35. $2(3x + 5)(x - 1)$
36. $3(2x - 3)(3x + 1)$
37. $(3x + 1)(x + 1)$
38. $(2x + 3)(3x + 2)$
39. $4(3x - 2)(x + 3)$
40. $3(2x + 1)(x + 5)$
41. $(2x + 1)(x - 1)$
42. $(5x - 3)(3x - 2)$
43. $(3x + 8)(3x - 2)$
44. $7(2x + 1)(x + 2)$
45. $5(3x + 1)(x - 2)$
46. $(6x - 5)(3x + 2)$
47. $(3x + 4)(4x + 5)$
48. $(5x - 2)(3x + 5)$
49. $(7x - 1)(2x + 3)$
50. $(5x + 2)(7x + 4)$
51. $(8x - 1)(7x - 1)$

Extension

Factor, if possible.

52. $9x^4 + 18x^2 + 8$ $(3x^2 + 2)(3x^2 + 4)$

53. $6 - 13x - 6x^2$ $(3 - 2x)(2 - 3x)$

54. $9x^2 - 42x + 49$ $(3x - 7)^2$

55. $15x^4 - 19x^2 + 6$ $(5x^2 - 3)(3x^2 - 2)$

56. $6x^3 + 4x^2 - 10x$ $2x(3x + 5)(x - 1)$

57. $18x^3 - 21x^2 - 9x$ $3x(2x - 3)(3x + 1)$

58. $x^2 + 3x - 7$ not factorable

59. $x^2 + 13x - 12$ not factorable

60. $x^5 + 2x^4 + 2x + 1$ not factorable

61. $27x^3 - 63x^2 - 147x + 343$ $(3x + 7)(3x - 7)(3x - 7)$

Challenge

Factor.

62. $20x^{2n} + 16x^n + 4$
63. $-15x^{2m} + 20x^m - 8$
    62. $(10x^n + 3)(2x^n + 1)$
    63. $(-3x^m + 4)(5x^m - 2)$

64. $3x^{6a} - 2x^{3a} - 1$
65. $x^{2n+1} - 2x^{n+1} + x$
    64. $(x^{3a} - 1)(3x^{3a} + 1)$
    65. $x(x^n - 1)^2$

66. $3(a + 1)^{n+1}(a + 3)^2 - 5(a + 1)^n(a + 3)^3$ $-2(a + 1)^n(a + 3)^2(a + 6)$

67. Here is how Bobbi factored $4y^2 + 36y + 80$.
    $2(y + 5)(y + 4)$. She argues that using the distributive law,
    $2(y + 5) = (2y + 10)$ and $2(y + 4) = (2y + 8)$. We know
    $(2y + 10)(2y + 8) = 4y^2 + 36y + 80$. So $2(y + 5)(y + 4)$
    $= 4y^2 + 36y + 18$. Evaluate Bobbi's argument.
    $(2y + 10)(2y + 8) = 2(y + 5) \cdot 2(y + 4) = \underline{4}(y + 5)(y + 4)$

Factoring by Grouping

The distributive law can be used to factor polynomials with four terms. Consider $x^3 + x^2 + 2x + 2$.

There is no factor common to all terms other than 1. But, we can factor $x^3 + x^2$ and $2x + 2$ separately.

$$x^3 + x^2 = x^2(x + 1) \quad \text{Factoring } x^3 + x^2$$
$$2x + 2 = 2(x + 1) \quad \text{Factoring } 2x + 2$$

Then, $x^3 + x^2 + 2x + 2 = x^2(x + 1) + 2(x + 1)$.

We can use the distributive law again.

$$x^2(x + 1) + 2(x + 1) = (x + 1)(x^2 + 2) \quad \text{Factoring out the common factor, } x + 1$$

EXAMPLES

Factor.

1. $x^3 + x^2 + x + 1 = (x^3 + x^2) + (x + 1)$ Separating into two binomials
$$= x^2(x + 1) + 1(x + 1) \quad \text{Factoring each binomial and writing a factor of 1}$$
$$= (x + 1)(x^2 + 1) \quad \text{Factoring out the common factor, } x + 1$$

2. $6x^3 - 9x^2 + 4x - 6 = (6x^3 - 9x^2) + (4x - 6)$ Separating into two binomials
$$= 3x^2(2x - 3) + 2(2x - 3) \quad \text{Factoring each binomial}$$
$$= (2x - 3)(3x^2 + 2) \quad \text{Factoring out the common factor, } 2x - 3$$

3. $x^3 + 2x^2 - x - 2 = (x^3 + 2x^2) + (-x - 2)$ Separating into two binomials
$$= x^2(x + 2) + 1(-x - 2) \quad \text{Common factor is not apparent.}$$
$$= x^2(x + 2) - 1(x + 2) \quad \text{Using } ab = (-a)(-b)$$
$$= (x + 2)(x^2 - 1)$$
$$= (x + 2)(x + 1)(x - 1) \quad \text{Factor completely.}$$

4. $x^3 + 2x^2 - x - 2 = (x^3 - x) + (2x^2 - 2)$ Rearranging terms first
$$= x(x^2 - 1) + 2(x^2 - 1)$$
$$= (x^2 - 1)(x + 2)$$
$$= (x + 1)(x - 1)(x + 2)$$

This method is called factoring by grouping. Not all expressions with four terms can be factored by this method.

TRY THIS Factor.

1. $8x^3 + 2x^2 + 12x + 3$ 2. $4x^3 - 6x^2 - 6x + 9$

3. $x^3 + x^2 - x - 1$ 4. $3x^5 - 12x^3 - x^2 + 4$

1. $(4x + 1)(2x^2 + 3)$
2. $(2x - 3)(2x^2 - 3)$
3. $(x + 1)(x + 1)(x - 1)$
4. $(x + 2)(x - 2)(3x^3 - 1)$

Exercises

Factor by grouping.

1. $x^3 + 3x^2 + 2x + 6$

2. $6x^3 + 3x^2 + 2x + 1$

3. $2x^3 + 6x^2 + x + 3$

4. $3x^3 + 2x^2 + 3x + 2$

5. $8x^3 - 12x^2 + 6x - 9$

6. $10x^3 - 25x^2 + 4x - 10$

7. $12x^3 - 16x^2 + 3x - 4$

8. $18x^3 - 21x^2 + 30x - 35$

9. $x^3 + 8x^2 - 3x - 24$

10. $2x^3 + 12x^2 - 5x - 30$

11. $14x^3 + 18x^2 - 21x - 27$

12. $24x^3 + 27x^2 - 8x - 9$

13. $2x^3 - 8x^2 - 9x + 36$

14. $20x^3 - 4x^2 - 25x + 5$

15. $24x^3 - 18x^2 - 20x + 15$

16. $24x^3 - 15x^2 - 56x + 35$

17. $x^3 + 5x^2 - x - 5$

18. $3x^3 + 2x^2 - 27x - 18$

19. $16x^3 - 48x^2 - 25x + 75$

20. $27x^3 - 18x^2 - 12x + 8$

1. $(x + 3)(x^2 + 2)$
2. $(2x + 1)(3x^2 + 1)$
3. $(x + 3)(2x^2 + 1)$
4. $(3x + 2)(x^2 + 1)$
5. $(2x - 3)(4x^2 + 3)$
6. $(2x - 5)(5x^2 + 2)$
7. $(3x - 4)(4x^2 + 1)$
8. $(6x - 7)(3x^2 + 5)$
9. $(x + 8)(x^2 - 3)$
10. $(x + 6)(2x^2 - 5)$
11. $(7x + 9)(2x^2 - 3)$
12. $(8x + 9)(3x^2 - 1)$
13. $(x - 4)(2x^2 - 9)$
14. $(5x - 1)(4x^2 - 5)$
15. $(4x - 3)(6x^2 - 5)$
16. $(8x - 5)(3x^2 - 7)$
17. $(x + 5)(x + 1)(x - 1)$
18. $(3x + 2)(x + 3)(x - 3)$
19. $(x - 3)(4x + 5)(4x - 5)$
20. $(3x + 2)(3x - 2)(3x - 2)$

Extension

Factor.

21. $4x^5 + 6x^3 + 6x^2 + 9$

22. $4x^5 + 6x^4 + 6x^3 + 9x^2$

23. $x^6 - x^4 - x^2 + 1$

24. $x^{13} + x^7 + x^6 + 1$

21. $(2x^2 + 3)(2x^3 + 3)$
22. $x^2(2x + 3)(2x^2 + 3)$
23. $(x^2 + 1)(x + 1)(x + 1)(x - 1)(x - 1)$
24. $(x^7 + 1)(x^6 + 1)$

Challenge

25. If a, b, c, and d are constants, factor $acx^{m+n} + adx^n + bcx^m + bd$ into two factors. $(ax^m + b)(cx^m + d)$

26. Find $ax^3 + bx^2 + cx + d$ so that a, b, c, and d are integers, $\frac{a}{c} = \frac{b}{d} = 4$, and $\frac{a}{b} = \frac{7}{5}$. Factor the result by grouping. $28x^3 + 20x^2 + 7x + 5, (7x + 5)(4x^2 + 1)$

27. Subtract $(x^2 + 1)^2$ from $x(x + 1)^2$ and factor the result.

    $x(x + 1)^2 - (x^2 + 1)^2 = x^4 + 2x^3 + x^2 - (x^4 + 2x^2 + 1) = $
    $2x^3 - 2x^2 + x^2 - 1 = 2x^2(x - 1) + (x + 1)(x - 1) = (2x^2 + x + 1)(x - 1)$

SQUARES OF DIGITS

Take any whole number. Square the digits and add them up. Do the same for this sum. If you continue, you will always end up with 89 or 1. Even mathematicians do not know why this is so. Try 2593.

83	$8^2 + 3^2 = 73$
73	$7^2 + 3^2 = 58$
58	$5^2 + 8^2 = 89$

Try this for the following numbers.

1. 1151   **2.** 9999   **3.** 89

28, 68,	324, 29,	145, 42,
100, 1	85, 89	20, 4,
		16, 37, 58, 89

2593	$2^2 + 5^2 + 9^2 + 3^2 = 119$
119	$1^2 + 1^2 + 9^2 = 83$

Here is a general strategy for factoring.

> 1. Always look first for a common factor.
> 2. Then look at the number of terms.
>
>   Two terms: Determine whether you have a difference of squares. Do not try to factor a sum of squares.
>
>   Three terms: Determine whether the trinomial is a square. If so, you know how to factor. If not, try trial and error.
>
>   Four terms: Try factoring by grouping.
> 3. Always factor completely. If a factor with more than one term can still be further factored, you should do so.

EXAMPLES

Factor.

1. $10x^3 - 40x$

   a. We look first for a common factor.

$$10x^3 - 40x = 10x(x^2 - 4) \quad \text{Factoring out the greatest common factor}$$

   b. Factor a difference of two squares.

$$10x(x + 2)(x - 2) \quad \text{Factoring } x^2 - 4$$

   c. Have we factored completely? Yes, because no factor can be factored further.

2. $t^4 - 16$

   a. We look for a common factor. There isn't one.

   b. There are only two terms. Factor a difference of squares.

$$(t^2)^2 - 4^2 = (t^2 + 4)(t^2 - 4)$$

   One of the factors is still a difference of two squares. We factor it.

$$(t^2 + 4)(t - 2)(t + 2)$$

   c. We have factored completely because no factors can be factored further.

3. $2x^3 + 10x^2 + x + 5$

   a. We look for a common factor. There isn't one.

   b. There are four terms. We try factoring by grouping.

$$2x^3 + 10x^2 + x + 5 = (2x^2 + 10x^2) + (x + 5) \quad \text{Separating into two binomials}$$
$$= 2x^2(x + 5) + 1(x + 5) \quad \text{Factoring each binomial}$$
$$= (x + 5)(2x^2 + 1) \quad \text{Factoring out the common factor, } x + 5$$

   c. No factor can be factored further, so we have factored completely.

4. $x^5 - 2x^4 - 35x^3$

   a. We look first for a common factor.

$$x^5 - 2x^4 - 35x^3 = x^3(x^2 - 2x - 35)$$

   b. The trinomial $x^2 - 2x - 35$ is not a trinomial square. We factor it using trial and error.

$$x^5 - 2x^4 - 35x^3 = x^3(x^2 - 2x - 35) = x^3(x - 7)(x + 5)$$

   c. No factor can be factored further, so we have factored completely.

5. $x^4 - 10x^2 + 25$

   a. We look first for a common factor. There isn't one.

   b. We factor a trinomial square.

$$x^4 - 10x^2 + 25 = (x^2)^2 - 2 \cdot 5x^2 + 5^2 = (x^2 - 5)^2$$

   c. No factor can be factored further, so we have factored completely.

TRY THIS Factor.

1. $3m^4 - 3$ **2.** $x^6 + 8x^3 + 16$ **3.** $2x^4 + 8x^3 + 6x^2$

4. $3x^3 + 12x^2 - 2x - 8$ **5.** $8x^3 - 200x$

1. $3(m^2 + 1)(m + 1)(m - 1)$
2. $(x^3 + 4)^2$
3. $2x^2(x + 3)(x + 1)$
4. $(x + 4)(3x^2 - 2)$
5. $8x(x + 5)(x - 5)$

5–7

Exercises

Factor.

1. $2x^2 - 128$ **2.** $3t^2 - 27$

3. $a^2 + 25 - 10a$ **4.** $y^2 + 49 + 14y$

5. $2x^2 - 11x + 12$ **6.** $8y^2 - 18y - 5$

7. $x^3 + 24x^2 + 144x$

9. $x^3 + 3x^2 - 4x - 12$

11. $24x^2 - 54$

13. $20x^3 - 4x^2 - 72x$

15. $x^2 + 4$

17. $x^4 + 7x^2 - 3x^3 - 21x$

19. $x^5 - 14x^4 + 49x^3$

21. $20 - 6x - 2x^2$

23. $x^2 + 3x + 1$

25. $4x^4 - 64$

27. $1 - y^8$

29. $x^5 - 4x^4 + 3x^3$

31. $36a^2 - 15a + \frac{25}{16}$

8. $x^3 - 18x^2 + 81x$

10. $x^3 - 5x^2 - 25x + 125$

12. $8x^2 - 98$

14. $9x^3 + 12x^2 - 45x$

16. $t^2 + 25$

18. $m^4 + 8m^3 + 8m^2 + 64m$

20. $2x^6 + 8x^5 + 8x^4$

22. $45 - 3x - 6x^2$

24. $x^2 + 5x + 2$

26. $5x^5 - 80x$

28. $t^8 - 1$

30. $x^6 - 2x^5 + 7x^4$

32. $\frac{1}{81}x^6 - \frac{8}{27}x^3 + \frac{16}{9}$

1. $2(x + 8)(x - 8)$
2. $3(t + 3)(t - 3)$
3. $(a - 5)^2$
4. $(y + 7)^2$
5. $(2x - 3)(x - 4)$
6. $(2y - 5)(4y + 1)$
7. $x(x + 12)^2$
8. $x(x - 9)^2$
9. $(x - 2)(x + 2)(x + 3)$
10. $(x - 5)^2(x + 5)$
11. $6(2x + 3)(2x - 3)$
12. $2(2x + 7)(2x - 7)$
13. $4x(x - 2)(5x + 9)$
14. $3x(x + 3)(3x - 5)$
15. not factorable
16. not factorable
17. $x(x - 3)(x^2 + 7)$
18. $m(m^2 + 8)(m + 8)$
19. $x^3(x - 7)^2$
20. $2x^4(x + 2)^2$
21. $-2(x - 2)(x + 5)$
22. $-3(2x - 5)(x + 3)$
23. not factorable
24. not factorable
25. $4(x^2 + 4)(x + 2)(x - 2)$
26. $5x(x^2 + 4)(x + 2)(x - 2)$
27. $(y^4 + 1)(y^2 + 1)(y + 1)(1 - y)$
28. $(t^4 + 1)(t^2 + 1)(t + 1)(t - 1)$
29. $x^3(x - 3)(x - 1)$
30. $x^4(x^2 - 2x + 7)$
31. $\left(6a - \frac{5}{4}\right)^2$
32. $\left(\frac{1}{9}x^3 - \frac{4}{3}\right)^2$
33. $(a + 1)(a + 1)(a - 1)(a - 1)$
34. not factorable
35. $(3.5x - 1)^2$
36. $\frac{1}{5}(x - 4)(x - 1)$
37. $5(x + 1.8)(x + 0.8)$
38. $(x + 3)(x + 1)(x - 1)$
39. $(y - 2)(y + 3)(y - 3)$
40. $-1(x^2 + 2)(x + 3)(x - 3)$
41. $(a + 4)(a^2 + 1)$
42. $(x + 2)(x - 2)(x + 1)$

Extension

Factor completely.

33. $a^4 - 2a^2 + 1$

34. $x^4 + 9$

35. $12.25x^2 - 7x + 1$

36. $\frac{1}{5}x^2 - x + \frac{4}{5}$

37. $5x^2 + 13x + 7.2$

38. $x^3 - (x - 3x^2) - 3$

39. $18 + y^3 - 9y - 2y^2$

40. $-(x^4 - 7x^2 - 18)$

41. $a^3 + 4a^2 + a + 4$

42. $x^3 + x^2 - (4x + 4)$

Challenge

43. Factor $y^5 + y^4 + y^3 + y^2 + y + 1$. $(y^3 + 1)(y^2 + y + 1)$ or $(y + 1)(y^4 + y^3 + 1)$

44. Factor $x^{2b} - 2^{2b}$ when $h = 4$. $x^{2 \cdot 4} - 2^{2 \cdot 4} = x^8 - 2^8 = x^8 - 256 = (x^4 + 16)(x^2 + 4)(x + 2)(x - 2)$

45. Is $(a - 3)$ a factor of $a^4 - 81$? If not, show why. If so, what is the other factor? Yes. $a^3 + 3a^2 + 9a + 27$ or $(a^2 + 9)(a + 3)$

MULTIPLES OR INCREASES

Sometimes, it is necessary to find a multiple of a value, other times we want to find how much a value has increased. Are we looking for the same thing in both cases? No.
Consider all these ways of writing the same thing.

y is $\frac{1}{5}$ larger than x. y is $\frac{6}{5}$ as large as x.

y is 20% more than x. y is 120% of x.

y is x increased by $\frac{1}{5}x$. y is $1\frac{1}{5}x$.

It is easy to see how we can arrive at a wrong solution if we incorrectly translate a problem.

Solving Equations by Factoring

The Principle of Zero Products

The product of two numbers is 0 if either of the factors is 0. If a product is 0, then at least one of the factors must be 0.

The Principle of Zero Products

For any numbers a and b, if $ab = 0$ then $a = 0$ or $b = 0$ and if $a = 0$ or $b = 0$ then $ab = 0$.

A statement in two parts is often abbreviated using if and only if For example, a sentence

If A then B and if B then A,

can be abbreviated

A if and only if B or B if and only if A.

Using such words we can restate the principle of zero products.

A product is 0 if and only if at least one of the factors is 0.

If we have an equation with 0 on one side and a factorization on the other, we can solve it by finding the values that make the factors 0.

EXAMPLE 1

Solve. $(5x + 1)(x - 7) = 0$

$$5x + 1 = 0 \quad \text{or} \quad x - 7 = 0 \quad \text{Using the principle of zero products}$$
$$5x = -1 \quad \text{or} \quad x = 7$$
$$x = -\frac{1}{5} \quad \text{or} \quad x = 7 \quad \text{Solving the two equations separately}$$

Check to see whether $\frac{-1}{5}$ and 7 are both solutions of the equation.

Check: for $-\frac{1}{5}$ · for 7

$$\frac{(5x + 1)(x - 7) = 0}{\left(5\left(-\frac{1}{5}\right) + 1\right)\left(-\frac{1}{5} - 7\right) \mid 0}$$
$$(-1 + 1)\left(-7\frac{1}{5}\right)$$
$$0\left(-7\frac{1}{5}\right)$$
$$0$$

$$\frac{(5x + 1)(x - 7) = 0}{(5 \cdot 7 + 1)(7 - 7) \mid 0}$$
$$(35 + 1)0$$
$$0$$

The solutions are $-\frac{1}{5}$ and 7.

Steps for Using the Principle of Zero Products

1. You must have a factorization on one side of the equation.
2. You must have 0 on the other side.
3. Set each factor equal to zero. This gives two or more simple equations.
4. Solve the simple equations.
5. Check for errors.

EXAMPLE 2

Solve. $x(2x - 9) = 0$

$x = 0$ or $2x - 9 = 0$ Using the principle of zero products
$x = 0$ or $2x = 9$
$x = 0$ or $x = \frac{9}{2}$

Check: for 0

$$\frac{x(2x - 9) = 0}{0(2 \cdot 0 - 9) \mid 0}$$
$$0(-9)$$
$$0$$

Check: for $\frac{9}{2}$

$$\frac{x(2x - 9) = 0}{\frac{9}{2}\left(2 \cdot \frac{9}{2} - 9\right) \mid 0}$$
$$\frac{9}{2}(0)$$
$$0$$

The solutions are 0 and $\frac{9}{2}$.

TRY THIS Solve by the principle of zero products.

1. $(x - 3)(x + 4) = 0$ 2. $(x - 7)(x - 3) = 0$ 3. $y(3y - 17) = 0$
4. $(4t + 1)(3t - 2) = 0$ 5. $3x(x - 5)(2x + 4) = 0$

1. $3, -4$
2. $7, 3$
3. $0, \frac{17}{3}$
4. $-\frac{1}{4}, \frac{2}{3}$
5. $0, 5, -2$

Factoring and Solving

To solve an equation using the principle of zero products, you must get 0 on one side and a factorization on the other.

EXAMPLE 3

Solve. $x^2 + 5x = -6$

$$x^2 + 5x + 6 = 0 \quad \text{Adding } -6, \text{ to get 0 on one side}$$
$$(x + 2)(x + 3) = 0 \quad \text{Factoring}$$
$$x + 2 = 0 \quad \text{or} \quad x + 3 = 0 \quad \text{Using the principle of zero products}$$
$$x = -2 \quad \text{or} \quad x = -3$$

Check:

$x^2 + 5x + 6 = 0$		$x^2 + 5x + 6 = 0$	
$(-2)^2 + 5(-2) + 6$	0	$(-3)^2 + 5(-3) + 6$	0
$4 - 10 + 6$		$9 - 15 + 6$	
$-6 + 6$		$-6 + 6$	
0		0	

The solutions are -2 and -3.

TRY THIS Solve.

6. $x^2 - x - 6 = 0$ $\quad$ 3, −2

EXAMPLES

Solve.

4. $x^2 - 8x + 16 = 0$
$(x - 4)(x - 4) = 0$ $\quad$ Factoring the square of a binomial
$x - 4 = 0$ or $x - 4 = 0$
$\quad x = 4$ or $\quad x = 4$

There is only one solution, 4. The check is left to the student.

5. $x^2 - 5x = 0$
$x(x - 5) = 0$ $\quad$ Factoring out a common factor
$x = 0$ or $x - 5 = 0$
$x = 0$ or $\quad x = 5$

The solutions are 0 and 5.

6. $4x^2 - 25 = 0$
$(2x - 5)(2x + 5) = 0$ $\quad$ Factoring a difference of two squares
$2x - 5 = 0$ or $2x + 5 = 0$
$\quad 2x = 5$ or $\quad 2x = -5$
$\quad x = \dfrac{5}{2}$ or $\quad x = -\dfrac{5}{2}$

Check:

$$\begin{array}{c|c} 4x^2 - 25 = 0 \\ \hline 4\left(\frac{5}{2}\right)^2 - 25 & 0 \\ 4 \cdot \frac{25}{4} - 25 \\ 25 - 25 \\ 0 \end{array} \qquad \begin{array}{c|c} 4x^2 - 25 = 0 \\ \hline 4\left(-\frac{5}{2}\right)^2 - 25 & 0 \\ 4 \cdot \frac{25}{4} - 25 \\ 25 - 25 \\ 0 \end{array}$$

The solutions are $\frac{5}{2}$ and $-\frac{5}{2}$.

TRY THIS Solve.

7. $x^2 - 3x = 28$ **8.** $x^2 + 9 = 6x$ **9.** $x^2 = 4x$ **10.** $25x^2 = 16$

7. $7, -4$
8. 3
9. $0, 4$
10. $-\frac{4}{5}, \frac{4}{5}$

5–8

Exercises

Solve.

1. $(x + 8)(x + 6) = 0$

2. $(x + 3)(x + 2) = 0$

3. $(x - 3)(x + 5) = 0$

4. $(x + 9)(x - 3) = 0$

5. $(x + 12)(x - 11) = 0$

6. $(x - 13)(x + 53) = 0$

7. $x(x + 5) = 0$

8. $y(y + 7) = 0$

9. $y(y - 13) = 0$

10. $v(v - 4) = 0$

11. $0 = y(y + 10)$

12. $0 = x(x - 21)$

13. $(2x + 5)(x + 4) = 0$

14. $(2x + 9)(x + 8) = 0$

15. $(3x - 1)(x + 2) = 0$

16. $(3x - 9)(x + 3) = 0$

17. $(5x + 1)(4x - 12) = 0$

18. $(4x + 9)(14x - 7) = 0$

19. $(7x - 28)(28x - 7) = 0$

20. $(12x - 11)(8x - 5) = 0$

21. $2x(3x - 2) = 0$

22. $75x(8x - 9) = 0$

23. $\frac{1}{2}x\left(\frac{2}{3}x - 12\right) = 0$

24. $\frac{5}{7}x\left(\frac{3}{4}x - 6\right) = 0$

25. $\left(\frac{1}{3} - 3x\right)\left(\frac{1}{5} - 2x\right) = 0$

26. $\left(\frac{1}{5} + 2x\right)\left(\frac{1}{9} - 3x\right) = 0$

27. $\left(\frac{1}{3}y - \frac{2}{3}\right)\left(\frac{1}{4}y - \frac{3}{2}\right) = 0$

28. $\left(\frac{7}{4}x - \frac{1}{12}\right)\left(\frac{2}{3}x - \frac{12}{11}\right) = 0$

29. $(0.3x - 0.1)(0.05x - 1) = 0$

30. $(0.1x - 0.3)(0.4x - 20) = 0$

31. $9x(3x - 2)(2x - 1) = 0$

32. $(x - 5)(x + 55)(5x - 1) = 0$

1. $-8, -6$
2. $-3, -2$
3. $3, -5$
4. $-9, 3$
5. $-12, 11$
6. $13, -53$
7. $0, -5$
8. $0, -7$
9. $0, 13$
10. $0, 4$
11. $0, -10$
12. $0, 21$
13. $-\frac{5}{2}, -4$
14. $-\frac{9}{2}, -8$
15. $\frac{1}{3}, -2$
16. $3, -3$
17. $-\frac{1}{5}, 3$
18. $-\frac{9}{4}, \frac{1}{2}$
19. $4, \frac{1}{4}$
20. $\frac{11}{12}, \frac{5}{8}$
21. $0, \frac{2}{3}$
22. $0, \frac{9}{8}$
23. $0, 18$
24. $0, 8$
25. $\frac{1}{9}, \frac{1}{10}$
27. $2, 6$
28. $\frac{1}{21}, \frac{11}{18}$
29. $0, 2$
30. $0, 2$
31. $\frac{1}{3}, 20$
32. $3, 50$

Solve.

33. $x^2 + 6x + 5 = 0$ _−5, −1_

34. $x^2 + 7x + 6 = 0$ _−6, −1_

35. $x^2 + 7x - 18 = 0$ _2, −9_

36. $x^2 + 4x - 21 = 0$ _−7, 3_

37. $x^2 - 8x + 15 = 0$ _5, 3_

38. $x^2 - 9x + 14 = 0$ _7, 2_

39. $x^2 - 8x = 0$ _0, 8_

40. $x^2 - 3x = 0$ _0, 3_

41. $x^2 + 19x = 0$ _0, −19_

42. $x^2 + 12x = 0$ _0, −12_

43. $x^2 - 16 = 0$ _4, −4_

44. $x^2 - 100 = 0$ _10, −10_

45. $9x^2 - 4 = 0$ _$\frac{2}{3}, \frac{-2}{3}$_

46. $4x^2 - 9 = 0$ _$\frac{3}{2}, -\frac{3}{2}$_

47. $x^2 + 6x + 9 = 0$ _−3_

48. $x^2 + 10x + 25 = 0$ _−5_

49. $x^2 - 8x - 16 = 0$ _4_

50. $x^2 - 2x + 1 = 0$ _1_

51. $5x^2 = 6x$ _$0, \frac{6}{5}$_

52. $7x^2 = 8x$ _$0, \frac{8}{7}$_

53. $6x^2 - 4x = 10$ _$-1, \frac{5}{3}$_

54. $3x^2 - 7x = 20$ _$4, \frac{-5}{3}$_

55. $12y^2 - 5y = 2$ _$\frac{2}{3}, \frac{-1}{4}$_

56. $2y^2 + 12y = -10$ _−5, −1_

57. $x(x - 5) = 14$ _7, −2_

58. $t(3t + 1) = 2$ _$\frac{2}{3}, -1$_

59. $64m^2 = 81$ _$\frac{9}{8}, \frac{-9}{8}$_

60. $100t^2 = 49$ _$\frac{7}{10}, \frac{-7}{10}$_

61. $3x^2 + 8x = 9 + 2x$ _−3, 1_

62. $x^2 - 5x = 18 + 2x$ _9, −2_

63. $10x^2 - 23x + 12 = 0$ _$\frac{4}{5}, \frac{3}{2}$_

64. $12x^2 - 17x - 5 = 0$ _$\frac{5}{3}, \frac{-1}{4}$_

Extension

Solve.

65. $b(b + 9) = 4(5 + 2b)$ _4, −5_

66. $y(y + 8) = 16(y - 1)$ _4_

67. $(t - 3)^2 = 36$ _9, −3_

68. $(t - 5)^2 = 2(5 - t)$ _5, 3_

69. $x^2 - \dfrac{1}{64} = 0$ _$\frac{1}{8}, \frac{-1}{8}$_

70. $x^2 - \dfrac{25}{36} = 0$ _$\frac{5}{6}, \frac{-5}{6}$_

71. $\dfrac{5}{16}x^2 = 5$ _4, −4_

72. $\dfrac{27}{25}x^2 = \dfrac{1}{3}$ _$\frac{5}{9}, \frac{-5}{9}$_

73. Find an equation that has the given numbers as solutions.
    For example, 3 and −2 are solutions to $x^2 - x - 6 = 0$.
    a. 1, −3   b. 3, −1   c. 2, 2   d. 3, 4   e. 3, −4
    f. −3, 4   g. −3, −4   h. $\dfrac{1}{2}, \dfrac{1}{2}$ i. 5, −5   j. 0, 0.1, $\dfrac{1}{4}$

74. Find an equation in the right column that has the same two
    solutions as each equation in the left column.

    a. $3x^2 - 4x + 8 = 0$ _i_   g. $4x^2 + 8x + 36 = 0$
    b. $(x - 6)(x + 3) = 0$ _k_   h. $(2x + 8)(2x - 5) = 0$
    c. $x^2 + 2x + 9 = 0$ _g_   i. $9x^2 - 12x + 24 = 0$
    d. $(2x - 5)(x + 4) = 0$ _h_   j. $(x + 1)(5x - 5) = 0$
    e. $5x^2 - 5 = 0$ _j_   k. $x^2 - 3x - 18 = 0$
    f. $x^2 + 10x - 2 = 0$ _l_   l. $2x^2 + 20x - 4 = 0$

    a. $x^2 + 2x - 3 = 0$
    b. $x^2 - 2x - 3 = 0$
    c. $x^2 - 4x + 4 = 0$
    d. $x^2 - 7x + 12 = 0$
    e. $x^2 + x - 12 = 0$
    f. $x^2 - x - 12 = 0$
    g. $x^2 + 7x + 12 = 0$
    h. $x^2 - x + \frac{1}{4}$ or $4x^2 - 4x + 1 = 0$
    i. $x^2 - 25 = 0$
    j. $x^3 - \frac{14}{40}x^2 - \frac{1}{40}x$ or $40x^3 - 14x^2 - x = 0$

Solving Problems

To solve:

1. Choose a variable to the unknown number.
2. Translate the problem to an equation. (Very often a drawing helps.)
3. Solve the equation.
4. Check the answers in the original problem.

EXAMPLE 1

Translate to an equation and solve.

The product of one more than a number and one less than the number is 8. Find the number.

Let $x =$ the number.

One more than a number times one less than that number is 8.

$$(x + 1) \quad \cdot \quad (x - 1) \quad = 8 \qquad \text{Translating}$$

$$
\begin{aligned}
(x + 1)(x - 1) &= 8 \\
x^2 - 1 &= 8 \qquad \text{Multiplying} \\
x^2 - 1 - 8 &= 0 \qquad \text{Adding } -8 \text{ on both sides} \\
x^2 - 9 &= 0 \qquad \text{to get 0 on one side} \\
(x - 3)(x + 3) &= 0 \qquad \text{Factoring}
\end{aligned}
$$

$$x - 3 = 0 \quad \text{or} \quad x + 3 = 0 \qquad \text{Using the principle of zero products}$$
$$x = 3 \quad \text{or} \qquad x = -3$$

Check for 3: One more than 3, or 4, times one less than 3, or 2, or $4 \cdot 2 = 8 = 8$. Check for -3: One more than -3, or -2, times one less than -3, or -4, is 8, or $(-2)(-4) = 8$.

TRY THIS Translate to an equation and solve.

1. Seven less than a number times eight less than the number is zero. 7 or 8
2. A number times one less than the number is zero. 0 or 1
3. One more than a number times one less than the number is 24. 5 or -5

EXAMPLE 2

Translate to an equation and solve.

The square of a number minus twice the number is 48. Let x = the number.

$$\underbrace{\text{The square of a number}}_{x^2} \;\; \underset{\downarrow}{\text{minus}} \;\; \underbrace{\text{twice the number}}_{2x} \;\; \underset{\downarrow\;\downarrow}{\text{is 48.}} \quad \text{Translating}$$

$$x^2 - 2x = 48$$
$$x^2 - 2x - 48 = 0$$
$$(x - 8)(x + 6) = 0$$

$$x - 8 = 0 \quad \text{or} \quad x + 6 = 0 \quad \text{Using the principle of zero products}$$
$$x = 8 \qquad\qquad x = -6$$

There are two such numbers, 8 and -6. They both check.

TRY THIS Translate to an equation and solve.

4. The square of a number minus the number is 20. 5 or −4

5. Twice the square of a number plus one is 73. 6 or −6

Sometimes it helps to reword before translating.

EXAMPLE 3

Translate to an equation and solve.

The height of a triangular sail is $1\frac{1}{2}$ meters more than the base. The area of the sail is $3\frac{1}{2}$ square meters. Find the base and height. (Area is $\frac{1}{2}$ × base × height).

First make a drawing. Then let b = the base and $b + 1\frac{1}{2}$ = the height.

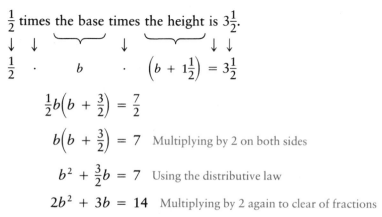

$$\underset{\downarrow\;\downarrow}{\tfrac{1}{2}} \; \underset{\downarrow}{\text{times}} \; \underbrace{\text{the base}}_{b} \; \underset{\downarrow}{\text{times}} \; \underbrace{\text{the height}}_{\left(b + 1\frac{1}{2}\right)} \; \underset{\downarrow\;\downarrow}{\text{is } 3\frac{1}{2}.}$$

$$\tfrac{1}{2} \cdot b \cdot \left(b + 1\tfrac{1}{2}\right) = 3\tfrac{1}{2}$$

$$\tfrac{1}{2}b\left(b + \tfrac{3}{2}\right) = \tfrac{7}{2}$$

$$b\left(b + \tfrac{3}{2}\right) = 7 \quad \text{Multiplying by 2 on both sides}$$

$$b^2 + \tfrac{3}{2}b = 7 \quad \text{Using the distributive law}$$

$$2b^2 + 3b = 14 \quad \text{Multiplying by 2 again to clear of fractions}$$

$$2b^2 + 3b - 14 = 0 \quad \text{Adding } -14 \text{ on both sides}$$
$$(2b + 7)(b - 2) = 0 \quad \text{to get } 0 \text{ on one side}$$
$$2b + 7 = 0 \quad \text{or} \quad b - 2 = 0 \quad \text{Using the principle of zero products}$$
$$b = -\frac{7}{2} \quad \text{or} \quad b = 2$$

The solutions of the equation are 2 and $-\frac{7}{2}$. The base of a triangle cannot have a negative length, so the base length is 2. The height is $1\frac{1}{2}$ meters greater than 2, so the height must be $3\frac{1}{2}$ meters.

TRY THIS Translate to an equation and solve.

6. The width of a rectangular card is 2 cm less than the length. The area is 15 cm². Find the length and width. $l(l - 2) = 15, 5 \text{ cm}, 3 \text{ cm}$

EXAMPLE 4

Translate to an equation and solve.

The product of two consecutive integers is 156. Find the integers. (Consecutive integers are next to each other, such as 49 and 50, or -6 and -5. The greater is 1 plus the lesser.)

Let x represent the first integer. Then $x + 1$ represents the second.

First integer times second integer is 156. Rewording
$$x \cdot (x + 1) = 156 \quad \text{Translating}$$

$$x(x + 1) = 156$$
$$x^2 + x = 156 \quad \text{Using the distributive law}$$
$$x^2 + x - 156 = 0 \quad \text{Adding } -156 \text{ on both sides}$$
$$(x - 12)(x + 13) = 0 \quad \text{to get } 0 \text{ on one side}$$
$$x - 12 = 0 \quad \text{or} \quad x + 13 = 0 \quad \text{Using the principle of zero products}$$
$$x = 12 \quad \text{or} \quad x = -13$$

The solutions of the equation are 12 and -13. When x is 12, then $x + 1$ is 13 and $12(13) = 156$. So, 12 and 13 are solutions to the problem. When x is -13, then $x + 1$ is -12, and $(-13)(-12) = 156$. Thus, in this problem we have two pairs of solutions, 12 and 13, and -12 and -13. Both are pairs of consecutive integers whose product is 156.

TRY THIS Translate to an equation and solve.

7. The product of two consecutive integers is 462. Find the integers. 21, 22; $-21, -22$

EXAMPLE 5

In a sports league of n teams in which each team plays every other team twice, the total number of games to be played is given by

$$N = n^2 - n.$$

a. A slow-pitch softball league has 17 teams. What is the total number of games to be played?

$$
\begin{aligned}
N &= n^2 - n \\
&= 17^2 - 17 \\
&= 289 - 17 \\
&= 272
\end{aligned}
$$

There is a total of 272 games to be played.

b. A basketball league plays a total of 90 games. How many teams are in the league?

$$
\begin{aligned}
n^2 - n &= N \\
n^2 - n &= 90 \qquad \text{Substituting 90 for } N \\
n^2 - n - 90 &= 0 \qquad \text{Adding } -90 \text{ on both sides} \\
(n - 10)(n + 9) &= 0 \qquad \text{to get 0 on one side} \\
n - 10 = 0 \quad \text{or} \quad n + 9 &= 0 \qquad \text{Using the principle of zero products} \\
n = 10 \quad \text{or} \qquad n &= -9
\end{aligned}
$$

Since the number of teams cannot be negative, -9 cannot be a solution. But, 10 checks, so there are 10 teams in the league.

TRY THIS Use $N = n^2 - n$ for each of the following.

8. A volleyball league has 19 teams. What is the total number of games to be played?   342

9. A slow-pitch softball league plays a total of 72 games. How many teams are in the league?   9

5–9	

Exercises

Translate to an equation and find all solutions.

1. If you subtract a number from four times its square, the result is three. $-\frac{3}{4}$ or 1

2. If seven is added to the square of a number the result is 32. -5 or 5

3. Eight more than the square of a number is six times the number.   2 or 4

4. Fifteen more than the square of a number is eight times the number.   3 or 5

5. The product of two consecutive integers is 182. 13 and 14, −13 and −14

6. The product of two consecutive integers is 56. 7 and 8, −7 and −8

7. The product of two consecutive even integers is 168. 12 and 14, −12 and −14

8. The product of two consecutive even integers is 224. 14 and 16, −14 and −16

9. The product of two consecutive odd integers is 255. 15 and 17, −15 and −17

10. The product of two consecutive odd integers is 143. 11 and 13, −11 and −13

11. The length of a rectangle is 4 m greater than the width. The area of the rectangle is 96 m². Find the length and width. 12 m, 8 m

12. The length of a rectangle is 5 cm greater than the width. The area of the rectangle is 84 cm². Find the length and width. 12 cm, 7 cm

13. The area of a square is 5 more than the perimeter. Find the length of a side. 5

14. The perimeter of a square is 3 more than the area. Find the length of a side. 1

15. The base of a triangle is 10 cm greater than the height. The area is 28 cm². Find the height and base. 4 cm, 14 cm

16. The height of a triangle is 8 m less than the base. The area is 10 m². Find the height and base. 2 m, 10 m

17. If the sides of a square are lengthened by 3 m, the area becomes 81 m². Find the length of a side of the original square. 6 m

18. If the sides of a square are lengthened by 7 km, the area becomes 121 km². Find the length of a side of the original square. 4 km

19. The sum of the squares of two consecutive odd positive integers is 74. 5 and 7

20. The sum of the squares of two consecutive odd positive integers is 130. 7 and 9

Use $N = n^2 - n$ for Exercises 21–24.

21. A slow-pitch softball league has 23 teams. What is the total number of games to be played? 506

22. A basketball league has 14 teams. What is the total number of games to be played? 182

23. A slow-pitch softball league plays a total of 132 games. How many teams are in the league? 12

24. A basketball league plays a total of 240 games. How many teams are in the league? 16

The number of possible handshakes within a group of n people is given by $N = \frac{1}{2}(n^2 - n)$.

25. At a meeting there are 40 people. How many handshakes are possible? 780

26. At a party there are 100 people. How many handshakes are possible? 4950

27. Everyone shook hands at a party. There were 190 handshakes in all. How many were at the party? 20

28. Everyone shook hands at a meeting. There were 300 handshakes in all. How many were at the meeting? 25

Extension

29. A cement walk of constant width is built around a 20 ft × 40 ft rectangular pool. The total area of the pool and walk is 1500 ft^2. Find the width of the walk.   5 ft

30. Mark launched a model rocket using an engine which will generate a speed of 180 feet per second. The formula $h = rt - 16t^2$ gives the height of an object projected upward at a rate of r feet per second after t seconds. After how many seconds will Mark's rocket reach a height of 464 feet? After how many seconds will it be at that height again? $(t - 4)(4t - 29) = 0$, so 4 sec, 7¼ sec

31. When the speed of an object is measured in meters per second and distance in meters, the formula of Exercise 30 becomes $h = rt - 4.9t^2$. A baseball is thrown upward with speed of 20.6 meters per second.
  a. After how many seconds will the ball reach a height of 21.6 meters? 2 seconds
  b. How long after it is thrown will it hit the ground? 4.2 seconds

32. The ones digit of a number less than 100 is four greater than the tens digit. The sum of the number and the product of the digit is 58. Find the number. 37

33. The total surface area of a box is 350 m^2. The box is 9 meters high and has a square base. Find the length of the side of the base. 7 m

34. The cube of a number is the same as twice the square of the number. Find the number. 2

35. **a.** Find three consecutive even integers such that the sum of the product of the first two and the product of the first and third is 1508. 26, 28, 30
  b. Find three consecutive odd integers which meet these conditions. −29, −27, −25

Challenge

36. Find two consecutive positive numbers such that the product of the sum and difference of the numbers plus eight is the sum of their squares. 2, 3

37. The length of a rectangle is three times its width. If the length is increased by 27 and the width decreased by 1, the area is 117. Find the original length and width. 12, 4

38. The pages of a book are 15 cm by 20 cm. Margins of equal width surround the printing on each page and comprise one half the area of the page. Find the width of the margins. $2\frac{1}{2}$ cm

39. A rectangular piece of cardboard is twice as long as it is wide. A 4 cm square is cut out of each corner, and the sides are turned up to make a box. The volume of the box is 616 cm³. Find the original dimensions of the cardboard. 30 cm by 15 cm

40. An open rectangular gutter is made by turning up the sides of a piece of metal 20 in. wide. The area of the cross-section of the gutter is 50 in². Find the depth of the gutter. 5 in.

50 in.²

20 in.

THE BINARY SYSTEM

Our method of counting uses 10 as a base. Other methods use different bases. Computers use a method known as binary arithmetic. All numbers are represented by a series of 0's and 1's, Here's how the numbers 1 to 10 appear in binary, or base 2.

$$1 = 1 \times 2^0 \qquad\qquad = \quad 1$$
$$2 = 1 \times 2^1 + 0 \times 2^0 \qquad = \quad 10$$
$$3 = 1 \times 2^1 + 1 \times 2^0 \qquad = \quad 11$$
$$4 = 1 \times 2^2 + 0 \times 2^1 + 0 \times 2^0 = \quad 100$$
$$5 = 1 \times 2^2 + 0 \times 2^1 + 1 \times 2^0 = \quad 101$$
$$6 = 1 \times 2^2 + 1 \times 2^1 + 0 \times 2^0 = \quad 110$$
$$7 = 1 \times 2^2 + 1 \times 2^1 + 1 \times 2^0 = \quad 111$$
$$8 = 1 \times 2^3 + 0 \times 2^2 + 0 \times 2^1 + 0 \times 2^0$$
$$= \quad 1000$$
$$9 = 1 \times 2^3 + 0 \times 2^2 + 0 \times 2^1 + 1 \times 2^0$$
$$= \quad 1001$$
$$10 = 1 \times 2^3 + 0 \times 2^2 + 1 \times 2^1 + 0 \times 2^0$$
$$= \quad 1010$$

In order to represent numbers in the system, a computer sets a series of switches either "on", to represent a 1, or "off", to represent a 0. Calculations are performed, and the output is converted to base 10 for the user.

Convert 100101101 to base 10.

$$1 \quad 0 \quad 0 \quad 1 \quad 0 \quad 1 \quad 1 \quad 0 \quad 1$$

with arrows pointing to 2^0, 2^2, 2^3, 2^5, 2^8

$$2^8 + 2^5 + 2^3 + 2^2 + 2^0$$
$$= 256 + 32 + 8 + 4 + 1 = 301$$

Convert to base 10.
1. 110111   2. 1000001   3. 111111010
   55   65   506

CAREERS/Graphic Arts

Graphic artists and designers are the people who put color and liveliness into the appearance of food products, books, displays, advertisements, and hundreds of other items. Certainly we are aware of the work done by these professionals when we see a clever billboard, or when we enter a building with wild bands of color spiraling around the walls.

The great majority of design jobs, though, do not draw attention to themselves. This algebra book is an example of quiet design with a purpose. The designers of this book decided what size and kind of print to use. They specified the sizes of the margins. All this was done with the intent of making pages uncomplicated and easy to read.

A look at the workplace of a design professional would quickly convince you that mathematics skills are important in this field. A graphic artist or designer will have a large collection of tools for drawing geometric forms. He or she will have instruments which give measurements according to different scales. A calculator for computing perimeters, areas, and volumes will be at hand. Charts giving proportions for enlarging or reducing photographs will be kept handy.

Why is measuring and calculating so important? All art and design work must fit the space available. A $4\frac{5}{32}''$ high label designed to cover a can $4\frac{1}{8}''$ high is a total waste of time and effort. Similarly, a cardboard display that is too wide for the average end-of-aisle space in a supermarket will not do the job it was intended to do.

Exercises

The problems that follow are similar to those that graphic artists and designers must solve as they create visual materials.

1. Sue is fashioning a new package from a 20″ square piece of cardboard. Squares with side x are cut out of the corners and the sides are folded up. The finished box will have a square bottom. The designer needs to determine the volume of the box, to make sure it will hold the proper amount of the product. Express the volume of the box as a polynomial in x. (Section 4–6.) $V = x(20 - 2x^2)$

2. Phil is preparing a trade show display with a giant-size replica of a breakfast cereal box. The designer wants to have the replica made in the same proportions as the real box. He will need to determine the surface area of the replica to find how much material must be purchased for its construction. The real box is 6 times as high as it is deep. It is twice as high as it is wide. Express the surface area of the real box in terms of its depth, d. (See Section 4–8.) $S = 54d^2$

3. Georgia is designing a book cover. She will use two colors in the design, one for the lettering and the other for the background. She has sixty colors from which to choose. How many possible combinations of colors for this design are there? Once she chooses a color for the lettering, how many possible combinations will there be? (See Section 5–9.) 3540, 59

CHAPTER 5   Review

Review the material in the chapter. Then see how you have done by trying these review exercises. If you miss an exercise, restudy the indicated lesson.

5–1   Find three factorizations of each monomial.

1. $-10x^2$ **2.** $36x^5$ 1. Answers may vary.
2. Answers may vary

5–1   Factor.

3. $x^2 - 3x$ **4.** $6x^3 + 12x^2 + 3x$ **5.** $8x^6 - 32x^5 + 4x^4$ 3. $x(x-3)$
4. $3x(2x^2 + 4x + 1)$
5. $4x^4(2x^2 - 8x + 1)$

5–2   Factor.

6. $9x^2 - 4$ **7.** $4x^2 - 25$ **8.** $2x^2 - 50$ 6. $(3x-2)(3x+2)$
7. $(2x-5)(2x+5)$
9. $3x^2 - 27$ **10.** $x^4 - 81$ **11.** $16x^4 - 1$ 8. $2(x-5)(x+5)$
9. $3(x-3)(x+3)$
10. $(x^2 + 9)(x-3)(x+3)$
11. $(4x^2 + 1)(2x+1)(2x-1)$

5–3   Factor.

12. $x^2 - 6x + 9$ **13.** $x^2 + 14x + 49$ **14.** $9x^2 - 30x + 25$ 12. $(x-3)^2$
13. $(x+7)^2$
14. $(3x-5)^2$
15. $25x^2 - 20x + 4$ **16.** $18x^2 - 12x + 2$ **17.** $12x^2 + 60x + 75$ 15. $(5x-2)^2$
16. $2(3x-1)^2$
17. $3(2x+5)^2$

5–4   Factor.

18. $x^2 - 8x + 15$ **19.** $x^2 + 4x - 12$ **20.** $x^3 - x^2 - 30x$ 18. $(x-5)(x-3)$
19. $(x+6)(x-2)$
20. $x(x-6)(x+5)$

5–5   Factor.

21. $2x^2 - 7x - 4$ **22.** $6x^2 - 5x + 1$ **23.** $6x^2 - 28x - 48$ 21. $(2x+1)(x-4)$
22. $(3x-1)(2x-1)$
23. $2(3x+4)(x-6)$

5–6   Factor by grouping.

24. $x^3 + x^2 + 3x + 1$ **25.** $x^4 + 4x^3 - 2x - 8$ 24. $(x^2 + 3)(x+1)$
25. $(x^3 - 2)(x+4)$

5–7   Factor.

26. $9x^3 + 12x^2 - 45x$ **27.** $5 - 20x^6$ 26. $3x(3x-5)(x+3)$
27. $5(1 + 2x^3)(1 - 2x^3)$

5–8   Solve.

28. $(x - 1)(x + 3) = 0$ 1, -3 **29.** $x^2 + 2x - 35 = 0$ $-7, 5$
30. $x^2 + x - 12 = 0$ 3, -4 **31.** $3x^2 + 2 = 5x$ $\frac{2}{3}, 1$
32. $2x^2 + 5x = 12$ $\frac{3}{2}, -4$ **33.** $16 = x(x - 6)$ 8, -2

Chapter 5 Review   **225**

Translate to an equation and find all solutions.

34. The square of a number is six more than the number. Find the number. -2 or 3

35. The product of two consecutive integers is 288. Find the integers. $16, 18$, or $-16, -18$

36. The product of two consecutive odd integers is 353. Find the integers. $17, 19$ or $-17, -19$

37. Twice the square of a number is 10 more than the number. Find the number. $\frac{5}{2}$ or -2

CHAPTER 5   Test

Factor.

1. $x(x - 5)$
2. $3x(2x^2 + 3x + 1)$
3. $2y^2 - 4y + 3$
4. $(2x + 3)(2x - 3)$
5. $3(x + 5)(x - 5)$
6. $3(x^2 + 4)(x + 2)(x - 2)$
7. $(x - 5)^2$
8. $(7x - 6)^2$
9. $5(3x + 2)^2$

1. $x^2 - 5x$
2. $6x^3 + 9x^2 + 3x$
3. $4y^4 - 8y^3 + 6y^2$
4. $4x^2 - 9$
5. $3x^2 - 75$
6. $3x^4 - 48$
7. $x^2 - 10x + 25$
8. $49x^2 - 84x + 36$
9. $45x^2 + 60x + 20$
10. $x^2 - 7x + 10$
11. $x^2 - x - 12$
12. $x^3 + 2x^2 - 3x$
13. $4x^2 - 4x - 15$
14. $5x^2 - 26x + 5$
15. $10x^2 + 28x - 48$
16. $x^3 + x^2 + 2x + 2$
17. $x^4 + 2x^3 - 3x - 6$
18. $6x^3 + 9x^2 - 15x$
19. $80 - 5x^4$

10. $(x - 2)(x - 5)$
11. $(x + 3)(x - 4)$
12. $x(x - 1)(x + 3)$
13. $(2x - 5)(2x + 3)$
14. $(x - 5)(5x - 11)$
15. $2(x + 4)(5x - 6)$
16. $(x^2 + 2)(x + 1)$
17. $(x^3 - 3)(x + 2)$
18. $3x(x - 1)(2x + 5)$
19. $5(4 + x^2)(2 + x)(2 - x)$

Solve.

20. $x^2 - x - 20 = 0$
21. $2x^2 + 7x = 15$
22. $x(x - 3) = 28$

20. $-4, 5$
21. $\frac{3}{2}, -5$
22. $7, -4$

Translate to an equation and find all solutions.

23. Find the number whose square is 24 more than five times the number. $8, -3$

24. The length of a rectangle is $6m$ more than the width. The area of the rectangle is $40m^2$. Find the length and the width. $4m, 10m$

Challenge

25. The length of a rectangle is 5 times its width. If the length is decreased by 3 and the width is increased by 2, the area is 60. Find the original length and width. $15, 3$

Ready for Polynomials in Several Variables?

4–3 Evaluate each polynomial for $x = -2$.

  1. $5x^2 - x + 8$ 30   **2.** $x^3 - x^2 + 3x + 3$ −15

4–3 Collect like terms.

  3. $3x^3 - 4 - 8x^3$ **4.** $6x^3 - 5x^4 - 3x^3 + 8x^4$ 3. $-5x^3 - 4$
                                                              4. $3x^4 + 3x^3$

4–4 Add.

  5. $4x^3 - x^2$ and $-5x^3 + 2x^2$ $-x^3 + x^2$
  6. $-6x + 2$ and $x^2 + x - 3$ $x^2 - 5x - 1$
  7. $4x^2 - 2x + 2$ and $-3x^2 + 5x - 7$ $x^2 + 3x - 5$

4–5 Subtract.

  8. $(3x + 4) - (-2x - 8)$ $5x + 12$
  9. $(3x^2 - 8) - (5x^2 + 11)$ $-2x^2 - 19$
  10. $(-7x^2 - 5x + 4) - (-2x^2 - 8x + 5)$ $-5x^2 + 3x - 1$

4–7, 4–8 Multiply.

  11. $(3x^2 + 4x - 2)(x - 5)$ **12.** $(x + 2)(x - 3)$ 11. $3x^3 - 11x^2 - 22x + 10$
                                                              12. $x^2 - x - 6$

4–8

  13. $(3t + 1)(3t - 1)$ **14.** $(p + 4)^2$ 13. $9t^2 - 1$
                                                     14. $p^2 + 8p + 16$

5–1 to 5–7 Factor.

  15. $3x^6 + 6x^3 - 9x^2$ 15. $3x^2(x^4 + 2x - 3)$
  16. $x^2 - 7x + 2x - 14$ 16. $(x + 2)(x - 7)$
                                    17. $(x + 2)(x + 6)$
  17. $x^2 + 8x + 12$ 18. $(3x + 1)(x - 2)$
                                    19. $(3t - 1)(3t - 1)$
  18. $3x^2 - 5x - 2$ 20. $x^3(x + 4)(x - 4)$
  19. $9t^2 - 6t + 1$
  20. $x^5 - 16x^3$

3–4

  21. Solve $3(x + 2) - 4 = 3 - 4(x - 5)$. 3

3–6

  22. Solve $d = rt$, for r. $r = \frac{d}{t}$

6

CHAPTER SIX

Polynomials
in Several Variables

6-1 Evaluating and Arranging Polynomials

Most of the polynomials you have studied so far have had only one variable. A polynomial in several variables is an expression like those you have already seen, but with more than one variable. Here are some examples.

$3x + xy^2 + 5y + 4$ polynomial in two variables, x and y

$8xy^2z - 2x^3z - 13x^4y^2 + 5$ polynomial in three variables, x, y, and z

Evaluating Polynomials

EXAMPLE 1

Evaluate the polynomial $4 + 3x + xy^2 + 8x^3y^3$ for $x = -2$ and $y = 5$.

We replace each x by -2 and each y by 5.

$$4 + 3(-2) + (-2) \cdot 5^2 + 8(-2)^3 \cdot 5^3 = 4 - 6 - 50 - 8000 = -8052$$

TRY THIS Evaluate.

1. $4 + 3x + xy^2 + 8x^3y^3$ for $x = 2$ and $y = -5$ -7940
2. $8xy^2 - 2x^3z - 13x^4y^2 + 5$ for $x = -1$, $y = 3$, and $z = 4$ -176

Area and volume formulas can be thought of as polynomials in two variables, r and h.

EXAMPLE 2

The area of a right circular cylinder is given by the polynomial $2\pi rh + 2\pi r^2$, where h is the height and r is the radius of the base.

A beverage can has height 12 cm and radius 3 cm. Evaluate the polynomial for $h = 12$ and $r = 3$ to find the area of this can. (Use 3.14 for π.)

$$2(3.14) \cdot 3 \cdot 12 + 2(3.14)3^2 = 226.08 + 56.52 = 282.6 \text{ cm}^2$$

TRY THIS

3. A beverage can has height $h = 16$ cm and radius $r = 3$ cm. Evaluate the polynomial in Example 2 for $h = 16$ and $r = 3$ to find the area of the can. (Use 3.14 for π.) 357.96 cm^2

Degree of a Polynomial

The degree of a term with several variables is the sum of the exponents of the variables. The degree of a polynomial is the same as that of the highest degree term.

EXAMPLE 3
Tell the degree of each term. Then find the degree of the polynomial.

$$9x^2y^3 - 14xy^2z^3 + xy + 4y + 5x^2 + 7$$

Term	Degree
$9x^2y^3$	$2 + 3 = 5$
$-14xy^2z^3$	$1 + 2 + 3 = 6$
xy	$1 + 1 = 2$
$4y$	$1 = 1$
$5x^2$	$2 = 2$
7	$0 = 0$

Thus, for the polynomial $9x^2y^3 - 14xy^2z^3 + xy + 4y + 5x^2 + 7$ the term of highest degree is $-14xy^2z^3$. Therefore the degree of the polynomial is 6.

Ascending and Descending Order

For polynomials in several variables we choose one of the variables and arrange the terms with respect to it.

EXAMPLE 4
Arrange the polynomial $7xy + 2 + 3x^5y + y^4 - 5x^3$ in descending powers of x.

$$3x^5y - 5x^3 + 7xy + y^4 + 2$$

There are two terms not containing x. We usually write the one with higher degree first in such a case.

EXAMPLE 5
Arrange the polynomial $8u^3v - 9uv^3 + 7u^2v + 5u^2v^2$ in descending powers of u.

$$8u^3v + 5u^2v^2 + 7u^2v - 9uv^3$$

In this case there are two terms containing u^2. One of them is of degree 4 and the other is of degree 3. When writing descending powers, we usually write the one with the greater degree first.

TRY THIS

4. Arrange in descending powers of y: $3xy - 7xy^2 + 5xy^4 - 3xy^3$. $\quad$ $5xy^4 - 3xy^3 - 7xy^2 + 3xy$

5. Arrange in ascending powers of x: $2x^2yz + 5xy^2z + 5x^3yz^2 - 2$. $\quad$ $-2 + 5xy^2z + 2x^2yz + 5x^3yz^2$

Like terms have exactly the same variables with exactly the same exponents.

EXAMPLE 6

Collect like terms and arrange in descending powers of x.

$$3xy - 5xy^2 + 3xy^2 + 9xy = -2xy^2 + 12xy$$

TRY THIS Collect like terms and arrange in descending powers of x.

6. $4x^2y + 3xy - 2x^2y - 2x^2 + 3xy^2$ $\quad$ $2x^2y - 2x^2 + 3xy^2 + 3xy$

6–1

Exercises

Evaluate each polynomial for $x = 3$ and $y = -2$.

1. $x^2 - y^2 + xy$ $\quad$ -1 $\quad$ **2.** $x^2 + y^2 - xy$ $\quad$ 19 $\quad$ **3.** $xy - x^2 - y^2$ $\quad$ -19

Evaluate each polynomial for $x = 2$, $y = -3$, and $z = -1$.

4. $xyz^2 + z$ $\quad$ -7 $\qquad$ **5.** $xy - xz + yz$ $\quad$ -1 $\quad$ **6.** $xyz^2 + xy^2z + x^2yz$ $\quad$ -12

An amount of money P is invested at interest rate r. In three years it will grow to an amount given by the polynomial $P + 3rP + 3r^2P + r^3P$.

7. Evaluate the polynomial for $P = 10,000$ and $r = 0.09$ to find the amount to which \$10,000 will grow at 9% interest for 3 years. $\quad$ 12,950.29

8. Evaluate the polynomial for $P = 10,000$ and $r = 0.12$ to find the amount to which \$10,000 will grow at 12% interest for 3 years. $\quad$ 14,049.28

The area of a right circular cylinder is given by the polynomial $2\pi rh + 2\pi r^2$, where h is the height and r is the radius of the base.

9. A 12-oz beverage can has height 4.7 in. and radius 1.2 in. Evaluate the polynomial for $h = 4.7$ and $r = 1.2$ to find the area of the can. (Use 3.14 for π.) 44.4624 in²

10. A 16-oz beverage can has height 6.3 in. and radius 1.2 in. Evaluate the polynomial for $h = 6.3$ and $r = 1.2$ to find the area of the can. Use 3.14 for π. 56.52 in.²

Tell the degree of each term of the following polynomials. Then find the degree of the polynomial.

11. $x^3y - 2xy + 3x^2 - 5$ 4, 2, 2, 0; 4   **12.** $5y^3 - y^2 + 15y + 1$ 3, 2, 1, 0; 3

13. $17x^2y^3 - 3x^3yz - 7$ 5, 5, 0; 5   **14.** $6 - xy + 8x^2y^2 - y^5$ 0, 2, 4, 5; 5

15. $a^4 - a^3b + a^2b^2 - ab^3 + b^4$ 4, 4, 4, 4, 4; 4

16. $x^3y^2z^3 + 5x^5yz + 25x^6z$ 8, 7, 7; 8

Arrange in descending powers of y.

17. $-xy^2 - y^3 + 5x^2y$ $-y^3 - xy^2 + 5x^2y$ **18.** $2xy^2 + 7xy + 4y^3$ $4y^3 + 2xy^2 + 7xy$

19. $-xy^2 + x^3 - y^3$ $-y^3 - xy^2 + x^3$ **20.** $4y^3 - x^2y^2 - 2x^2y + xy^4 - y^5$ $-y^5 + xy^4 + 4y^3 - x^2y^2 - 2x^2y$

Arrange in ascending powers of m.

21. $5m^2n - 3mn^3 + 4n^2 - m^4n$ $4n^2 - 3mn^3 + 5m^2n - m^4n$ **22.** $5m^3n - 8mn^2 + 7m^2n - 3m^4n^3$ $-8mn^2 + 7m^2n + 5m^3n - 3m^4n^3$

Arrange in descending powers of the specified variable. Collect like terms if possible.

24. $5n^2 - 4mn + 6m^2$
25. $-11uv^2 + 7u^2v + 5uv$

23. $x^2 + 3y^2 + 2xy$; y $3y^2 + 2xy + x^2$ **24.** $4n^2 - 3mn + m^2 - mn + n^2 + 5m^2$; n

25. $5uv - 8uv^2 + 7u^2v - 3uv^2$; v **26.** $6r^2s + 11 + 3r^2s - 5r + 3$; s $6r^2s - 5r + 14$

27. $a - a^2b + ab^2 + a^2b - ab^2$; a a   **28.** $x^2 + x^2y + xy^2 - x^2y - xy^2 - xy^3$; x $x^2 - xy^3$

Extension

29. Construct a polynomial in the variables x and y of degree 7 with six terms and coefficients which are integers.   Answers may vary.

30. Construct a polynomial in the variables x, y and z of degree 9 with eight terms and coefficients that are integers.   Answers may vary.

31. In the sixth degree term of a polynomial in the variables x and y, the exponent of y is twice that of x. The coefficient of the term is 1 more than the exponent of y. Write the term. $5x^2y^4$

32. In the eighth degree term of a polynomial in the variables x and y, the exponent of x is one third that of y. The coefficient is the inverse of the four times the exponent of x. $-8x^2y^6$

33. A polynomial of degree 1 is called a linear polynomial. Write a two term linear polynomial in the variables v and w.   Answers may vary.

34. A polynomial of degree 2 is called a quadratic polynomial. Write a three term quadratic polynomial in the variables m and n. Answers may vary.

35. A polynomial of degree 3 is called a cubic polynomial. Write a five term cubic polynomial in the variables x and y. Answers may vary.

Challenge

36. The polynomial $0.524hD^2 + 0.262hd^2$ gives the approximate

volume of certain barrels where d is the smaller diameter, D is the larger diameter and h is the height. Find the approximate volume of a barrel which is 48 inches high, has a smaller diameter of 18 inches and a larger diameter of 24 inches. 18,562.2 in.³ or 10.7 ft³

37. The polynomial $3.14(R^2 - r^2)$ gives the approximate area of a ring with inner radius r and outer radius R. Find the area of a ring with outer radius 20 cm and inner radius 15 cm. 549.5 cm²

38. The polynomial $0.49W + 0.45P - 6.36R + 8.7$ gives an estimate of the percent of body fat for a man.

W is the waist circumference in centimeters.
P is the skin fold above the pectoral muscle in millimeters.
R is the wrist diameter in centimeters.

Find the percent of body fat for Frank Scavone. $W = 83.9$ cm, $P = 6.0$ mm and $R = 7.1$ cm 7.36%

39. The polynomial $0.041h - 0.018A - 2.69$ gives the lung capacity in liters for a woman.

h is the height in centimeters. A is the age in years.

Find the lung capacity for Diane Wild. $h = 139.8$ cm, $A = 41$ years 2.304

Find the value for a so that each term has degree n.

40. $x^n y^a$ 0   **41.** $x^{(n-2)} y^a$ 2   **42.** $x^a y^{\frac{n}{2}}$ $\frac{n}{2}$ **43.** $x^5 y^a z^a$ $\frac{n-5}{2}$

44. How many ways can you write a term of degree 3 with three or fewer variables and a coefficient of 1? 10 ways; x^3, y^3, z^3, x^2y, x^2z, y^2z, xy^2, xz^2, yz^2, and xyz

Calculations with Polynomials

Calculations with polynomials in several variables are very much like those for polynomials in one variable.

Addition and Subtraction

To add polynomials in several variables, we collect like terms.

EXAMPLE 1
Add $(3ax^2 + 4bx - 2)$ and $(2ax^2 - 5bx + 4)$.
$$(3ax^2 + 4bx - 2) + (2ax^2 - 5bx + 4) = (3 + 2)ax^2 + (4 - 5)bx + (-2 + 4)$$
$$= 5ax^2 - bx + 2$$

TRY THIS Add.

1. $(13x^3y + 3x^2y - 5y) + (x^3y + 4x^2y - 3xy + 3y)$ $14x^3y + 7x^2y - 3xy - 2y$
2. $(-5p^2q^4 + 2p^2q^2 - 3q) + (6pq^2 + 3p^2q^4 + 3p)$ $-2p^2q^4 + 2p^2q^2 + 6pq^2 + 3p - 3q$

We subtract a polynomial by adding its inverse. The additive inverse of a polynomial is found by replacing each coefficient by its additive inverse.

EXAMPLE 2
Subtract.

$$(4x^2y + x^3y^2 + 3x^2y^3 + 6y) - (4x^2y - 6x^3y^2 + x^2y^2 - 5y)$$
$$= 4x^2y + x^3y^2 + 3x^2y^3 + 6y - 4x^2y + 6x^3y^2 - x^2y^2 + 5y \quad \text{Adding the inverse}$$
$$= 7x^3y^2 + 3x^2y^3 - x^2y^2 + 11y \quad \text{Collecting like terms}$$

TRY THIS Subtract. Try to write just the answer.

3. $(-4s^4t + s^3t^2 + 2s^2t^3) - (4s^4t - 5s^3t^2 + s^2t^2)$ $-8s^4t + 6s^3t^2 + 2s^2t^3 - s^2t^2$

Multiplication

Multiplication of polynomials is based on the distributive laws. Recall that this means we multiply each term of one polynomial by every term of the other. For most polynomials in several variables having three or more terms, you will probably want to use columns.

EXAMPLE 3
Multiply.

$$3x^2y - 2xy + 3y$$
$$\underline{xy + 2y}$$
$$3x^3y^2 - 2x^2y^2 + 3xy^2 \qquad \text{Multiplying by } xy$$
$$\underline{ 6x^2y^2 - 4xy^2 + 6y^2} \qquad \text{Multiplying by } 2y$$
$$3x^3y^2 + 4x^2y^2 - xy^2 + 6y^2 \qquad \text{Adding}$$

TRY THIS Multiply. 4. $x^5y^5 + 2x^4y^2 + 3x^3y^3 + 5x^2$
5. $p^5q + 3pq^3 - 4p^3q^3 + 6q^4$

4. $(x^2y^3 + 2x)(x^3y^2 + 3x)$ **5.** $(p^4q - 2p^3q^2 + 3q^3)(p + 2q)$

For products of two binomials use FOIL.

EXAMPLES
Multiply.

$$\overset{F}{} \overset{O}{} \overset{I}{} \overset{L}{}$$

4. $(x^2y + 2x)(xy^2 + y^2) = x^3y^3 + x^2y^3 + 2x^2y^2 + 2xy^2$

5. $(p + 5q)(2p - 3q) = 2p^2 - 3pq + 10pq - 15q^2$
$$= 2p^2 + 7pq - 15q^2$$

TRY THIS Multiply.
6. $(3xy + 2x)(x^2 + 2xy^2)$ **7.** $(x - 3y)(2x - 5y)$ 6. $3x^3y + 6x^2y^3 + 2x^3 + 4x^2y^2$
7. $2x^2 - 11xy + 15y^2$

Special Products

The square of a binomial is the square of the first expression, plus or minus twice the product of the two expressions, plus the square of the last.

$$(A + B)^2 = A^2 + 2AB + B^2 \qquad (A - B)^2 = A^2 - 2AB + B^2$$

EXAMPLES
Multiply.

$$(A + B)^2 = A^2 + 2 A B + B^2$$
$$\downarrow \quad \downarrow \qquad \downarrow \quad \downarrow \quad \downarrow \qquad \downarrow$$

6. $(3x + 2y)^2 = (3x)^2 + 2(3x)(2y) + (2y)^2$
$$= 9x^2 + 12xy + 4y^2$$

7. $(2y^2 - 5x^2y)^2 = (2y^2)^2 - 2(2y^2)(5x^2y) + (5x^2y)^2$
$$= 4y^4 - 20x^2y^3 + 25x^4y^2$$

TRY THIS Multiply.

8. $(4x + 5y)^2$ **9.** $(3x^2 - 2xy^2)^2$ 8. $16x^2 + 40xy + 25y^2$
                                                   9. $9x^4 - 12x^3y^2 + 4x^2y^4$

The product of the sum and difference of two expressions is the square of the first expression minus the square of the second.

$$(A + B)(A - B) = A^2 - B^2$$

EXAMPLES
Multiply.

$$(A \; + \; B) \; (A \; - \; B) \; = \; A^2 \; - \; B^2$$
$$\downarrow \quad \downarrow \quad \downarrow \quad \downarrow \qquad \downarrow \qquad \downarrow$$

8. $(3x^2y + 2y)(3x^2y - 2y) = (3x^2y)^2 - (2y)^2$
$$= 9x^4y^2 - 4y^2$$

9. $(-2x^3y^2 + 5t)(2x^3y^2 + 5t) = (5t - 2x^3y^2)(5t + 2x^3y^2)$ Rearranging
$$= (5t)^2 - (2x^3y^2)^2$$
$$= 25t^2 - 4x^6y^4$$

$$(\; A \; - \; B)(\; A \; + \; B\;) \; = \; A^2 \; - \; B^2$$
$$\downarrow \qquad \downarrow \quad \downarrow \qquad \downarrow \qquad \downarrow \qquad \downarrow$$

10. $(2x + 3 - 2y)(2x + 3 + 2y) = (2x + 3)^2 - (2y)^2$
$$= 4x^2 + 12x + 9 - 4y^2$$

11. $(4x + 3y + 2)(4x - 3y - 2) = (4x + 3y + 2)(4x - [3y + 2])$
$$= 16x^2 - (3y + 2)^2$$
$$= 16x^2 - (9y^2 + 12y + 4)$$
$$= 16x^2 - 9y^2 - 12y - 4$$

10. $4x^2y^4 - 9x^2$
11. $16y^2 - 9x^2y^4$
12. $9y^2 + 24y + 16 - 9x^2$
13. $4a^2 - 25b^2 - 10bc - c^2$

TRY THIS Multiply.

10. $(2xy^2 + 3x)(2xy^2 - 3x)$ **11.** $(3xy^2 + 4y)(-3xy^2 + 4y)$
12. $(3y + 4 - 3x)(3y + 4 + 3x)$ **13.** $(2a + 5b + c)(2a - 5b - c)$

6–2	

Exercises
Add.

1. $(xy - ab) + (2xy - 3ab)$ $3xy - 4ab$

2. $(pq + st) + (-4pq - 5st)$ $-3pq - 4st$

3. $(2x^2 - xy + y^2) + (-x^2 - 3xy + 2y^2)$ $x^2 - 4xy + 3y^2$

4. $(3x^2 + xy - y^2) + (-x^2 - xy - 3y^2)$ $_{2x^2 - 4y^2}$

5. $(3p^4q^2 + 2p^3q - 3p) + (2p^4q^2 + 2p^3q - 4p - 2q)$ $_{5p^4q^2 + 4p^3q - 7p - 2q}$

6. $(2x^2 - 3xy + y^2) + (-4x^2 - 6xy - y^2) + (x^2 + xy - y^2)$ $_{-x^2 - 8xy - y^2}$

Subtract.

7. $(xy - ab) - (2xy - 3ab)$ $_{-xy + 2ab}$

8. $(pq + st) - (-4pq - 5st)$ $_{5pq + 6st}$

9. $(x^3 - y^3) - (-2x^3 + x^2y - xy^2 + 2y^3)$ $_{3x^3 - x^2y + xy^2 - 3y^3}$

10. $(a^3 - b^3) - (-4a^3 - a^2b + ab^2 + 5b^3)$ $_{5a^3 + a^2b - ab^2 - 6b^3}$

11. $(p^4q^3 - p^3q^2 + 4p^2q + 9) - (p^4q^3 + 4p^3q^2 - p^2q - 8)$ $_{-5p^3q^2 + 5p^2q + 17}$

12. $(2s^2t^3 - s^3t^2 - 5s^4t^3 - 16) - (5s^3t^2 - 3s^2t^3 - 4)$ $_{5s^2t^3 - 6s^3t^2 - 5s^4t^3 - 12}$

13. Find the sum of $2a + b$ and $3a - 4b$. Then subtract $5a + 2b$. $_{-5b}$

14. Find the sum $3p - q$ and $4p + 5q$. Then subtract $4p - q$. $_{3p + 5q}$

Multiply.

15. $(3z - u)(2z + 3u)$

16. $(x - y)(x^2 + xy + y^2)$

17. $(xy + 7)(xy - 4)$

18. $(p^2q^2 + 3)(pq^2 - 4)$

19. $(a^2 + a - 1)(a^2 - y + 1)$

20. $(tx + r)(vx + s)$

21. $(a^3 + bc)(a^3 - bc)$

22. $(m^2 + n^2 - mn)(m^2 + mn + n^2)$

23. $(a^2 - ab + b^2)(a^2 + ab + b^2)$

24. $(p^3q^4 - p^2 + 2)(p^2 - 3)$

25. $(a - b)(a^3 + a^2b + ab^2 + b^3)$

26. $(c + d)(c^3 - c^2d + cd^2 - d^3)$

27. $(3xy - 1)(4xy + 2)$

28. $(m^3n + 8)(m^3n - 6)$

29. $(3 - c^2d^2)(4 + c^2d^2)$

30. $(6x - 2y)(5x - 3y)$

31. $(m^2 - n^2)(m + n)$

32. $(p^2 + q^2)(p - q)$

33. $(x^5y^5 + xy)(x^4y^4 - xy)$

34. $(a^3b^4 - ab)(a^4b^3 + ab)$

35. $(x - y^3)(x + 2y^3)$

36. $(5st^2 + 4t)(2st^2 - t)$

Multiply.

37. $(3a + 2b)^2$

38. $(r^3t^2 - 4)^2$

39. $(3a^2b - b^2)^2$

40. $(p^4 + m^2n^2)^2$

41. $(ab + cd)^2$

42. $(2a^3 - \frac{1}{2}b^3)^2$

43. $-5x(x + 3y)^2$

44. $(a^2 + b + 2)^2$

45. $(x - y)(x + y)$

46. $(2a - b)(2a + b)$

47. $(c^2 - d)(c^2 + d)$

48. $(p^3 - 5q)(p^3 + 5q)$

49. $(ab + cd^2)(ab - cd^2)$

50. $(c + d + 5)(c + d - 5)$

51. $(x + y - 3)(x + y + 3)$

52. $(-a + b)(a + b)$

53. $(-m^2n^2 + p^4)(m^2n^2 + p^4)$

54. $[a + b + c][a - (b + c)]$

55. $(a + b + c)(a - b - c)$

56. $(3x + 2 - 5y)(3x + 2 + 5y)$

57. $(3x + 5y + 1)(3x - 5y - 1)$

58. $(h - k + 4)(h + k - 4)$

Extension

Express the area of the shaded region as a polynomial. (Leave results in terms of π where appropriate.)

59.

$4xy - 4y^2$

60.

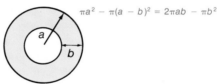

$\pi a^2 - \pi(a - b)^2 = 2\pi ab - \pi b^2$

61.

$\pi x^2 + 2xy$

62.

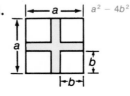

$a^2 - 4b^2$

Multiply. Look for patterns.

63. $(x + y)^3$ **64.** $(x - y)^3$ **65.** $(x + y)^4$

66. $(x - y)^4$ **67.** $(x + y)^5$ **68.** $(x - y)^5$

63. $x^3 + 3x^2y + 3xy^2 + y^3$
64. $x^3 - 3x^2y + 3xy^2 - y^3$
65. $x^4 + 4x^3y + 6x^2y^2 + 4xy^3 + y^4$
66. $x^4 - 4x^3y + 6x^2y^2 - 4xy^3 + y^4$
67. $x^5 + 5x^4y + 10x^3y^2 + 10x^2y^3 + 5xy^4 + y^5$
68. $x^5 - 5x^4y + 10x^3y^2 - 10x^2y^3 + 5xy^4 - y^5$

Challenge

The expression you get when you multiply out $(x + y)^n$ is called the *expansion* of $(x + y)^n$. Answer exercises 69–73 on the basis of the patterns observed in the expansions of the preceding exercises.

69. How many terms are there in the expansion of $(x + y)^6$?   7

70. What is the coefficient of the xy^7 term in the expansion of $(x + y)^8$?   8

71. In the expansion of $(x - y)^{10}$ how many terms have negative coefficients and how many have positive coefficients?   5, 6

72. One term in the expansion of $(x + y)^{12}$ is $220x^3y^9$. What other term has the same coefficient? $220x^9y^3$

73. What is the value of n in the term $6435x^7y^n$, if the term occurs in the expansion of $(x + y)^{15}$?   8

74. Multiply out the compound interest formula $A = P(1 + r)^4$. (Hint: Use your solution to Exercise 64) $P + 4Pr + 6Pr^2 + 4Pr^3 + Pr^4$

75. Express the area of the shaded region as a polynomial.

$(x - 2y)^2 - (x - 2y - 2z)^2 = 4xz - 4z^2 - 8yz$

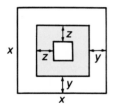

Recall these steps for factoring.

1. Always look first for a common factor.
2. Then look at the number of terms.
   Two terms: Determine whether you have a difference of of squares.
   Three terms: Determine whether the trinomial is a square. If not, try to find binomial factors.
   Four terms: Try factoring by grouping.
3. Factor completely.

Terms with Common Factors

Always look for the greatest common factor. To factor $20x^3y + 12x^2y$ we see that 4 is the greatest numerical factor. Each term contains x^2 as a factor and y as a factor.

$$20x^3y + 12x^2y = (4x^2y)(5x) + (4x^2y)3 \quad \text{\small $4x^2y$ is the greatest common factor}$$
$$= 4x^2y(5x + 3)$$

EXAMPLE 1
Factor. Write the answer directly.

$$6x^2 - 21x^3y^2 + 3x^2y^3 = 3x^2(2 - 7xy + y^2)$$

TRY THIS Factor.

1. $x^4y^2 + 2x^3 + 3x^2y$ 　 2. $10p^6q^2 - 4p^5q^3 + 2p^4q^4$ 　 1. $x^2(x^2y^2 + 2x + 3y)$
2. $2p^4q^2(5p^2 - 2pq + q^2)$

Differences of Squares

Recall $A^2 - B^2 = (A + B)(A - B)$.

EXAMPLES
Factor.

2. $36x^2 - 25y^6 = (6x)^2 - (5y^3)^2$ 　 Writing as a difference of squares
$$= (6x + 5y^3)(6x - 5y^3)$$

3. $32x^4y^4 - 50 = 2(16x^4y^4 - 25)$ Removing a common factor
$$= 2[(4x^2y^2)^2 - (5)^2]$$ Writing as a difference of squares
$$= 2(4x^2y^2 + 5)(4x^2y^2 - 5)$$

4. $5x^4 - 5y^4 = 5(x^4 - y^4)$
$$= 5(x^2 + y^2)(x^2 - y^2)$$
$$= 5(x^2 + y^2)(x + y)(x - y)$$ Factoring $x^2 - y^2$ as a difference of squares

TRY THIS Factor.   3. $(3a + 4x^2)(3a - 4x^2)$ 4. $2(5xy^2 + 2a)(5xy^2 - 2a)$ 5. $5(1 + x^2y^2)(1 + xy)(1 - xy)$
3. $9a^2 - 16x^4$ **4.** $50x^2y^4 - 8a^2$ **5.** $5 - 5x^4y^4$

Trinomials

Whenever you have a trinomial to factor, check to see whether it is the square of a binomial. $A^2 + 2AB + B^2 = (A + B)^2$, $A^2 - 2AB + B^2 = (A - B)^2$

EXAMPLES
Factor.

5. $25x^2 + 20xy + 4y^2 = (5x)^2 + 2(5x)(2y) + (2y)^2$
$$= (5x + 2y)^2$$

6. $x^6 - 8x^3y + 16y^2 = (x^3)^2 - 2(x^3)(4y) + (4y)^2$
$$= (x^3 - 4y)^2$$

TRY THIS Factor.   6. $(x^2 + y^2)^2$ 7. $(2x - 3y)^2$ 8. $(x^3 + 2y)^2$
6. $x^4 + 2x^2y^2 + y^4$ **7.** $4x^2 - 12xy + 9y^2$ **8.** $x^6 + 4x^3y + 4y^2$

If a trinomial is not a square we try to find binomial factors.

EXAMPLES
Factor.

7. $p^2q^2 + 7pq + 12 = (pq + 3)(pq + 4)$

8. $8x^4 - 20x^2y - 12y^2 = 4(2x^4 - 5x^2y - 3y^2)$
$$= 4(2x^2 + y)(x^2 - 3y)$$

Look first for common factors. Not all trinomials can be factored.

TRY THIS Factor.   9. $(xy + 4)(xy + 1)$ 10. $2(x^2y^3 + 5)(x^2y^3 - 2)$
9. $x^2y^2 + 5xy + 4$ **10.** $2x^4y^6 + 6x^2y^3 - 20$

Factoring by Grouping

EXAMPLES

Factor.

9. $x^2y^2 + ay^2 + ab + bx^2 = y^2(x^2 + a) + b(x^2 + a)$
$$= (x^2 + a)(y^2 + b)$$

10. $2x^2 + 4ax - 3a^2x - 6a^3 = 2x(x + 2a) - 3a^2(x + 2a)$
$$= (2x - 3a^2)(x + 2a)$$

TRY THIS Factor. 11. $(x^2 - y)(a - b)$ 12. $(a - 2b)(3 + 5a)$

11. $ax^2 - ay - bx^2 + by$ 12. $3a - 6b + 5a^2 - 10ab$

6-3	

Exercises

Factor. $12n^2(1 + 2n)$

1. $12n^2 + 24n^3$ 2. $9x^2y^2 - 36xy$ $9xy(xy - 4)$ 3. $5c^2d^2 + 10cd$ $5cd(cd + 2)$

4. $x^2y - xy^2$ $xy(x - y)$ 5. $r^2t + rt^2$ $rt(r + t)$ 6. $2\pi rh + 2\pi r^2$ $2\pi r(h + r)$

7. $\pi r^2 + \pi rh$ $\pi r(r + h)$ 8. $10p^4q^4 + 35p^3q^3 + 10p^2q^2$ 9. $12a^4b^4 - 9a^3b^3 + 6a^2b^2$
$5p^2q^2(2p^2q^2 + 7pq + 2)$ $3a^2b^2(4a^2b^2 - 3ab + 2)$

Factor.

10. $a^2b^2 - 9$ 11. $x^2y^2 - 25$ 10. $(ab + 3)(ab - 3)$ 12. $p^2q^2 - r^2$
                                     11. $(xy + 5)(xy - 5)$
13. $c^2d^2 - t^2$ 14. $9x^4y^2 - b^2$ 12. $(pq + r)(pq - r)$ 15. $16a^4b^2 - c^2$
                                       13. $(cd + t)(cd - t)$
16. $36t^2 - 49p^2q^2$ 17. $64z^2 - 25c^2d^2$ 18. $3x^2 - 48y^2$
                             17. $(8z + 5cd)(8z - 5cd)$
19. $5t^2 - 20m^2$ 20. $9s^4 - 9s^2$ 18. $3(x + 4y)(x - 4y)$ 21. $16a^4 - 16a^2$
                14. $(3x^2y + b)(3x^2y - b)$ 19. $5(t + 2m)(t - 2m)$
                15. $(4a^2b + c)(4a^2b - c)$ 20. $9s^2(s + 1)(s - 1)$

Factor.   16. $(6t + 7pq)(6t - 7pq)$ 21. $16a^2(a + 1)(a - 1)$

22. $a^2 + 4ab + 4b^2$ 23. $9c^2 - 6cd + d^2$

24. $16x^2 + 24xy + 9y^2$ 25. $49m^4 - 112m^2n + 64n^2$

26. $4x^2y^2 + 12xyz + 9z^2$ 27. $y^4 + 10y^2z^2 + 25z^4$

28. $0.01x^4 - 0.1x^2y^2 + 0.25y^4$ 29. $0.04a^4 + 0.12a^2b^2 + 0.09b^4$

30. $\frac{1}{16}p^2 - \frac{1}{10}pq + \frac{1}{25}q^2$ 31. $\frac{1}{4}a^2 + \frac{1}{3}ab + \frac{1}{9}b^2$

32. $9a^4 - 12a^3b + 4a^2b^2$ 33. $4p^2q + pq^2 + 4p^3$

34. $a^2 - ab - 2b^2$ 35. $x^2 + 2xy - 3y^2$

22. $(a + 2b)^2$
23. $(3c - d)^2$
24. $(4x + 3y)^2$
25. $(7m^2 - 8n)^2$
26. $(2xy + 3z)^2$
27. $(y^2 + 5z^2)^2$
28. $(0.1x^2 - 0.5y^2)^2$
29. $(0.2a^2 + 0.3b^2)^2$
30. $(\frac{1}{4}p - \frac{1}{5}q)^2$
31. $(\frac{1}{2}a + \frac{1}{3}b)^2$
32. $a^2(3a - 2b)^2$
33. $p(2p + q)^2$
34. $(a + b)(a - 2b)$
35. $(x + 3y)(x - y)$

36. $m^2 + 2mn - 360n^2$

37. $n^2 + 23nr - 420r^2$

38. $x^2y^2 + 8xy + 15$

39. $a^2b^2 - 3ab - 10$

40. $a^5b^2 + 3a^4b - 10a^3$

41. $m^2n^6 + 4mn^5 - 32n^4$

42. $x^4y + x^3y + x^2y$

43. $ab^4 + ab^3 - ab^2$

44. $-k^2 + 36kt - 324t^2$

45. $-p^2 - 20pt - 100t^2$

46. $z^2 + 18zab + 81a^2b^2$

47. $d^2 - 6bcd + 9b^2c^2$

48. $-16a^2b - 10a^2hr - a^2br^2$

49. $a^2 - b^2 + (a - b)^2$

50. $k^2t^2 - 9s^2 - 9t^2 + k^2s^2$

51. $42m^2n - 24mn^2 - 18n^3$

52. $p^2 - q^2 - (p - q)^2$

53. $5ac - 5ad + 5bc - 5bd$

54. $18m^4 + 12m^3 + 2m^2$

55. $75a^3 + 60a^2b + 12ab^2$

Factor.

56. $(x - 1)(x + 1) - y(x + 1)$

57. $(x - 1)(x + 1) - y(x - 1)$

58. $x^2 + x + xy + y$

59. $x^2 - x + xy - y$

60. $ax - bx + ay - by$

61. $bx + 2b + cx + 2c$

62. $n^2 + 2n + np + 2p$

63. $2x^2 - 4x + xz - 2z$

64. $a^2 - 3a + ay - 3y$

65. $6y^2 - 3y + 2py - p$

Extension

66. $3ay^2 - 3ax^2 + 2by^2 - 2bx^2$

67. $4a^2 - 9b^2 - 2a + 3b$

68. $c^2x + c^3 - d^2x - cd^2$

69. $c(x - 2y) - 3d(2y - x)$

70. $7p^4 - 7q^4$

71. $a^4b^4 - 16$

72. $81a^4 - b^4$

73. $1 - 16x^{12}y^{12}$

74. $xy^2 + 3y^2 - 4x - 12$

75. $ay^2 - a - y^2 + 1$

76. $a^2c^2 - 4a^2 - b^2c^2 + 4b^2$

77. $2x^4 - 2x^2y^2 - 24y^4$

78. $a^2 + 2ab - 16 + b^2$

79. $25 - 9x^2 - 6xy - y^2$

Challenge

Under what conditions is each polynomial equal to 0? (Hint: Factor and use the principle of zero products.)

80. $x^4 - y^4$ **81.** $9x^2 - y^2$ **82.** $x^2y^2 - 3xy^2 - 4y^2$ **83.** $y^3 - x^4y^3$

84. Factor $(x + h)^2 - x^2$ $h(h + 2x)$

Use the answer to find $(4.1)^2 - 4^2$ and $(4.01)^2 - 4^2$ $0.1(0.1 + 8) = 0.81, 0.01(0.01 + 8) = 0.0801$

85. Factor.

a. $x^3 - y^3$ **b.** $x^3 + y^3$ **c.** $x^6 - y^6$ **d.** $x^5 - y^5$

86. a. Find a rule or pattern for factoring $x^n - y^n$, where n is any positive integer. $(x - y)(x^{n-1} + x^{n-2}y + x^{n-3}y^2 + \cdots xy^{n-2} + y^{n-1})$

      b. Find a rule or pattern for factoring $x^n + y^n$, where n is any positive odd integer. $(x + y)(x^{n-1} - x^{n-2}y + x^{n-3}y^2 - \cdots xy^{n-2} + y^{n-1})$

Sometimes a letter represents a specific number, although we may not know what the number is. It is called a constant rather than a variable. In this lesson we agree that letters near the end of the alphabet will be variables. Letters at the beginning of the alphabet will be constants. This is a common agreement. We treat unknown constants the same way as known ones.

EXAMPLE 1

Solve $cx + b^2 = 2$ for x.

$$cx + b^2 = 2 \quad \text{x is a variable, b and c are constants.}$$
$$cx = 2 - b^2 \quad \text{Adding $-b^2$ on both sides}$$
$$x = \frac{2 - b^2}{c} \quad \text{Multiplying by $\frac{1}{c}$ on both sides}$$

We treated b and c as if they were known. In that sense they are like the 2 in the equation.

TRY THIS Solve.

1. $ay - b^2 = 3$ for y **2.** $2abx - 6a = abx$ for x 1. $\frac{b^2 + 3}{a}$ 2. $\frac{6}{b}$

To solve an equation we try to get the variable alone on one side. If the variable appears in several terms we usually collect like terms, or factor out the variable. We may need to multiply to remove parentheses.

In Examples 2 and 3, remember that x is used as a variable and a, b, and c are used as constants.

EXAMPLES

Solve

2. $(x - a)(x + a) = x^2 - x$
$$x^2 - a^2 = x^2 - x \quad \text{Multiplying}$$
$$-a^2 = -x \quad \text{Adding $-x^2$ on both sides}$$
$$a^2 = x \quad \text{Multiplying by -1 on both sides}$$

We can check our solution:

$$\frac{(x - a)(x + a) = x^2 - x}{\begin{array}{c|c} (a^2 - a)(a^2 + a) & (a^2)^2 - a^2 \\ a^4 - a^2 & a^4 - a^2 \end{array}}$$

The solution is a^2.

3.

$$(x + a)(x + 2b) = x^2 + a^2 + b^2$$
$$x^2 + ax + 2bx + 2ab = x^2 + a^2 + b^2 \quad \text{Multiplying}$$
$$ax + 2bx + 2ab = a^2 + b^2$$
$$(a + 2b)x + 2ab = a^2 + b^2 \quad \text{Collecting } x\text{- terms}$$
$$(a + 2b)x = a^2 + b^2 - 2ab$$
$$x = \frac{a^2 + b^2 - 2ab}{a + 2b} \quad \text{Multiplying by } \frac{1}{a + 2b}$$
$$x = \frac{(a - b)^2}{a + b} \quad \text{Factoring the numerator}$$

TRY THIS Solve.

3. $(x + a)(x + b) = x^2 + 2$ $\quad \frac{2 - ab}{a + b}$

4. $2(x + a) + 3(x + b) = 4(x - 2)$ $\quad {-3b - 2a - 8}$

6–4	

Exercises

Solve for x, y or z.

1. $2a - 3x = 12$ $\quad \frac{2a - 12}{3}$

2. $z - k = 3k$ $\quad {4k}$

3. $3b - 2y = 1$ $\quad \frac{3b - 1}{2}$

4. $5a + 2x = 3b$ $\quad \frac{3b - 5a}{2}$

5. $rxt = c$ $\quad \frac{c}{rt}$

6. $a^2x = a^6$ $\quad {a^4}$

7. $bx - b^2 = 3x + b - 12$ $\quad {b + 4}$

8. $m^2x = m + 1$ $\quad \frac{m + 1}{m^2}$

9. $ax + b^2 = a^2 + bx$ $\quad {a + b}$

10. $cy - 1 = c^2 + 2c - y$ $\quad {c + 1}$

11. $ax + bx = 3ax - c$ $\quad \frac{c}{2a - b}$

12. $b^2x = 4b$ $\quad \frac{4}{b}$

13. $ax - bx = a^2 - 2ab + b^2$ $\quad {a - b}$

14. $cy + dy = c^2 + 2cd + d^2$ $\quad {c + d}$

15. $3z - a = b + 11$ $\quad \frac{a + b + 11}{3}$

16. $24a - 3x = 5x$ $\quad {3a}$

17. $b(x - b) = x - (2 - b)$ $\quad {b + 2}$

18. $a(3 + 2x) = 5 + x$ $\quad \frac{5 - 3a}{2a - 1}$

19. $4(x - a) + 4a = 7(b + 3) - 21$ $\quad \frac{7b}{4}$

20. $-3(c + y) + 3c = 6(c - 2) + 12$ $\quad {-2c}$

21. $5(2a - z) + 6 = -2(z - 5a)$ $\quad {2}$

22. $x(a + 2) - 3 = b(x + 7)$ $\quad \frac{3 + 7b}{a - b + 2}$

23. $m(m - x) = n(n - x)$ $\quad {m + n}$

24. $b^2(ay - 1) = a^2(1 - ay)$ $\quad \frac{1}{a}$

25. $(x - a)(x + b) = x^2 + 3$ $\quad \frac{ab + 3}{b - a}$

26. $(z + c)(z - d) = z^2 + 5$ $\quad \frac{5 + cd}{c - d}$

27. $(x - c)^2 = (x - d)^2$ $\quad \frac{d + c}{2}$

28. $(y + a)^2 = (y - b)^2$ $\quad \frac{b - a}{2}$

29. $(x + c)^2 = (x + d)^2$ $\quad \frac{-(d + c)}{2}$

30. $(y + a)^2 - ay = (y + b)^2 - by$ $\quad {-b - a}$

31. $dx + x = (d + 1)(d - 1)$ $\quad {d - 1}$

32. $(2x - 5)(3x + 6) = 6x^2 - 9$ $\quad {-7}$

Extension

Solve for x, y, or z.

33. $(x - a)(x - b) = 0$ a, b

34. $(y + a)(y - c) = 0$ $-a, c$

35. $(x - a)(x + b)(x - c) = 0$ $a, -b, c$

36. $(z + d)^2(z - a) = 0$ $-d, a$

37. $x^2 - a^2 = 0$ $a, -a$

38. $4y^2 - 16b^2 = 0$ $2b, -2b$

39. $x^2 - cx + ax - ac = 0$ $c, -a$

40. $y^2 - y + by - b = 0$ $-b, 1$

41. $6z^2 + bz - b^2 = 0$ $\frac{-b}{2}, \frac{b}{3}$

42. $x^2 + 2ax + a^2 = 0$ $-a$

43. $4x^2 + dx - 3d^2 = 0$ $-d, \frac{3d}{4}$

44. $10x^2 - 7ax + a^2 = 0$ $\frac{a}{2}, \frac{a}{5}$

Challenge

Solve for x.

45. $|x| = b$ $b, -b$

46. $|x| - a = b$ $b + a, -b - a$

47. $2x^5 - 26x^3 + 72x = 0$ $0, 2, -2, 3, -3$

48. $36x^4 - 109x^2 + 25 = 0$ $\frac{1}{2}, \frac{-1}{2}, \frac{5}{3}, \frac{-5}{3}$

49. $x^2 = (k - 1)^2$ $k - 1, 1 - k$

50. $(x - 1)^2 = k^2$ $k + 1, -k - 1$

PASCAL'S TRIANGLE

Pascal's Triangle is a triangular array of numbers. The rows and diagonals are numbered as shown below.

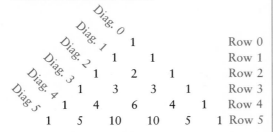

Notice that 1 is the number at each end of a row. All other numbers are the sum of the two numbers above them. Diagonal number 1 gives the numbers 1, 2, 3, 4, 5—the natural, or counting numbers. The triangle can be continued indefinitely by adding the numbers in each row in pairs. Thus, the 6th row contains $(1 + 5)$, $(5 + 10)$, $(10 + 10)$, $(10 + 5)$, and $(5 + 1)$. So, the 6th row is 1, 6, 5, 20, 15, 6, 1. Find the 7th row. 1 7 21 35 35 21 7 1

Each row has one more number than its row number. So, row n has $n + 1$ numbers. How many numbers in the 155th row? 156

To find the sum of all the numbers in any diagonal, look at the number directly below and to the left of the last number in the series to be added. For example, the sum of the natural numbers 1 through 4 is 10. To find this sum, move down diagonal 1 to the number 4. Then move down one row and to the left to the sum, 10. Make a Pascal's Triangle with ten rows. Then find the sum of the first seven numbers in the third diagonal. 210

Each row n of the triangle also gives the coefficients of the binomial $(x + y)^n$. For instance, $(x + y)^3 = x^3 + 3x^2y + 3xy^2 + y^3$. The coefficients are 1, 3, 3, and 1—the third row of the triangle. What are the coefficients of $(x + y)^5$? 1, 5, 10, 10, 5, 1

Pascal's Triangle has many other properties and is often used in applications. It is named after Blaise Pascal, the 17th-century mathematician and philosopher who was the first to write a paper about it. The triangle was known before 1653 when Pascal wrote about it. A drawing in a book published in 1303 by a Chinese mathematician shows the triangle.

6—5 Solving Formulas

EXAMPLE 1

The gravitational force f between planets of mass M and m, at a distance d from each other is given by

$$f = \frac{kMm}{d^2},$$

where k is constant. Solve for m.

$fd^2 = kMm$ Multiplying on both sides by d^2 to clear of fractions

$\dfrac{fd^2}{kM} = m$ Multiplying on both sides by $\frac{1}{kM}$

TRY THIS

1. Solve $f = \dfrac{kMm}{d^2}$ for M. $\frac{fd^2}{km}$

It is not possible to look at a formula and tell which symbols are variables and which are constants. In fact, a certain letter may be a variable at one time and a constant at another time, depending on how the formula is used.

EXAMPLE 2

The area A of a trapezoid is half the product of the height h and the sum of the lengths b_1 and b_2 of the parallel sides.

$$A = \frac{1}{2}(b_1 - b_2)h$$

Solve for b_2.

The variables b_1 and b_2 represent different numbers. The numbers 1 and 2 are called subscripts. It is important not to forget to write them.

$A = \dfrac{1}{2}(b_1 - b_2)h$

$2A = (b_1 + b_2)h$ Multiplying by 2 on both sides
$2A = b_1h + b_2h$
$2A - b_1h = b_2h$ Adding $-b_1h$ on both sides
$\dfrac{2A - b_1h}{h} = b_2$ Multiplying by $\frac{1}{h}$ on both sides

Each of the following is also a correct answer: $\frac{2A}{h} - b_1 = b_2$ and $\frac{1}{h}(2A - b_1h) = b_2$.

TRY THIS

2. Solve $V = \frac{1}{6}\pi h (h^2 - 3a^2)$ for a^2. $\quad \frac{h^2}{3} - \frac{2v}{\pi h}$

Solving Problems

To solve some problems involving formulas, we first solve the formula for a certain letter and then evaluate it.

EXAMPLE 3

The area of a certain trapezoid is 18 cm². The bases have lengths 11 cm and 13 cm. What is the height?

The formula for the area is given in Example 2. We solve it for h.

$$A = \frac{1}{2}(b_1 + b_2)h$$

$$2A = (b_1 + b_2)h$$

$$\frac{2A}{b_1 + b_2} = h \quad \text{Dividing by } b_1 + b_2 \text{ on both sides}$$

We now substitute for A, b_1 and b_2.

$$h = \frac{2 \cdot 18}{11 + 13} = \frac{36}{24}, \text{ or } 1\frac{1}{2}.$$

The height should be $1\frac{1}{2}$ cm. That checks in the problem, so the answer is $1\frac{1}{2}$ cm.

EXAMPLE 4

The approximate length L of a belt around two pulleys whose centers are a distance D apart and whose circumferences are C_1 and C_2 is given by the formula

$$L = \frac{1}{2}C_1 + \frac{1}{2}C_2 + 2D.$$

Find the distance between centers of two pulleys, having a 36-inch belt around them, where their circumferences are 8 in. and 4 in.

$$L = \frac{1}{2}C_1 + \frac{1}{2}C_2 + 2D \quad \text{Solve for } D.$$

$$L - \frac{1}{2}C_1 - \frac{1}{2}C_2 = 2D \quad \text{Adding } -\left(\frac{1}{2}C_1 + \frac{1}{2}C_2\right) \text{ on both sides}$$

$$\frac{L - \frac{1}{2}C_1 - \frac{1}{2}C_2}{2} = D \quad \text{Multiplying by } \frac{1}{2} \text{ on both sides}$$

$$D = \frac{36 - \frac{1}{2} \cdot 8 - \frac{1}{2} \cdot 4}{2} \quad \text{Substituting } L = 36, c_1 = 8, c_2 = 4$$

$$= 15$$

The number 15 checks, so the pulley centers are 15 in. apart.

TRY THIS

3. A belt around two pulleys has a length of 100 cm. The distance between the pulley centers is 30 cm and the circumference of one pulley is 50 cm. Find the circumference of the other pulley. 30 cm

4. The area of a trapezoid is 210 cm². The height is 7.5 cm and one base has length 23 cm. What is the length of the other base? 33 cm

6–5

Exercises

Solve.

1. $S = 2\pi rk$ for r

2. $A = P(1 + rt)$ for t

3. $A = \frac{1}{2}bk$ for b

4. $s = \frac{1}{2}gt^2$ for g

5. $S = 180(n - 2)$ for n

6. $S = \frac{n}{2}(a + 1)$ for a

7. $V = \frac{1}{6}k(B + b + 4M)$ for b

8. $A = P + Prt$ for P

9. $S(r - 1) = rl - a$ for r

10. $T = mg - mf$ for m

11. $A = \frac{1}{2}h(b_1 + b_2)$ for h

12. $S = 2\pi r(r + k)$ for k

13. $r = \frac{v^2 pL}{a}$ for a

14. $L = \frac{Mt - g}{t}$ for M

15. $A = \frac{1}{2}h(b_1 + b_2)$ for b_1

16. $l = a + (n - 1)d$ for n

17. $A = \frac{\pi r^2 E}{180}$ for E

18. $R = \frac{WL - x}{L}$ for W

1. $r = \frac{S}{2\pi k}$

2. $t = \frac{A - P}{Pr}$

3. $b = \frac{2A}{k}$

4. $g = \frac{2S}{t^2}$

5. $n = \frac{S + 360}{180}$

6. $a = \frac{2s - n}{n}$

7. $b = \frac{6V - Bk - 4kM}{k}$

8. $P = \frac{A}{1 + rt}$

9. $r = \frac{S - a}{S - l}$

10. $m = \frac{T}{g - f}$

11. $h = \frac{2A}{b_1 + b_2}$

12. $k = \frac{S - 2\pi r^2}{2\pi r}$

13. $a = \frac{v^2 pL}{r}$

14. $M = \frac{Lt + g}{t}$

15. $b_1 = \frac{2A - hb_2}{h}$

16. $n = \frac{l - a + d}{d}$

17. $E = \frac{180A}{\pi r^2}$

18. $W = \frac{RL + x}{L}$

19. $V = -h(B + c + 4M)$ for M **20.** $W = I^2R$ for R

21. $y = \frac{v^2pL}{a}$ for L **22.** $V = \frac{1}{3}bh$ for b

23. $r = \frac{v^2pL}{a}$ for p **24.** $P = 2(l + w)$ for l

25. $\frac{a}{c} = n + bn$ for n **26.** $C = \frac{Ka - b}{a}$ for K

27. $C = \frac{5}{9}(F - 32)$ for F **28.** $V = \frac{4}{3}\pi r^3$ for π

29. $f = \frac{gm - t}{m}$ for g **30.** $S = \frac{rl - a}{r - l}$ for a

31. The area of a trapezoid is 92 cm². The height is 8 cm and one of the bases has length 10 cm. How long is the other base? <small>13 cm</small>

32. The circumference C of a circle is given by $C = 2\pi r$, where r is the length of a radius. Find the length of a radius of a circle whose circumference is 314 cm. Use 3.14 for π. <small>50 cm</small>

33. The formula $W = EI$ tells the power in Watts given E, the number of volts and I, the current in amperes. Find the current used by a 75-watt light bulb which uses a voltage of 120. <small>0.625 amp</small>

34. The formula $E = \frac{9r}{I}$ tells the earned run average of a baseball pitcher who has pitched I innings and given up r earned runs. Find the number of innings pitched by a pitcher with an earned run average of 3.24 who gave up 24 earned runs. <small>66⅔</small>

35. The formula $P = 176 - 0.8A$ gives the recommended maximum pulse rate for exercising for a person of age A. Find Bonnie Klinefellir's age, if her recommended pulse rate is 140. <small>45</small>

36. The formula $n = [a(b + e)] - h$ tells the number of hits n needed to obtain a desired batting average a. The number of times at bat is b, the expected times at bat to come is e and the present number of hits is h. Find the desired batting average of a player who has 95 hits in 240 times at bat, expects to be at bat 64 more times and hopes to get 27 more hits. <small>.401</small>

Extension

37. The amount A to which P dollars will grow at interest rate r, compounded annually, in three years is given by $A = P + 3rP + 3r^2P + r^3P$. If an amount grows to $136 in three years at 10% compounded annually, how much was originally invested? <small>$102.18</small>

38. The formula $C = \frac{5}{9}(F - 32)$ is used to convert Farenheit temperatures to Celsius temperatures. At what temperature are the Farenheit and Celsius readings the same? <small>−40</small>

19. $M = -\frac{V + hB + hc}{4h}$

20. $R = \frac{W}{I^2}$

21. $L = \frac{ay}{v^2p}$

22. $b = \frac{3V}{h}$

23. $p = \frac{ar}{v^2L}$

24. $l = \frac{P - 2w}{2}$

25. $n = \frac{a}{c(1 + b)}$

26. $K = \frac{aC + b}{a}$

27. $F = \frac{9C + 160}{5}$

28. $\pi = \frac{3V}{4r^3}$

29. $g = \frac{fm + t}{m}$

30. $a = rl - S(r - 1)$

Using a Calculator

Algebraic Logic

What is the result if you enter $10 - 3 \times 2$ on your calculator?

Problem: $10 - 3 \times 2$

Enter: 10 (−) 3 (×) 2 (=)

Display: 10   3   2   4

Perhaps your calculator gave the following results.

Problem: $10 - 3 \times 2$

Enter: 10 (−) 3 (×) 2 (=)

Display: 10   3   7   2   14

Different calculators follow different rules for the order of operations in problems that mix addition or subtraction with multiplication or division. If your calculator gave the first result above, it follows the algebraic order of operations you have learned in this book. If your calculator gave the second result (or some other result), then it does not use algebraic logic and you cannot enter some problems from left to right and get the correct answer.

Memory Keys

Most calculators have one or more memory keys.

(M+) or (M) adds the display to the number in the memory.

(M−) subtracts the display from the number in the memory.

(STO) or (M) or (Min) stores a number in the memory.

(RCL) or (MR) or (RM) recalls the number in memory to the display.

(MC) or (CM) clears the memory.

Note that the clear and clear entry keys do not usually clear the memory. The store and recall memory keys can be used with calculators that do not follow algebraic logic.

EXAMPLE 1

This calculator does not have algebraic logic.

Problem: $10 - 3 \times 2$

Enter: 3 (×) 2 (=) (STO) 10 (−) (RCL) (=)

Display: 3   2   6   6   10   6   4

Instead of using the store and recall keys, you can also write the result of the first calculation on a sheet of paper.

Problem: $10 - 3 \times 2$

Equivalent Problems: $3 \times 2 = M$; $10 - M$

Enter: 3 $\boxed{\times}$ 2 $\boxed{=}$

Display: 3   2   6

Enter: 10 $\boxed{-}$ 6 $\boxed{=}$

Display: 10   6   4

Practice Problem: $26 + 13 \div 2$ 32.5

EXAMPLE 2

Many problems with fractions require you to use memory keys to record intermediate results. Notice that denominators are usually computed first. (In this problem and in the following examples, the answers have been rounded to three decimal places.)

Problem: $\dfrac{7.5}{2.4 + 0.8}$

Equivalent Problems: $2.4 + 0.8 = m$; $7.5 \div m$

Enter: 2.4 $\boxed{+}$ 0.8 $\boxed{=}$ $\boxed{\text{Min}}$ 7.5 $\boxed{\div}$ $\boxed{\text{MR}}$ $\boxed{=}$

Display: 2.4   0.8 3.2 3.2 7.5   3.2 2.344

Practice Problem: $\dfrac{0.92}{3.08 - 1.79}$ 0.713

EXAMPLE 3

Problems with parentheses, and some problems with fractions, can often be solved without using memory. Instead, the equals key is used. (For a calculator without algebraic logic, the first equals sign of Examples 3 and 4 may be omitted.)

Problem: $(45 + 32) \times 8$

Enter: 45 $\boxed{+}$ 32 $\boxed{=}$ $\boxed{\times}$ 8 $\boxed{=}$

Display: 45   32   77   8   616

Practice Problem: $(2.6 - 0.71) \times 3$ 5.67

EXAMPLE 4

Problem: $\dfrac{8 - 3}{0.2}$

Equivalent Problem: $(8 - 3) \div 2$

Enter: 8 $\boxed{-}$ 3 $\boxed{=}$ $\boxed{\div}$ 2 $\boxed{=}$

Display: 8   3   5   2   2.5

Practice Problem: $(\$15 + \$35 + \$49) \div 6$

                        $16.50

EXAMPLE 5

Problem: $\dfrac{5}{9} \times 56$

Equivalent Problem: $5 \div 9 \times 56$

Enter: 5 $\boxed{\div}$ 9 $\boxed{\times}$ 56 $\boxed{=}$

Display: 5   9   45   56   31.111

Practice Problem: $\dfrac{2}{3} + \dfrac{4}{5} + \dfrac{1}{8}$ 1.592

EXAMPLE 6

This problem uses both the memory and the equals keys.

Problem: $\dfrac{456 + 78 - 201}{735 - 324}$

Equivalent Problems: $735 - 324 = m$; $(456 + 78 - 201) \div m$

Enter: 735 ⟨ − ⟩ 324 ⟨ = ⟩ ⟨Min⟩ 456 ⟨ + ⟩ 78 ⟨ − ⟩ 201 ⟨ = ⟩ ⟨ ÷ ⟩ ⟨MR⟩ ⟨ = ⟩

Display: 735   324 411 411 456   78 534 201 333   411 0.810

Practice Problem: $\dfrac{0.6 - 0.07}{0.003 + 0.8 - 0.04}$ 0.695

The Change-Sign Key

The change-sign key, marked $+/-$ or CHS, changes the sign of the number in the display. This key is used to enter negative numbers. Notice, in the examples below, that the change-sign key is pressed *after* the number. For example, -9 is entered by pressing 9 and then ⟨ +/− ⟩ .

EXAMPLE 7

Problem: $-9 \times 5 + (-8)$

Enter: 9 ⟨+/−⟩ ⟨ × ⟩ 5 ⟨ + ⟩ 8 ⟨+/−⟩ ⟨ = ⟩

Display: 9 -9 5 -45 8 -8 -53

Practice Problem: $-18 \div 5 - (-3)$ −0.6

EXAMPLE 8

Problem: $0.1 \times [3 + (-1) - (-7)]$

Equivalent Problem: $[3 + (-1) - (-7)] \times 0.1$

Enter: 3 ⟨ + ⟩ 1 ⟨+/−⟩ ⟨ − ⟩ 7 ⟨+/−⟩ ⟨ = ⟩ ⟨ × ⟩ 0.1 ⟨ = ⟩

Display: 3   1 -1 2   7 -7 9   0.1   0.9

Practice Problem: $(-4 + 6 - 5) \div -8$ 0.375

EXAMPLE 9

The change-sign key can also be used to change the sign of an intermediate result. Here is another way to work Example 9.

Problem: $-[4 + 3 + (-2)]$

Enter: 4 ⟨ + ⟩ 3 ⟨ + ⟩ 2 ⟨+/−⟩ ⟨ = ⟩ ⟨+/−⟩

Display: 4   3 7 2 -2 5 -5

Practice Problem: $-[6 \times (-13 + 25)]$ −72

If your calculator does not have a change-sign key, you can work some problems with negative numbers by rewriting them and using the subtraction key.

EXAMPLE 10

Problem: $-9 \times 5 + (-8)$

Equivalent Problem: $-(9 \times 5 + 8)$

Enter: 9 $\boxed{\times}$ 5 $\boxed{+}$ 8 $\boxed{=}$

Display: 9   5   45   8   53

Now, mentally change the sign. The answer is -53.

Practice Problem: $40 \div -16 + (-12)$ −14.5

The Reciprocal Key

The reciprocal key, marked $1/x$, replaces the number in the display with its reciprocal. This key can be used to solve many problems with fractions. In the examples below, all answers are rounded to three decimal places.

EXAMPLE 11

Problem: $\frac{1}{15} + 36$

Enter: 15 $\boxed{1/x}$ $\boxed{+}$ 36 $\boxed{=}$

Display: 15   0.067   36   36.067

Practice Problem: $\frac{1}{32} - 2$ −1.969

EXAMPLE 12

This shows another way of working the problem in Example 2.

Problem: $\frac{7.5}{2.4 + 0.8}$

Enter: 2.4 $\boxed{+}$ 0.8 $\boxed{=}$ $\boxed{\div}$ 7.5 $\boxed{=}$ $\boxed{1/x}$

Display: 2.4   0.8   3.2   7.5   0.427   2.34375

Practice Problem: $\frac{32}{118 - 76}$ 0.762

Solving Equations

A calculator cannot solve an equation, but it can help you do any computation that is involved. First, solve the equation using algebra. Then do all the calculations.

EXAMPLE 13

Problem: Solve $8x - 35 = 9$.

Solve for x: $8x - 35 = 9$ $8x = 9 + 35$ $x = \frac{9 + 35}{8}$

Enter: 9 $\boxed{+}$ 35 $\boxed{=}$ $\boxed{\div}$ 8 $\boxed{=}$

Display: 9   35   44   8   5.5

Practice Problem: $14 + 6x = 11$ $x = -0.5$

Managing a Checking Account

Checks provide a safe way to pay bills. They enable you to buy without carrying cash and they provide a record of your payments.

A checking account is opened by depositing money in a bank. The bank assigns an account number and issues a checkbook containing deposit slips, checks, and a register.

A deposit slip lists cash and checks for deposit in your account.

A check contains the information required by the bank to turn your money over to someone else. It must be correctly written to be valid.

A checkbook register contains the record of checks and deposits. Each time a check is written, the amount is subtracted from the previous balance. Deposits are added.

The monthly statement from the bank shows the opening balance, the transactions, and the closing balance.

NATIONAL SAVINGS			ACCOUNT NUMBER 000000000 000 00000	
ALLAN W. BOOK 18 PAGE STREET AVON, N.J.			PREVIOUS BALANCE 320.98	
DATE	CHECKS		DEPOSITS	BALANCE
6-23-85	101	35.75		285.23
6-23-85	102	19.48		265.75
6-30-85			198.50	464.25
7-1-85	104	42.10		422.15

You should determine if your records agree with the bank's records. Most banks provide a simple form for balancing your account.

CLOSING BALANCE ON BANK STATEMENT	$422.15◄	Copy from the bank statement
DEPOSITS NOT YET CREDITED	+ 50.00◄	Add deposits not yet credited to your account
	472.15	
TOTAL OF OUTSTANDING CHECKS	- 10.00◄	Subtract checks not paid by the bank
BALANCE	$462.15◄	This balance should agree with your checkbook balance

Exercises

Find whether each account balances or not.

1. Checkbook balance: $482.80
   Closing balance on bank statement: $324.91
   Deposits not yet credited: $170.85
   Outstanding checks: $43.96 No

2. Checkbook balance: $346.07
   Closing balance on bank statement: $97.63
   Deposits not yet credited: $280.45
   Outstanding checks: $32.01 Yes

CHAPTER 6   Review

Review the material in the chapter. Then see how you have done by trying these review exercises. If you miss an exercise, restudy the indicated lesson.

6–1

1. Evaluate $x^2 - xy - 1$ for $x = 5$ and $y = -1$. 29
2. Evaluate $xy + xz - yz$ for $x = -1$, $y = 2$, and $z = 1$. −5

6–1   Tell the degree of each term of the following polynomials. Then find the degree of the polynomial.

3. $a^3 + a^2b - 3$ 4. $3x^5 + x^3y^2 - xy^3 + y^2 + 7$
3. 3, 3, 0; 3
4. 5, 5, 4, 2, 0; 5

6–1   Arrange in descending powers of the specified variable. Collect like terms if possible.

5. $b^3 + 3a^2b + 3ab^2 + a^3$; a $a^3 + 3a^2b + 3ab^2 + b^2$
6. $3x^3 + 4x^2y + 7y^3 - 5x^4y$; x $-5x^4y + 4x^2y + 3x + 7y^3$
7. $3x^2yz^3 - 2xy^2 + x^2yz^3 + x^2y^2 + 2xy^2$; y $x^2y^2 + 4x^2yz^3$

6–2   Add.

8. $(a^3b - 6a^2b^2 - ab^3 + 3) + (a^3b - 4a^2b^2 + 8)$ $2a^3b - 10a^2b^2 - ab^3 + 11$

6–2   Subtract.

9. $(18s^2t^3 + 12st^2 + 4) - (6st^2 - s^2t^2 - 3)$ $18s^2t^3 + 6st^2 + s^2t^2 + 7$

6–2   Multiply.

10. $(y^3z^2 - 2yz - 3)(2yz - 1)$ 11. $(3x^2 - 4y)(x + y)$
12. $(3x - 4y)^2$ 13. $(p - 4t^2)(p + 4t^2)$

6–3   Factor.

14. $x^5b^2 - x^4b^3 - x^3b^2$ 15. $16x^2y^2 - 1$
16. $4x^2 - 12xy + 9y^2$ 17. $8x^2 + 10xy - 3y^2$
18. $8ab - 12ac + 6bc - 9c^2$

6–4   Solve for x.

19. $ax + 6a = -2x - 3a^2$ $x = -3a$
20. $r(x - r) + s(x - s) = s(s + x) - (r + s)$ $x = \frac{r^2 + 2s^2 - r - s}{r}$

6–5

21. Solve for p: $A - p = prt$ $p = \frac{A}{1 + rt}$
22. The area of a trapezoid is given by $A = \frac{1}{2}(b_1 - b_2)h$. A trapezoid has area 64 cm². The bases have lengths 35 cm and 19 cm. What is the height?   18 cm

CHAPTER 6   Test

1. Evaluate $3x - xy + 5z$ for $x = 2$, $y = 1$, and $z = -1$. -1
2. Tell the degree of each term of the polynomial and the degree of the polynomial.
   $x^4 - x^3y + x^2 - 4y^3 + 6$ 4, 4, 2, 3, 0; 4
3. Arrange in descending powers of x.
   $3x + 4x^2y + 7y^3 - 5x^4y$ $-5x^4y + 4x^2y + 3x + 7y^3$

Add.

4. $(3xy - 4x^2y^2 - 3x^3y) + (7x^2y^2 + 4xy - 5x^3y + 4)$ $7xy + 3x^2y^2 - 8x^3y + 4$

Subtract.

5. $(18x^3y^3 - 5xy + 4x) - (3x^2y^2 + 4xy - 7x)$ $18x^3y^3 - 3x^2y^2 - 9xy + 11x$

Multiply.

6. $(a^2b - 3ab^2 + 4)(2ab - 4)$ $2a^3b^2 - 6a^2b^3 + 8ab - 4a^2b + 12ab^2 - 16$
7. $(3x^2 - 4y)(x + y)$ $3x^3 - 4xy + 3x^2y - 4y^2$
8. $(a^2 + 2b)^2$ $a^4 + 4a^2b + 4b^2$
9. $(c^2 + d)(c^2 - d)$ $c^4 - d^2$

Factor.

10. $x^5b^2 - x^4b^3 - x^3b^2$

11. $36x^2 - 25y^2$

12. $4x^2 - 12xy + 9y^2$

13. $8x^2 + 10xy - 3y^2$

14. $2xy - 6xz - 3y^2 + 9yz$

10. $x^3b^2(x^2 - xb - 1)$
11. $(6x + 5y)(6x - 5y)$
12. $(2x - 3y)^2$
13. $(4x - y)(2x + 3y)$
14. $(2x - 3y)(y - 3z)$

15. Solve for x. $-bx - 3b^2 = 3x + 9b$ $\quad x = -3b$

16. Solve for t. $R = st - s$ $\quad t = \frac{R + s}{s}$

17. The area of a triangle is given by $A = \frac{1}{2}bh$. For a triangle with area 18 cm² and height 6 cm, find the base. 6 cm

Challenge

18. Solve for x. $16x^4 - 13x^2 + 9 = 0$ $\quad \pm\frac{1}{2}, \pm\frac{3}{2}$

Ready for Graphs and Linear Equations?

1–3

1. What is the meaning of y^2? $y \cdot y$ 2. Write exponential notation for nnn. n^3

2–1 Make true sentences using a number line and $<$ or $>$.

3. $-3 \quad 2$ $<$ 4. $-2 \quad -6$ $>$ 5. $0 \quad -8$ $>$ 6. $5 \quad -2$ $>$

3–1 to 3–3 Solve and check.

7. $\frac{5}{2} - y = \frac{1}{3}$ $\frac{13}{6}$ 8. $w + 8 = -3$ -11 9. $-4 + x = 8$ 12
10. $6x = -12$ -2 11. $\frac{7}{8}w = -\frac{2}{3}$ $-\frac{16}{21}$ 12. $\frac{2}{3}t = \frac{1}{8}$ $\frac{3}{16}$
13. $5x + 8 = 43$ 7 14. $-2x + 9 = -11$ 10 15. $-8x + 3x = 25$ -5

3–6 Solve for the indicated letter.

16. $d = \frac{5k}{s}$, for k $\quad \frac{ds}{5}$ 17. $S = \frac{Mp^2}{mv}$, for v $\quad \frac{Mp^2}{mS}$

4–3 Evaluate each polynomial for $y = 4$.

18. $9 - 5y$ -11 19. $-4y - 8$ -24
20. $3y^2 - y + 8$ 52 21. $-y^2 + 2y + 1$ -7

7

CHAPTER SEVEN

Graphs
and Linear Equations

Plotting Points

On a number line each point is the graph of a number. On a plane each point is the graph of an ordered pair. We use two perpendicular number lines called axes. The horizontal axis is called the *x*-axis and the vertical axis is called the *y*-axis. The axes cross at a point called the origin. The arrows show the positive directions.

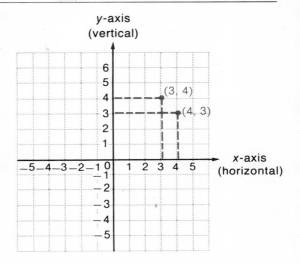

The numbers in an ordered pair are called coordinates. In the ordered pair (4,3) the first number 4 is the *x*-coordinate and the second number 3 is the *y*-coordinate. The *x*-coordinate tells the distance right (positive) or left (negative) from the origin. The *y*-coordinate tells the distance up (positive) or down (negative) from the horizontal axis. The *x*-coordinate is called the abscissa and the *y*-coordinate is called the ordinate.

EXAMPLE 1

Plot the points $(-3, 4)$, $(2, -5)$, and $(-4, -4)$.

The *x*-coordinate -3 is negative. We move 3 units left. The *y*-coordinate 4 is positive. We move 4 units up. The graphs of $(2, -5)$ and $(-4, -4)$ are shown.

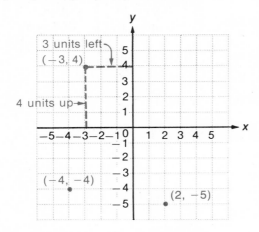

TRY THIS Use graph paper. Draw and label an x-axis and a y-axis. Plot these points on the same graph. Write the ordered pair close to each point.

1. $(4, 6)$ **2.** $(6, 4)$ **3.** $(-2, 5)$ **4.** $(-3, -4)$ **5.** $(5, -3)$ **6.** $(-4, -3)$

When one coordinate is 0, the point is on one of the axes. The origin has coordinates $(0, 0)$.

EXAMPLE 2
Plot the points $(0, -3)$ and $(-2, 0)$.

The x-coordinate, 0, tells us 0 units left or right. The y-coordinate, -3, tells us to move 3 units down. The point $(0, -3)$ is on the y-axis. For the point $(-2, 0)$, the x-coordinate, -2, tells us to move 2 units left. The y-coordinate, 0, tells us not to move. The point $(-2, 0)$ is on the x-axis.

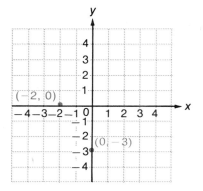

TRY THIS Plot the following points.

7. $(0, 7)$ **8.** $(5, 0)$ **9.** $(0, 0)$ **10.** $(0, -5)$

Quadrants

A plane is divided into four quadrants as shown. The graph shows some points and their coordinates. In the first quadrant both coordinates of any point are positive. In the second quadrant, the x-coordinate is negative and the y-coordinate is positive.

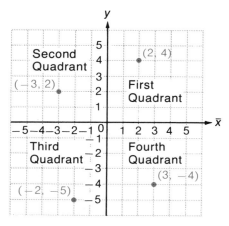

TRY THIS

11. What are the signs of the coordinates of a point in the third quadrant? Both coordinates are negative.

12. What are the signs of the coordinates of a point in the fourth quadrant? x-coordinate is positive, y-coordinate is negative.

In which quadrant is each point located?

13. $(5, 3)$ first **14.** $(-6, -4)$ third **15.** $(10, -14)$ fourth **16.** $(-13, 4)$ second

Finding Coordinates

EXAMPLE 3

Find the coordinates of point B.

Point B is 3 units to the left and 5 units up. Its coordinates are $(-3, 5)$.

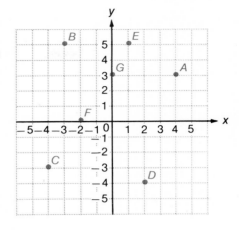

TRY THIS

17. Find the coordinates of points A, C, D, E, F, and G in the graph of Example 3. $(4, 3), (-4, -3), (2, -4), (1, 5), (-2, 0), (0, 3)$

7–1	

Exercises

Use graph paper. Draw and label an x-axis and a y-axis. Plot these points. Write the ordered pair close to each point.

1. $(2, 5)$ 2. $(4, 6)$ 3. $(-1, 3)$ 4. $(-2, 4)$
5. $(3, -2)$ 6. $(5, -3)$ 7. $(-2, -4)$ 8. $(-5, -7)$
9. $(0, 4)$ 10. $(0, 6)$ 11. $(0, -5)$ 12. $(0, -7)$
13. $(5, 0)$ 14. $(6, 0)$ 15. $(-7, 0)$ 16. $(-8, 0)$

In which quadrant is each point located?

17. $(-5, 3)$ 18. $(-12, -1)$ 19. $(100, -1)$ 20. $(35.6, -2.5)$
21. $(-6, -29)$ 22. $(-3.6, 10.9)$ 23. $(3.8, 9.2)$ 24. $(1895, 1492)$

17. second
18. third
19. fourth
20. fourth
21. third
22. second
23. first
24. first

25. In the second quadrant, x-coordinates are always ___ and y-coordinates are always ___. negative, positive

26. In the fourth quadrant, _x_ coordinates are always positive and _y_ coordinates are always negative.

Find the coordinates of points A, B, C, D, and E.

27.

A (3,3), B (0, −4), C (−5,0), D (−1, −1), E (2,0)

28.

A (4,1), B (0, −5), C (−4,0), D (−3, −2), E (2,0)

Extension

Use graph paper. Plot a point which satisfies each of the following conditions. Answers may vary.

29. The x-coordinate is the same as the y-coordinate. Ex. (−2, −2), (0, 0), (1, 1)

30. The absolute values of the ordinate and the abscissa are equal. Ex. (−3, 3), (−4, −4)

31. The x-value and the y-value are inverses of each other. Ex. (−1, 1), (0,0)

32. The x-coordinate is the square of the y-coordinate. Ex. (−2, 4), (3, 9)

33. The first coordinate is 3 less than the second coordinate. Ex. (−3, 0), (−2, 1), (1, 4)

34. The product of the coordinates is 2. Ex. (−2, −1), (1, 2)

35. The sum of the x and y values is 5. Ex. (2, 3), (4, 1), (0,5)

36. The product of the first and second coordinates is 0. Ex. (0, 1), (1, 0)

37. Graph 12 points such that the sum of the coordinates of the points is 6. Ex. (−2, 8), (−1, 7), (0, 6), (1, 5)

38. Graph twelve points such that the difference between x and y is 1. Ex. (−2, −3), (0, −1), (2, 1); (−1, 0), (0, 1), (2, 3)

Challenge

39. Find the perimeter of a rectangle whose vertices have coordinates (5, 3), (5, −2), (−3, −2) and (−3, 3). 26

40. Find the area of a triangle whose vertices have coordinates (0, 9), (0, −4) and (5, −4). 32.5

Equations in Two Variables

Solutions of Equations

An equation such as $3x + 2 = 7$ has the number $\frac{5}{3}$ as its solution.

An equation in two variables, such as $y = 2x + 1$, has ordered pairs of numbers as solutions. We usually take variables in alphabetical order. For an equation such as $y = 2x + 1$ we write an ordered pair in the form (x, y).

EXAMPLE 1
Determine whether $(3, 7)$ is a solution of $y = 2x + 1$.

$$
\begin{array}{c|c}
\multicolumn{2}{c}{y = 2x + 1} \\
\hline
7 & 2 \cdot 3 + 1 \quad \text{\footnotesize Substituting 3 for x and 7 for y} \\
 & 7
\end{array}
$$

The equation is true. $(3, 7)$ is a solution.

EXAMPLE 2
Determine whether $(-2, 3)$ is a solution of $2y = 4x - 8$.

$$
\begin{array}{c|c}
\multicolumn{2}{c}{2y = 4x - 8} \\
\hline
2 \cdot 3 & 4(-2) - 8 \quad \text{\footnotesize Substituting -2 for x and 3 for y} \\
6 & -16
\end{array}
$$

The equation is false. $(-2, 3)$ is not a solution.

TRY THIS

1. Determine whether $(2, 3)$ is a solution of $y = 2x + 3$. No
2. Determine whether $(-2, 4)$ is a solution of $4y - 3x = 22$. Yes

EXAMPLE 3
Find three solutions of $y - 3x = -2$.

We first solve for y.

$$y = 3x - 2$$

We choose any value for x. The easiest is 0.

$$y = 3 \cdot 0 - 2 \quad \text{Substituting 0 for } x$$
$$y = -2$$

We have a solution, an ordered pair, $(0, -2)$. We choose another number for x.

$$y = 3 \cdot 2 - 2 \quad \text{Substituting 2 for } x$$
$$y = 4$$

A second solution is $(2, 4)$. Let's choose -2 for x.

$$y = 3(-2) - 2 \quad \text{Substituting } -2 \text{ for } x$$
$$y = -8$$

A third solution is $(-2, -8)$.

TRY THIS

3. Find three solutions of $y - 2x = 3$. Answers may vary. Ex. $(0, 3), (1, 5), (-1, 1), (-2, -1)$

Graphing Equations

We know that a solution of an equation with two variables is an ordered pair of numbers. The numbers in each ordered pair are the coordinates of a point and can be plotted. Thus, we can graph an equation with two variables by plotting enough points to see a pattern.

> To graph an equation means to make a drawing of its solutions.

EXAMPLE 4

Graph the equation $y - x = 1$.
Use a table to list several solutions.

x	0	-1	-5	1	3
y	1	0	-4	2	4

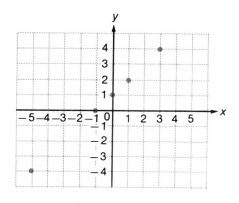

The points all lie on a straight line. We can see that if we were to plot a million solutions, the points would resemble a solid line. If we take all of the solutions we do get the entire line. Here is the graph of the equation.

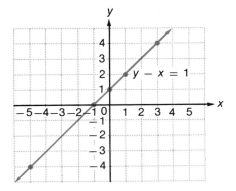

TRY THIS Graph each equation.

4. $y = x$ 5. $y - x = 3$.

7-2

Exercises

Determine whether the given point is a solution of the equation.

1. $(2, 5), y = 3x - 1$ Yes
2. $(1, 7), y = 2x + 5$ Yes
3. $(2, -3), 3x - y = 3$ No
4. $(-1, 4), 2x + y = 2$ Yes
5. $(-2, -1), 2x + 3y = -7$ Yes
6. $(0, -4), 4x + 2y = 8$ No

Find three solutions of each equation. Answers may vary.

7. $y = 2x + 1$
8. $y = 3x + 2$
9. $x + y = 6$
10. $x + y = 8$
11. $2x + y = 10$
12. $3x - y = 11$
13. $4x + 3y = 14$
14. $5x + 7y = 19$
15. $6x - 5y = 23$

Make a table like Example 4. Graph each of the following equations.

16. $y = x$
17. $y = -x$
18. $y = -2x$
19. $y = 2x$
20. $y = x + 1$
21. $y = x - 1$
22. $y = 2x + 1$
23. $y = 3x - 1$
24. $y = -3x + 2$
25. $y = -4x + 1$
26. $2x + y = 3$
27. $5x + y = 7$
28. $3x + 9y = 12$
29. $2x + 8y = -4$
30. $2x - 3y = 6$

31. $3x - 4y = 12$ **32.** $y = \frac{1}{2}x + 1$ **33.** $y = \frac{1}{3}x - 1$

34. Complete the table for $y = x^2 + 1$. Plot the points on graph paper and draw the graph.

x	0	-1	1	-2	2	-3	3
y	1	2	2	5	5	10	10

Extension

35. Find all whole number solutions of $x + y = 6$. (0, 6), (1, 5), (2, 4), (3, 3), (4, 2), (5, 1), (6, 0)

36. Find all whole number solutions of $x + 3y = 15$. (15, 0), (12, 1), (9, 2), (6, 3), (3, 4), (0, 5)

37. Write an equation that n nickels and d dimes total 1.95.
Find three solutions. $5n + 10d = 195$; Ex. (d, n) form, (10, 19), (0, 39), (15, 9)

38. Write an equation that n nickels and q quarters total 2.35.
Find three solutions. $5n + 25q = 235$; Ex. (27, 4), (7, 8), (47, 0)

39. Find three solutions of $y = |x|$. Ex. $(-3, 3)$, (2, 2), (0, 0)

40. Find three solutions of $y = |x| + 1$. Ex. $(-3, 4)$, (2, 3), (0, 1)

Challenge

41. Two machines x and y produce rivets. Machine x produces 68 rivets per hour while machine y produces 76 rivets per hour. Let x represent the number of hours machine x runs and y represent the number of hours machine y runs. Write an equation telling that the combined production of x and y on a given day is 864. Find a solution to the equation. Explain your solution. $68x + 76y = 864$, let $x = y$, 6 hr each machine

---

USING A CALCULATOR/Graphing

A calculator can be used to help you graph equations. First solve the equation. Then use a calculator to do any computations.

EXAMPLE 1
Problem: Graph $3x - 4y = 12$.

Solve for y: $y = \frac{3x - 12}{4}$

Let $x = 6$: $y = \frac{3 \times 6 - 12}{4}$

Enter: 3 $\times$ 6 $-$ 12 $=$
Display: 3   6   18   12   6
Enter: $\div$ 4 $=$
Display: 4   1.5

Repeat for other values of x until you have enough ordered pairs to draw the graph.

EXAMPLE 2
Problem: Graph $3.56x + 4.8y = 0.234$.

Solve for y: $y = \frac{0.234 - 3.56x}{4.8}$

Let $x = 3$: $y = \frac{0.234 - 3.56x \times 3}{4.8}$

Enter: 0.234 $-$ 3.56 $\times$ 3 $=$
Display: 0.234   3.56   3 -10.446
Enter: $\div$ 4.8 $=$
Display: 4.8 -2.17625

7–3 Graphing Linear Equations

Equations whose graphs are straight lines are called linear equations. The standard form of a linear equation is $ax + by = c$, where a, b, and c are constants and a and b are not both 0. An equation is linear if the variables occur to the first power only, there are no products of variables, and no variable appears in a denominator. Linear equations are also called first degree equations. The following are examples of linear equations.

$$3x + 5 = 3y \qquad 5y = -4 \qquad 9x - 15y = y$$

Graphing Using Two Points

The graph of a linear equation is a straight line. Plotting two points is sufficient. Use one more point as a check.

EXAMPLE 1

Graph the equation $2y - 4 = 4x$.

We solve for y and find two solutions.

$$y = 2x + 2$$

If $x = 1$, then $y = 2 \cdot 1 + 2$, or 4. If $x = -2$, then $y = 2(-2) + 2$, or -2. Plot the points $(1, 4)$ and $(-2, -2)$ and draw the line. The point $(3, 8)$ is also a solution. We plot it as a check.

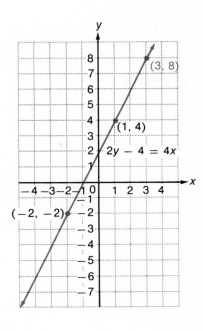

TRY THIS Use graph paper. Graph these linear equations. Use a third point to check.

1. $3y - 12 = 9x$ **2.** $4y + 8 = -16x$ **3.** $6x - 2y = -2$ **4.** $-10x - 2y = 8$

Graphing Using Intercepts

Another method of graphing linear equations involves the use of intercepts. In the graph of $y - 2x = 4$, we could graph it by solving for y and proceed as before, but we want to develop a faster method. The y-intercept is $(0, 4)$. It occurs where the line crosses the y-axis and always has 0 as the first coordinate. The x-intercept is $(-2, 0)$. It occurs where the line crosses the x-axis and always has 0 as the second coordinate.

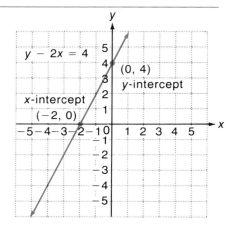

To find the x-intercept, let $y = 0$ and solve for x. The x-intercept is in the form $(a, 0)$.

To find the y-intercept, let $x = 0$ and solve for y. The y-intercept is in the form $(0, b)$.

EXAMPLE 2

Graph $4x + 3y = 12$.

To find the x-intercept, let $y = 0$ and solve for x.

$$4x + 3 \cdot 0 = 12$$
$$4x = 12$$
$$x = 3$$

The x-intercept is $(3, 0)$.

To find the y-intercept, let $x = 0$ and solve for y.

$$4 \cdot 0 + 3y = 12$$
$$3y = 12$$
$$y = 4$$

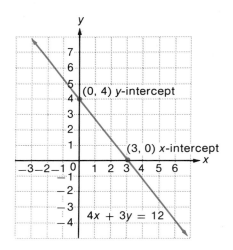

The y-intercept is $(0, 4)$. We plot these two points and draw the line.

TRY THIS Use graph paper. Graph using intercepts.

5. $2y = 3x - 6$ 6. $5x + 7y = 35$ 7. $8x + 2y = 24$

Graphing Equations with a Missing Variable

Consider the equation $y = 3$. We can think of it as $y = 0 \cdot x + 3$. No matter what number we choose for x, we find that y is 3.

EXAMPLE 3
Graph $y = 3$.

Any ordered pair of the form $(x, 3)$ is a solution, such as $(2, 3)$, $(4, 3)$, or $(-1, 3)$. So the line is parallel to the x-axis with y-intercept $(0, 3)$.

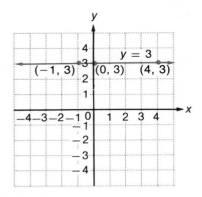

EXAMPLE 4
Graph $x = -4$.

Any ordered pair of the form $(-4, y)$ is a solution, such as $(-4, 3)$, $(-4, 1)$, or $(-4, -1)$. So the line is parallel to the y-axis with x-intercept $(-4, 0)$.

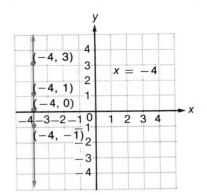

TRY THIS Graph these equations using the same axes.

8. $x = 5$ **9.** $y = -2$ **10.** $x = 0$ **11.** $x = -6$

The graph of $y = b$ is a horizontal line parallel to the x-axis.

The graph of $x = a$ is a vertical line parallel to the y-axis.

Steps for Graphing Linear Equations

1. If the equation is of the type $x = a$ or $y = b$, the graph will be a line parallel to an axis.
2. If the equation is not of the type $x = a$ or $y = b$, find the intercepts. Graph using the intercepts if this is feasible. If the intercepts are too close together, choose another point farther from the origin.
3. Use a third point as a check.

7–3

Exercises

Use graph paper. Graph these linear equations using two points. Use a third point to check.

1. $x + 3y = 6$ 2. $x + 2y = 8$ 3. $-x + 2y = 4$
4. $-x + 3y = 9$ 5. $3x + y = 9$ 6. $2x + y = 6$
7. $2y - 2 = 6x$ 8. $3y - 6 = 9x$ 9. $3x - 9 = 3y$
10. $5x - 10 = 5y$ 11. $2x - 3y = 6$ 12. $2x - 5y = 10$
13. $4x + 5y = 20$ 14. $2x + 6y = 12$ 15. $2x + 3y = 8$

Use graph paper. Graph using intercepts.

16. $x - 1 = y$ 17. $x - 3 = y$ 18. $2x - 1 = y$
19. $3x - 2 = y$ 20. $4x - 3y = 12$ 21. $6x - 2y = 18$
22. $7x + 2y = 6$ 23. $3x + 4y = 5$ 24. $y = -4 - 4x$
25. $y = -3 - 3x$ 26. $-3x = 6y - 2$ 27. $-4x = 8y - 5$

Graph the following equations.

28. $x = -4$ 29. $x = -3$ 30. $y = -7$ 31. $y = -9$

32. $x = 5$ 33. $x = 7$ 34. $y = \frac{1}{2}$ 35. $y = \frac{1}{4}$

Extension

36. Write the equation of the y-axis. $\; x = 0$

37. Write the equation of the x-axis. $\; y = 0$

38. Find the coordinates of the point of intersection of the graphs of the equations $x = -3$ and $y = 6$. $\; (-3, 6)$

39. Write the equation of a line parallel to the x-axis and 5 units below it. $\; y = -5$

40. Write the equation of a line parallel to the y-axis and 13 units to the right of it. $\; x = 13$

41. Write the equation of a line parallel to the x-axis and intersecting the y-axis at $(0, 2.8)$ $\; y = 2.8$

Challenge

42. Plot the points $(10, 10)$, $(10, -10)$, $(-10, -10)$, and $(-10, 10)$. Connect the points to form a square. Then graph the following equations, but only draw the part of the line that is inside the square.

    a. $y = x - 7$ **b.** $y = x - 5$ **c.** $y = 5$ **d.** $y = 2x$

    e. $y = -x$ **f.** $y = -x + 7$ **g.** $y = -x + 5$ **h.** $2y = x$

43. The part of each line that is inside the square is called a line segment. Which of the eight line segments is the longest? Which pairs of line segments have the same length? Find an equation whose segment has the same length as the segment, inside the square, of $y = -3x + 5$. $\; \text{e; b and g, a and f; b}$

THE FOUR COLOR MAP PROBLEM

Suppose you draw a map showing many countries. How many colors do you need so that no two neighboring countries have the same color? (Countries that touch at just one point do not count as neighboring.)

Experimentation shows that four colors are enough for any map. Many mathematicians have tried, unsuccessfully, to construct a map that requires five colors. However, for many years, no one could *prove* that four colors were sufficient to color any map.

Then, in 1976, mathematicians at the University of Illinois found a proof. Their proof is unusual. It includes a computer program and lengthy computer calculations. It is not an elegant proof. But it solves the problem.

Of course, some maps can be colored with fewer than four colors. For example, a chessboard requires only two different colors. A drawing made up of equilateral triangles requires only three. Try constructing maps that require two, three, and four colors.

What is Slope?

Graphs of some linear equations slant upward from left to right. Others slant downward. Some slant more steeply than others. Consider a line with two points marked. As we move from P to Q, the x-coordinate changes from 2 to 6 and the y-coordinate changes from 1 to 3. The change in x is 4, or $6 - 2$. The change in y is 2, or $3 - 1$.

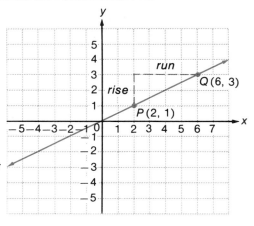

We call the change in y the rise. The change in x is called the run. The ratio $\frac{\text{rise}}{\text{run}}$ is the same for any two points on a line. We call this ratio slope. Slope describes the slant of a line. The slope of the line in the graph above has a $\frac{\text{rise}}{\text{run}}$ ratio of $\frac{2}{4}$.

$$\text{The slope of a line} = \frac{\text{rise}}{\text{run}} = \frac{\text{the change in } y}{\text{the change in } x}$$
$$= \frac{\text{difference of } y\text{-coordinates}}{\text{difference of } x\text{-coordinates}}.$$

EXAMPLE 1

Graph the line containing points $(-4, 3)$ and $(2, -6)$ and find the slope. To find the slope of a line find two points on it. We know that the given points $(-4, 3)$ and $(2, -6)$ are on the line. From $(-4, 3)$ to $(2, -6)$ the change in y, or rise, is $3 - (-6) = 9$. The change in x, or run, is $-4 - 2 = -6$.

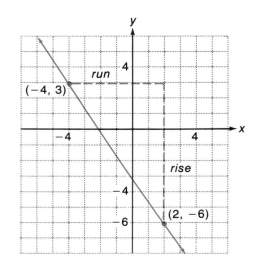

$$\text{Slope} = \frac{\text{rise}}{\text{run}} = \frac{\text{change in } y}{\text{change in } x} = \frac{3 - (-6)}{-4 - 2}$$
$$= \frac{9}{-6}$$
$$= -\frac{9}{6}, \text{ or } -\frac{3}{2}$$

TRY THIS Graph the lines containing these points and find each slope.

1. $(-2, 3)$ $(3, 5)$ **2.** $(0, -3)$ $(-3, 2)$ 1. slope $= \frac{2}{5}$ 2. slope $= \frac{-5}{3}$

To find slope we subtract coordinates of points. We can subtract in two ways. Let's do Example 1 again.

$$\text{slope} = \frac{\text{change in } y}{\text{change in } x} = \frac{-6 - 3}{2 - (-4)} = \frac{-9}{6} = -\frac{3}{2}$$

This is the same slope. In finding slope we must choose one point and write its y-coordinate first in the numerator and its x-coordinate first in the denominator of the slope formula.

EXAMPLE 2

The points $(3, 5)$ and $(1, 1)$ are on a line. Find its slope. We will usually use the letter m for slope.

The change in y is $5 - 1$, or 4. The change in x is $3 - 1$, or 2.

$$\text{The slope, } m, \text{ is } \frac{\text{change in } y}{\text{change in } x} = \frac{5 - 1}{3 - 1} = \frac{4}{2} = 2$$

TRY THIS Find the slopes of the lines containing these points.

3. $(2, 2)$ $(8, 9)$ $\frac{7}{6}$ **4.** $(-4, -6)$ $(3, -2)$ $\frac{4}{7}$
5. $(-2, 3)$ $(2, 1)$ $-\frac{1}{2}$ **6.** $(5, -11)$ $(-9, 4)$ $\frac{-15}{14}$

The slope of a line tells us how it slants. A line with a large slope slants up steeply. A line with a negative slope slants downward to the right.

$m = \frac{10}{3}$

$m = \frac{3}{10}$

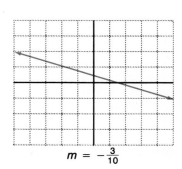

$m = -\frac{3}{10}$

Horizontal and Vertical Lines

What about the slope of a horizontal or vertical line?

EXAMPLE 3

Find the slope of the line $y = 4$.

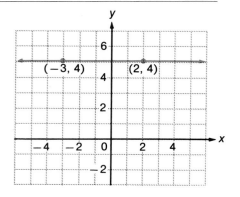

change in $y = 4 - 4 = 0$

change in $x = -3 - 2 = -5$

$$m = \frac{4 - 4}{-3 - 2} = \frac{0}{-5} = 0$$

Any two points on a horizontal line have the same y-coordinate. Thus, the change in y is 0, so the slope is 0.

EXAMPLE 4

Find the slope of the line $x = -3$.

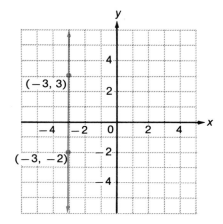

change in $y = 3 - (-2) = 5$

change in $x = -3 - (-3) = 0$

$$m = \frac{3 - (-2)}{-3 - (-3)} = \frac{5}{0}$$

Since division by 0 is not defined, this line has no slope.

> A horizontal line has slope 0. A vertical line has no slope.

TRY THIS Find the slopes, if they exist, of the lines containing these points.

7. $(9, 7)$ $(3, 7)$ 0   **8.** $(4, -6)$ $(4, 0)$ $\overset{\text{No}}{\text{slope}}$ **9.** $(2, 4)$ $(-1, 5)$ $-\frac{1}{3}$

7–4	

Exercises

Graph the lines containing these points and find their slopes.

1. $(3, 2)$ $(-1, 2)$ **2.** $(4, 1)$ $(-2, -3)$ **3.** $(-2, 4)$ $(3, 0)$

4. $(-4, 2)$ $(2, -3)$ **5.** $(0, 5)$ $(-4, -3)$ **6.** $(1, 6)$ $(-2, -4)$

Find the slope of each line.

7.

8.

9.

10.

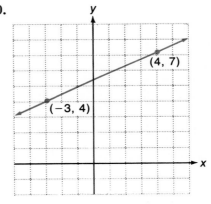

Find the slopes of the lines containing these points.

11. $(4, 0)$ $(5, 7)$ ₇   **12.** $(3, 0)$ $(6, 2)$ $\frac{2}{3}$

13. $(0, 8)$ $(-3, 10)$ $-\frac{2}{3}$ **14.** $(0, 9)$ $(4, 7)$ $-\frac{1}{2}$

15. $(3, -2)$ $(5, -6)$ ₋₂   **16.** $(-2, 4)$ $(6, -7)$ $-\frac{11}{8}$

17. $(0, 0)$ $(-3, -9)$ ₃   **18.** $(0, 0)$ $(-4, -8)$ ₂

19. $(-2, -3)$ $(-5, -7)$ $\frac{4}{3}$ **20.** $\left(\frac{1}{2}, \frac{2}{3}\right)$ $\left(\frac{5}{2}, \frac{1}{3}\right)$ $-\frac{1}{6}$

21. $\left(\frac{3}{4}, \frac{1}{2}\right)$ $\left(\frac{1}{4}, -\frac{1}{2}\right)$ ₂   **22.** $\left(\frac{1}{4}, \frac{1}{8}\right)$ $\left(\frac{1}{2}, \frac{3}{4}\right)$ $\frac{5}{2}$

Tell the slope, if it exists, of each of these lines.

23. $x = -8$ **24.** $x = -4$ **25.** $y = 2$ **26.** $y = 17$

27. $x = 9$ **28.** $x = 6$ **29.** $y = -9$ **30.** $y = -4$

23. No slope   27. No slope
24. No slope   28. No slope
25. Zero slope   29. Zero slope
26. Zero slope   30. Zero slope

Extension

31. Graph the following equations on the same set of axes.

$$y = x, y = x + 1, y = x - 2$$

What is true about the slopes of these lines? The slopes are the same.

32. Graph the following equations on the same set of axes.

$$y = x, y = 2x, y = 3x, y = 5x$$

What is true about the slopes of these lines? The slopes increase.

33. A line contains $(4, 3)$ and $(x, 7)$. It has slope 2. Find x. 6

34. A line contains $(9, y)$ and $(-6, 3)$. It has slope $\frac{2}{3}$. Find y. 13

35. A line containing $(-4, y)$ and $(2, 4y)$ has slope 6. Find y. 12

36. The grade of a road is really its slope. Grade is usually expressed as percent. What is the slope of a road with a 7% grade? $\frac{7}{100}$

37. The rate of climb of an airplane is really the slope of its path while climbing. Suppose a plane climbs 11.7 ft for every 30 ft it moves horizontally. Express the slope or rate of climb as a percent. 39%

Challenge

38. A line contains points $\left(p, \frac{p}{q}\right)$ and $\left(q, \frac{q}{p}\right)$ where p and q are not 0. Find the slope. $\frac{p + q}{pq}$

39. Use the idea of slope to determine whether $(-1, 3)$, $(1, 1)$, and $(10, -8)$ are on the same line. Yes, the slopes of any two points are the same.

40. In the chessboard drawing, the knight may move to any of the eight squares shown. If the beginning and end squares of any move determine a line, what slopes are possible? $2, \frac{1}{2}, -\frac{1}{2}, -2$

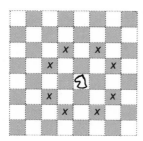

Equations and Slope

Finding Slope from an Equation

It is possible to find the slope of a line from its equation. We begin by finding two points on the line.

EXAMPLE 1

Find the slope of the line $y = 2x + 3$. We choose the points $(0, 3)$ and $(1, 5)$.

$$m = \frac{\text{change in } y}{\text{change in } x} = \frac{5 - 3}{1 - 0}$$

$$= \frac{2}{1}$$

$$= 2$$

The slope is 2. This is also the coefficient of the x-term in the equation $y = 2x + 3$.

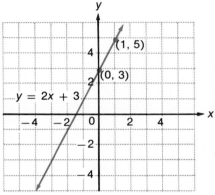

To find the slope of a nonvertical linear equation in x and y, first solve the equation for y. The resulting equation has the form $y = mx + b$. The coefficient of the x-term, m, is the slope of the line.

EXAMPLE 2

Find the slope of $2x + 3y = 7$.

We solve for y.

$$2x + 3y = 7$$
$$3y = -2x + 7$$
$$y = \frac{-2}{3}x + \frac{7}{3}$$

The slope is $-\frac{2}{3}$.

TRY THIS Find the slope of each equation by solving for y.

1. $4x + 5y = 7$ $-\frac{4}{5}$ **2.** $3x + 8y = 9$ $-\frac{3}{8}$ **3.** $x + 5y = 7$ $-\frac{1}{5}$ **4.** $5x - 4y = 8$ $\frac{5}{4}$

Slope-Intercept Equation of a Line

In the equation $y = mx + b$, we stated that m is the slope. If $x = 0$ then $y = b$, so the y-intercept is $(0, b)$. We also say that the number b is the y-intercept. In this graph the line $y = 2x - 3$ has slope 2 and y-intercept -3.

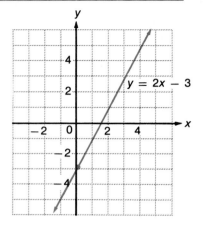

An equation $y = mx + b$ is called the slope-intercept equation of a line with slope, m, and y-intercept, b.

EXAMPLE 3

Find the slope and y-intercept of $y = 3x - 4$.

We simply read from the equation.

$y = 3x - 4 \leftarrow$ y-intercept: -4
$\uparrow$
slope: 3

EXAMPLE 4

Find the slope and y-intercept of $2x + 3y = 8$.

We first solve for y.

$$3y = -2x + 8$$
$$y = -\frac{2}{3}x + \frac{8}{3}$$

The slope is $-\frac{2}{3}$. The y-intercept is $\frac{8}{3}$.

TRY THIS Find the slope and y-intercept of each line.

5. $y = 5x$ 6. $y = -\frac{3}{2}x - 6$ 7. $2y = 4x - 17$

8. $3x + 4y = 15$ 9. $-7x - 5y = 22$

5. $5, (0, 0)$
6. $-\frac{3}{2}, (0, -6)$
7. $2, (0, -\frac{17}{2})$
8. $-\frac{3}{4}, (0, \frac{15}{4})$
9. $-\frac{7}{5}, (0, -\frac{22}{5})$

Graphing Using the Slope-Intercept Equation

Graphs of lines described by the slope-intercept equations are easy to draw.

EXAMPLE 5

From the equation $y = -\frac{2}{3}x + 3$ we know the slope is $-\frac{2}{3}$ and the y-intercept is 3.

First, we plot $(0, 3)$, the y-intercept. We find another point by moving -2 units vertically and 3 units horizontally. The point is $(3, 1)$. We connect the points to graph the line.

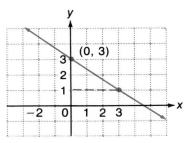

TRY THIS   Use graph paper. Graph each equation using y-intercept and slope.

10. $y = 3x - 4$ **11.** $y = -\frac{1}{3}x + 4$ **12.** $y = -\frac{3}{4}x + 2$ **13.** $y = -2x - 5$

7–5

Exercises

Find the slope of each equation by solving for y.

1. $3x + 2y = 6$ $-\frac{3}{2}$ **2.** $4x - y = 5$ 4 **3.** $x + 4y = 8$ $-\frac{1}{4}$

4. $x + 3y = 6$ $-\frac{1}{3}$ **5.** $-2x + y = 4$ 2 **6.** $-5x + y = 5$ 5

7. $4x - 3y = -12$ $\frac{4}{3}$ **8.** $3x - 4y = -12$ $\frac{3}{4}$ **9.** $x - 2y = 9$ $\frac{1}{2}$

10. $x - 3y = -2$ $\frac{1}{3}$ **11.** $-2x + 4y = 8$ $\frac{1}{2}$ **12.** $-5x + 7y = 2$ $\frac{5}{7}$

13. $-7x + 5y = 16$ $\frac{7}{5}$ **14.** $-3x + 2y = 9$ $\frac{3}{2}$ **15.** $-6x - 9y = 13$ $-\frac{2}{3}$

16. $-8x - 5y = 18$ $-\frac{8}{5}$ **17.** $8x + 9y = 10$ $-\frac{8}{9}$ **18.** $7x + 4y = 13$ $-\frac{7}{4}$

Find the slope and y-intercept of each line.

19. $y = -4x - 9$ **20.** $y = -3x - 5$ **21.** $2x + 3y = 9$

22. $5x + 4y = 12$ **23.** $-8x - 7y = 21$ **24.** $-2x - 9y = 13$

25. $9x = 3y + 5$ **26.** $4x = 9y + 7$ **27.** $-6x = 4y + 2$

19. -4, $(0, -9)$
20. -3, $(0, -5)$
21. $-\frac{2}{3}$, $(0, 3)$
22. $-\frac{5}{4}$, $(0, 3)$
23. $-\frac{8}{7}$, $(0, -3)$
24. $-\frac{2}{9}$, $(0, -\frac{13}{9})$
25. 3, $(0, -\frac{5}{3})$
26. $\frac{4}{9}$, $(0, -\frac{7}{9})$
27. $-\frac{3}{2}$, $(0, -\frac{1}{2})$

Use graph paper. Graph each equation using y-intercept and slope.

28. $y = 2x + 3$
29. $y = -3x + 4$
30. $y = -x + 7$

31. $y = \frac{2}{3}x - 3$
32. $y = \frac{3}{4}x - 3$
33. $y = \frac{1}{2}x + 2$

34. $y = -\frac{1}{3}x + 2$
35. $y = \frac{2}{3}x$
36. $y = -\frac{3}{5}x - 3$

Extension

Graph these equations using the same axes.

37. $y = 2x + 1$
38. $y = 2x + 3$
39. $y = 2x - 3$

40. $y = 2x$
41. $y = 2x - 5$
42. $y = 2x - 1$

43. What appears to be true of lines with the same slope? Lines are parallel.

44. Write the equation of a line which has the same slope as $y = \frac{2}{3}x + 5$ with a y-intercept of -8. $y = \frac{2}{3}x - 8$

45. Consider the equation $ky + 2x = 7$. For what value of k will the slope be 1? -2

Find the slope and y-intercept of each line. Do not graph.

46. $3(x + 4) = y - 8x + 3$ 47. $2y + 4x = 3(y - x) + 8$

    $11, (0, 9)$ $7, (0, -8)$

Challenge

48. A linear equation of the form $ax + by + c = 0$ where a and b are not both 0 is in standard form. Find the slope and y-intercept in terms of a, b, and c. $-\frac{a}{b}, \left(0, -\frac{c}{b}\right)$

FIELDS OF MATHEMATICS/Cryptography

Codebreaking techniques have been used throughout history for such applications as military strategy and reconstructing the languages of lost civilizations. For hundreds of years secret codes and ciphers were thought of as an isolated specialty. Then, in 1922, William Friedman published a paper connecting cryptography with mathematical statistics. His work led to many new codebreaking techniques and the success of these methods proved an important factor in World War II.

In a dramatic application of these methods, Friedman's team painstakingly broke the most secret and complex Japanese cipher, the PURPLE cipher, by constructing a duplicate of the rotor mechanism that produced it.

One simple code is created by shifting the letters of the alphabet up or down a certain number of letters. For example, if we shift up one letter, A becomes B, B becomes C, and so on. To break the code, shift down one letter. Thus CVMMFU is the coded word for BULLET.

Complete the code alphabet in which A becomes G, B becomes H, and so on. Then decipher the message KTKSE RKLZ LRGTQ ATVXUZKIZKJ. YZXOQK GZ SOJTOMNZ.

ENEMY LEFT FLANK UNPROTECTED. STRIKE AT MIDNIGHT.

The Slope-Intercept Equation

We know that the graph of any linear equation is a straight line. If we know some information about a line, we can write an equation to describe it.

EXAMPLE 1

Write an equation for the line with slope 3 that contains the point (4, 1).

Step 1. Use the given point (4, 1) and substitute 4 for x and 1 for y in $y = mx + b$. Also substitute 3 for m, the slope.

$$y = mx + b$$
$$1 = 3 \cdot 4 + b \quad \text{Substituting}$$
$$-11 = b \quad \text{Solving for } b, \text{ the } y\text{-intercept}$$

Step 2. Write the slope-intercept values in the equation $y = mx + b$.

$$y = mx + b$$
$$y = 3x - 11$$

TRY THIS Write an equation for the line that contains the given point and has the given slope. Use method 1.

1. (4, 2), $m = 5$ **2.** (−2, 1), $m = -3$

1. $y = 5x - 18$
2. $y = -3x - 5$

EXAMPLE 2

Write an equation for the line containing (3, 6) and (−1, 4).

Step 1. Find the slope from the definition.

$$m = \frac{\text{difference of } y\text{-coordinates}}{\text{difference of } x\text{-coordinates}} = \frac{6 - 4}{3 - (-1)} = \frac{1}{2}$$

Step 2. Choose either point and substitute 3 for x and 6 for y in $y = mx + b$. Also substitute $\frac{1}{2}$ for m, the slope.

$$y = mx + b$$
$$6 = \frac{1}{2}(3) + b$$
$$\frac{9}{2} = b \quad \text{Solving for } b, \text{ the } y\text{-intercept}$$

Step 3. Write the slope-intercept values in the equation $y = mx + b$.

$$y = mx + b$$

$$y = \frac{1}{2}x + \frac{9}{2}$$

TRY THIS Write an equation for the line that contains the given two points. Use method 1.

3. $(8, 2)$ $(2, 6)$ **4.** $(-1, 4)$ $(-3, -5)$ 3. $y = -\frac{2}{3}x + \frac{22}{3}$
4. $y = \frac{9}{2}x + \frac{17}{2}$

The Point-Slope Equation

Now consider a line with slope 2 and containing the point $(1, 3)$ as shown. Suppose (x, y) is any other point on this line. Using the definition of slope we substitute the two points, $(1, 3)$ and (x, y).

$$m = \frac{\text{difference of } y\text{-coordinates}}{\text{difference of } x\text{-coordinates}} = \frac{y - 3}{x - 1}$$

We know that slope equals 2.

$$2 = \frac{y - 3}{x - 1} \quad \text{or} \quad \frac{y - 3}{x - 1} = 2$$

This equation has meaning for all values except $x = 1$, which would give a zero denominator.

We multiply on both sides by $x - 1$ to get a linear equation.

$$y - 3 = 2(x - 1)$$
$$y = 2x + 1$$

This equation is satisfied by every point of the line.

THEOREM

The Point-Slope Equation

A nonvertical line that contains a point (x_1, y_1) with slope m has an equation

$$y - y_1 = m(x - x_1).$$

EXAMPLE 3

Write an equation for the line with slope 3 that contains the point $(4, 1)$.

$$y - y_1 = m(x - x_1) \quad \text{Using the point-slope equation}$$
$$y - 1 = 3(x - 4) \quad \text{Substituting } (4, 1) \text{ for } (x_1, y_1)$$
$$y - 1 = 3x - 12$$
$$y = 3x - 11 \quad \text{Simplifying}$$

TRY THIS Write an equation for the line that contains the given point and has the given slope. Use method 2.

5. $(3, 5), m = 6$ **6.** $(1, 4), m = -\dfrac{2}{3}$ $\begin{aligned} y &= 6x - 13 \\ y &= -\tfrac{2}{3}x + \tfrac{14}{3} \end{aligned}$

EXAMPLE 4

Write an equation for the line containing $(2, 3)$ and $(-6, 1)$. First find the slope.

$$m = \frac{3 - 1}{2 - (-6)} = \frac{1}{4}$$

Then use the point-slope equation.

$$y - y_1 = m(x - x_1)$$
$$y - 3 = \frac{1}{4}(x - 2) \quad \text{Substituting } (2, 3) \text{ for } (x_1, y_1)$$
$$y - 3 = \frac{1}{4}x - \frac{1}{2}$$
$$y = \frac{1}{4}x + \frac{5}{2}$$

TRY THIS Write an equation for the line that contains the given two points. Use method 2.

7. $(2, 4) \quad (3, 5)$ **8.** $(-1, 2) \quad (-3, -2)$ $\begin{aligned} y &= x + 2 \\ y &= 2x + 4 \end{aligned}$

7–6

Exercises

Write an equation for each line containing the given point and having the given slope.

$\begin{aligned} &1.\ y = 5x - 5 \\ &2.\ y = -2x - 6 \\ &3.\ y = \tfrac{3}{4}x + \tfrac{5}{2}x \end{aligned}$

1. $(2, 5), m = 5$ **2.** $(-3, 0), m = -2$ **3.** $(2, 4), m = \dfrac{3}{4}$

4. $\left(\frac{1}{2}, 2\right)$, $m = -1$ **5.** $(2, -6)$, $m = 1$ **6.** $(4, -2)$, $m = 6$

4. $y = -x + \frac{5}{2}$
5. $y = x - 8$
6. $y = 6x - 26$

7. $(-3, 0)$, $m = -3$ **8.** $(0, 3)$, $m = -3$ **9.** $(4, 3)$, $m = \frac{3}{4}$

7. $y = -3x - 9$
8. $y = -3x + 3$
9. $y = \frac{3}{4}x$

10. $(5, 6)$, $m = \frac{2}{3}$ **11.** $(2, 7)$, $m = \frac{5}{6}$ **12.** $(-3, -5)$, $m = -\frac{3}{5}$

10. $y = \frac{2}{3}x + \frac{8}{3}$
11. $y = \frac{5}{6}x + \frac{16}{3}$
12. $y = -\frac{3}{5}x - \frac{34}{5}$

Write an equation for each line that contains the given pair of points.

13. $(-6, 1)$ $(2, 3)$ **14.** $(12, 16)$ $(1, 5)$

15. $(0, 4)$ $(4, 2)$ **16.** $(0, 0)$ $(4, 2)$

17. $(3, 2)$ $(1, 5)$ **18.** $(-4, 1)$ $(-1, 4)$

19. $(5, 0)$ $(0, -2)$ **20.** $(-2, -2)$ $(1, 3)$

21. $(-2, -4)$ $(2, -1)$ **22.** $(-3, 5)$ $(-1, -3)$

13. $y = \frac{1}{4}x + \frac{5}{2}$
14. $y = x + 4$
15. $y = -\frac{1}{2}x + 4$
16. $y = \frac{1}{2}x$
17. $y = -\frac{3}{2}x + \frac{13}{2}$
18. $y = x + 5$
19. $y = \frac{2}{5}x - 2$
20. $y = \frac{5}{3}x + \frac{4}{3}$
21. $y = \frac{3}{4}x - \frac{5}{2}$
22. $y = -4x - 7$

Extension

23. Write an equation for the line that has the same slope as the line described by $3x - y + 4 = 0$ and contains the point $(2, -3)$. $y = 3x - 9$

24. Write an equation for the line that has the same y-intercept as the line described by $x - 3y = 6$ and contains the point $(5, -1)$. $y = \frac{1}{5}x - 2$

25. Write an equation with the same slope as $3x - 2y = 8$ and the same y-intercept as $2y + 3x = -4$. $y = \frac{3}{2}x - 2$

26. Write an equation for a line with the same slope as $2x = 3y - 1$ and containing the point $(8, -5)$. $y = \frac{2}{3}x - \frac{31}{3}$

27. Write the equation of a line containing $(a, 0)$ and $(0, b)$ in standard form. $bx + ay - ab = 0$

Challenge

28. Write an equation in standard form that has the same slope as $2x - 3y = 6$ and the same y-intercept as $3x + 4y = 12$. $-2x + 3y - 9 = 0$

29. Find the value of m in $y = mx + 3$ so that the point $(-2, 5)$ will be on the graph. -1

30. Find the value of b in $y = -5x + b$ so that the point $(3, 4)$ will be on the graph. 19

31. Write equations of six lines that all go through the point $(4, -2)$. Answers may vary. Ex. $y = x - 6$

32. Plot and connect the points $(-2, 1)$, $(-1, -2)$, $(4, 3)$, and $(5, 0)$ to form a rectangle. What is the product of the slopes of adjacent sides? $\frac{1}{3}(-3) = -1$

7–7 Proofs (Optional)

Before beginning to write a proof we must organize our ideas and see exactly what we want to prove. Making a proof is somewhat like putting together a jigsaw puzzle. It always helps to have the completed picture in front of you as a goal.

We have stated that in the equation $y = mx + b$, m is the slope. Before writing a proof of this statement we must think about what it means to prove that m is the slope. We know

$$\text{slope} = \frac{\text{change in } y}{\text{change in } x}.$$

We must show that the m-value in $y = mx + b$ is also change in y/change in x.

Plan: Start with two points on a line $y = mx + b$. Call the points (x_1, y_1) and (x_2, y_2). Find the slope m. Show that this slope m matches our definition of slope.

Proof

Consider any linear equation $y = mx + b$. Suppose that (x_1, y_1) and (x_2, y_2) are any two points on the line. Then, since each of these points must satisfy the equation, we have

$$y_2 = mx_2 + b \quad \text{and} \quad y_1 = mx_1 + b.$$

(Our strategy will be to work with these two equations and try to show $m = (y_2 - y_1)/(x_2 - x_1)$.)

From the second equation we know that y_1 and $mx_1 + b$ are the same number. Thus, $-y_1$ and $-(mx_1 + b)$ are also the same number. We add this number on both sides of the first equation.

$$y_2 - y_1 = (mx_2 + b) - (mx_1 + b)$$
$$y_2 - y_1 = mx_2 - mx_1 \quad \text{Simplifying}$$
$$y_2 - y_1 = m(x_2 - x_1) \quad \text{Factoring out } m$$

$$\frac{y_2 - y_1}{x_2 - x_1} = m \quad \text{Solving for } m$$

Since $\frac{y_2 - y_1}{x_2 - x_1}$ is the $\frac{\text{change in } y}{\text{change in } x}$ for the given two points,

then the m-value in $y = mx + b$ is the slope.

TRY THIS

1. Write a narrative proof to show that in the equation $y = mx + b$, b is the y-intercept. (Hint: Think about what is true of a y-intercept.)

We have also stated that a horizontal line has slope 0. Before we begin to write the proof we think about horizontal lines. On any horizontal line each point has the same y-coordinate. This is the key to the proof.

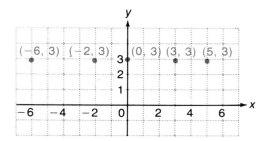

> **Proof**
>
> Consider any horizontal line. Suppose that (x_1, y_1) and (x_2, y_2) are any two points on the line. Then the slope of the slope of the line is
>
> $\frac{y_2 - y_1}{x_2 - x_1}$. Since the y-coordinates are the same, $\frac{y_2 - y_1}{x_2 - x_1} = \frac{0}{x_2 - x_1} = 0$.

TRY THIS

2. Prove that a vertical line has no slope. (Hint: Think about the coordinates of the points on a vertical line and division by 0.)

7–7

Exercises

1. Prove the Point-Slope Equation Theorem. Suppose (x, y) is any other point on the line. Then the slope of the line is $\frac{y - y_1}{x - x_1}$. Complete the proof.

2. Prove that if a line has slope m and y-intercept b, then its equation is $y = mx + b$. (Hint: Use the Point-Slope Equation Theorem.)

CAREERS/Health Care

Until the middle of the nineteenth century, medicine depended on folklore more than on science for treatments of many diseases. During the past 125 years, though, medicine has become a precise science.

Medical researchers use statistics and probability theory to turn their observations into judgments about the effectiveness of a method of treatment. Statistics are numerical records of events. The health of patients receiving a particular kind of treatment is recorded by medical researchers in the form of statistics. Probability theory involves predicting outcomes based on past events. Researchers use probability theory to predict the effectiveness of a treatment on the basis of how it helped or did not help a particular group of patients.

Doctors use mathematics, too, in evaluating the health of patients and in prescribing treatment. For example, the health of a patient's heart is reflected in the number of times it beats per minute (*pulse rate*) and the force with which it circulates blood through the body (*blood pressure*). Doctors use graphs of normal ranges of pulse rate and blood pressure for people of similar age, height, and weight to determine whether a particular patient runs a higher than normal risk of heart problems.

Even a task as seemingly simple as deciding how much medicine to give a child with an ear infection involves mathematics. A doctor usually will not write a prescription unless he or she knows the age and weight of the child. The doctor substitutes these figures into a mathematical equation; the answer to the equation is the volume of medicine that the child of that age and weight should be given.

Exercises

The problems that follow resemble problems that health care professionals must solve on the job.

1. A doctor needs to estimate the percent of body fat for an injured wrestler. The polynomial $0.49W + 0.45P - 6.36R + 8.7$ gives an estimate of the percent of body fat for a man. W is the waist circumference in centimeters; P is the skinfold above the pectoral muscle in millimeters; and R is the wrist diameter in centimeters. These are the wrestler's measure-ments: $W = 94.2$ cm, $P = 6.3$ mm, $R = 7.5$ cm. Find the wrestler's percentage of body fat. (See Section 6–1). 9.9%

2. Herb, a physical therapist, is working with a disabled patient. He has found that the patient has a lung capacity of 2.41 L. He needs to compare this with the average lung capacity for a person of similar height and age. The patient, a woman, is 138.7 cm tall and is 29 years of age. Use the polynomial $0.041h - 0.018A - 2.69$ to compute the average lung capacity in liters. Find how much greater or smaller than average the patient's lung capacity is. (See Section 6–1.) 2.47 L, 0.06 greater

3. Celine is studying to be a laboratory technician. Her assignment is to find the percent of oxygen in the hemoglobin in a certain blood sample. The formula she must use is $H = 1.36gs$. This tells the number H of milliliters (mL) of oxygen in the hemoglobin of 100 mL of whole blood. The letter g represents the number of grams of hemoglobin in 100 mL of whole blood. The letter s represents the percent of oxygen in the hemoglobin. In Celine's sample, $H = 14.77$ and $g = 11$. Using the formula given above, complete the calculation. (See Section 6–5.) 98.7%

Review the material in the chapter. Then see how you have done by trying these review exercises. If you miss an exercise, restudy the indicated lesson.

7–1   Use graph paper. Plot these points.

1. $(2, 5)$ **2.** $(0, -3)$ **3.** $(-4, -2)$

7–1   In which quadrant is each point located?

4. $(3, -8)$ **5.** $(-20, -14)$ **6.** $(4.9, 1.3)$

4. fourth
5. third
6. first

7–1   Find the coordinates of each point.

7. A **8.** B **9.** C

7. (4, 3)
8. (−3, 5)
9. (−4 −3)

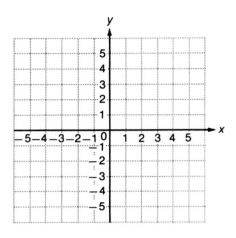

7–2   Determine whether the given point is a solution $3x + y = 4$.

10. $(0, 4)$ **11.** $(1, -1)$

10. Yes
11. No

7–2

12. Make a table of solutions of $2x - y = 1$. Graph the equation.

7–3   Graph each equation.

13. $2x - 7y = 14$ Use intercepts.   **14.** $y = -4$

Find the slopes, if they exist, of the lines containing these points.

15. $(6, 8)(-2, -4)$ **16.** $(5, 1)(-1, 1)$ **17.** $(-3, 0)(-3, 5)$

15. $\frac{3}{2}$
16. 0
17. No slope

18. Find the slope and y-intercept of the equation $3x - 5y = 4$. $\frac{3}{5}, -\frac{4}{5}$

7–6   Write an equation for the line containing the given point and having the given slope.

19. $(1, 2)$, $m = 3$ **20.** $(0, 4)$, $m = -2$

18. $y = 3x + 1$
19. $y = -2x + 4$

7–6   Write an equation for the line containing the given two points.

21. $(5, 7)$ $(-1, 1)$ **22.** $(2, 0)$ $(-4, -3)$

20. $y = x + 2$
21. $y = \frac{1}{2}x - 1$

Use graph paper. Plot these points.

1. $(-5, 3)$ 2. $(0, -4)$

In which quadrant is each point located?

3. $(-1, -4)$ 4. $(-1, 8, 4)$ 3. fourth
   4. second

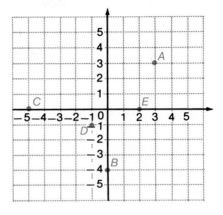

Find the coordinates of each point.

5. A 6. B 5. (3, 3)
   6. (0, −4)

Graph each equation.

7. $3x + y = 10$. Make a table of solutions.
8. $2x - 3y = -6$. Use intercepts.
9. $x = 8$ 10. $y = -2$

Find the slopes, if they exist, of the lines containing these points.

11. $(9, 2)$ $(-3, -5)$ $\frac{7}{12}$
12. $(4, 7)$ $(4, -1)$ No slope

Use the equation $-4x + 3y = -6$.

13. Find the slope and y-intercept. $\frac{4}{3}, -2$
14. Graph the equation.

Write an equation for the line containing the given point and having the given slope.

15. $(3, 5)$ $m = 1$ $y = x + 2$
16. $(-2, 0)$ $m = -3$ $y = -3x - 6$

Write an equation for the line containing the given two points.

17. $(1, 1)$ $(2, -2)$ $y = 3x + 4$
18. $(4, -1)$ $(-4, -3)$ $y = \frac{1}{4}m - 2$

Challenge
19. Find the area of a rectangle whose vertices have coordinates $(-3, 1)$, $(5, 1)$, $(5, 8)$, and $(-3, 8)$.   56

1–1 Write an algebraic expression for each of the following.

1. 7 less than twice y **2.** the difference of x and three times y 1. $2y - 7$ 2. $x - 3y$

1–2 Simplify.

3. $\dfrac{1800}{156}$ $\frac{150}{13}$ **4.** $\dfrac{72xz}{90xy}$ $\frac{4z}{5y}$ **5.** $\dfrac{144ab}{108abc}$ $\frac{4}{3c}$

1–3, 1–4 Evaluate.

6. $x^2 - 5$ for $x = 3$ 4 **7.** $(y - 1)^2$ for $y = 6.$ 25

1–5 Multiply.

8. $3(2x + y)$ **9.** $4(3x + 4y + z)$ $12x + 16y + 4z$
  $6x + 3y$

1–5 Collect like terms.

10. $7a + 7b + a + 7c$ **11.** $x + 2y + 2z + x$ $2x + 2y + 2z$
  $8a + 7b + 7c$

1–6 Solve.

12. $x + \dfrac{5}{6} = \dfrac{17}{12}$ $\frac{7}{12}$ **13.** $2.3y = 12.88$ 5.6

1–7 Translate to an equation and solve.

14. A scale drawing shows a bolt enlarged 5 times. If the drawing is 3.7 cm long, how long is the actual bolt? 0.74 cm

2–2 Use $<$, $>$, or $=$ to write a true sentence.

15. -10 -14 $>$ **16.** -3.1 -3.15 $>$ **17.** 0.01 0.1 $<$

2–3, 2–4 Simplify.

18. $-\dfrac{1}{2} + \dfrac{3}{8} + (-6) + \dfrac{3}{4}$ **19.** $-2.6 + (-7.5) + 2.6 + (-7.5)$ 18. $\frac{-43}{8}$ 19. -15

20. $-6.1 - (-3.1) + 7.9 - 3.1 + 1.8$ 3.6 **21.** $-7 - 2x + 5 - (-x) - 1$ $-3 - x$

2–5 Multiply.

22. $-\dfrac{2}{3}\left(\dfrac{18}{15}\right)$ **23.** $\dfrac{3}{5} \cdot \left(-\dfrac{3}{5}\right) \cdot \left(\dfrac{-25}{9}\right)$ **24.** $-2 \cdot (-7) \cdot (-3) \cdot 0$ 22. $\frac{-12}{5}$ 23. 1 24. 0

2–6 Divide.

25. $\dfrac{-4}{3} \div \left(-\dfrac{2}{9}\right)$ **26.** $-6.262 \div 1.01$ **27.** $-\dfrac{72}{108} \div \left(-\dfrac{2}{3}\right)$ 25. 6 26. -6.2 27. 1

2–7 Factor.

28. $121x - 55$
$11(11x - 5)$

29. $36 - 81y$
$9(4 - 9y)$

30. $-6 - 2x - 12y$
$-2(3 + x + 6y)$ or $2(-3 - x - 6y)$

2–8 Simplify.

31. $-8x - (9 - 4x)$
$-4x - 9$

32. $-2(y + 3) - 3y$
$-5y - 6$

33. $-4[2(x - 3) - 1]$
$-8x + 28$

3–1 to 3–4 Solve.

34. $x - \dfrac{3}{8} = \dfrac{1}{2}$

35. $-3.2 = y - 5.8$

36. $-\dfrac{2}{3} = x - \dfrac{8}{12}$ 34. $\frac{7}{8}$ 35. 2.6 36. 0

37. $-4x = -18$

38. $\dfrac{-x}{3} = -16$

39. $-\dfrac{5}{6} = x - \dfrac{1}{3}$ 37. $\frac{9}{2}$ 38. 48 39. $-\frac{1}{2}$

40. $6y + 3 = -15$ $_{-3}$ **41.** $5x + 7 = -3x - 9$ $_{-2}$ **42.** $\dfrac{1}{3}x - \dfrac{2}{9} = \dfrac{2}{3} + \dfrac{4}{9}x$ $_{-8}$

43. $3(x - 2) = 24$ $_{10}$ **44.** $4(y - 5) = -2(y + 2)$ $\frac{8}{3}$ **45.** $-6x - 2(x - 4) = 10$ $-\frac{1}{4}$

3–5, 3–7 Solve.

46. After a 20% reduction, an item is on sale for \$144. What was the marked price (the price before reduction)? $180

47. In an election, candidate A was elected over candidate B by a ratio of 3 to 2. If candidate A received 240 votes, how many did B receive? 160

4–1 Simplify.

48. $x^8 \cdot x^2$ $_{x^{10}}$ **49.** $\dfrac{z^4}{z^7}$ $\frac{1}{z^3}$ **50.** $(4y^3)^2$ $16y^6$ **51.** $(3x^2y)^3$ $(27x^6y^3)$

4–2 Collect like terms.

52. $-3x^2 + 4x - 5x^3 - 6x^2 + 2 - 3x$
$-5x^3 - 9x^2 + x + 2$

53. $2x^3 - 7 + 3x^2 - 6x^3 - 4x^2 + 5$
$-4x^3 - x^2 - 2$

4–4 Add.

54. $(3x^4 + 2x^3 - 6x^2) + (-2x^4 - 3x^2 - 7) + (-5x^3 - 4x^2 + 2)$ $x^4 - 3x^3 - 13x^2 - 5$

4–5 Subtract.

55. $(-8y^2 - y + 2) - (y^3 - 6y^2 + y - 5)$ $-y^3 - 2y^2 - 2y + 7$

4–6 to 4–9 Multiply.

56. $4x^3(2x^2 - x + 7)$

57. $(2x - 5)(3x + 4)$

58. $(2.5a + 7.5)(0.4a - 1.2)$

59. $(6x^2 - 3x + 2)(2x - 1)$

60. $(2x^2 - 1)(x^3 + x - 3)$

61. $(1 - 3x^2)(2 - 4x^2)$

62. $(2x^5 + 3)(3x^2 - 6)$

63. $(2x^3 + 1)(2x^3 - 1)$

64. $(8x + 3)^2$

65. $(6x - 5)^2$

66. $(4x^3 - x + 1)(x - 1)$

5–1 to 5–7   Factor.

67. $x^2 - 4x$

68. $6x^5 - 36x^3 + 9x^2$

69. $12x - 4x^2 - 48x^4$

70. $9x^2 - 1$

71. $2x^2 - 18$

72. $16x^4 - 81$

73. $x^2 - 14x + 49$

74. $16x^2 + 40x + 25$

75. $18x^2 - 48x + 32$

76. $x^2 - 10x + 24$

77. $x^2 - 2x - 35$

78. $x^3 - 4x^2 - 21x$

79. $8x^2 + 10x + 3$

80. $3x^2 + 10x - 8$

81. $6x^2 - 28x + 16$

82. $x^3 + x^2 + 2x + 2$

83. $x^4 + 2x^3 - 3x - 6$ 84. $3 - 12x^6$

5–8   Solve for x.

85. $x^2 + 4x - 12 = 0$ $2, -6$

86. $2x^2 + 7x - 4 = 0$ $\frac{1}{2}, -4$

5–9

87. The product of two consecutive integers is 224. Find the integers. $14, 16$ or $-14, -16$

6–2   Simplify.

88. $(4a^3b - 5a^2b^2 - 2ab^3 + 4) + (2ab^3 - 3a^2b^2 - 2a^3b - 1)$ $2a^3b - 8a^2b^2 + 3$

89. $(5xy^2 - 6x^2y - 3xy^3) - (-4xy^3 + 7xy^2 - 2x^2y^2)$ $xy^3 - 2xy^2 - 4x^2y^2$

90. $(3x^2 + 4y)(3^2 - 4y)$ $9x^4 - 16y^2$

91. $(2a^2b - 5ab^2)^2$ $4a^4b^2 - 20a^3b^3 + 25a^2b^4$

6–3   Factor.

92. $4x^4 - 12x^2y + 9y^2$ $(2x^2 - 3y)^2$

93. $x^5 - x^3y + x^2y^2 - y^3$ $(x^3 + y^2)(x^2 - y)$

6–4

94. Solve for x: $ax + 3x = -2ab - 6b$. $x = -2b$

95. Solve for h: $S = 2\pi rh + 2\pi r^2$. $\frac{S}{2\pi r} - r$

96. The surface area of a right circular cylinder with altitude h is $s = 2\pi rh + 2\pi r^2$. If $r = 6$ cm and $h = 10$ cm, find S, the surface area (use 3.14 for π).   602.88 cm²

7–1   In which quadrant is each point located?

97. $(-3, -2.3)$ third

98. $(2, -1)$ fourth

99. $(-4.2, 5)$ second

7–2

100. Make a table of solutions for $3x - y = 2$. Graph the equation.

Ex.

x	0	1	2
y	-2	1	4

Graph each equation.

101. $3x - 5y = 15$. Use intercepts.

102. $x = -3$ **103.** $y = 2$

7–4 Find the slope, if it exists, of the line containing these points.

104. $(-2, 6), (-2, -1)$ **105.** $(-4, 1), (3, -2)$ **106.** $(2, 3), (-1, 3)$
No slope $-\frac{3}{7}$ 0

7–5 Use the equation $4x - 3y = 6$.

107. Find the slope and y-intercept. $\frac{4}{3}, -2$

108. Graph the equation using slope and y-intercept.

7–6 Write an equation for the line containing the given point and
     having the given slope.

109. $(-2, 3), m = -4$ **110.** $(0, -3), m = 6$
$y = -4x - 5$ $y = 6x - 3$

7–6 Write an equation for the line containing the given two points.

111. $(-1, -3), (5, -2)$ **112.** $(-5, 6), (2, -4)$ 111. $y = \frac{1}{6}x - \frac{17}{6}$ 112. $y = \frac{-10}{7}x - \frac{8}{7}$

Ready for Functions and Variation?

1–1, 1–5 Evaluate for $x = 5$ and $y = -3$.

1. $\frac{-2x}{y}$ $\frac{10}{3}$ **2.** $x^2 + 1$ 26 **3.** $y^3 - 4$ -31

1–6 Solve.

4. $x + 3.8 = 1.5$ **5.** $\frac{2}{3} + y = \frac{3}{8}$ 4. -2.3 5. $\frac{-7}{24}$

3–6

6. Solve $A = \frac{1}{2}h(b_1 + b_2)$ for h. $h = \frac{2A}{b_1 + b_2}$

3–7

7. Translate to a proportion and solve. The winner of an election
won by a vote of 5 to 3, getting 1750 votes. How many votes
did the loser get? 1050

7–3 Graph each equation.

8. $5y - 4 = 2x$ **9.** $3x + y = 8$
Line through $\left(0, \frac{4}{5}\right)$ and $(-2, 0)$ Line through $(0, 8)$ and $\left(\frac{8}{3}, 0\right)$

8

CHAPTER EIGHT

Functions and Variation

Functions

Identifying Functions

Consider a set of people. To each person there corresponds a number called the height of the person.

Person	Height (cm)
Lora	120
Jason	202
Carolyn	142
Elaine	138
Saul	142

To each person there corresponds *exactly* one height. Such a correspondence is called a function.

> A function is a correspondence (or rule) that assigns to each member of one set (called the *domain*) exactly one member of some set. The set of assigned values is called the *range*.

The members of the domain are also called inputs and the members of the range are called outputs. Arrows can be used to describe functions.

Domain (Set of inputs)	Range (Set of outputs)
Lora ──────────→	120
Jason ─────────→	202
Carolyn ───────→	142
Elaine ────────→	138
Saul ─────────⟋	

EXAMPLE 1

Are the following correspondences functions?

f:
Domain Range
a ──────→ 4
b ──────→ 0
c ──────⟋

g:
Domain Range
3 ──────→ 5
4 ──────→ 9
5 ──────→ −7
6 ──────⟋

The correspondence f is a function since each input is matched to only one output. The correspondence g is not a function since the input 4 has more than one output.

EXAMPLE 2

Which of the following correspondences are functions?

Domain	Range
4	0
h: 6	
2	

Domain	Range
Cheese pizza	$9.75
p: Tomato pizza	$7.25
Meat pizza	$8.50

Correspondence h is a function. Correspondence p is not a function since the input cheese pizza has two outputs. In a function an element in the domain can be matched with only one element in the range.

TRY THIS Are the following correspondences functions?

1. Domain Range Yes

1 ⟶ 1
−1

2. Domain Range Yes

(12, 3) ⟶ 36
(5, 7) ⟶ 35
(6, 6)

Function Notation

The input-output process can be thought of in terms of a function machine. Inputs from the domain are put into the machine. The machine then gives the proper output.

This function machine, for the correspondence f, assigns to each input the output $x + 2$. It adds 2 to each input. The outputs for the inputs 8, -3, 0, and 5 are as follows.

$$8 \rightarrow 10 \qquad -3 \rightarrow -1 \qquad 0 \rightarrow 2 \qquad 5 \rightarrow 7$$

The symbol $f(x)$, read "f of x", denotes the number assigned to x by the correspondence f. If x is the input, $f(x)$ is the output. We can write the above results as follows where $f(x) = x + 2$.

$$f(8) = 8 + 2 = 10 \qquad f(-3) = -3 + 2 = -1$$
$$f(0) = 0 + 2 = 2 \qquad f(5) = 5 + 2 = 7$$

EXAMPLE 3

A function P assigns to each input x the output 5. Find $P(x)$, $P(0)$, and $P(2)$.

$$P(x) = 5 \qquad P(0) = 5 \qquad P(2) = 5$$

EXAMPLE 4

$f(t) = 2t^2 + 5$; find $f(-2)$, $f(0)$, and $f(3)$.

$$f(-2) = 2(-2)^2 + 5 \qquad f(0) = 2(0)^2 + 5 \qquad f(3) = 2(3)^2 + 5$$
$$= 2 \cdot 4 + 5 \qquad\qquad\quad = 5 \qquad\qquad\quad = 2 \cdot 9 + 5$$
$$= 13 \qquad\qquad\qquad\qquad\qquad\qquad\qquad\qquad = 23$$

TRY THIS

3. Find $f(5)$, $f(-8)$, and $f(-2)$ for the function machine shown. <small>8, −5, 1</small>
4. $G(x) = 3x - x^2$; find $G(0)$, $G(-2)$, and $G(1)$. <small>0, −10, 2</small>
5. $f(y) = 8y^2 + 3$; find $f(-1)$, $f(2)$, and $f(\frac{1}{2})$. <small>11, 35, 5</small>
6. $p(x) = 2x^2 + x - 1$; find $p(0)$, $p(-2)$, and $p(3)$. <small>−1, 5, 20</small>

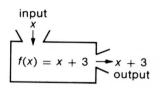

8–1	

Exercises

Which of the following correspondences are functions? <small>1, 2, 3, 4, 6</small>

1. Domain → Range
2 → 9
5 → 8
19

2. Domain → Range
5 → 3
−3 → 7
7
−7

3. Domain → Range
−5 → 1
5
8

4. Domain → Range
6 → −6
7 → −7
3 → −3

5. Domain → Range
Los Angeles → Mets
New York → Lakers
Dodgers
Yankees

6. Domain → Range
(3, 4) → 12
(8, 10) → −11
(4, −2) → 18
(−3, −8) → 2

Find the indicated output for each function machine.

7.

Find $f(3)$, $f(7)$, and $f(-9)$. <small>8, 12, −4</small>

8.
$g(t) = t - 6 \rightarrow t - 6$

Find $g(0)$, $g(6)$, and $g(18)$. <small>−6, 0, 12</small>

9.
$h(p) = 3p \rightarrow 3p$

Find $h(-2)$, $h(5)$, and $h(24)$. <small>−6, 15, 72</small>

10.

Find $f(6)$, $f\left(-\frac{1}{2}\right)$, and $f(20)$. <small>−24, 2, −80</small>

Find the indicated outputs for these functions.

11. $g(s) = 2s + 4$; find $g(1)$, $g(-7)$, and $g(6)$. 6, −10, 16

12. $h(x) = 19$; find $h(4)$, $h(-6)$, and $h(12)$. 19, 19, 19

13. $F(x) = 2x^2 - 3x + 2$; find $F(0)$, $F(-1)$, and $F(2)$. 2, 9, 4

14. $P(x) = 3x^2 - 2x + 5$; find $P(0)$, $P(-2)$, and $P(3)$. 5, 21, 26

15. $h(x) = |x|$; find $h(-4)$, $h(5)$, and $h(-3)$. 4, 5, 3

16. $f(t) = |t| + 1$; find $f(-5)$, $f(0)$, and $f(-9)$. 6, 1, 10

17. $f(x) = |x| - 2$; find $f(-3)$, $f(93)$, and $f(-100)$. 1, 91, 98

18. $g(t) = t^3 + 3$; find $g(1)$, $g(-5)$, and $g(0)$. 4, −122, 3

19. $h(x) = x^4 - 3$; find $h(0)$, $h(-1)$, and $h(3)$. −3, −2, 78

20. $f(m) = 3m^2 - 5$; find $f(4)$, $f(-3)$, and $f(6)$. 43, 22, 103

Extension

In many physical situations we speak of one quantity being "a function of" another. For instance, the cost of replacing a defective tire is a function of the tread depth. For Exercises 21–24, the chart below gives a rule for this function for a tire with original tread depth of 9mm.

Tread Depth in Millimeters									
	9	8	7	6	5	4	3	2	1
% charged	No charge	20%	30%	40%	55%	70%	80%	90%	100%

21. Find the cost of replacing a tire whose regular price is $64.50 and whose tread depth is 4 mm. $45.15

22. Find the cost of replacing a tire whose regular price is $78.50 and whose tread depth is 7 mm. $23.55

23. Find the cost of replacing a tire whose regular price is $67.80 and whose tread depth is 3 mm. $54.24

24. Find the cost of replacing a tire whose regular price is $72.40 and whose tread depth is 5 mm. $39.82

25. The function $P(d) = 1 + \frac{d}{33}$ gives the pressure of salt water in atmosphere as a function of d, the depth in feet. Find the pressure at 20 feet, 30 feet and 100 feet. 1.606, 1.909, 4.03

26. The function $R(t) = 33\frac{1}{3}t$ gives the number of revolutions of a $33\frac{1}{3}$ R.P.M. record as a function of t, the time it is on the turntable. Find the number of revolutions at 5 minutes, 20 minutes and 25 minutes. $166\frac{2}{3}$, $666\frac{2}{3}$, $833\frac{1}{3}$

27. The function $T(d) = 10d + 20$ gives the temperature in degrees Celsius inside the earth as a function of d, the depth in kilometers. Find the temperature at 5 km, 20 km, 1000 km. 70, 220, 10,020

28. The function $W(d) = 0.112d$ gives the depth of water in centimeters as a function of d, the depth of snow in cm. Find the depth of water that results from these depths of snow: 16 cm, 25 cm, and 100 cm. 1.792 cm, 2.8 cm, 11.2 cm

Find the range of each function for the given domain.

29. $f(x) = 3x + 5$ when the domain is the whole numbers less than 4 5, 8, 11, 14

30. $g(t) = t^2 - 5$ when the domain is the integers between -4 and 2 -5, -4, -1, 4

31. $h(x) = |x| - x$ when the domain is the integers between -2 and 20. 0, 2

32. $f(m) = m^3 + 1$ when the domain is the integers between -3 and 3 -7, 0, 1, 2, 9

Challenge

Suppose $f(x) = 3x$ and $g(x) = -4x^2$. Find each of the following.

33. $f(8) - g(2)$ 8   34. $f(0) - g(-5)$ 100

35. $2f(1) + 3g(4)$ -186 36. $g(-3) \cdot f(-8) + 16$ 880

37. If $f(-1) = -7$ and $f(3) = 8$, find a linear equation for $f(x)$. $f(x) = \frac{15}{4}x - \frac{13}{4}$

38. $H(x - 1) = 5x$; find $H(6)$. 35

39. When you flip a coin, is the number of "heads" a function of the number of flips? No. One flip may correspond to 0 or 1 heads.

COMPUTER GRAPHICS

The early computers could display only numbers and letters on the screens of their terminals. Modern computers use graphic-display devices that show not only numbers and letters, but drawings and graphs as well.

Each point on the screen can be identified by a pair of x-y coordinates. A device called a *digitizer* is used to scan a drawing and convert it to coordinates that can be shown on the screen. A computer graphic may have as many as 1000 points per square inch.

Graphic display devices are used to display colorful graphs, maps, and charts that can help people make decisions in business and science. Recently, dramatic photographs have been taken by space vehicles. A photo is converted into many dots, each with a certain color and brightness. Each dot is converted to a number, which is radioed from the space vehicle to Earth. Then the numbers are interpreted by computer and a color picture is made.

Graphing Functions

The two elements related by a function rule can be written as ordered pairs. The first coordinate, x, is the input and the second coordinate, $f(x)$, is the output. Since we know how to graph ordered pairs we can draw graphs of functions.

EXAMPLE 1

Graph the function f described by $f(x) = x + 2$ where the domain is the set $\{-4, -3, -2, -1, 0, 1, 2, 3, 4, 5\}$.

The list of function values is shown in this chart.

x	-4	-3	-2	-1	0	1	2	3	4	5
$f(x)$	-2	-1	0	1	2	3	4	5	6	7

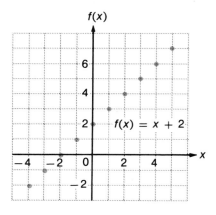

We can write these as ordered pairs $(-4, -2)$, $(-3, -1)$, $(-2, 0)$, $(-1, 1)$, $(0, 2)$, $(1, 3)$, $(2, 4)$, $(3, 5)$, $(4, 6)$, and $(5, 7)$. The graph of the function is simply the graph of all the ordered pairs of the function.

EXAMPLE 2

Graph the function g described by $g(x) = |x|$.

First, find some values of the function.

x	0	1	-1	2	-2	3	-3
$g(x)$	0	1	1	2	2	3	3

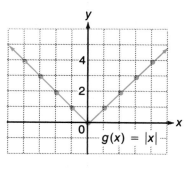

These values give the ordered pairs $(0, 0)$, $(1, 1)$, $(-1, 1)$, $(2, 2)$, $(-2, 2)$, $(3, 3)$, $(-3, 3)$. Note that these are solutions of the equation $g(x) = |x|$. When graphing a function we agree that the domain is the set of all sensible replacements. Next, plot the points and connect them to form a pattern.

TRY THIS Use graph paper. Graph the functions described below.

1. $f(x) = |x| - 1$ **2.** $h(x) = |x| + 1$

Recognizing Graphs of Functions

To recognize the graph of a function we can use a vertical line test. If any vertical line crosses the graph in more than one place, then the graph is not the graph of a function.

EXAMPLE 3
Which of the following are graphs of functions?

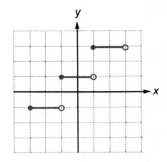

A function.
No vertical line
crosses the graph
more than once.

Not a function.
A vertical line
crosses the graph
more than once.

A function.
No vertical line
crosses the graph
more than once.

TRY THIS Which of the following are graphs of functions?

3. Yes

4. No

5. No

8–2

Exercises
Graph the functions described below.

1. $f(x) = x + 4$, where the domain is $\{-2, -1, 0, 1, 2, 3\}$

2. $g(x) = x + 3$, where the domain is $\{-5, -4, -3, -2, -1, 0, 1\}$

3. $h(x) = 2x - 3$, where the domain is $\{-3, -1, 1, 3\}$

4. $f(x) = 3x - 1$ where the domain is $\{-1, 0, 2, 4, 6\}$

Graph each function.

5. $g(x) = x - 6$ **6.** $h(x) = x - 5$ **7.** $f(x) = 2x - 7$

8. $g(x) = 4x - 13$ **9.** $f(x) = \frac{1}{2}x + 1$ **10.** $f(x) = -\frac{3}{4}x - 2$

11. $g(x) = 2|x|$ **12.** $h(x) = -|x|$ **13.** $g(x) = -2|x| + 2$

Which of the following are graphs of functions?

14.

15.

16.

17.

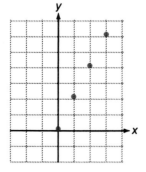

Extension

domain {0, 1, 2, 3}, range {0, 2, 4, 6}, $f(x) = 2x$

18. Here is the graph of a function. List the domain and range of the function. Write an equation for this function.

19. Sketch a graph which is not a function. Answers may vary.

20. Draw the graph of $|y| = x$. Is this the graph of a function? No

21. Draw the graph of $g(x) = \frac{1}{x}$. Is this the graph of a function?
Yes (The domain excludes 0)

Challenge

22. Describe the graph of any function of the form $g(x) = a|x| + b$.

V shaped, ∧ if a negative, with "point" on the y axis b units up or down from the origin.

23. For the function defined by $g(x) = a|x| + b$, what effect does changing the value of a have on the graph? What effect does changing the value of b have on the graph?

If |a| increases, the graph is stretched horizontally; if b increases, the graph is moved upwards.

24. If $d(x^2) = x$ for $x = -2, 0,$ and 2. Is d a function?

No, g(4) is both −2 and 2.

8-3 Linear Functions and Problems

A linear function is any function that can be described by a linear equation. For instance, $f(x) = x + 3$ and $g(x) = 3x$ are linear functions. Many physical situations can be described in mathematical language by linear functions.

EXAMPLE 1

The amount of antifreeze needed to protect a radiator against freezing to a temperature of $-18°C$ is about half the capacity of the radiator. How much antifreeze is needed to protect a radiator with a capacity of 15 liters?

$$\underbrace{\text{Amount needed}}_{y} \underset{\downarrow}{\text{is}} \underset{\downarrow}{\text{half}} \underset{\downarrow}{\text{of}} \underbrace{\text{the capacity}}_{x}$$

$$y \quad = \quad \tfrac{1}{2} \quad \cdot \quad x$$

We see that we have a linear function with ordered pairs of the form (x, y). The inputs are radiator capacities. The outputs are amounts of antifreeze needed.

$$y = \frac{1}{2}x$$

$$y = \frac{1}{2} \cdot 15$$

$$= 7.5$$

The amount of antifreeze needed is 7.5 L.

EXAMPLE 2

The City Cab Company charges sixty cents plus forty-eight cents per km as the fare. What is the cost of a 9 km ride?

$$\underset{c}{\text{Cost}} \underset{=}{\text{is}} \underbrace{\text{sixty cents}}_{0.60} \underset{+}{\text{plus}} \underbrace{\text{forty-eight cents}}_{0.48} \underset{\cdot}{\text{times}} \underbrace{\text{the distance in km.}}_{d} \quad \text{Rewording}$$

Translating

In the linear function $c = 0.60 + 0.48d$, the inputs are distances. The outputs are costs.

$$c = 0.60 + 0.48$$
$$= 0.60 + 0.48(9) \quad \text{The distance } d, \text{ is 9 km}$$
$$= 4.92 \quad \text{The cost is \$4.92}$$

1. Frank's baby-sitting service charges $3.50 per day plus $1.65 per hour. What is the input and output, and what is the cost of a nine-hour baby-sitting job? Input-9 hours, output-cost ($18.35)

8–3

Exercises

Translate each situation to an equation which describes a linear function. Find the input and output for each. Then solve the problem.

1. The Triad car rental Company charges $35 per day plus 21¢ per kilometer. Find the cost of renting a car for a one day trip of 340 kilometers. $c = 35 + 0.21k$, input 340 km, output $106.40 cost

2. The Dialum phone company charges 55¢ per long distance call plus 25¢ per minute. Find the cost of a 12 minute long distance call. $c = 0.55 + 0.25m$, input 12 min, output $3.55 cost

3. A certain 40 cm spring will stretch (in cm) one third the weight (in kg) attached to it. How long will the spring be if a 15 kg weight is attached? $L = \frac{1}{3}w + 40$, input 15 kg, output 45 cm

4. A certain 60 cm spring will stretch (in cm) one fifth the weight (in kg) attached to it. How long will the spring be if a 20-kg weight is attached? $L = \frac{1}{5}w + 60$, input 20 kg, output 64 cm

5. The cost of renting a floor waxer is $4.25 per hour plus $5.50 for the wax. Find the cost of waxing a floor if the time involved was 4.5 hours. $c = 5.50 + 4.25h$, input 4.5 hr, output $24.63 cost

6. Sally rents a compact car for $29 per day plus 19¢ per km. Compute the cost of a one day trip of 280 km. $c = 29 + 0.19m$, input 280 km, output $82.20 cost

7. To rent a chain saw it costs $3.90 per hour plus $6.50 for a can of gas. Find the cost of using the chain saw for 7.5 hours. $c = 6.50 + 3.90h$, input 7.5 hr, output $35.75 cost

8. The airport parking garage charges $1.25 for the first hour and 70¢ for each additional hour. Find the cost of parking 18 hours. $c = 0.70(h - 1) + 1.25$ or $0.70h + 0.55$, input 18 hr, output $13.15 cost

Extension

9. A woman's phone bill is based on a 15¢ per message unit charge plus a base charge. Her July bill was $18 and included 62 message units. Find the base charge. $8.70

10. The city's water department charges 23¢ per kiloliter plus a fixed charge for the first 50 kiloliters used. Mr. Ahmed's water bill for the use of 70 kiloliters was $26.60. Find the fixed charge. $10.50

11. Sketch the graph of a linear function. A nonvertical straight line

12. Sketch the graph of a non-linear function. A curve with no vertical sections

13. A constant function is any function that can be described by an equation of the form $y = k$. Sketch the graph of constant function. A horizontal line

Challenge

14. Make up a real-world example of a constant function. Ex. People in a house to house address

15. Draw the graph of the function described by $f(t) = t^3$.

16. If a value of a function is 0 for some inputs, these inputs are called zeros of the function. Graphically, the zeros of a function are the x-coordinates of the points where the graph crosses the x-axis. Graph the following functions. Estimate their zeros.

    a. $f(x) = x^2 - 6$ **b.** $f(x) = x^2 - x - 7$
    c. $f(x) = x^2 - 2$ **d.** $f(x) = x^2 + 3$

    a. 2.5, −2.5
    b. 3.2, −2.2
    c. 1.4, −1.4
    d. no zeros

PHYSICS/Formulas and Functions

Physics is a quantitative science. This means that physicists are interested in accurate measurements and precise relationships to describe and predict events in the natural world. The findings of physics about the natural world are almost always best expressed in mathematical formulas. Formulas summarize the results of experiments and make it possible for physicists to draw conclusions that are not obvious from experimental results alone.

Formulas in physics express relationships between two or more measurable quantities. For example, $C = \frac{5}{9}(F - 32)$ gives the relationship between temperature in degrees Celsius and temperature in Fahrenheit. A formula can be thought of as a function. In this case, C is a function of F.

Many formulas in physics have more than two variables. The formula $I = \frac{V}{R}$ gives the current

I that flows in an electrical circuit in terms of the resistance R of the circuit and the potential difference V across its end. This formula shows that I is a function of the quantities V and R. So, $I = f(V, R)$. The domain of this function is the set of ordered pairs (V, R). The function assigns one value to each ordered pair.

There are examples in mathematics, too, of functions in more than one variable. Later in this book (Section 13–4), you will read about the Quadratic Formula. This formula is expressed as follows.

$$x = \frac{-b \pm \sqrt{b^2 - 4ac}}{2a}$$

In the Quadratic Formula, x is a function of the three variables, a, b, and c. So, $x = f(a, b, c)$ and its domain is a set of ordered triples.

8—4 Direct Variation

A bicycle is traveling at 10 km/h. In 1 hour it goes 10 km. In 2 hours it goes 20 km. In 3 hours it goes 30 km, and so on. We will use the number of hours as the first coordinate and the number of km traveled as the second coordinate (1, 10), (2, 20), (3, 30), (4, 40), and so on. The ratio of distance to time for each of these ordered pairs is always $\frac{10}{1}$, or 10.

Whenever a situation produces pairs of numbers in which the ratio is constant, we say that there is direct variation. Here the distance varies directly as the time.

$$\frac{d}{t} = 10 \text{ (a constant), or } d = 10t$$

> If a situation translates to a function described by $y = kx$, where k is a constant, $y = kx$ is called an *equation of direct variation*, and k is called the *variation constant*.

When there is direct variation $y = kx$, the variation constant can be found if one pair of values of x and y is known. Then other values can be found.

EXAMPLE 1
Find an equation of variation where y varies directly as x, and $y = 7$ when $x = 25$.

We substitute to find k.

$$y = kx$$
$$7 = k \cdot 25$$
$$\frac{7}{25} = k, \text{ or } k = 0.28$$

Then the equation of variation is $y = 0.28x$.

TRY THIS Find an equation of variation where y varies directly as x.

1. $y = 84$ when $x = 12$ **2.** $y = 50$ when $x = 80$
1. $y = 7x$
2. $y = 0.625x$

EXAMPLE 2

The amount F which a family spends on food varies directly as its income I. A family making $19,600 a year will spend $5096 on food. At this rate, how much would a family making $20,500 spend on food?

First find an equation of variation. We substitute to find k. Then we can use our equation to find F for any value of I.

$$F = kI$$
$$5096 = k \cdot 19,600 \quad \text{Substituting}$$
$$\frac{5096}{19,600} = k$$
$$0.26 = k$$

The equation of variation is $F = 0.26I$.

Use the equation to find how much a family making $20,500 will spend on food.

$$F = 0.26I$$
$$= 0.26(20,500)$$
$$= 5330$$

The family will spend $5330 for food.

EXAMPLE 3

The weight J of an object on Jupiter varies directly as its weight E on Earth. An object which weighs 225 kg on Earth has a weight of 594 kg on Jupiter. What is the weight on Jupiter of an object which has a weight of 115 kg on Earth?

First find an equation of variation. We substitute to find k. Then we can use our equation to find J for any value of E.

$$J = kE$$
$$594 = k \cdot 225$$
$$\frac{594}{225} = k$$
$$2.64 = k$$

The equation of variation is $J = 2.64E$.

Use the equation to find the weight on Jupiter of the 115 kg object.

$$J = 2.64E$$
$$J = 2.64(115)$$
$$J = 303.6$$

The object would have a weight of 303.6 kg on Jupiter.

3. The cost c of operating a TV varies directly as the number n of hours it is in operation. It costs \$14.00 to operate a standard size color TV continuously for 30 days. At this rate, how much would it cost to operate the TV for 1 day? 1 hour? 46⅔¢, 1¹⁷⁄₁₈¢

4. The weight V of an object on Venus varies directly as its weight E on Earth. A person weighing 75 kg on earth would weigh 66 kg on Venus. How much would a person weighing 90 kg weigh on Venus? 79.2 kg

---

8–4	

Exercises

Find an equation of variation where y varies directly as x, and the following are true.

1. $y = 28$ when $x = 7$ $y = 4x$

2. $y = 30$ when $x = 8$ $y = 3.75x$

3. $y = 0.7$ when $x = 0.4$ $y = 1.75x$

4. $y = 0.8$ when $x = 0.5$ $y = 1.6x$

5. $y = 400$ when $x = 125$ $y = 3.2x$

6. $y = 630$ when $x = 175$ $y = 3.6x$

7. $y = 200$ when $x = 300$ $y = \frac{2}{3}x$

8. $y = 500$ when $x = 60$ $y = \frac{25}{3}x$

Solve these problems.

9. A person's paycheck P varies directly as the number H of hours worked. For working 15 hours the pay is \$78.75. Find the pay for 35 hours work. $183.75

10. The number B of bolts a machine can make varies directly as the time it operates. It can make 6578 bolts in 2 hours. How many can it make in 5 hours? 16,445

11. The number of servings S of meat which can be obtained from a turkey varies directly as its weight W. From a turkey weighing 14 kg one can get 40 servings of meat. How many servings can be obtained from an 8-kg turkey? 22

12. The number of servings S of meat which can be obtained from round steak varies directly as the weight W. From 9 kg of round steak one can get 70 servings of meat. How many servings can one get from 12 kg of round steak? 93

13. The weight M of an object on the moon varies directly as its weight E on earth. A person who weighs 78 kg on earth weighs 13 kg on the moon. How much would a 100-kg person weigh on the moon? 16⅔ kg

14. The weight M of an object on Mars varies directly as its weight E on earth. A person who weighs 95 kg on earth weighs 36.1 kg on Mars. How much would an 80-kg person weigh on Mars? 30.4 kg

15. The number of kg of water W in a human body varies directly as the total body weight B. A person weighing 75 kg contains 54 kg of water. How many kilograms of water are in a person weighing 95 kg? 68.4 kg

16. The amount C which a family gives to charity varies directly as its income I. Last year, the family earned $25,880 and gave $4011 to charity. How much will they give if they make $30,000 this year? $4,650

Extension

Which of the following vary directly?

17. The amount of a gas in a tank in liters and the amount in gallons. Yes

18. The temperature in Fahrenheit degrees and in Celsius. No

19. The price per pound of carrots and the number of pounds. No

20. The total price of tomatoes and the number of pounds. Yes

21. A number and its reciprocal. No

Write an equation of direct variation for each situation. If possible, give a value for k.

22. The perimeter P of an equilateral polygon varies directly with the length S of a side. $P = kS$ (k = number of sides)

23. The circumference of a circle C varies directly with the radius r. $C = kr$ ($k = 2\pi$)

24. The number of bags B of peanuts sold at a baseball game varies directly with the number N of people in attendance. $B = kN$

25. The cost C of building a new house varies directly as A, the area of the floor space of the house. $C = kA$

26. Describe the graph of any equation of direct variation $y = kx$. What is k, the constant of variation for such an equation? a line, its slope

Challenge

Write an equation of variation to describe these situations.

27. In a stream, the amount S of salt carried varies directly as the sixth power of the speed V of the stream. $S = kV^6$

28. The square of the pitch P of a vibrating string varies directly as the tension t on the string. $P^2 = kt$

The volume of a box varies directly as its length. It also varies directly as the height. We then say that the volume varies *jointly* as the length and the height. An equation of variation can be written using the *product* of variables $V = k \cdot l \cdot h$. Write an equation of variation for each of the following.

29. The power P required in an electric circuit varies jointly as the resistance R and the square of the current I. $P = kRI^2$

Equations of Inverse Variation

A car is traveling a distance of 10 km. At a speed of 10 km/h it will take 1 hour. At 20 km/h, it will take $\frac{1}{2}$ hour. At 30 km/h it will take $\frac{1}{3}$ hour, and so on. This determines a set of pairs of numbers, all having the same product.

$$(10, 1), \left(20, \frac{1}{2}\right), \left(30, \frac{1}{3}\right), \left(40, \frac{1}{4}\right), \text{ and so on.}$$

Note that as the first number gets larger the second number gets smaller. Whenever a situation produces pairs of numbers whose product is constant, we say that there is inverse variation. Here the time varies inversely as the speed.

$$rt = 10 \text{ (a constant), or } t = \frac{10}{r}$$

> If a situation translates to a function described by $y = \frac{k}{x}$, where k is a constant, $y = \frac{k}{x}$ is called an *equation of inverse variation*. We say that y varies inversely as x.

EXAMPLE 1
Find an equation of variation where y varies inversely as x, and $y = 145$ when $x = 0.8$.

We substitute to find k.

$$y = \frac{k}{x}$$
$$145 = \frac{k}{0.8}$$
$$(0.8)145 = k$$
$$116 = k$$

The equation of variation is $y = \frac{116}{x}$.

TRY THIS Find an equation of variation where y varies inversely as x.

1. $y = 105$ when $x = 0.6$ **2.** $y = 45$ when $x = 20$ 1. $y = \frac{63}{x}$ 2. $y = \frac{900}{x}$

Inverse Variation Problems

EXAMPLE 2

The time T required to do a certain job varies inversely as the number of people N working (assuming all work at the same rate). It takes 4 hours for 20 people to wash and wax the floors in a building. How long would it take 25 people to do the job?

First, find an equation of variation.

$$T = \frac{k}{N}$$

$$4 = \frac{k}{20} \quad \text{Substituting 4 for } T \text{ and 20 for } N$$

$$20 \cdot 4 = k$$

$$80 = k$$

The equation of variation is $T = \frac{80}{N}$.

Use the equation to find the time it would take 25 people to do the job.

$$T = \frac{80}{N}$$

$$T = \frac{80}{25}$$

$$= 3.2$$

It would take 3.2 hours.

EXAMPLE 3

The pitch P of a musical tone varies inversely as its wavelength W. One tone has a pitch of 660 vibrations per second and a wavelength of 1.6 feet. Find the wavelength of another tone which has a pitch of 440 vibrations per second.

Find an equation of variation.

$$P = \frac{h}{w}$$

$$660 = \frac{h}{1.6}$$

$$1.6(660) = h$$

$$1056 = h$$

The equation of variation is $P = \frac{1056}{w}$.

Use the equation to find the wavelength of the second tone.

$$P = \frac{1056}{w}$$

$$440 = \frac{1056}{w}$$

$$440w = 1056$$

$$w = 2.4$$

The wavelength is 2.4 feet.

TRY THIS

3. In Example 2, how long would it take 10 people to do the job? 8 hr

4. The time t required to drive a fixed distance varies inversely as the speed r. It takes 5 hours at 60 km/h to drive a fixed distance. How long would it take at 40 km/h? $7\frac{1}{2}$ hr

---

| **8–5** | |

Exercises

Find an equation of variation where y varies inversely as x, and the following are true.

1. $y = 25$ when $x = 3$ $y = \frac{75}{x}$

2. $y = 45$ when $x = 2$ $y = \frac{90}{x}$

3. $y = 8$ when $x = 10$ $y = \frac{80}{x}$

4. $y = 7$ when $x = 10$ $y = \frac{70}{x}$

5. $y = 0.125$ when $x = 8$ $y = \frac{1}{x}$

6. $y = 6.25$ when $x = 0.16$ $y = \frac{1}{x}$

7. $y = 42$ when $x = 25$ $y = \frac{1050}{x}$

8. $y = 42$ when $x = 50$ $y = \frac{2100}{x}$

9. $y = 0.2$ when $x = 0.3$ $y = \frac{0.06}{x}$

10. $y = 0.4$ when $x = 0.6$ $y = \frac{0.24}{x}$

Solve these problems.

11. It takes 16 hours for 2 people to resurface a gym floor. How long would it take 6 people to do the job? $5\frac{1}{3}$ hr

12. It takes 4 hours for 9 cooks to prepare a school lunch. How long would it take 8 cooks to prepare the lunch? $4\frac{1}{2}$ hr

13. The volume V of a gas varies inversely as the pressure P upon it. The volume of a gas is 200 cubic centimeters (cm^3) under a pressure of 32 kg/cm². What will be its volume under a pressure of 20 kg/cm²? 320 kg

14. The current I in an electrical conductor varies inversely as the resistance R of the conductor. The current is 2 amperes when the resistance is 960 ohms. What is the current when the resistance is 540 ohms? $3\frac{5}{9}$ amp

15. The time t required to empty a tank varies inversely as the rate r of pumping. A pump can empty a tank in 90 minutes at the rate of 1200 ℓ/min. How long will it take the pump to empty the tank at 2000 ℓ/min? 54 min

16. The height H of triangles of fixed area varies inversely as the base B. Suppose the height is 50 cm when the base is 40 cm. Find the height when the base is 8 cm. What is the fixed area? 250 cm, 1000 cm²

Extension

Write an equation of inverse variation for each situation.

17. The cost per person C of chartering a fishing boat varies inversely as the number N of persons sharing the cost. $C = \frac{k}{N}$

18. The number N of revolutions of a tire rolling over a given distance varies inversely as the circumference C of the tire. $N = \frac{k}{C}$

19. The amount of current I flowing in an electrical circuit varies inversely with the resistance R of the circuit. $I = \frac{k}{R}$

20. The density D of a given mass varies inversely as its volume V. $D = \frac{k}{V}$

21. The intensity of illumination I from a light source varies inversely as the square of the distance d from the source. $I = \frac{k}{d^2}$

Which of the following vary inversely?

22. The cost of mailing a letter in the U.S. and the distance it travels. No

23. A runner's speed in a race and the time it takes to run it. Yes

24. The number of plays to go 80 yards for a touchdown and the average gain per play. Yes

25. The weight of a turkey and the cooking time. No

Challenge

26. Graph the equation of inverse variation $y = \frac{6}{x}$.

The times it takes n people to do s jobs varies directly as the number of jobs and inversely as the number of people. An equation of variation is $T = ks \cdot \frac{1}{n}$. This is *combined variation*.

Write an equation of variation for each of the following.

27. The force F needed to keep a car from skidding on a curve varies directly as the square of the car's speed S and its mass m and inversely as the radius of the curve r. $F = \frac{kSm}{r}$

28. For a horizontal beam supported at both ends, the maximum safe load L varies directly as its width w and the square of its thickness t and inversely as the distance d between the supports. $L = \frac{kWt^2}{d}$

The Square and Power Keys

Many calculators have a key marked x^2 or x^y. These keys can be used to find powers of numbers and to evaluate functions of degree greater than 1. The x^2 key replaces a number in the display with the square of that number. The x^y key is used to find the yth power of a number in the display. It is important to remember that the square and power keys act only on the number in the display.

EXAMPLE 1

Problem: Let $g(x) = -4x^2$. Find $g(0.35)$.

Enter: 4   (+/−)   (×)   0.35   (x^2)   (=)

Display: 4   −4   0.35   0.1225   −0.49

Practice Problem: Let $h(x) = \dfrac{x^2}{-6}$. Find $h(2.4)$.   −0.96

EXAMPLE 2

Notice in this problem that you must press the equals key before pressing the x^2 key. Also, the change sign key must be used last.

Problem: Let $g(x) = -(4x)^2$. Find $g(0.35)$.

Enter: 4   (×)   0.35   (=)   (x^2)   (+/−)

Display: 4   0.35   1.4   1.96   −1.96

Practice Problem: Let $h(x) = -\left(\dfrac{x}{6}\right)^2$. Find $h(2.4)$.   −0.16

The memory keys are also useful in evaluating functions. In this example, the value of x is first stored in the memory. Then it is recalled later in the problem. *Min* stands for memory in. *MR* stands for memory recall. (Your calculator may have an *STO* key instead of one marked *Min*. A key marked *RCL* will work in the same way as one marked *MR*.)

EXAMPLE 3

Problem: Let $p(x) = 2x^3 - x^2 + 3x + 8$. Find $p(14)$.

Enter: 14   (Min)   2   (×)   (MR)   (x^y)   3   (−)   (MR)   (x^2)

Display: 14   14   2   14   3   5488   14   196

Enter: (+)   3   (×)   (MR)   (+)   8   (=)

Display: 5292   3   14   5334   8   5342

Practice Problem: Let $q(x) = x^4 + 3x^3 - x + 7$. Find $q(0.5)$.   6.9375

Scientific Notation

The displays of most calculators show 8 or 10 digits. However, most calculators can be used to compute with much larger numbers. To do this, they use *scientific notation.*

Scientific notation is used to express a very large number by showing it as the product of a number between 1 and 10, and a power of ten.

EXAMPLE 4

If your calculator has a key marked *EE,* that key will work in the same way as a key marked *EXP.*

Problem: Write 456,879 in scientific notation.

Handwritten Answer: $456,879 = 4.56879 \times 100,000 = 4.56879 \times 10^5$

Enter: 4.56879   (EXP)   (5)

Display: 4.56879 4.56879 00 4.56879 05

Practice Problem: Write 345,700,000 in scientific notation. 3.457×10^8
Then enter it into your calculator. 3.457 08

EXAMPLE 5

Scientific notation can also be used to write very small numbers. To do so, remember that $\frac{1}{x^a}$ can also be written as x^{-a}.

Problem: Write 0.00654 in scientific notation.

Handwritten Answer: $0.00654 = 6.54 \times 0.001 = 6.54 \times \frac{1}{1000}$
$$= 6.54 \times \frac{1}{10^3} = 6.54 \times 10^{-3}$$

Enter: 6.54   (EXP)   3   (+/−)

Display: 6.54 6.54 00 6.54 03 6.54 − 03

Practice Problem: Write 0.000045 in scientific notation. 4.5×10^{-5}
Then enter it into your calculator. 4.5 − 05

EXAMPLE 6

If your calculator does not express numbers in scientific notation, you can still use it to compute with very large and small numbers. In the example below, notice that the exponent in the answer is the sum of the exponents in the two factors.

Problem: 328,000 × 78,600

Equivalent Problem: $(3.28 \times 10^5)(7.86 \times 10^4)$

Enter: 3.28   (×)   7.86   (=)

Display: 3.28   7.86 25.7808

Answer: 25.7808×10^9, or 2.57808×10^{10}

Practice Problem: Find 45,300,000 × 6,800,000. 3.0804×10^{14}

CAREERS/Financial Institutions

Banks, savings and loan institutions, and credit unions play a key part in the economic growth of society. These financial institutions protect money saved by individuals. They also put this money to work by lending it out at interest, so it earns more money.

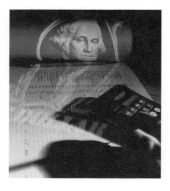

In modern financial institutions, workers at all levels must have strong mathematical skills. For example, tellers must take in and give out money hundreds of times each day without making any mistakes. Bookkeepers must enter figures accurately, keeping track of which moneys are to be *credited* (added) to an account, and which are to be *debited* (subtracted). *Trust officers,* people who manage money for customers, must compare interest rates available on various types of investments.

Among the most important decision-making jobs in any financial institution is the job of *loan officer*. The loan officer must decide which of the people and businesses who want loans should be given them. The loan officer must decide whether a loan applicant is likely to pay back the money borrowed and the interest owed. To make this decision, the loan officer looks at the person's or company's *financial statement.*

A financial statement is a report that shows such things as the dollar value of property owned, inventories of products, and salary or cash on hand. It also shows how much money is already owed by the person or company, and when it must be paid back. The loan officer must use the numbers on the financial statement to try to foresee how well the individual or company will do in the future—how likely they are to be able to pay back the loan. A loan officer must thus

interpret the meanings of numbers, and risk large amounts of dollars on the basis of these interpretations.

The exercises that follow are similar to those that workers in financial institutions must solve.

Exercises

1. A person's interest income from a six-month certificate of deposit account varies directly as the amount of money deposited. For a deposit of $10,000, the person earns $506.75 interest during a six month period. How much would the person earn during the same period for a deposit of $45,000? (See Section 8–4.) $2280.38

2. Sue, a bank lending officer, knows that the value of a house in a certain neighborhood varies directly as A, the area of the floor space of the house. A house in this neighborhood with 1200 square feet of floor space is worth about $80,000. Find the approximate value of a 2000-sq.-foot house in this neighborhood. (See Section 8–4.) $133,333

3. The number of customers C that tellers in a bank can handle varies directly with the number of tellers on duty and the number of hours they work. Two tellers can handle a total of 98 customers during a four-hour shift. How many customers can be handled by 6 tellers during an eight-hour shift? (See Section 8–4.) 588

CHAPTER 8   Review

Review the material in the chapter. Then see how you have done by trying these review exercises. If you miss an exercise, restudy the indicated lesson.

8–1   Are the following correspondences functions?

1. Domain   Range No

$-1 \longleftrightarrow 3$
$0 \longrightarrow 4$
$1 \longrightarrow 5$

2. Domain   Range Yes

$-2 \longrightarrow 0$
$5 \longrightarrow 1$
$7 \longrightarrow 4$

8–1   Find the indicated outputs for these functions.

3. $f(x) = 3x - 4$; find $f(2)$, $f(0)$, and $f(-1)$. 2, −4, −7
4. $g(t) = |t| - 3$; find $g(3)$, $g(-5)$, and $g(0)$. 0, 2, −3
5. $h(x) = x^3 + 1$; find $h(-2)$, $h(0)$, and $h(1)$. −7, 1, 2

8–2   Graph each function.

6. $g(x) = x + 7$ **7.** $f(x) = x^2 - 3$ **8.** $h(x) = 3|x|$

8–2   Which of the following are graphs of functions?

9. No

10. Yes

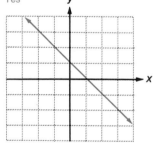

8–3   Translate to an equation that describes a linear function. Find the input and output. Then solve the problem.

11. A long distance phone call from Houston to San Francisco costs 35¢ for the first minute and 25¢ for each additional minute. Find the cost of a five-minute call. $c = 0.35 + 0.25\,m$; input 5, output 1.60; cost is $1.60

8–4   Find an equation of variation where y varies directly as x, and the following are true.

12. $y = 12$ when $x = 4$ **13.** $y = 4$ when $x = 8$ **14.** $y = 0.4$ when $x = 0.5$

8–4 Solve.

15. A person's paycheck P varies directly as the number H of hours worked. The pay is $165.00 for working 20 hours. Find the pay for 30 hours of work. $247.50

8–5 Find an equation of variation where y varies inversely as x, and the following are true.

16. $y = 5$ when $x = 6$ **17.** $y = 0.5$ when $x = 2$ **18.** $y = 1.3$ when $x = 0.5$

8–5 Solve.

19. It takes 5 hours for 2 washing machines to wash a fixed amount. How long would it take 10 washing machines? 1 hour

---

CHAPTER 8   Test

Find the indicated outputs for these functions.

1. $f(x) = \frac{1}{2}x + 1$, find $f(0)$, $f(1)$, and $f(2)$. $1, \frac{3}{2}, 2$

2. $g(t) = -2|t| + 3$, find $t(-1)$, $t(0)$, and $t(3)$. $1, 3, -3$

Graph each function.

3. $h(x) = x - 4$ **4.** $g(x) = x^2 - 1$

Which of the following are graphs of functions?

5. Yes

6. No

Find an equation of variation where y varies directly as x, and the following are true.

7. $y = 6$ when $x = 3$ **8.** $y = 1.5$ when $x = 3$ 7. $y = 2x$ 8. $y = 0.5x$

Solve.

9. The distance d traveled by a train varies directly as the time t it travels. The train travels 60 km in $\frac{1}{2}$ hour. How far will it travel in 2 hours? 240 km

Find an equation of variation where y varies inversely with x and the following are true.

10. $y = 6$ when $x = 2$ **11.** $y = \frac{1}{3}$ when $x = -3$ 10. $y = \frac{12}{x}$ 11. $y = \frac{-1}{x}$

Solve.

12. It takes 3 hours for 2 cement mixers to mix a certain amount. How long would it take 5 cement mixers to do the job? $1\frac{1}{5}$ hours

Challenge

13. If $f(-1) = -1$ and $f(7) = 2$, find a linear equation for $f(x)$. $f(x) = \frac{3}{8}x - \frac{5}{8}$

Ready for Systems of Equations?

3–1 to 3–3   Solve.

1. $y + 3 = -2$ -5

2. $9y = 2$ $\frac{2}{9}$

3. $-3x + 2 = -10$ 4

4–3   Evaluate each polynomial for $w = -2$.

4. $3 + 4w$ -5   **5.** $-7w - 8$ 6   **6.** $w^2 - 2w + 3$ 11

7–2

7. Determine whether $(3, -2)$ is a solution of $y = 4x - 14$.   Yes
8. Determine whether $(-1, 5)$ is a solution of $y = -3x - 2$.   No
9. Determine whether $(3, 4)$ is a solution of $4x - 2y = 3$.   No

7–2   Find three solutions of each equation.   Answers may vary.

10. $y = 3x - 1$ **11.** $2w + 4x = -7$ **12.** $-4y - 2z = 10$

7–3   Use graph paper. Graph these linear equations.

13. $2x - 4y = 1$ **14.** $-x + 3y = 5$
15. $y = -2$ **16.** $x = 5$

9

CHAPTER NINE

Systems of Equations

Solving Systems by Graphing

Identifying Solutions

A set of equations with the same variable is called a system of equations. A solution of a system of two equations is an ordered pair that makes both equations true.
Consider the system of equations.

$$x + y = 8$$
$$2x - y = 1$$

The ordered pair $(3, 5)$ is the solution of the system because both equations are true when $x = 3$ and $y = 5$.

$x + y = 8$		$2x - y = 1$	
$3 + 5$	8	$2(3) - 5$	1
8		1	

Since the solution of a system satisfies both equations simultaneously we sometimes say we have a system of simultaneous equations.

EXAMPLES

1. Determine whether $(1, 2)$ is a solution of the system.

$$y = x + 1$$
$$2x + y = 4$$

$y = x + 1$		$2x + y = 4$	
2	$1 + 1$	$2(1) + 2$	4
2	2	$2 + 2$	
		4	

$(1, 2)$ is a solution of the system.

2. Determine whether $(-3, 2)$ is a solution of the system.

$$a + b = -1$$
$$b + 3a = 4$$

$a + b = -1$		$b + 3a = 4$	
$-3 + 2$	-1	$2 + 3(-3)$	4
-1		$2 - 9$	
		-7	

$(-3, 2)$ is not a solution of $b + 3a = 4$. Thus, it is not a solution of the system. When we find all the solutions of a system, we say that we have solved the system.

Determine whether the given ordered pair is a solution of the system.

1. $(2, -3)$; $x = 2y + 8$
$2x + y = 1$ Yes

2. $(20, 40)$; $a = \frac{1}{4}b + 10$
$b - a = -20$ No

Finding Solutions by Graphing

One way to solve a system of equations is to graph the equations and find the coordinates of the point(s) of intersection. These coordinates are the solutions of the system.

EXAMPLE 3
Solve.

$x + 2y = 7$
$x = y + 4$

We graph the equations. Point P appears to have coordinates $(5, 1)$.

Check $(5, 1)$:

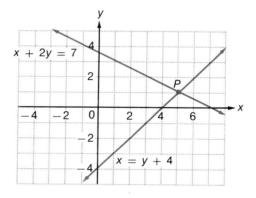

$x + 2y = 7$	$x = y + 4$
$5 + 2(1) \mid 7$	$5 \mid 1 + 4$
$7 \mid$	$5 \mid 5$

$(5, 1)$ is a solution of the system.

When we graph a system of two equations, one of the three things may happen.

1. The lines have one point of intersection, as in Example 3. The point of intersection is the only solution of the system.
2. The lines are parallel. If so, there is no point which satisfies both equations. The system has no solution.
3. The lines coincide. Thus the equations have the same graph, and every solution of one equation is a solution of the other. There are an unlimited number of solutions.

Use graph paper. Solve each system graphically and check.

3. $x + 4y = -6$
$2x - 3y = -1$ $(-2, -1)$

4. $y + 2x = 5$
$2y - 5x = 10$ $(0, 5)$

Exercises

Determine whether the given ordered pair is a solution of the system of equations. Remember to use alphabetical order of variables.

1. $(3, 2)$; $2x + 3y = 12$
$x - 4y = -5$ Yes

2. $(1, 5)$; $5x - 2y = -5$
$3x - 7y = -32$ Yes

3. $(3, 2)$; $3t - 2s = 0$
$t + 2s = 15$ No

4. $(2, -2)$; $b + 2a = 2$
$b - a = -4$ Yes

5. $(15, 20)$; $3x - 2y = 5$
$6x - 5y = -10$ Yes

6. $(-1, -3)$; $3r + s = -6$
$2r = 1 + s$ Yes

7. $(-1, 1)$; $x = -1$
$x - y = -2$ Yes

8. $(-3, 4)$; $2x = -y - 2$
$y = -4$ No

9. $(12, 3)$; $y = \frac{1}{4}x$

$3x - y = 33$ Yes

10. $(-3, 1)$; $y = -\frac{1}{3}x$

$3y = -5x - 12$ No

Use graph paper. Solve each system graphically and check.

11. $x + y = 3$
$x - y = 1$

12. $x - y = 2$
$x + y = 6$

13. $x + 2y = 10$
$3x + 4y = 8$

14. $x - 2y = 6$
$2x - 3y = 5$

15. $8x - y = 29$
$2x + y = 11$

16. $4x - y = 10$
$3x + 5y = 19$

17. $x = y$
$4x = 2y - 6$

18. $x = 3y$
$3y - 6 = 2x$

19. $x = -y$
$x + y = 4$

20. $-3x = 5 - y$

$2y = 6x + 10$

21. $a = \frac{1}{2}b + 1$

$a - 2b = -2$

22. $x = \frac{1}{3}y + 2$

$-2x - y = 1$

11. $(2, 1)$
12. $(4, 2)$
13. $(-12, 11)$
14. $(-8, -7)$
15. $(4, 3)$
16. $(3, 2)$
17. $(-3, -3)$
18. $(-6, -2)$
19. No solution
20. Infinitely many solutions
21. $(2, 2)$
22. $(1, -3)$
23. $(5, 3)$
24. $(\frac{1}{3}, 1)$
25. Infinitely many solutions
26. No solution

Extension

Solve these systems graphically.

23. $y = 3$
$x = 5$

24. $y = 3x$
$y = -3x + 2$

25. $x + y = 9$
$3x + 3y = 27$

26. $x + y = 4$
$x + y = -4$

27. The solution of the following system is $(2, -3)$. Find A and B.

$Ax - 3y = 13$ A = 2, B = 2
$x - By = 8$

28. A system of equations which has one or more solutions is called consistent. What must be true of the slopes of the equations in a system with exactly one solution? They are not equal.

29. A system of equations which has infinitely many solutions is called consistent and dependent. What must be true of the slopes and y-intercepts of the equations in a consistent-dependent system? The slopes are equal, the intercepts are equal.

30. A system of equations which has no solution is called inconsistent. What must be true of the slopes and y-intercepts in an inconsistent system? The slopes are equal, the intercepts are not equal.

Challenge

31. Solve this system by graphing. What happens when you check your solution? Non-integer solutions are difficult to approximate from graphs. Other methods are needed, $(\frac{2}{3}, \frac{3}{7})$.

$$3x + 7y = 5$$
$$6x - 7y = 1$$

GEAR RATIOS

A gear ratio compares the number of times one wheel turns to the number of times another wheel turns. A gear ratio of 3 to 1 means one wheel turns 3 times for every revolution of the other wheel. On a bicycle, the ratio is the number of teeth on the *chainwheel* divided by the number of teeth on the *freewheel* (see illustration). The 10-speed bicycle shown below has 2 chainwheels and 5 freewheels or $2 \times 5 = 10$ gears. Calculate all ten gear ratios and complete the table so the gears are in increasing order of their gear ratios.

Gear	Ratio	Gear	Ratio
1st	$\frac{40}{28} = 1.43$	6th	40/17 = 235
2nd	40/24 = 1.67	7th	52/20 = 2.60
3rd	52/28 = 1.86	8th	40/14 = 2.86
4th	40/20 = 2	9th	52/17 = 3.06
5th	52/24 = 2.17	10th	$\frac{52}{14} = 3.71$

Which gears use the small (40 tooth) chainwheel? 1st, 2nd, 4th, 6th, 8th

Which gears use the large chainwheel? 3rd, 5th, 7th, 9th, 10th

Which gears use the middle freewheel? 4th, 7th

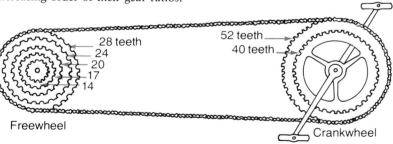

28 teeth
24
20
17
14

52 teeth
40 teeth

Freewheel

Crankwheel

The Substitution Method

Substituting for One Variable

How can we find the solution to a system? One method that can be used is the substitution method.

EXAMPLE 1

Solve the system.

$$x + y = 6$$
$$x = y + 2$$

The second equation says that x and $y + 2$ name the same thing. Thus in the first equation, we can substitute $y + 2$ for x.

$$x + y = 6$$
$$y + 2 + y = 6 \quad \text{Substituting } y + 2 \text{ for } x$$

This last equation has only one variable. We solve for y.

$$2y + 2 = 6 \quad \text{Collecting like terms}$$
$$2y = 4$$
$$y = 2$$

We return to the original pair of equations and substitute 2 for y in either of them. We use the first equation.

$$x + y = 6$$
$$x + 2 = 6 \quad \text{Substituting 2 for } y$$
$$x = 4$$

The ordered pair (4, 2) may be a solution. We check.

Check (4, 2):

$x + y = 6$		$x = y + 2$	
$4 + 2$	6	4	$2 + 2$
6	6	4	4

Since (4, 2) checks, we have the solution. This can also be expressed as $x = 4$, $y = 2$.

It is easy to make arithmetical errors when solving systems, so you should always check your solution by evaluating the ordered pair in the original equations. We will not always show the check, so be sure to verify each solution.

TRY THIS Solve by the substitution method.

1. $x + y = 5$ **2.** $a - b = 4$
    $x = y + 1$ (3, 2) $b = 2 - 5a$ (1, −3)

Solving for the Variable First

Sometimes neither equation of a pair has a variable alone on one side. Then we solve one equation for one of the variables and proceed as before.

EXAMPLE 2

Solve.

$$x - 2y = 6$$
$$3x + 2y = 4$$
$$x = 6 + 2y \quad \text{Solving the first equation for } x$$
$$3(6 + 2y) + 2y = 4 \quad \text{Substituting for } x \text{ in the second equation}$$
$$18 + 8y = 4$$
$$8y = -14$$
$$y = \frac{-7}{4}$$

We go back to either of the original equations and substitute $-\frac{7}{4}$ for y. It will be easier to solve for x in the first equation.

$$x - 2\left(-\frac{7}{4}\right) = 6$$

$$x + \frac{7}{2} = 6$$

$$x = \frac{5}{2}$$

Check $\left(\frac{5}{2}, \frac{-7}{4}\right)$:

$x - 2y = 6$		$3x + 2y = 4$	
$\frac{5}{2} - 2\left(-\frac{7}{4}\right)$	6	$3 \cdot \frac{5}{2} + 2\left(-\frac{7}{4}\right)$	4
$\frac{5}{2} + \frac{7}{2}$		$\frac{15}{2} - \frac{7}{2}$	
6		4	

TRY THIS Solve.

3. $x - 2y = 8$ **4.** $4x - y = 5$ 3. $\left(\frac{24}{5}, \frac{-8}{5}\right)$
    $2x + y = 8$ $2x + y = 10$ 4. $\left(\frac{5}{2}, 5\right)$

Problems Using Substitution

Translating a problem to mathematical language is often easier if we translate to a system of equations.

EXAMPLE 3

Translate to a system of equations and solve.

The sum of two numbers is 82. One number is twelve more than the other. Find the larger number.

Let x = one number and y = the other number. There are two statements in this problem.

The sum of two numbers is 82.

$$x + y \qquad = 82$$

One number is twelve more than the other number.

$$x \qquad = \quad 12 \quad + \qquad y$$

Now we have a system of equations.

$$x + y = 82$$
$$x = 12 + y$$

We solve, substituting $12 + y$ for x in the first equation.

$$x + y = 82$$
$$12 + y + y = 82 \qquad \text{Substituting } 12 + y \text{ for } x$$
$$12 + 2y = 82$$
$$2y = 70$$
$$y = 35$$

Next, we solve for x by substituting 35 for y in the second equation.

$$x = 12 + 35$$
$$x = 47$$

We check in the original problem. The sum of 35 and 47 is 82 and 47 is twelve more than 35. The larger number is 47.

TRY THIS Translate to a system of equations and solve.

5. The sum of two numbers is 84. One number is three times the other. Find the numbers. 63, 21

6. One number is five times another number. Their sum is 102. Find the numbers. 85, 17

Exercises

Solve by the substitution method.

1. $x + y = 4$
   $y = 2x + 1$

2. $x + y = 10$
   $y = x + 8$

3. $y = x + 1$
   $2x + y = 4$

4. $y = x - 6$
   $x + y = -2$

5. $y = 2x - 5$
   $3y - x = 5$

6. $y = 2x + 1$
   $x + y = -2$

7. $x = -2y$
   $x + 4y = 2$

8. $r = -3s$
   $r + 4s = 10$

Solve by the substitution method. Get one variable alone first.

9. $s + t = -4$
   $s - t = 2$

10. $x - y = 6$
    $x + y = -2$

11. $y - 2x = -6$
    $2y - x = 5$

12. $x - y = 5$
    $x + 2y = 7$

13. $2x + 3y = -2$
    $2x - y = 9$

14. $x + 2y = 10$
    $3x + 4y = 8$

15. $x - y = -3$
    $2x + 3y = -6$

16. $3b + 2a = 2$
    $-2b + a = 8$

17. $r - 2s = 0$
    $4r - 3s = 15$

18. $y - 2x = 0$
    $3x + 7y = 17$

19. $x - 3y = 7$
    $-4x + 12y = 28$

20. $8x + 2y = 6$
    $4x = 3 - y$

1. (1, 3)
2. (1, 9)
3. (1, 2)
4. (2, −4)
5. (4, 3)
6. (−1, −1)
7. (−2, 1)
8. (−30, 10)

9. (−1, −3)
10. (2, −4)
11. $(\frac{17}{3}, \frac{16}{3})$
12. $(\frac{17}{3}, \frac{2}{3})$
13. $(\frac{25}{8}, -11)$
14. (−12, 11)
15. (−3, 0)
16. (4, −2)
17. (6, 3)
18. (1, 2)
19. No solution
20. infinitely many solutions

Translate to a system of equations and solve.

21. The sum of two numbers is 27. One number is 3 more than the other. Find the numbers. 15, 12

22. The sum of two numbers is 36. One number is 2 more than the other. Find the numbers. 19, 17

23. Find two numbers whose sum is 58 and whose difference is 16. 37, 21

24. Find two numbers whose sum is 66 and whose difference is 8. 37, 29

25. The difference between two numbers is 16. Three times the larger number is seven times the smaller. What are the numbers? 28, 12

26. The difference between two numbers is 18. Twice the smaller number plus three times the larger is 74. What are the numbers? 22, 4

27. The perimeter of a rectangle is 400 m. The length is 40 m more than the width. Find the length and width. 120 m, 80 m

28. The perimeter of a rectangle is 76 cm. The length is 17 cm more than the width. Find the length and width. $27\frac{1}{2}$ cm, $10\frac{1}{2}$ cm

29. The perimeter of a football field is $306\frac{2}{3}$ yards. The length is $46\frac{2}{3}$ yards longer than the width. Find the length and width. 100 yd, $53\frac{1}{3}$ yd

Extension

Solve by the substitution method.

30. $\frac{1}{4}(a - b) = 2$ **31.** $\frac{x}{2} + \frac{3y}{2} = 2$ **32.** $0.4x + 0.7y = 0.1$ 30. $(7, -1)$
31. $(10, -2)$
32. $(2, -1)$

$\frac{1}{6}(a + b) = 1$ $\frac{x}{5} - \frac{y}{2} = 3$ $0.5x - 0.1y = 1.1$

33. Determine whether $(2, -3)$ is a solution of this system of three equations.

$$x + 3y = -7$$
$$-x + y = -5 \quad \text{No}$$
$$2x - y = 1$$

34. A rectangle has a perimeter of x feet. The width is 5 feet less than the length. Find the length in terms of x. $\ell = \frac{x + 10}{4}$

35. A rectangle has a perimeter of y meters. The length is 8 meters longer than the width. Find the width in terms of y. $w = \frac{y - 16}{4}$

Challenge

Here are systems of three equations in three variables. Use the substitution method to solve.

36. $x + y + z = 4$ **37.** $x + y + z = 180$ 36. $(2, -1, 3)$
 $x - 2y - z = 1$ $x = z - 70$ 37. $(30, 50, 100)$
 $y = -1$ $2y - z = 0$ 38. The x-terms drop out and leave
            $12 = 14$. The lines are parallel, so
            there is no solution.

38. Consider this system of equations.

$$3y + 3x = 14$$
$$y = -x + 4$$

Try to solve by the substitution method. Can you explain your results?

39. Consider this system of equations.

$$y = x + 5$$
$$3x + 3y = 15$$

Try to solve by the substitution method. Can you explain your results?   The x-terms drop out and leave $15 = 15$. The lines coincide, so all solutions to one equation are solutions of the system.

40. Why is there no solution to the following system? (Hint: Use substitution more than once.)

$$x + y = 10 \quad \text{Answers may vary. Ex.} \quad x = 10 - z, y = 10 - z, \text{ so}$$
$$y + z = 10 \qquad\qquad\qquad\qquad (10 - z) + (10 - z) + z = 10 \text{ or}$$
$$x + z = 10 \qquad\qquad\qquad\qquad z = 10. x = 10 - z \text{ so } x = 0,$$
$$x + y + z = 10 \qquad\qquad\qquad y = 10 - z \text{ so } y = 0, \text{ then } x + y =$$
$$\qquad\qquad\qquad\qquad\qquad 0. \text{ But we know } x + y = 10, \text{ so there}$$
$$\qquad\qquad\qquad\qquad\qquad \text{is no solution.}$$

The Addition Method

Solving by the Addition Method

Another method of solving systems of equations is called the addition method.

EXAMPLE 1
Solve.

$$x + y = 5$$
$$x - y = 1$$

We will use the addition principle for equations. According to the second equation, $x - y$ and 1 are the same thing. Thus, we can add $x - y$ to the left side of the first equation and 1 to the right side.

$$
\begin{array}{rl}
x + y = 5 & \\
\underline{x - y = 1} & \\
2x + 0y = 6 & \text{Adding} \\
2x = 6 & \text{Note that we now have an equation with just one variable.} \\
x = 3 & \text{Solving for } x
\end{array}
$$

Next substitute 3 for x in either of the original equations.

$$
\begin{array}{rl}
x + y = 5 & \\
3 + y = 5 & \text{Substituting 3 for } x \text{ in the first equation} \\
y = 2 &
\end{array}
$$

Check to see that (3, 2) is the solution of the system.

TRY THIS Solve using the addition method.

1. $x + y = 5$ $\quad$ **2.** $3x - 3y = 6$
   $2x - y = 4$ $\qquad\quad\;\; 3x + 3y = 0$

Using the Multiplication Principle First

The addition method allows us to eliminate a variable. We may need to multiply an equation by -1 for this to happen.

EXAMPLE 2
Solve.

$$2x + 3y = 8$$
$$x + 3y = 7$$

If we add, we do not eliminate a variable. However, if the $3y$ were $-3y$ in the second equation we could. We multiply on both sides of the second equation by -1 and then add.

$$2x + 3y = 8$$
$$\underline{-x - 3y = -7} \quad \text{Multiplying by } -1 \text{ on both sides}$$
$$x \qquad = 1 \quad \text{Adding}$$

Note that this is the same as subtracting the second equation in the original equations. We can now solve the system as before.

$$x + 3y = 7$$
$$1 + 3y = 7 \quad \text{Substituting 1 for } x \text{ in the second equation}$$
$$3y = 6$$
$$y = 2 \quad \text{Solving for } y$$

Check to see that $(1, 2)$ is the solution of the system.

TRY THIS Solve. Multiply one equation by -1 first.

3. $5x + 3y = 17$ 4. $8x + 11y = 37$
    $5x - 2y = -3$ $-2x + 11y = 7$ 3. (1, 4)   4. $(3, \frac{13}{11})$

In Example 2 we used the multiplication principle, multiplying by -1. We often need to multiply by something other than -1.

EXAMPLE 3
Solve.

$$3x + 6y = -6$$
$$5x - 2y = 14$$

Multiplying by -1 and adding will not eliminate a variable. Look at the coefficients of each variable. For the x-terms, 3 does not divide 5 evenly, but for the y-terms, we only need to multiply by 3 in the second equation to eliminate the y variable. Multiply by 3 on both sides of the second equation.

$$3x + 6y = -6$$
$$\underline{15x - 6y = 42} \quad \text{Multiplying by 3 on both sides}$$
$$18x \qquad = 36 \quad \text{Adding}$$
$$x \qquad = 2$$

We can now substitute 2 for x in the first equation.

$$3(2) + 6y = -6 \quad \text{Substituting 2 for } x$$
$$6 + 6y = -6$$
$$6y = -12$$
$$y = -2 \quad \text{Solving for } y$$

Check to see that $(2, -2)$ is the solution of the system.

TRY THIS Solve.

5. $4a + 7b = 11$ 6. $7x - 5y = 76$
    $2a + 3b = 5$ (1, 1) $4x + y = 55$ (13, 3)

When we use the addition method for solving systems of equations, we sometimes need to use the multiplication principle more than once.

EXAMPLE 4
Solve.

$$3x + 5y = 30$$
$$5x + 8y = 49$$

We use the multiplication principle with both equations. We choose the variable that looks easier to work with, in this case x. If we multiply on both sides of the first equation by 5 and the second by -3, we can eliminate the x-variable.

$$15x + 25y = 150 \quad \text{Multiplying by 5 on both sides}$$
$$\underline{-15x - 24y = -147} \quad \text{Multiplying by } -3 \text{ on both sides}$$
$$y = 3 \quad \text{Adding}$$

We substitute 3 for y in one of the original equations.

$$3x + 5y = 30$$
$$3x + 5(3) = 30 \quad \text{Substituting 3 for } y$$
$$3x + 15 = 30$$
$$3x = 15$$
$$x = 5$$

Check to see that $(5, 3)$ is the solution of the system.

TRY THIS Solve.

7. $5x + 3y = 2$ 8. $6x + 2y = 4$
    $3x + 5y = -2$ $10x + 7y = -8$ 7. $(1, -1)$ 8. $(2, -4)$

Solving Problems Using the Addition Method

Once we have translated a problem to a system of equations we can use the addition method to solve.

EXAMPLE 5

Translate to a system of equations and solve. The sum of two numbers is 56. One third of the first number plus one fourth of the second number is 16. Find the numbers.

Let $x =$ the first number and $y =$ the second number. We translate the first statement.

$$x + y = 56$$

We translate the second statement.

$$\frac{1}{3}x + \frac{1}{4}y = 16$$

We now have a system of equations.

$$x + y = 56$$
$$\frac{1}{3}x + \frac{1}{4}y = 16$$

First we clear the second equation of fractions by multiplying on both sides by 12.

$$x + y = 56$$
$$4x + 3y = 192$$

We then use the addition method, multiplying on both sides of the first equation by -4.

$$
\begin{array}{r}
-4x - 4y = -224 \\
4x + 3y = 192 \\
\hline
-y = -32 \\
y = 32
\end{array}
$$

Substituting for y in the first equation, we have

$$x + 32 = 56$$
$$x = 24. \quad \text{The two numbers are 24 and 32.}$$

TRY THIS Translate to a system of equations and solve.

9. The difference between two numbers is 36. One sixth of the larger number minus one ninth of the smaller number is 11. Find the numbers. 126, 90

EXAMPLE 6

Translate to a system of equations and solve.

Badger Rent-a-Car rents compact cars at a daily rate of $23.95 plus 20¢ per mile. Thrifty Rent-a-Car rents compact cars at a daily rate of $22.95 plus 22¢ per mile. For what mileage is the cost the same?

If we let m represent the mileage and c the cost, we see that the cost for Badger will be

$$23.95 + 0.2m = c.$$

The cost for Thrifty will be

$$22.95 + 0.22m = c.$$

We solve the system.

$$23.95 + 0.20m = c$$
$$22.95 + 0.22m = c$$

We clear the system of decimals and multiply the second equation by -1. Then we use the addition method.

$$2395 + 20m = 100c$$
$$-2295 - 22m = -100c$$
$$100 - 2m = 0$$
$$100 = 2m$$
$$50 = m$$

Thus, if the cars are driven 50 miles, the cost will be the same.

TRY THIS Translate to a system of equations and solve.

10. Acme rents a station wagon at a daily rate of $21.95 plus 23¢ per mile. Speedo Rentzit rents a wagon for $24.95 plus 19¢ per mile. For what mileage is the cost the same? 75 miles

---

9–3

Exercises

Solve using the addition method.

1. $x + y = 10$
   $x - y = 8$

2. $x - y = 7$
   $x + y = 3$

3. $x + y = 8$
   $-x + 2y = 7$

4. $x + y = 6$
   $-x + 3y = -2$

5. $3x - y = 9$
   $2x + y = 6$

6. $4x - y = 1$
   $3x + y = 13$

7. $4a + 3b = 7$
$-4a + b = 5$

8. $7c + 5d = 18$
$c - 5d = -2$

9. $8x - 5y = -9$
$3x + 5y = -2$

10. $3a - 3b = -15$
$-3a - 3b = -3$

11. $4x - 5y = 7$
$-4x + 5y = 7$

12. $2x + 3y = 4$
$-2x - 3y = -4$

Solve using the multiplication principle first. Then add.

13. $-x - y = 8$
$2x - y = -1$

14. $x + y = -7$
$3x + y = -9$

15. $x + 3y = 19$
$x - y = -1$

16. $3x - y = 8$
$x + 2y = 5$

17. $x + y = 5$
$5x - 3y = 17$

18. $x - y = 7$
$4x - 5y = 25$

19. $2w - 3z = -1$
$3w + 4z = 24$

20. $7p + 5q = 2$
$8p - 9q = 17$

21. $2a + 3b = -1$
$3a + 5b = -2$

22. $3x - 4y = 16$
$5x + 6y = 14$

23. $x - 3y = 0$
$5x - y = -14$

24. $5a - 2b = 0$
$2a - 3b = -11$

25. $3x - 2y = 10$
$5x + 3y = 4$

26. $2p + 5q = 9$
$3p - 2q = 4$

27. $3x - 8y = 11$
$x + 6y - 8 = 0$

28. $m - n = 32$
$3m - 8n - 6 = 0$

Translate to a system of equations and solve. Check your solution in the original problem.

29. The sum of two numbers is 92. One eighth of the first number plus one third of the second number is 19. Find the numbers. 56, 36

30. The difference of two numbers is 49. One half of the larger number plus one seventh of the smaller number is 56. Find the numbers. 98, 49

31. The sum of two numbers is 115. The difference is 21. Find the numbers. 68, 47

32. The sum of two numbers is 26.4. One is five times the other. Find the numbers. 22, 4.4

33. Badger rents an intermediate-size car at a daily rate of $21.95 plus 19¢ per mile. Fleet Vehicles rents an intermediate-size car for $18.95 plus 21¢ per mile. For what mileage is the cost the same? 150 mi

34. Badger rents a basic car at a daily rate of $17.99 plus 18¢ per mile. Fleet Vehicles rents a basic car for $18.95 plus 16¢ per mile. For what mileage is the cost the same? 48 mi

35. Two angles are supplementary. One is 8° more than three times the other. Find the angles. (Supplementary angles are angles whose sum is 180°.) 137, 43

1. $(9, 1)$
2. $(5, -2)$
3. $(3, 5)$
4. $(5, 1)$
5. $(3, 0)$
6. $(2, 7)$
7. $(\frac{-1}{2}, 3)$
8. $(2, \frac{4}{5})$
9. $(-1, \frac{1}{5})$
10. $(-2, 3)$
11. No solution
12. Infinitely many solutions

13. $(-3, -5)$
14. $(-1, -6)$
15. $(4, 5)$
16. $(3, 1)$
17. $(4, 1)$
18. $(10, 3)$
19. $(4, 3)$
20. $(1, -1)$
21. $(1, -1)$
22. $(4, -1)$
23. $(-3, -1)$
24. $(2, 5)$
25. $(2, -2)$
26. $(2, 1)$
27. $(5, \frac{1}{2})$
28. $(50, 18)$

36. Two angles are supplementary. One is 30° more than two times the other. Find the angles. 130, 50

37. Two angles are complementary. Their difference is 34°. Find the angles. (Complementary angles are angles whose sum is 90°.) 62, 28

38. Two angles are complementary. One angle is 42° more than $\frac{1}{2}$ the other. Find the angles. 58, 32

39. In a vineyard a grower uses 820 hectares to plant Chardonnay and Riesling grapes. The grower knows that profits will be greatest by planting 140 hectares more of Chardonnay than Riesling. How many hectares of each grape should be planted? 480, 340

40. The West Valley Horse Farm allots 650 hectares to plant wheat and oats. The owners know that their needs are best met if they plant 180 hectares more wheat than oats. How many hectares of each should they plant? 415, 235

Extension

Solve each system.

41. $3(x - y) = 9$
    $x + y = 7$ (5, 2)

42. $5(a - b) = 10$
    $a + b = 2$ (2, 0)

43. $2(x - y) = 3 + x$
    $x = 3y + 4$ (1, −1)

44. $2(5a - 5b) = 10$
    $-5(6a + 2b) = 10$
    (0, −1)

45. $1.5x + 0.85y = 1637.5$
    $0.01(x + y) = 15.25$
    (525, 1000)

46. $\frac{x}{3} + \frac{y}{2} = 1\frac{1}{3}$
    $x + 0.05y = 4$ (4, 0)

Challenge

Solve each system.

47. $y = ax + b$
    $y = x + c$ $\left(\frac{b - c}{1 - a}, \frac{b - ac}{1 - a}\right)$

48. $ax + by + c = 0$
    $ax + cy + b = 0$ $\left(\frac{-b - c}{a}, 1\right)$

49. $3(7 - a) - 2(1 + 2b) + 5 = 0$
    $3a + 2b - 18 = 0$ (4, 3)

50. $\frac{2}{x} - \frac{3}{y} = -\frac{1}{2}$ $\frac{1}{x} + \frac{2}{y} = \frac{11}{12}$ (4, 3)

51. Suppose we can get a system into the form
    $$ax + by = c$$
    $$dx + ey = f,$$
    where $a, b, c, d, e,$ and f are any positive or negative rational numbers.
    a. Solve the system for x and y. $x = \frac{ce - bf}{ae - bd}$ $y = \frac{af - cd}{ae - bd}$
    b. Use the pattern of your solution to part a to solve the following system. Use a calculator. (2722.4, 1.4)
    $$1.425x - 2044y = 1000$$
    $$0.875x + \frac{1088}{13}y = 2500.$$

9–4 Applying Systems

When we have translated a problem to a system, we must decide whether to use the substitution or addition method. Which method is better?

Although there are exceptions, the substitution method is probably better when a variable has a coefficient of 1, as in the following.

$$8x + 4y = 180 \qquad x + y = 561$$
$$-x + y = 3 \qquad\qquad x = 2y$$

Otherwise, the addition method is better. Both methods work. When in doubt use the addition method.

EXAMPLE 1

A baseball team played 162 games. They won 44 more games than they lost. How many games did they lose?

Let $x =$ the number of games won and $y =$ the number of games lost. There are two statements in this problem.

The number of games won plus the number of games lost is 162   Rewording

$$x \qquad\qquad + \qquad\qquad y \qquad\qquad = 162 \quad \text{Translating}$$

The number of games won minus the number of games lost is 44   Rewording

$$x \qquad\qquad - \qquad\qquad y \qquad\qquad = 44 \quad \text{Translating}$$

We solve the system of equations by the addition method.

$$
\begin{aligned}
x + y &= 162 \\
x - y &= 44 \\
\hline
2x \phantom{{}+y} &= 206 \quad \text{Adding} \\
x &= 103 \\
x + y &= 162 \quad \text{Choosing the easier equation} \\
103 + y &= 162 \quad \text{Substituting 103 for } x \\
y &= 59 \quad \text{The team lost 59 games.}
\end{aligned}
$$

We check in the original problem. Adding 103 and 59 gives a total of 162. Subtracting 59 from 103 gives a difference of 44. The team lost 59 games.

TRY THIS Translate to a system of equations and solve.

1. The sum of two integers is 36 and their difference is 4. Find the integers. 16, 20

EXAMPLE 2

Translate to a system of equations and solve.
Ramon sells cars and trucks. He has room on his lot for 510 vehicles. From experience he knows that his profits will be greatest if he has 190 more cars than trucks. How many of each vehicle should he have? Let x = the number of cars and y = the number of trucks.

Let x = the number of cars and y = the number of trucks.

$$
\underbrace{\text{Number of cars}}_{x} \quad \underset{+}{\text{plus}} \quad \underbrace{\text{number of trucks}}_{y} \quad \underset{= 510}{\text{is 510}} \qquad \text{Rewording}
$$

Translating

$$
\underbrace{\text{Number of cars}}_{x} \quad \underset{= 190 \; +}{\text{is 190 plus}} \quad \underbrace{\text{number of trucks}}_{y} \qquad \text{Rewording}
$$

Translating

We now have a system of equations.

$$x + y = 510$$
$$x = 190 + y$$

We use the substitution method, substituting $190 + y$ for x.

$$(190 + y) + y = 510$$
$$190 + 2y = 510$$
$$2y = 320$$
$$y = 160$$

Substituting 160 for y in the second equation we have

$$x = 190 + 160$$
$$x = 350$$

We check in the original problem. The number of cars is 350. This plus 160 trucks is 510 vehicles. Also, 350 is 190 more than 160. Ramon should have 350 cars and 160 trucks in his lot.

TRY THIS Translate to a system of equations and solve.

2. A family went camping at a place 45 km from town. They drove 13 km more than they walked to get to the campsite. How far did they walk? 16 km

EXAMPLE 3

Shirley is 21 years older than Laura. In six years, Shirley will be twice as old as Laura. How old are they now?

Let x = Shirley's age and y = Laura's age.

	Age now	Age in 6 years
Shirley	x	$x + 6$
Laura	y	$y + 6$

Shirley's age now is 21 more than Laura's age now.

$$x = 21 + y$$

Shirley's age in 6 years will be twice Laura's age in 6 years.

$$x + 6 = 2 \quad (y + 6)$$

We solve the system of equations.

$$x = 21 + y$$
$$x + 6 = 2(y + 6)$$

Simplifying the second equation gives $x = 2y + 6$, so we now have

$$x = 21 + y$$
$$x = 2y + 6.$$

Again we use the substitution method.

$$2y + 6 = 21 + y \quad \text{Substituting } 2y + 6 \text{ for } x$$
$$y = 15 \quad \text{Laura's age now}$$

We substitute 15 for y in $x = 21 + y$.

$$x = 21 + 15$$
$$x = 36 \quad \text{Shirley's age now}$$

Shirley's age is 36, which is 21 more than Laura's age, 15. In six years, Shirley will be 42 and Laura will be 21.

TRY THIS Translate to a system of equations and solve.

3. Wilma is 13 years older than Bev. In nine years, Wilma will be twice as old as Bev. How old is Bev? 4

4. Stan is two thirds as old as Adam. In 7 years, Stan will be three fourths as old as Adam. How old are they now? 14, 21

A two-digit number is 10 times the tens' digit plus the ones' digit. If we let x = the tens' digit and y = the ones' digit, then $10x + y$ is the original number. Reversing the digits means that the new value is $10y + x$. We use this pattern in the next example.

EXAMPLE 4

The sum of the digits of a two-digit number is 14. If the digits are reversed, the new number is 36 greater than the original number. Find the original number.

There are two statements in this problem.

$$\underbrace{\text{The sum of the digits}}_{x + y} \underbrace{\text{is}}_{} \underbrace{14.}_{}$$
$$x + y = 14 \quad \text{Translating}$$

$$\underbrace{\text{The original number}}_{10x + y} + 36 \text{ is } \underbrace{\text{the new number.}}_{} \quad \text{Rewording}$$
$$10x + y + 36 = 10y + x \quad \text{Translating}$$

This equation can be simplified.

$$9x - 9y = 36$$

We have a system of equations.

$$x + y = 14$$
$$9x - 9y = 36.$$

The solution is $x = 5$ and $y = 9$. The original number is 59.

TRY THIS Translate to a system of equations and solve.

5. The sum of the digits of a two-digit number is 5. If the digits are reversed, the new number is 27 more than the original number. Find the original number. 14

9–4	

Exercises

Translate to a system of equations and solve.

1. Marco has 150 coins, all nickels and dimes. He has 12 more dimes than nickels. How many nickels and how many dimes does he have? 69 nickels, 81 dimes

2. There are 37 students in an algebra class. There are 9 more girls than boys. How many girls and how many boys are in the class? 23 girls, 14 boys

3. Marge is twice as old as Consuelo. The sum of their ages seven years ago was 13. How old are they now? 18, 9

4. Andy is four times as old as Wendy. In twelve years Wendy's age will be half of Andy's. Find their ages now. 24, 6

5. A hot dog and a milk shake cost $2.10. Two hot dogs and three shakes cost $5.15. Find the cost of a hot dog and a shake. $1.15, $.95

6. Four oranges and five apples cost $2.00. Three oranges and four apples cost $1.56. Find the cost of an orange and the cost of an apple. 20¢, 24¢

7. Zelma is eighteen years older than her son. She was three times as old one year ago. How old is each? 28, 10

8. Tyrone is twice as old as his daughter. In six years Tyrone's age will be three times what his daughter's age was six years ago. How old is each at present? 48, 24

9. Frederique is two years older than her brother. She was twice as old twelve years ago. How old is each? 16, 14

10. The perimeter of a rectangle is 160 feet. One fourth the length is the same as twice the width. Find the dimensions of the rectangle. $71\frac{1}{9}$, $8\frac{8}{9}$

11. On a fishing trip, Rachael caught twenty four fish. She caught some rockfish averaging 2.5 lbs. and some bluefish averaging 8 lbs. The total weight of the fish was 137 lbs. How many of each kind of fish did she catch? 10 rock, 14 blue

12. The sum of the digits of a two-digit number is 9. If the digits are reversed the new number is 63 greater than the original number. Find the original number. 18

13. The sum of the digits of a two-digit number is 10. When the digits are reversed, the new number is 36 less than the original number. Find the original number. 73

Extension

14. In Lewis Carroll's "Through the Looking Glass" Tweedledum says to Tweedledee, "The sum of your weight and twice mine is 361 pounds." Then Tweedledee says to Tweedledum, "Contrariwise, the sum of your weight and twice mine is 362 pounds. Find the weight of Tweedledum and Tweedledee. 120, 121

15. During a publicity campaign, a cycle shop gave away 5000 miniature cycles and bumper stickers. The cycles cost 21¢ and the bumper stickers cost 14¢ each. The cycle shop spent $826 on the gifts. How many of each gift did they buy? 3200 bumper stickers, 1800 cycles

16. Fenton Rent-a-Car charges $22.85 plus 19¢ per mile for a certain car. Classic Auto Rents charges $21.95 plus 18¢ per mile for the same car. For what mileage is the cost the same? no solution

17. Several ancient Chinese books included problems that can be solved by translating to systems of equations. Arithmetical Rules in Nine Sections is a book of 246 problems compiled by a Chinese mathematician, Chang Tsang, who died in 152 B.C. One of the problems is: Suppose there are a number of rabbits and pheasants confined in a cage. In all there are 35 heads and 94 feet. How many rabbits and how many pheasants are there? Solve the problem. 12 rabbits, 23 pheasants

Challenge

18. Francine earned $288 on investments. She invested $1100 at one yearly rate and $1800 at a rate which was 1.5% higher. Find the two rates of interest. $1100x + 1800(x + 0.015) = 288$; 9%, 10.5%

19. In a two-digit number, the sum of the units' digit and the number is 43 more than five times the tens' digit. Find the number. $5x + 2y = 43$, 74 is the only possible solution.

20. The sum of the digits of a three-digit number is 9. If the digits are reversed, the number increases by 495. The sum of the tens' and hundreds' digit is half the units' digit. Find the number. 126

21. Together, a bat, ball, and glove cost $99.00. The bat costs $9.95 more than the ball, and the glove costs $65.45 more than the bat. How much does each cost? glove $79.95, bat $14.50, ball $4.55

9–5 Motion Problems

Many problems involve distance, time, and speed. These three quantities are related by the formula

distance = rate (or speed) × time.

We have considered some general steps for problem solving. The following are also helpful when solving motion problems.

1. Organize the information in a chart, keeping the formula $d = rt$ in mind.
2. Use drawings to show when distances are the same or when distances are added.

EXAMPLE 1

A train leaves Slaton traveling east at 35 kilometers per hour (km/h). An hour later another train leaves Slaton on a parallel track at 40 km/h. How far from Slaton will the trains meet? First make a drawing showing distances.

From the drawing we see that the distances are the same. Call the distance d. We don't know the times. Let t represent the time for the faster train. Then the time for the slower train will be $t + 1$. We can organize the information in a chart, keeping the formula $d = rt$ in mind.

	distance	rate	time
slow train	d	35	$t + 1$
fast train	d	40	t

For each row of the chart, we write an equation of the form $d = rt$.

$$d = 35(t + 1) \qquad d = 40t$$

Thus, we have a system of equations. We solve the system by the substitution method.

$$40t = 35(t + 1) \quad \text{Substituting } 40\,t \text{ for } d \text{ in the first equation}$$
$$40t = 35t + 35$$
$$5t = 35$$
$$t = 7$$

The problem asks us to find how far from Slaton the trains meet. Thus, we need to find d. By substituting 7 for t in the equation $d = 40t$, we have $d = 40(7) = 280$. The trains meet 280 km from Slaton. Note also that $280 = 35(7 + 1)$, so 280 checks in the problem.

TRY THIS Translate to a system of equations and solve.

1. A car leaves Hartford traveling north at 56 km/h. Another car leaves Hartford one hour later traveling north at 84 km/h. How far from Hartford will the second car overtake the first? (Hint: The cars travel the same distance.) 168 km

---

EXAMPLE 2

A motorboat took 3 hours to make a downstream trip with a current of 6 km/h. The return trip against the same current took 5 hours. Find the speed of the boat in still water.

Let r represent the speed of the boat in still water. Then, when traveling downstream, the speed of the boat is $r + 6$ (the current helps the boat along). When traveling upstream the speed of the boat is $r - 6$ (the current holds the boat back). We can organize the information in a chart, keeping the formula $d = rt$ in mind.

	distance	rate	time
downstream	d	$r + 6$	3
upstream	d	$r - 6$	5

From each row of the chart, we write an equation of the form $d = rt$.

$$d = (r + 6)3$$
$$d = (r - 6)5$$

Thus we have a system of equations.

We solve the system by the substitution method.

$$(r + 6)3 = (r - 6)5 \quad \text{Substituting } (r + 6)3 \text{ for } d$$
$$3r + 18 = 5r - 30$$
$$-2r = -48$$
$$r = 24$$

We check in the original problem. When $r = 24$, $r + 6 = 30$ and the distance is $30 \cdot 3$, or 90. When $r = 24$, $r - 6 = 18$ and the distance is $18 \cdot 5$, or 90. In both cases we get a distance of 90 km. Thus, the speed in still water is 24 km/h.

TRY THIS Translate to a system of equations and solve.

2. An airplane flew for 5 hours with a tail wind of 25 km/h. The return flight against the same wind took 6 hours. Find the speed of the airplane in still air. (Hint: The distance is the same both ways. The speeds are $r + 25$ and $r - 25$, where r is the speed in still air.) 275 km/h

---

EXAMPLE 3

Two cars leave town at the same time going in opposite directions. One of them travels 60 mi/h and the other 30 mi/h. In how many hours will they be 150 miles apart?

We first make a drawing.

From the wording of the problem and the drawing, we see that the distances are *not* the same. We also see that the distance of the slow car plus the distance of the fast car is 150. Both cars travel for the same amount of time, so we use t for both times. We organize the information in a chart.

	distance	rate	time
slow car	distance of slow car	30	t
fast car	distance of fast car	60	t

Using the chart, we translate this information.

$$30t + 60t = 150$$
$$90t = 150$$
$$t = \frac{5}{3}, \text{ or } 1\frac{2}{3} \text{ hours}$$

This checks in the original problems, so in $1\frac{2}{3}$ hours the cars will be 150 miles apart.

TRY THIS Translate to a system of equations and solve.

3. Two cars leave town at the same time in opposite directions. One travels 35 km/h and the other 40 km/h. In how many hours will they be 200 kilometers apart? $35t + 40t = 200, t = 2\frac{2}{3}$ h

4. Two cars leave town at the same time in the same direction. One travels 35 mi/h and the other 40 mi/h. In how many hours will they be 15 miles apart? $d = 35t, d + 15 = 40t, t = 3$ hr, $d = 105$ mi

---

9–5

Exercises

Translate to a system of equations and solve.

1. Two cars leave town at the same time going in opposite directions. One travels 55 mi/h and the other travels 48 mi/h. In how many hours will they be 206 miles apart? 2 hr

2. Two cars leave town at the same time going in opposite directions. One travels 44 mi/h and the other travels 55 mi/h. In how many hours will they be 297 miles apart? 3 hr

3. Two cars leave town at the same time going in the same direction. One travels 30 mi/h and the other travels 46 mi/h. In how many hours will they be 72 miles apart? 4.5 hr

4. Two cars leave town at the same time going in the same direction. One travels 32 mi/h and the other travels 47 mi/h. In how many hours will they be 69 miles apart? 4.6 hr

5. A train leaves a station and travels east at 72 km/h. Three hours later a second train leaves on a parallel track and travels east at 120 km/h. When will it overtake the first train? $7\frac{1}{2}$ hours after first train leaves

6. A private airplane leaves an airport and flies due south at 192 km/h. Two hours later a jet leaves the same airport and flies due south at 960 km/h. When will the jet overtake the plane? $2\frac{1}{2}$ hours after private plane leaves

7. A canoeist paddled for 4 hours with a 6-km/h current to reach a campsite. The return trip against the same current took 10 hours. Find the speed of the canoe in still water. 14 km/h

8. An airplane flew for 4 hours with a 20-km/h tail wind. The return flight against the same wind took 5 hours. Find the speed of the plane in still air. 180 km/h

9. It takes a passenger train 2 hours less time than it takes a freight train to make the trip from Central City to Clear Creek. The passenger train averages 96 km/h while the freight train averages 64 km/h. How far is it from Central City to Clear Creek? 384 km

10. It takes a small jet plane 4 hours less time than it takes a propeller-driven plane to travel from Glen Rock to Oakville. The jet plane averages 637 km/h while the propeller plane averages 273 km/h. How far is it from Glen Rock to Oakville? 1911 km

11. An airplane took 2 hours to fly 600 km against a head wind. The return trip with the wind took $1\frac{2}{3}$ hours. Find the speed of the plane in still air. 330 km/h

12. It took 3 hours to row a boat 18 km against the current. The return trip with the current took $1\frac{1}{2}$ hours. Find the speed of the rowboat in still water. 9 km/h

13. A motorcycle breaks down and the rider has to walk the rest of the way to work. The motorcycle was being driven at 45 mi/h and the rider walks at a speed of 6 mi/h. The distance from home to work is 25 miles and the total time for the trip was 2 hours. How far did the motorcycle go before it broke down? 15 mi

14. A student walks and jogs to college each day. The student averages 5 km/h walking and 9 km/h jogging. The distance from home to college is 8 km and the student makes the trip in 1 hour. How far does the student jog? $6\frac{3}{4}$ km

Extension

15. An airplane flew for 4.23 hours with a 25.5-km/h tail wind. The return flight against the same wind took 4.97 hours. Find the speed of the plane in still air. ≈317.03 km/h

16. An airplane took $2\frac{1}{2}$ hours to fly 625 miles with the wind. It took 4 hours and 10 minutes to make the return trip against the same wind. Find the wind speed and the speed of the plane in still air. 50 mi/h, 200 mi/h

17. To deliver a package, a messenger must travel at a speed of 60 miles per hour on land and then use a motorboat whose speed is 20 miles per hour in still water. While delivering the package, the messenger goes by land to a dock and then travels on a river against a current of 4 miles per hour. The messenger reaches the destination in 4.5 hours and then returns to the starting point in 3.5 hours. How far did the messenger travel by land and how far by water? 90 mi, 48 mi

18. Against a headwind, Gary computes his flight time for a trip of 2900 miles at 5 hours. The flight would take 4 hours and 50 minutes if the headwind were half as much. Find the headwind and the plane's air speed. 40 mi/h, 620 mi/h

19. A car travels from one town to another at a speed of 32 mph. If it had gone 4 mph faster, it could have made the trip in $\frac{1}{2}$ hour less time. How far apart are the towns? 144 mi

20. Two airplanes start at the same time and fly toward each other from points 1000 km apart at rates of 420 km/h and 330 km/h. When will they meet? 1 hr, 20 min

21. A truck and a car leave a service station at the same time and travel in the same direction. The truck travels at 55 mph and the car at 40 mph. They can maintain CB radio contact within a range of 10 miles. When will they lose contact? 40 min

Challenge

22. Charles Lindbergh flew the Spirit of St. Louis in 1927 from New York to Paris at an average speed of 107.4 miles per hour. Eleven years later, Howard Hughes flew the same route, averaged 217.1 miles per hour and took 16 hours, 57 minutes less time. Find the length of their route. ≈3603 miles

EXAMPLE 1

A student has some nickels and dimes. The value of the coins is $1.65. There are 12 more nickels than dimes. How many of each kind of coin are there?

Let d = the number of dimes and n = the number of nickels. We write an equation for the number of coins.

$$d + 12 = n$$

The value of the nickels, in cents, is $5n$ since each nickel is worth 5¢. The value of the dimes is $10d$. Since we have the values of the coins in cents, we must use 165 cents for the total value. We write an equation for the value of the coins.

$$10d + 5n = 165$$

Solve the system by substitution.

$$
\begin{aligned}
d + 12 &= n \\
10d + 5n &= 165 \\
10d + 5(d + 12) &= 165 \quad \text{Substituting } d + 12 \text{ for } n \\
10d + 5d + 60 &= 165 \\
15d &= 105 \\
d &= 7 \\
d + 12 &= n \quad \text{Choosing the easier equation} \\
7 + 12 &= n \quad \text{Substituting 7 for } d \\
19 &= n
\end{aligned}
$$

The solution of this system is $d = 7$ and $n = 19$. The student has 7 dimes and 19 nickels.

TRY THIS Translate to a system of equations and solve.

1. On a table are 20 coins, quarters and dimes. Their value is $3.05. How many of each are there? 7 quarters, 13 dimes

2. Calvin paid his $1.35 skate rental with dimes and nickels only. There were 19 coins altogether. How many of each coin were there? 8 dimes, 11 nickels

Certain other types of problems are very much like coin problems. Although they are not about coins, they are solved in the same way.

EXAMPLE 2

There were 411 people at a play. Admission was $1 for adults and $0.75 for children. The receipts were $395.75. How many adults and how many children attended?

Let a = the number of adults and c = the number of children. Since the total number of people is 411, we have this equation.

$$a + c = 411$$

The receipts from adults and from children equal the total receipts.

$$1.00a + 0.75c = 395.75$$

Solve the system of equations. Clear the second equation of decimals.

$$a + c = 411$$
$$100a + 75c = 39575$$

We multiply on both sides of the first equation by -100 and then add.

$$-100a - 100c = -41100 \quad \text{Multiplying by } -100$$
$$\underline{100a + 75c = 39575}$$
$$-25c = -1525 \quad \text{Adding}$$
$$c = \frac{-1525}{-25}$$
$$c = 61$$
$$a + c = 411 \quad \text{Choosing the easier equation}$$
$$a + 61 = 411 \quad \text{Substituting 61 for } c$$
$$a = 350$$

The solution of the system is $a = 350$ and $c = 61$. This checks, so 350 adults and 61 children attended.

TRY THIS Translate to a system of equations and solve.

3. There were 166 paid admissions to a game. The price was $2 for adults and $0.75 for children. The amount taken in was $293.25. How many adults and how many children attended? 135, 31

EXAMPLE 3

A chemist has one solution that is 80% acid and another that is 30% acid. How much of each solution is needed to make a 200 liter solution that is 62% acid?

The chemist uses x liters of the first solution and y liters of the second. Since the total is to be 200 liters, we have

$$x + y = 200.$$

The amount of acid is to be 62% of 200 liters, or 124 liters. The amounts of acid from the solutions are 80% of x and 30% of y. Thus,

$$0.8x + 0.3y = 124$$

We clear the decimals by multiplying on both sides by 10.

$$8x + 3y = 1240$$

We can then solve this system of equations.

$$x + y = 200$$
$$8x + 3y = 1240$$

We use the addition method, first multiplying on both sides of the first equation by -3.

$$
\begin{array}{rl}
-3x - 3y = -600 & \text{Multiplying by } -3 \\
\underline{8x + 3y = 1240} & \\
5x = 640 & \text{Adding} \\
x = 128 &
\end{array}
$$

We substitute 128 for x in $x + y = 200$.

$$128 + y = 200$$
$$y = 72$$

The solution is $x = 128$ and $y = 72$. The sum is 200. 80% of 128 plus 30% of 72 is $102.4 + 21.6$, or 124. The chemist must use 128 liters of the stronger acid and 72 liters of the weaker acid.

TRY THIS Translate to a system of equations and solve.

4. A grocer wishes to mix some candy worth 90¢ per kilogram and some worth $1.60 per kilogram to make 175 kg of a mixture worth $1.30 per kilogram. How much of each should be used? 75 kg of 90¢, 100 kg of $1.60

9–6

Exercises

Translate to a system of equations and solve.

1. A collection of dimes and quarters is worth $15.25. There are 103 coins in all. How many of each are there? 70 dimes, 33 quarters

2. A collection of quarters and nickels is worth $1.25. There are 13 coins in all. How many of each are there? 3 quarters, 10 nickels

3. A collection of nickels and dimes is worth $25. There are three times as many nickels as dimes. How many of each are there?   300 nickels, 100 dimes

4. A collection of nickels and dimes is worth $2.90. There are 19 more nickels than dimes. How many of each are there?   13 dimes, 32 nickels

5. There were 429 people at a play. Admission was $1 for adults and 75¢ for children. The receipts were $372.50. How many adults and how many children attended?   203 adults, 226 children

6. The attendance at a school concert was 578. Admission was $2 for adults and $1.50 for children. The receipts were $985. How many adults and how many children attended?   236 adults, 342 children

7. There were 200 tickets sold for a college basketball game. Tickets for students were $0.50 and for adults were $0.75. The total amount of money collected was $132.50. How many of each type of ticket were sold?   130 adults, 70 students

8. There were 203 tickets sold for a wrestling match. For activity cardholders the price was $1.25 and for non-cardholders the price was $2. The total amount of money collected was $310. How many of each type of ticket were sold?   128 cardholders, 75 non-cardholders

9. Solution A is 50% acid and solution B is 80% acid. How much of each should be used to make 100 grams of a solution that is 68% acid? (Hint: What quantity is 68% acid?)   40 g of A, 60 g of B

10. Solution A is 30% alcohol and solution B is 75% alcohol. How much of each should be used to make 100 liters of a solution that is 50% alcohol? $55\frac{5}{9}$ l of A, $44\frac{4}{9}$ l of B

11. Farmer Jones has 100 liters of milk that is 4.6% butterfat. How much skim milk (no butterfat) should be mixed with it to make milk that is 3.2% butterfat?   43.75 l

12. A tank contains 8000 liters of a solution that is 40% acid. How much water should be added to make a solution that is 30% acid?   ~2666.7 l

13. A solution containing 30% insecticide is to be mixed with a solution containing 50% insecticide to make 200 liters of a solution containing 42% insecticide. How much of each solution should be used?   80 L of 30%, 120 L of 50%

14. A solution containing 28% fungicide is to be mixed with a solution containing 40% fungicide to make 300 liters of a solution containing 36% fungicide. How much of each solution should be used?   100 L of 28%, 200 L of 40%

15. The "Nutshell" has 10 kg of mixed cashews and pecans worth $8.40 per kilogram. Cashews alone sell for $8 per kilogram and pecans sell for $9 per kilogram. How many kilograms of each are in the mixture?   6 kg of cashews, 4 kg of pecans

16. A coffee shop mixes Brazilian coffee worth $5 per kilogram with Turkish coffee worth $8 per kilogram. The mixture is to sell for $7 per kilogram. How much of each type of coffee should be used to make a mixture of 300 kg? 100 kg of Brazilian, 200 kg of Turkish

Extension

17. A basketball player averages 14 points per game. If the player scores 34 points in the next game, (s)he will be averaging 14.5 points per game. How many games has the player played? 39

18. On one page of his stamp collection, Bill Fritz has stamps currently valued at $4 each. On another page he has stamps currently valued at $8.50 each. There are 33 stamps in all with a total value of $213. How many stamps are on each page? 15 at $4, 18 at $8.50

19. Penny Booth invested $27,000, part of it at 12% and part at 13%. The total yield is $3385. How much was invested at each rate? 12,500 at 12%, 14,500 at 13%

20. Northern Maywood voted 60% to 40% in favor of a water project. Southern Maywood voted 90% to 10% against the project. The project passed, 55% to 45%. If 5900 people voted, how many were from Southern Maywood? 590

21. An employer has a daily payroll of $325 when employing some workers at $20 per day and others at $25 per day. When the number of $20 workers is increased by 50% and the number of $25 workers is decreased $\frac{1}{5}$ the new daily payroll is $400. Find how many were originally employed at each rate. 10 at $20, 5 at $25

22. A two-digit number is 6 times the sum of its digits. The tens digit is 1 more than the units digit. Find the number. 54

23. A mixture weighing 100 pounds contains 15% silver and 30% lead. How much silver and lead must be added to obtain an alloy containing 25% silver and 50% lead? 40 lb silver, 80 lb lead

Challenge

24. Bottle A containing 12 liters of 15% acid is combined with bottle B containing 3 liters of 25% acid. Bottle C is 26% acid. How much of each solution is needed to have 24 liters of a 20% acid solution? Need 16 liters of A + B and 8 liters of C, but there are only 15 liters of A + B, so it can't be done.

25. An automobile radiator contains 16 liters of antifreeze and water. This mixture is 30% antifreeze. How much of this mixture should be drained and replaced with pure antifreeze so that the mixture will be 50% antifreeze? 4$\frac{4}{7}$ liters

26. Find all possible combinations of quarters and dimes that will total $2.20. What is the fewest number of coins? Possible combinations of quarters and dimes: 8, 2; 6, 7; 4, 12; 2, 17; 0, 22; fewest is 10.

CONSUMER APPLICATION/Determining Earnings

As an employee, the pay you receive may be determined in various ways.

Fixed Salary

You are paid a certain salary per year. This salary is paid on a regular basis, perhaps weekly, monthly, or bi-weekly (every two weeks). Usually you do not receive additional pay for working extra hours.

For example, Rick is a computer programmer. He receives a yearly salary of $29,000.00. Every two weeks his earnings before deductions are:

$$\$29,000.00 \div 26 = \$1115.38$$

Hourly Wages

You are paid a certain amount per hour. This is your regular hourly rate. Hours that you work beyond a certain number (usually 40) are paid at a higher, overtime rate.

Jenny is an electrician. She is paid $12.50 per hour regular time and $18.75 per hour overtime. She worked 49 hours this week (40 hours regular time and 9 hours overtime). Her week's pay before deductions is:

$$(40 \times \$12.50) + (9 \times \$18.75) = \$668.75$$

Commissions

You are paid according to how much you sell. Usually it is a percent of your sales.

Martha is a sales representative. She sold $50,000.00 in laboratory equipment one month. She is paid 5% commission on her monthly sales. Her earnings this month before deductions are:

$$0.05 \times \$50,000.00 = \$2500.00$$

Salary and Commissions

You are paid a base salary plus commissions on sales.

Ed is a salesperson. He makes a base salary of $900.00 per month plus 6% commission on sales over $1,000.00. He sold $4500.00 of his product one month. His earnings this month before deductions are:

$$\$900.00 + .06(\$4500.00 - \$1000.00) = \$1110.00$$

Typical deductions from your pay are Social Security Tax (FICA), Federal Income Tax, State Income Tax, Pension Fund, and Insurance. These deductions are subtracted from your gross earnings to determine your net, or take home pay.

In many companies, these payroll computations are performed by a computer. The required data is accumulated in the computer and then processed to produce the paychecks and earnings statements each pay period.

Joanne Thomas works in a restaurant. She gets an earnings statement with her paycheck. It shows the gross pay, deductions, and net pay.

EARNINGS STATEMENT			
Joanne Thomas Soc. Sec. No. 999–99–9999 Pay Period Ending 10-21-86			
Hours	Amount	Deductions	
40.0 Regular 7.0 Overtime	$160.00 42.00	Fed. Withholding Tax FICA United Fund Credit Union	$48.21 16.02 1.00 25.00
Gross Pay	$202.00		
Net Pay	$111.77		

$$\begin{aligned} \text{Gross pay} &= \text{regular pay} + \text{overtime pay} \\ &= \$160.00 + \$42.00 \\ &= \$202.00 \end{aligned}$$

$$\begin{aligned} \text{Net pay} &= \text{Gross pay} - \text{deductions} \\ &= \$202.00 - \$90.23 \\ &= \$111.77 \end{aligned}$$

Exercises

Find the gross pay (that is, earnings before deductions) for each of the following.

1. Shirley earns $19,500 per year. She is paid once a month. Find her gross pay on her monthly check. $1625

2. Jason receives a yearly salary of $20,400. He is paid bi-weekly. Find his gross pay every two weeks. $784.62

3. Nick makes $6.35 per hour. One week he worked 36 hours. Find his gross pay. $228.60

4. Olga makes $7.20 per hour regular time and $10.80 per hour overtime. One week she worked 40 hours regular time and 5 hours overtime. Find her gross pay. $342.00

5. Larry makes a commission of 5% on his monthly sales. One month he made sales of $62,000. Find his gross pay. $3100

6. Lilian makes a base salary of $800 per month plus 4% commission on sales. One month she had sales of $3800. Find her gross pay. $952

Find the net pay for each of the following.

7.

Hours	Amount	Deductions	
40.0 Regular at $8.20/h	$328.00	Fed. Withholding Tax	$77.58
2.0 Overtime at $12.30/h	24.60	FICA	24.96
		State Withholding Tax	13.19
Gross Pay	$352.60		
Net Pay	$236.87		

8.

Hours	Amount	Deductions	
36.0 Regular at $5.40/h	$194.40	Fed. Withholding Tax	$40.10
3.5 Overtime at $8.10/h	28.35	FICA	15.37
		Pension Fund	23.60
		Insurance	8.29
Gross Pay	$222.75		
Net Pay	$135.39		

9.

Hours	Amount	Deductions	
40.0 Regular at $10.50/h	$420.00	Fed. Withholding Tax	$104.48
6.5 Overtime at $15.75/h	102.38	FICA	37.09
		State Withholding Tax	15.67
		Health Insurance	5.92
Gross Pay	$522.38		
Net Pay	$359.22		

10. A secretary is paid a monthly salary of $1100.00. Deductions are: FICA, $74.80; Federal Income Tax, $180.33; State Tax, $22.00; and Insurance, $23.00. $799.87

11. The regular hourly rate of a store clerk is $3.80. The overtime rate is $5.70. The clerk worked 45 hours, 40 hours regular time and 5 hours overtime. Deductions totaled $44.75. $135.75

12. A real estate salesperson is paid a commission of 4% on the selling price of homes. The salesperson sold two homes, one at $62,000.00 and one at $73,500.00. Deductions totaled $2,120.50. $3299.50

13. A salesperson earns $850.00 in salary per month plus 7% commission on sales over $500.00. Sales amounted to $3,300.00 one month. Deductions totaled $301.00. $745.00

CHAPTER 9   Review

Review the material in the chapter. Then see how you have done by trying these review exercises. If you miss an exercise, restudy the indicated lesson.

9–1   Determine whether the given ordered pair is a solution of the system of equations.

1. $(6, -1)$; $x - y = 3$ No
$2x + 5y = 6$

2. $(2, -3)$; $2x + y = 1$ Yes
$x - y = 5$

3. $(-2, 1)$; $x + 3y = 1$ Yes
$2x - y = -5$

4. $(-4, -1)$; $x - y = 3$ No
$x + y = -5$

9–1   Use graph paper. Solve each system graphically.

5. $x + y = 4$
$x - y = 8$

6. $x + 3y = 12$
$2x - 4y = 4$

5. $(6, -2)$ 6. $(6, 2)$

7. $2x + y = 1$
$x = 2y + 8$

8. $3x - 2y = -4$
$2y - 3x = -2$

7. $(2, -3)$ 8. No solution; lines are parallel

9–2   Solve by the substitution method.

9. $y = 5 - x$ $(0, 5)$
$3x - 4y = -20$

10. $x + 2y = 6$ $(-2, 4)$
$2x + 3y = 8$

11. $3x + y = 1$ $(1, -2)$
$x = 2y + 5$

12. $x + y = 6$ $(-3, 9)$
$y = 3 - 2x$

13. $s + t = 5$ $(1, 4)$
$s = 13 - 3t$

14. $x - y = 4$ $(3, -1)$
$y = 2 - x$

9–2   Translate to a system of equations and solve.

15. The sum of two numbers is 8. Their difference is 12. Find the numbers. $10, -2$

9–3   Solve by the addition method.

16. $x + y = 4$ $(3, 1)$
$2x - y = 5$

17. $x + 2y = 9$ $(1, 4)$
$3x - 2y = -5$

18. $x - y = 8$ $(5, -3)$
$2x + y = 7$

19. $2x + 3y = -5$ **20.** $2x + 3y = 8$ (-2, 4) **21.** $5x - 2y = 2$ (-2, -5)
$3x - y = -13$ (-4, 1) $5x + 2y = -2$ $3x - 7y = 36$

9–3   Solve. Multiply one equation by -1 first.

22. $-x - y = -5$ (3, 2)**23.** $6x + 2y = 4$ (2, -4)
$2x - y = 4$ $10x + 7y = -8$

9–3   Translate to an equation and solve.

24. The sum of two numbers is 27. One half of the first number plus one third of the second number is 11. Find the numbers. 12, 15

9–4   Translate to systems of equations and solve.

25. The sum of two numbers is 27. One number is 3 more than the other. Find the numbers. 12 and 15

26. The perimeter of a rectangle is 76 *cm*. The length is 17 *cm* more than the width. Find the length and width. Length $27\frac{1}{2}$ cm, width $10\frac{1}{2}$ cm

9–5

27. An airplane flew for 4 hours with a 5 *km/h* tail wind. The return flight against the same wind took 5 hours. Find the speed of the airplane in still air. 135 km/h

28. There were 508 people at an organ recital. Orchestra seats cost $5.00 per person with balcony seats costing $3.00. The total receipts were $2118. Find the number of orchestra and the number of balcony seats sold. 297 orchestra seats, 211 balcony seats

9–6

29. Solution A is 30% alcohol and solution B is 60% alcohol. How much of each is needed to make 80 liters of a solution that is 45% alcohol? 40L of each

---

CHAPTER 9   Test

Use graph paper. Solve each system graphically.

1. $x - y = 3$ (4, 1)   **2.** $x + 2y = 6$ (10, -2)
$x - y = 5$ $2x - 3y = 26$

Solve by the substitution method.

3. $y = 6 - x$ (8, -2) 4. $x + 2y = 5$ (-1, 3)
   $2x - 3y = 22$ $x + y = 2$

Solve by the addition method.

5. $x - y = 6$ (1, -5) 6. $3x - 4y = 7$ 7. $4x + 5y = 5$ (0, 1) 8. $2x + 3y = 13$ (5, 1)
   $3x + y = -2$ $x + 4y = 5$ $\left(3, \frac{1}{2}\right)$ $6x + 7y = 7$ $3x - 5y = 10$

Translate to a system of equations and solve.

9. A motorboat traveled for 2 hours with an 8 *km/h* current. The
   return trip agains the same current took 3 hours. Find the
   speed of the motorboat in still water. 40 *km/h*

10. Solution A is 25% acid and solution B is 40% acid. How much
    of each is needed to make 60 liters of a solution that is 30% acid? 40L of A, 20L of B

Challenge

11. For a two-digit number, the sum of the unit's digit and the
    ten's digit is 6. When the digits are reversed, the new number
    is 18 more than the original number. Find the original number. 24

Ready for Inequalities?

2–1 Find the absolute value of each integer.

1. 9 9   2. -3 3   3. 0 0   4. -8 8

2–2 Graph each number on a number line.

5. $\frac{5}{3}$ 6. $\frac{7}{9}$

2–2 Use the proper symbol >, <, or =.

7. $\frac{5}{2}$ $\frac{8}{2}$ <   8. $\frac{4}{9}$ $\frac{5}{11}$ <

3–1 Solve and check.

9. $x + 8 = -2$ -10   10. $5 - y = 1$ 4   11. $w - 3 = -4$ -1   12. $4 + x = -5$ -9

3–2

13. $4x = -12$ -3   14. $2x = 7$ $\frac{7}{2}$ 15. $\frac{1}{2}y = 10$ 20   16. $-\frac{3}{4}x = \frac{1}{8}$ $-\frac{1}{6}$

10

Inequalities

10–1 Using the Addition Principle

In Chapter Two we learned the meaning of the symbols $<$ (is less than) and $>$ (is greater than). We now include these symbols.

$\leq$ is less than or equal to
$\geq$ is greater than or equal to

Sentences containing $<$, $>$, $\leq$, or $\geq$ are called inequalities.

Solutions of Inequalities

A solution of an inequality is any number that makes it true.

EXAMPLE 1
Determine whether each number is a solution of $x > 5$.

    5   5 is a solution because $5 \geq 5$ is true.
   12   12 is a solution because $12 \geq 5$ is true.
   4   4 is not a solution because $4 \geq 5$ is not true.
 -7 -7 is not a solution because $-7 \geq 5$ is not true.

TRY THIS Determine whether the given number is a solution of the inequality.

1. $x < 3$ **a.** 2 Yes **b.** 0 Yes **c.** -5 Yes **d.** 15 No **e.** 3 No
2. $x \geq 6$ **a.** 6 Yes **b.** 0 No **c.** -4 No **d.** 25 Yes **e.** -6 No

The Addition Principle

Consider the true inequality

   $3 < 7.$

If we add 2 to both numbers, we get another true inequality, $5 < 9$.

> **The Addition Principle for Inequalities**
>
> If any number is added on both sides of a true inequality, we get another true inequality.

The addition principle can be applied when solving inequalities, just as the addition principle is applied when solving equations.

EXAMPLE 2

Solve.

$$x + 2 > 4$$
$$x + 2 + (-2) > 4 + (-2) \quad \text{Using the addition principle}$$
$$x > 2$$

Any number greater than 2 makes the last sentence true and is a solution of that sentence. Any such number is also a solution of the original sentence.

We could not possibly check all of the solutions by substituting them in the original inequality. There are too many. However, we do not need to check. Let us see why. Consider the first and last inequalities in Example 2.

$$x + 2 > 4 \quad x > 2$$

Any number that makes the first one true must make the second one true. We know this by the addition principle. Will any number that makes the (second) one true also be a solution of the first one?

$$x > 2$$
$$x + 2 > 2 + 2 \quad \text{Using the addition principle}$$
$$x + 2 > 4$$

Now we know that any number that makes $x > 2$ true also makes $x + 2 > 4$ true. Therefore the sentences $x > 2$ and $x + 2 > 4$ have the same solutions. Whenever we use the addition principle with inequalities, the first and second sentences will have the same solutions.

TRY THIS Solve using the addition principle.

3. $x + 3 > 5$ 4. $x - 5 < 8$ 5. $x - 2 > 7$ 6. $x + 1 < 3$

       $x > 2$ $x < 13$ $x > 9$ $x < 2$

EXAMPLE 3

Solve.

$$3x + 1 < 2x - 3$$
$$3x + 1 - 1 < 2x - 3 - 1 \quad \text{Adding} -1$$
$$3x < 2x - 4 \quad \text{Simplifying}$$
$$3x - 2x < 2x - 4 - 2x \quad \text{Adding} -2x$$
$$x < -4 \quad \text{Simplifying}$$

Any number less than -4 is a solution.

EXAMPLE 4

Solve.

$$x + \frac{1}{3} \geq \frac{3}{4}.$$

$$x + \frac{1}{3} - \frac{1}{3} \geq \frac{3}{4} - \frac{1}{3} \quad \text{Adding } -\frac{1}{3}$$

$$x \geq \frac{3}{4} - \frac{1}{3}$$

$$x \geq \frac{9}{12} - \frac{4}{12} \quad \text{Finding a common denominator}$$

$$x \geq \frac{5}{12}$$

Any number greater than or equal to $\frac{5}{12}$ is a solution.

7. $x < -3$
8. $y \leq -3$
9. $y < -21$
10. $y > \frac{9}{8}$

TRY THIS Solve using the addition principle.

7. $5x + 1 < 4x - 2$ 8. $5y + 2 \leq -1 + 4y$ 9. $y + 16 < -5$ 10. $y - \frac{1}{2} > \frac{5}{8}$

10-1

Exercises

Determine whether the given number is a solution of the inequality.

1. $x > 4$ **a.**   4 No **b.**   0 No **c.** -4 No **d.**   6 Yes

2. $y < 5$ **a.**   0 Yes **b.**   5 No **c.** -1 Yes **d.** -5 Yes

3. $x \geq 6$ **a.** -6 No **b.**   0 No **c.**   6 Yes **d.**   8 Yes

4. $x \leq 10$ **a.**   4 Yes **b.** -10 Yes **c.**   0 Yes **d.**   11 No

5. $x < -8$ **a.**   0 No **b.** -8 No **c.** -9 Yes **d.** -7 No

6. $x \geq 0$ **a.**   2 Yes **b.** -3 No **c.**   0 Yes **d.**   3 Yes

7. $y \geq -5$ **a.**   0 Yes **b.** -4 Yes **c.** -5 Yes **d.** -6 No

8. $y \leq -\frac{1}{2}$ **a.** -1 Yes **b.** $-\frac{2}{3}$ Yes **c.**   0 No **d.** -0.5 Yes

Solve using the addition principle.

9. $x + 7 > 2$ $x > -5$ 10. $x + 6 > 3$ $x > -3$

11. $y + 5 > 8$ $y > 3$ 12. $y + 7 > 9$ $y > 2$

13. $x + 8 \leq -10$ $x \leq -18$ 14. $x + 9 \leq -12$ $x \leq -21$

15. $a + 12 < 6$ $a < -6$ 16. $a + 20 < 8$ $a < -12$

17. $x - 7 \leq 9$ $x \leq 16$ **18.** $x - 3 \leq 14$ $x \leq 17$

19. $x - 6 > 2$ $x > 8$ **20.** $x - 9 > 4$ $x > 13$

21. $y - 7 > -12$ $y > -5$ **22.** $y - 10 > -16$ $y > -6$

23. $2x + 3 > x + 5$ $x > 2$ **24.** $2x + 4 > x + 7$ $x > 3$

25. $3x + 9 \leq 2x + 6$ $x \leq -3$ **26.** $3x + 10 \leq 2x + 8$ $x \leq -2$

27. $3x - 6 \geq 2x + 7$ $x \geq 13$ **28.** $3x - 9 \geq 2x + 11$ $x \geq 20$

29. $5x - 6 < 4x - 2$ $x < 4$ **30.** $6x - 8 < 5x - 9$ $x < -1$

31. $3y + 4 \geq 2y - 7$ $y \geq -11$ **32.** $4y + 5 \leq 3y - 8$ $y \leq -13$

33. $7 + c > 7$ $c > 0$ **34.** $-9 + c > 9$ $c > 18$

35. $y + \frac{1}{4} \leq \frac{1}{2}$ $y \leq \frac{1}{4}$ **36.** $y + \frac{1}{3} \leq \frac{5}{6}$ $y \leq \frac{1}{2}$

37. $x - \frac{1}{3} > \frac{1}{4}$ $x > \frac{7}{12}$ **38.** $x - \frac{1}{8} > \frac{1}{2}$ $x > \frac{5}{8}$

39. $-14x + 21 > 21 - 15x$ $x > 0$ **40.** $-10x + 15 > 18 - 11x$ $x > 3$

Extension

Solve.

41. $3(r + 2) < 2r + 4$ $r < -2$ **42.** $4(r + 5) \geq 3r + 7$ $r \geq -13$

43. $0.8x + 5 \geq 6 - 0.2x$ $x \geq 1$ **44.** $0.7x + 6 \leq 7 - 0.3x$ $x \leq 1$

45. $2x + 2.4 > x - 9.4$ $x > -11.8$ **46.** $5x + 2.5 > 4x - 1.5$ $x > -4$

47. $12x + 1.2 \leq 11x$ $x \leq -1.2$ **48.** $x + 0.8 \leq 7.8 - 6$ $x \leq 1$

Challenge

Determine whether the following statements are true or false.

49. $x + c < y + d$ when $x < y$ and $c < d$. True

50. $x - c > y - d$ when $x > y$ and $c > d$. False

51. If x is an integer, write a statement equivalent to $x > 5$ using $\geq$. $x \geq 6$

52. If y is an integer, write a statement equivalent to $y < 5$ using $\leq$. $y \leq 4$

53. Does the transitive property hold for $>$? Does it hold for $\leq$? Yes, if $a > b$ and $b > c$, $a > c$;
Yes if $a \leq b$ and $b \leq c$, $a \leq c$

54. Other inequality symbols include $\not>$, which means "is not greater than", $\not<$, "is not less than", and $\neq$, "is not equal to." Write statements equivalent to each of the following using $>$, $<$, $\geq$, $\leq$, or $=$.

   a. $x \not> 5$ **b.** $x \not< -3$ **c.** $x \neq -\frac{3}{2}$ a. $x \leq 5$ b. $x \geq -3$ c. $x < \frac{-3}{2}$ or $x > \frac{-3}{2}$

   d. $x \not< y$ **e.** $x \not> -y$ **f.** $-x \neq y$ d. $x \geq y$ e. $x \leq -y$ f. $-x > y$ or $-x < y$

Consider the true inequality

$$3 < 7.$$

If we multiply both numbers by 2, we get another true inequality.

$$6 < 14$$

If we multiply both numbers by -3, we get a false inequality.

$$-9 < -21$$

However, if we reverse the inequality symbol, we get a true inequality.

$$-9 > -21$$

The Multiplication Principle

The Multiplication Principle for Inequalities
If we multiply on both sides of a true inequality by a positive number, we get another true inequality.
If we multiply on both sides by a negative number and reverse the inequality symbol, we get another true inequality.

EXAMPLE 1
Solve.

$$4x < 28$$
$$\frac{1}{4} \cdot (4x) < \frac{1}{4} \cdot 28 \quad \text{Multiplying on both sides by } \frac{1}{4}$$
$$x < 7$$

Any number less than 7 is a solution.

TRY THIS Solve using the multiplication principle.
1. $8x < 64$ $x < 8$ **2.** $5y \geq 160$ $y > 32$ **3.** $2t < 56$ $t < 28$ **4.** $9s > 81$ $s > 9$

EXAMPLE 2

Solve.

$$-2y < 18$$

$$-\frac{1}{2}(-2y) > -\frac{1}{2} \cdot 18 \quad \text{Multiplying on both sides by } -\frac{1}{2} \text{ and reversing the inequality sign}$$

$$y > -9$$

Any number greater than -9 is a solution.

TRY THIS Solve using the multiplication principle.

5. $-4x \geq 24$ 6. $-5y < 13$ 7. $-t < -5$ 8. $-n > 2$

5. $x \leq -6$
6. $y > -\frac{13}{5}$
7. $t > 5$
8. $n < -2$

EXAMPLE 3

Solve.

$$-3x \geq \frac{5}{6}$$

$$-\frac{1}{3}(-3x) \leq -\frac{1}{3} \cdot \frac{5}{6} \quad \text{Multiplying on both sides by } -\frac{1}{3} \text{ and reversing the inequality sign}$$

$$x \leq -\frac{5}{18}$$

Any number less than or equal to $-\frac{5}{18}$ is a solution.

TRY THIS Solve using the multiplication principle.

9. $-y \geq \frac{1}{2}$ 10. $-3x < \frac{1}{6}$ 11. $-2x \leq \frac{5}{8}$ 12. $-4y \geq -\frac{3}{7}$

9. $y \leq -\frac{1}{2}$
10. $x > -\frac{1}{18}$
11. $x \geq -\frac{5}{16}$
12. $y \leq \frac{3}{28}$

10–2

Exercises

Solve using the multiplication principle.

1. $5x < 35$ $x < 7$
2. $8x \geq 32$ $x \geq 4$
3. $9y \leq 81$ $y \leq 9$
4. $10x > 240$ $x > 24$
5. $6y > 72$ $y > 12$
6. $9x \leq 63$ $x \leq 7$
7. $7x < 13$ $x < \frac{13}{7}$
8. $8y < 17$ $y < \frac{17}{8}$
9. $4y \geq 15$ $y \geq \frac{15}{4}$
10. $3y \geq 19$ $y \geq \frac{19}{3}$
11. $6y \leq 3$ $y \leq \frac{1}{2}$
12. $14x \leq 4$ $x \leq \frac{2}{7}$
13. $7y \geq -21$ $y \geq -3$
14. $6x \geq -18$ $x \geq -3$
15. $12x < -36$ $x < -3$

16. $16y < -64$ $y < -4$ **17.** $5y \geq -2$ $y \geq -\frac{2}{5}$ **18.** $7x \geq -4$ $x \geq -\frac{4}{7}$

19. $-2x \leq 12$ $x \geq -6$ **20.** $-3y \leq 15$ $y \geq -5$ **21.** $-4y \leq 16$ $y \geq -4$

22. $-7y \leq 21$ $y \geq -3$ **23.** $-6y > 360$ $y < -60$ **24.** $-9x > 540$ $x < -60$

25. $-12x < -24$ $x > 2$ **26.** $-14y < -70$ $y > 5$ **27.** $-18y \geq -36$ $y \leq 2$

28. $-20x \geq -400$ $x \leq 20$ **29.** $-2x < -17$ $x > \frac{17}{2}$ **30.** $-5y < -23$ $y > \frac{23}{5}$

31. $-8y \geq -31$ $y \leq \frac{31}{8}$ **32.** $-7x \geq -43$ $x \leq \frac{43}{7}$ **33.** $-3y < \frac{1}{7}$ $y > -\frac{1}{21}$

34. $-2x < \frac{1}{9}$ $x > -\frac{1}{18}$ **35.** $-5x \geq -\frac{5}{7}$ $x \leq \frac{1}{7}$ **36.** $-6y \geq -\frac{6}{11}$ $y \leq \frac{1}{11}$

Extension

Solve using the multiplication principle.

37. $-7x \geq -6.3$ $x \leq 0.9$ **38.** $-\frac{5}{6}y \leq -\frac{3}{4}$ $y \geq \frac{9}{10}$ **39.** $-8x < 40.5$ $x > 5.0625$

40. $-\frac{3}{4}x \geq -\frac{1}{8}$ $x \leq \frac{1}{6}$ **.41.** $0.13y \geq 91$ $y \geq 700$ **42.** $-0.89x \geq 0.00178$ $x \leq 0.002$

43. $-1.34q < -241.2$ **44.** $\frac{1}{7}x < -142.857$ **45.** $\frac{-45x}{0.4} \geq 1$ $x \leq \frac{-1}{112.5}$ 43. $q > 180$ 44. $x < 999.999$

Challenge

46. Solve $3x > 4x$. $x < 0$

Determine whether the following statements are true or false.

47. $x^2 > y^2$ when $x > y$.   False. $-2 > -3$ but $4 < 9$

48. $\frac{x}{z} < \frac{y}{z}$ when $x < y$ and $z \neq 0$.   True

---

DISCOVERY/Thomas Harriot

One of the important mathematicians in the seventeenth century was the Englishman Thomas Harriot. Like other mathematicians of his time he was not interested only in math. He had been sent by Sir Walter Raleigh as a surveyor on an expedition to the New World in 1585 and was the first well-known mathematician to set foot in North America. On his return he published a book about his travels.

Harriot was among the first to use some of the symbols of algebra we use today. In a book published in 1631, ten years after his death, he used the inequality symbols $<$ and $>$ for the first time. He wrote the cube of a number A as AAA—a great improvement over the Latin phrase A *cubus*. In other writing he found methods of factoring higher degree polynomials and of determining the areas of spherical triangles.

The invention and standardization of the symbols we use in algebra today were important steps in the history of mathematics. If you were to invent symbols of *greater than* and *less than*, what choices would you make?

10–3 Using the Principles Together

We use the addition and multiplication principles together in solving inequalities in much the same way as for equations. We usually use the addition principle first.

EXAMPLES

1. Solve.

$$6 - 5y > 7$$
$$-5y > 1 \quad \text{Adding } -6 \text{ on both sides}$$
$$-\frac{1}{5} \cdot (-5y) < -\frac{1}{5} \cdot 1 \quad \text{Multiplying on both sides by } -\frac{1}{5} \text{ and}$$
$$\text{reversing the inequality sign}$$
$$y < -\frac{1}{5} \quad \text{Simplifying}$$

2. Solve.

$$15x + 4 \le 4x + 3$$
$$15x \le 4x - 1 \quad \text{Adding } -4 \text{ on both sides}$$
$$11x \le -1 \quad \text{Adding } -4x \text{ on both sides}$$
$$x \le -\frac{1}{11} \quad \text{Multiplying on both sides by } \frac{1}{11}$$

TRY THIS Solve using both principles.

1. $7 - 4x < 8$ 2. $13x + 5 \le 12x + 4$ 3. $5x - 7 \ge 14$ 4. $4x - 4 > 8 + 2x$

1. $x > -\frac{1}{4}$
2. $x \le -1$
3. $x \ge \frac{21}{5}$
4. $x > 6$

EXAMPLE 3
Solve.

$$17 - 5y < 8y - 5$$
$$-5y < 8y - 22 \quad \text{Adding } -17 \text{ on both sides}$$
$$-13y < -22 \quad \text{Adding } -8y \text{ on both sides}$$
$$-\frac{1}{13} \cdot (-13y) > -\frac{1}{13} \cdot (-22) \quad \text{Multiplying on both sides by } -\frac{1}{13} \text{ and}$$
$$\text{reversing the inequality sign}$$
$$y > \frac{22}{13} \quad \text{Simplifying}$$

TRY THIS Solve using both principles.

5. $24 - 7y < 11y - 14$ 6. $5 - y > 3y + 2$

7. $18 - 6x \ge 9x - 6$ 8. $4 - 3x \le x + 9$

5. $y > \frac{19}{9}$
6. $y < \frac{3}{4}$
7. $x \le \frac{8}{5}$
8. $x \ge \frac{-5}{4}$

Exercises

Solve using both principles.

1. $4 + 3x < 28$ $x < 8$
2. $5 + 4y < 37$ $y < 8$
3. $6 + 5y \geq 36$ $y \geq 6$
4. $7 + 8x \geq 71$ $x \geq 8$
5. $3x - 5 \leq 13$ $x \leq 6$
6. $5y - 9 \leq 21$ $y \leq 6$
7. $10y - 9 > 31$ $y > 4$
8. $12y - 6 > 42$ $y > 4$
9. $13x - 7 < -46$ $x < -3$
10. $8y - 4 < -52$ $y < -6$
11. $5x + 3 \geq -7$ $x \geq -2$
12. $7y + 4 \geq -10$ $y \geq -2$
13. $4 - 3y > 13$ $y < -3$
14. $6 - 8x > 22$ $x < -2$
15. $3 - 9x < 30$ $x > -3$
16. $5 - 7y < 40$ $y > -5$
17. $3 - 6y > 23$ $y < -\frac{10}{3}$
18. $8 - 2y > 14$ $y < -3$
19. $4x + 2 - 3x \leq 9$ $x \leq 7$
20. $15x + 3 - 14x \leq 7$ $x \leq 4$
21. $8x + 7 - 7x > -3$ $x > -10$
22. $9x + 8 - 8x > -5$ $x > -13$
23. $6 - 4y > 4 - 3y$ $y < 2$
24. $7 - 8y > 5 - 7y$ $y < 2$
25. $5 - 9y \leq 2 - 8y$ $y \geq 3$
26. $6 - 13y \leq 4 - 12y$ $y \geq 2$
27. $19 - 7y - 3y < 39$ $y > -2$
28. $18 - 6y - 9y < 63$ $y > -3$
29. $21 - 8y < 6y + 49$ $y > -2$
30. $33 - 12x < 4x + 97$ $x > -4$
31. $14 - 5y - 2y \geq -19$ $y \leq \frac{33}{7}$
32. $17 - 6y - 7y \leq -13$ $y \geq \frac{30}{13}$
33. $27 - 11x > 14x - 18$ $x < \frac{9}{5}$
34. $42 - 13y > 15y - 19$ $y < \frac{61}{28}$

Extension

Solve.

35. $5(12 - 3t) \geq 15(t + 4)$ $t \leq 0$
36. $6(z - 5) < 5(7 - 2z)$ $z < \frac{65}{16}$
37. $4(0.5 - y) + y > 4y - 0.2$ $y < \frac{2.2}{7}$
38. $3 + 3(0.6 + y) > 2y + 6.6$ $y > 1.8$
39. $\frac{x}{3} - 2 \leq 1$
40. $\frac{2}{3} - \frac{x}{5} < \frac{4}{15}$
41. $\frac{y}{5} + 1 \leq \frac{2}{5}$
42. $\frac{3x}{5} \geq -15$
39. $x \leq 9$
40. $x > 2$
43. $\frac{-x}{4} - \frac{3x}{8} + 2 > 3 - x$ $x > \frac{8}{3}$
44. $11 - x > 5 + \frac{2x}{5}$ $x < \frac{30}{7}$
41. $y \leq -3$
42. $x \geq -25$

Challenge

Solve for x.

45. $-(x + 5) \geq 4a - 5$ $x \leq -4a$
46. $\frac{1}{2}(2x + 2b) > \frac{1}{3}(21 + 3b)$ $x > 7$
47. $-6(x + 3) \leq -9(y + 2)$ $x \geq \frac{3y}{2}$
48. $y < ax + b$ $x > \frac{y - b}{a}$
49. If $x \geq y$ and $-x \geq -y$, what can we conclude about x and y?

$x \geq y$ and $x \leq y$, so $x = y$.

Solving Problems with Inequalities

We can solve certain problems by translating to inequalities.

EXAMPLE 1

Your goal in the school seed sale is to sell more than 50 packages. Yesterday you sold 22, today 18. How many must you sell by the deadline to make your goal?

$$22 + 18 + x > 50 \quad \text{Translating}$$
$$40 + x > 50 \quad \text{Collecting like terms}$$
$$x > 10 \quad \text{Using the addition principle}$$

Thus, by selling more than 10 additional packages you will reach or exceed your goal.

TRY THIS

1. In an algebra course you must get a total score of at least 360 points on four tests for an A. You get 85, 89, and 92 on the first three tests. What score on the last test will give you an A? 94

2. An airline gives each passenger a 105-pound weight limit for baggage. Gilles has suitcases weighing 43 pounds and 28 pounds. How much more weight can he take on his flight? $w \le 34$

EXAMPLE 2

The sum of three consecutive integers is less than 30. What are the three greatest possible integers?

$$x + (x + 1) + (x + 2) < 30 \quad \text{Translating}$$
$$3x + 3 < 30 \quad \text{Collecting like terms}$$
$$3x < 27 \quad \text{Using the addition principle}$$
$$x < 9 \quad \text{Using the multiplication principle}$$

Thus, the greatest value for x is 8, and the three numbers are 8, 9, and 10.

TRY THIS

3. The sum of two consecutive integers is less than 35. What is the greatest possible pair? 16,17

Exercises

Solve these by translating them into inequalities.

1. Your quiz grades are 73, 75, 89, and 91. What is the lowest grade you can obtain on the last quiz and still achieve an average of at least 85? 97

2. The sum of three consecutive odd integers is less than 100. What are the greatest possible values of these integers? 31, 33, 35

3. The sum of two consecutive odd integers is less than or equal to 20. What is the greatest possible pair? 9, 11

4. Find the greatest possible pair of integers such that one integer is twice the other and their sum is less than 30. 9, 18

5. The sum of two integers is greater than 12. One integer is ten less than twice the other. What are the least values of the integers? 8, 6

6. Find all sets of four consecutive even whole numbers whose sum is less than 35. 0, 2, 4, 6; 2, 4, 6, 8; 4, 6, 8, 10

7. Find all numbers such that the sum of the number and 15 is less than four times the number. $n < 5$

8. Find the length of the base of a triangle when one side is 2 cm shorter than the base and the other side is 3 cm longer than the base. The perimeter is greater than 19 cm. $b > 6$ cm

9. Grace and Joan do volunteer work at a hospital. Joan worked 3 more hours than Grace and together they worked more than 27 hours. What is the least number of hours each worked? $J > 15$, $G > 12$

10. Joe is shopping for a new pair of jeans and a sweater. He is determined to spend less than $40.00 for the outfit. If he buys jeans for $21.98, how much can he spend for the sweater? $s \leq$ $18.01

11. Mrs. Hays has promised her two teenagers that they may go to a concert if together they save more than $25.00 of their spending money. The older teenager agrees to save twice as much as the younger. How much must each save? $16.68, $8.34

12. Mr. Britt has an $80.00 daily budget for car rental. He has rented a car for $15.00 per day, plus 12 cents a mile. What mileage will keep him within his budget? $m \leq 541\frac{2}{3}$

13. A saleswoman made 18 customer calls last week and 22 calls this week. How many calls must she make next week to maintain an average number of calls of at least 20 for the three-week period? 20

Extension

14. The length of a rectangle is 26 cm. What width will make the perimeter greater than 80 cm? $w > 14$ cm

15. The width of a rectangle is 8 cm. What length will make the area at least 150 cm²? $l \geq 18.75$ cm

16. The height of a triangle is 20 cm. What length base will make the area greater than 40 cm²? $b > 4$ cm

17. The area of a square can be no more than 64 cm². What is the length of a side? $s \leq 8$ cm

Challenge

18. To qualify for a secretarial position, an applicant must type two pages, averaging at least 60 words per minute. On the first page, Ken typed 50 w/m. At what rate must he type the second page in order to qualify for the position? (Assume each page has an equal number of words.) $\frac{w}{50} + \frac{w}{x} \geq \frac{2w}{60}$, $x \geq 75$ w/m

---

SCIENTIFIC NOTATION

Large numbers can be simplified for calculation by using exponents. For example, the Cambrian period of Earth history is that time which began 570,000,000 years ago. This number can also be written as $5.7 \times 100{,}000{,}000$, or 5.7×10^8. The last form is called *scientific notation* and shows the product of a number between 1 and 10 and a power of ten. Write the following distances in scientific notation.

Earth to Sun   149,600,000 km 1.496×10^8
Moscow to New York   7503 km 7.503×10^3
One mile   1.609 km 1.609×10^0

Astronomers express the great distances between galaxies and stars using units of measure called *light years*. A light year is the distance light travels through space in one year and is roughly equal to 9.46×10^{12} km. The light we see from a distant star may have taken years to reach us. Even the light from the Sun is about 8 minutes old by the time we see it.

Scientific notation can also be used to write very small numbers. For example, $0.0000834 = 8.34 \times \frac{1}{100{,}000}$. In scientific notation, the number is written 8.34×10^{-5}.

Physicists, as well as astronomers and other scientists, also use scientific notation. For example, the mass of an electron at rest is 9.11×10^{-31} kg. Write the following physical units in scientific notation.

Proton rest mass 1.67×10^{-27}
0.00000000000000000000000000167
Planck's constant 6.63×10^{-34}
0.000000000000000000000000000000000663

Using scientific notation prevents giving a false impression about the degree of accuracy of a measurement. Suppose the distance from the earth to the moon is written as 236,000 miles. Does this mean that the distance has been measured so precisely that we know it to be exactly 236,000 miles? Of course not. The last three zeros are used to show the correct location of the decimal point. So, 2.36×10^5 miles shows both how large the distance is and how accurately we know it.

10–5 Graphing Inequalities in One Variable

Graphing Simple Inequalities

A graph of an inequality in one variable is a picture of all its
solutions on a number line.

EXAMPLE 1

Graph $x < 2$ on a number line.

The solutions of $x < 2$ are all numbers less than 2. They are shown
by shading all points to the left of 2 on a number line.

Note that 2 is not a solution. We indicate this by an open circle
at 2.

EXAMPLE 2

Graph $x \geq -3$ on a number line.

The solutions of $x \geq -3$ are 3 and all points to the right of 3.

Note that -3 is a solution and is shaded.

EXAMPLE 3

Graph $3x + 2 < 5x - 1$ on a number line. First solve.

$2 < 2x - 1$ Adding $-3x$
$3 < 2x$ Adding 1
$\dfrac{3}{2} < x$ Multiplying by $\dfrac{1}{2}$

Then graph.

TRY THIS Graph on a number line.

1. $x < 8$ **2.** $y \geq -5$ **3.** $x + 2 > 5$ **4.** $4x + 6 \leq 7x - 3$

Graphing Inequalities with Absolute Value

Recall that the absolute value of a number is its distance from 0 on a number line.

EXAMPLE 4

Graph $|x| < 3$ on a number line.

For the absolute value of a number to be less than 3, its distance from 0 must be less than 3. So x must be between -3 and 3.

We write the solution as $x < 3$ and $x > -3$. We can abbreviate this by writing $-3 < x < 3$. Absolute value expressions which are less than a constant b are solved using the pattern

$x < b$ and $x > -b$.

Again, we can write this as $-b < x < b$.

EXAMPLE 5

Graph $|x| > 2$ on a number line.

For the absolute value of a number to be greater than 2, its distance from 0 must be greater than 2. So x must be greater than 2 or less than -2.

We write the solution as $x > 2$ or $x < -2$. Absolute value expressions which are greater than a constant b are solved using the pattern

$x > b$ or $x < -b$.

TRY THIS Graph on a number line.

5. $|x| < 5$ **6.** $|x| > 1$ **7.** $|x| \leq 4$ **8.** $|x| \geq 3$

EXAMPLE 6

Graph $|x - 3| \leq 2$ on a number line.

We know from Example 4 this means $x - 3 \leq 2$ and $x - 3 \geq -2$.
After solving these inequalities, we get $x \leq 5$ and $x \geq 1$, or $1 \leq x \leq 5$.

We then graph the solution.

EXAMPLE 7

Graph $|x - 8| \geq 5$ on a number line.

We know from Example 5 this means $x - 8 \geq 5$ or $x - 8 \leq -5$.
After solving the inequalities, we get $x \geq 13$ or $x \leq 3$.

We graph the solution.

TRY THIS Graph on a number line.

9. $|x - 7| \leq 20$ 10. $|x + 9| < 4$ 11. $|2x - 5| > 5$

10–5	

Exercises

Graph on a number line.

1. $x < 5$ 2. $y < 0$ 3. $t < -3$

4. $y > 5$ 5. $x \geq 6$ 6. $y \geq -4$

7. $x + 2 > 7$ 8. $x + 3 > 9$ 9. $z - 3 < 4$

10. $x - 2 < 6$ 11. $t - 3 \leq -7$ 12. $x - 4 \leq -8$

13. $x - 8 \geq 0$ 14. $2x + 6 < 14$ 15. $3y + 5 < 26$

16. $4x - 8 \geq 12$ 17. $5y - 4 > 11$ 18. $3x + 7 < 8x - 3$

19. $4y + 9 > 11y - 12$ 20. $5t + 8 \geq 12t - 27$ 21. $6x + 11 \leq 14x + 7$

Graph on a number line.

22. $|x| < 2$ 23. $|y| < 6$ 24. $|t| \leq 1$ 25. $|x| \leq 7$

26. $|y| > 3$ 27. $|t| > 4$ 28. $|x| \geq 7$ 29. $|y| \geq 9$

Graph on a number line.

30. $|x - 3| < 12$ **31.** $|x + 2| \le 5$ **32.** $|x - 1| \ge 6$ **33.** $|x + 5| > 19$

34. $|2y - 4| < 7$ **35.** $|4y - 2| < 7$ **36.** $|x + \frac{1}{3}| \ge 3$ **37.** $|\frac{1}{5}x - \frac{1}{4}| \ge 1$

Extension

38. When is $-|x|$ negative?   **39.** When is $-|x|$ positive? Never

When x is not zero

Tell whether each sum or difference is positive, negative, or zero.

40. $|n| > |m|$; n is negative; m is positive. $n + m$ is _____. negative

41. $|n| > |m|$; $n > 0$; $m < 0$. $n + m$ is _____. positive

42. $|n| = |m|$; $n > 0$; $m < 0$. $-n - m$ is _____. zero

43. Tell which of the following statements are always true. If a statement is *not* always true, given an example for which it is false.

    a. $|x| \ge 0$ **b.** $|-x| \ge -|x|$ **c.** $x < |x|$ a, b, and d are always true.

    d. $-|x| \le |x^2|$ **e.** $|x| < |x|^2$ **f.** $-|x| < x$ c. Not true when $x \ge 0$

                                                               e. Not true when $-1 \le x \le 1$

                                                               f. Not true when $x \le 0$

Challenge

44. $m < 0$, $n > 0$. $m + n = s$, where $s > 0$. Is $|m| > |n|$? No

45. $m < 0$, $n > 0$. $m + n = s$, where $s < 0$. Is $|m| > |n|$? Yes

46. $m < 0$, $n > 0$. $m + n = 0$. Is $|m| > |n|$? No

47. a. Give all integer solutions for $|x| \le 3$. $-3, -2, -1, 0, 1, 2, 3$

    b. If b is an integer, how many integer solutions are there for $|x| \le b$? $2b$ and zero, or $2b + 1$

48. a. Give all integer solutions for $|x| < 3$. $-2, -1, 0, 1, 2$

    b. If c is a nonzero integer, how many integer solutions are there for $|x| < c$? $2b - 2$ and zero, or $2b - 1$

LOGIC/Truth Tables

The solution to $|x| > 2$ is written as the following statement.

    $x > 2$ or $x < -2$

The solution includes both values of x greater than 2 and less than -2. Any statement "A or B" is true if either A, or B, is true.

The solution to $|x| < 3$ is written in the following way.

    $x < 3$ and $x > -3$

For the statement above, and any statement "A and B" to be true, *both* part A and part B must be true.

These ways of using the words *or* and *and* can be shown in a truth table.

A	B	A and B	A or B
True	True	True	True
True	False	False	True
False	True	False	True
False	False	False	False

Solutions of Inequalities in Two Variables

The solutions of an inequality in two variables are the ordered pairs of numbers which make the inequality true.

EXAMPLE 1

Determine whether $(5, -3)$ is a solution of the inequality $2x - y > 5$.

First replace x by 5 and y by -3.

$$\begin{array}{c|c} 2x - y > 5 \\ \hline 2(5) - (-3) & 5 \\ 10 + 3 \\ 13 \end{array}$$

Since $13 > 5$ is true, $(5, -3)$ is a solution.

TRY THIS

1. Determine whether $(2, 1)$ is a solution of $x + y < 4$. Yes
2. Determine whether $(4, 8)$ is a solution of $y > 2x + 1$. No

Graphing Inequalities in Two Variables

Inequalities in two variables are graphed on a plane.

EXAMPLE 2

Graph $x + y < 4$ on a plane.

First we graph $x + y = 4$. We use a dashed line to show that the points on the line are not solutions of $x + y < 4$.

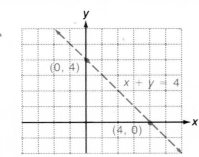

The solutions of $x + y < 4$ must lie on either side of the dashed line, so we test a point not on the line such as $(0, 0)$. $0 + 0 < 4$ is true, so the half-plane containing $(0, 0)$ is the solution. We shade it to show that every point in that half plane is a solution.

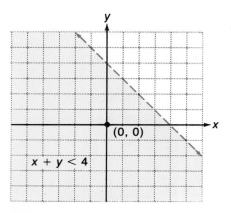

EXAMPLE 3

Graph $y > x + 2$ on a plane.

First we graph $y = x + 2$ using a dashed line. Then we determine which half-plane contains the solutions to $y > x + 2$ by testing $(0, 0)$.

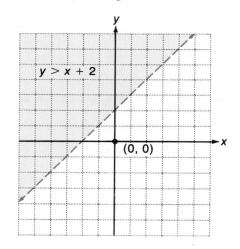

$0 > 0 + 2$ is not true, so the half-plane containing $(0, 0)$ is not the solution. We shade the opposite half-plane.

TRY THIS Graph on a plane.

3. $2x + y < 4$ 4. $y > x - 1$ 5. $y - 3x < 0$ 6. $y - 4 > x$

EXAMPLE 4

Graph $x - y \geq 5$ on a plane.

First we graph $x - y = 5$. We use a solid line to show that the points on the line are solutions.

Then we test a point not on the line, (0, 0). $0 - 0 \geq 5$ is not true, so the half-plane containing (0, 0) is not the solution. We shade the opposite half-plane.

 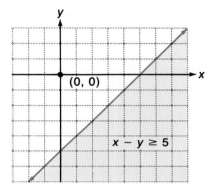

EXAMPLE 5

Graph $2x + 3y \leq 0$ on a plane.

First we graph $2x + 3y = 0$ using a solid line. Then we test a point not on the line.

Since the origin is on the line, we test (1, 1). $2(1) + 3(1) \leq 0$ is false, so the half-plane containing (1, 1) is not the solution. We shade the opposite half-plane.

 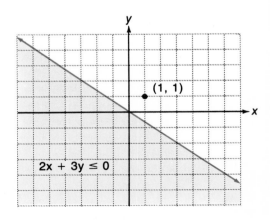

Thus, the graph of any linear inequality in two variables is either a half-plane or a half-plane together with its boundary line.

10–6

Exercises

1. Determine whether $(-3, -5)$ is a solution of $-x - 3y < 18$.   No

2. Determine whether $(5, -3)$ is a solution of $-2x + 4y \leq -2$.   No

3. Determine whether $\left(\frac{1}{2}, -\frac{1}{4}\right)$ is a solution of $7y - 9x > -3$.   Yes

Graph on a plane.

4. $x > 2y$	**5.** $x > 3y$	**6.** $y \leq x - 3$
7. $y \leq x - 5$	**8.** $y < x + 1$	**9.** $y < x + 4$
10. $y \geq x - 2$	**11.** $y \geq x - 1$	**12.** $y \leq 2x - 1$
13. $y \leq 3x + 2$	**14.** $x + y \leq 3$	**15.** $x + y \leq 4$
16. $x - y > 7$	**17.** $x - y > -2$	**18.** $x - 3y < 6$
19. $x - y < -10$	**20.** $2x + 3y \leq 12$	**21.** $5x + 4y \geq 20$
22. $y \geq 1 - 2x$	**23.** $y - 2x \leq -1$	**24.** $y + 4x > 0$
25. $y - x < 0$	**26.** $y > -3x$	**27.** $y < -5x$

Extension

Graph on a plane.

28. $y \leq \frac{2}{3}x + 1$	**29.** $y < \frac{1}{2}x - 1$	**30.** $y > 0.5x - 6.5$
31. $y > 1.3x + 9.6$	**32.** $y > 2$	**33.** $x \geq 3$
34. $x > 0$	**35.** $y \leq 0$	**36.** $3(x - y) \leq 2x + 6$

Challenge

Graph on a plane

37. $|x| \leq y$ **38.** $|y| \geq x$

39. $|x| + |y| > 4$ **40.** $|x| - |y| \geq 6$

41. What inequality is shown in the graph? $xy \leq 0$

A pair of linear inequalities is called a system of inequalities. The solutions of a system of inequalities are those ordered pairs which make both inequalities true. One way to find the solutions to such a system is to graph both inequalities and find their intersection.

EXAMPLE 1

Solve this system by graphing. $2x + y > 8$
$2x - y > 1.$

Graph $2x + y > 8$.   Graph $2x - y > 1$.

 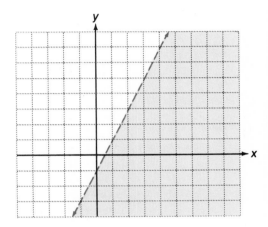

The intersection of these graphs is the solutions of the system.

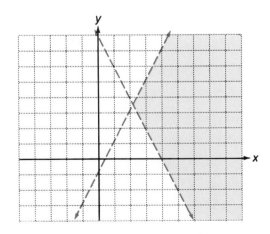

EXAMPLE 2

Solve this system by graphing. $y \geq x$
$$x - 3y \leq 5$$

Graph $y \geq x$.   Graph $x - 3y \leq 5$.

Graph their intersection.

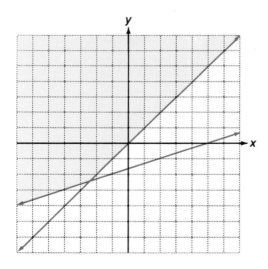

TRY THIS Solve by graphing.

1. $x + y < -1$ 2. $y > 4x - 1$ 3. $x - 2y \geq 6$ 4. $y \geq x$
   $3x - y > 4$ $y < -2x + 3$ $x + 2y \leq 4$ $y \leq -x + 1$

EXAMPLE 3

Solve this system by graphing. $x + y < 4$
$$y \geq 1.$$

Graph $x + y < 4$.   Graph $y \geq 1$.

Graph their intersection.

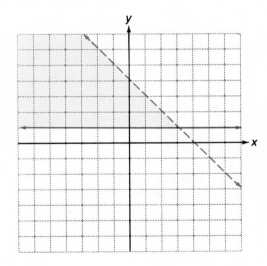

TRY THIS Solve by graphing.

5. $x + y \geq -1$ 6. $x \leq 0$ 7. $x + 2y \geq 12$ 8. $y < 2x$
   $\quad y < -2$ $\quad x - y > 1$ $\quad 3x + y < 8$ $\quad y \geq x - 5$

Exercises

Solve these systems by graphing.

1. $x > 2 + y$
   $y > 1$

2. $y < 3x$
   $x + y < 4$

3. $y < x$
   $y < -x + 1$

4. $y > x$
   $y > -x + 2$

5. $2y - y < 2$
   $x > 3$

6. $y > 4$
   $2y + x > 5$

7. $y > 4x - 1$
   $y \le -2x + 3$

8. $y > 5x + 2$
   $y \le -x + 1$

9. $x - 2y > 6$
   $x + 2y \le 4$

10. $2y - x > 5$
    $x + y \le 4$

11. $2x - 3y \ge 9$
    $2y + x > 6$

12. $3x - 2y \le 8$
    $2x + y > 6$

13. $x + y < 3$
    $x - y \le 4$

14. $x - y < 3$
    $x + y \ge 4$

15. $5x + 2y \ge 12$
    $2x + 3y \le 10$

Extension

Solve these systems by graphing.

16. $-\frac{1}{3}x \le -4$

    $\frac{1}{2}y > x$

17. $-0.5y \ge -18$
    $2.5x + y > 10$

18. $4(2y - 2) \le x$
    $2y - 7 < 1$

19. $2x + 7 < 19$
    $2(3 - x) > 10$

20. $4x + 6y \ge -2$
    $-2x - 3y \le 1$

21. $-x + 3y < 4$
    $3x - 9y < -12$
    $-x + 3y < 4$ and $-x + 3y > 4$, so there is no solution.

Challenge

Solve these systems of three inequalities by graphing.

22. $x \le 4$
    $x + y \le 3$
    $y \le x$

23. $x - y \le 1$
    $x + 3y < 2$
    $y < 1$

24. $y \le x$
    $x \ge -2$
    $x \le -y$

25. $y > 0$
    $2y + x \le 6$
    $x + 2 \le 2y$

26. Graph $(x - y - 3)(x + y + 2) > 0$. Shade the area where the product is greater than 0. (Hint: Under what conditions is a product of two numbers positive?)

27. Graph the following system.

    $$y \ge -\frac{2}{5}x + 5$$
    $$y \ge -3x + 18 \qquad x \ge 0, \quad y \ge 0$$

    Find the coordinates of the point in the system that gives the largest value to $2x + 3y$. What is the value of $2x + 3y$ at that point? (Hint: Graph $2x + 3y = 0$, $2x + 3y = 12$, and $2x + 3y = 18$ in a different color.) (5, 3), 19

CHAPTER 10   Review

Review the material in the chapter. Then see how you have done by trying these review exercises. If you miss an exercise, restudy the indicated lesson.

10–1   Determine whether the given number is a solution of the inequality $x \leq 4$.

1. -3 Yes **2.** 7 No **3.** 4 Yes

10–1   Solve using the addition principle.

4. $y + 9 \geq 3$ **5.** $3x + 5 < 2x - 6$ 4. $y \geq -6$ 5. $x < -11$

10–2   Solve using the multiplication principle.

6. $9x \geq 63$ **7.** $-4y < 28$ **8.** $-3y \geq -21$ **9.** $-4x \leq \dfrac{1}{3}$ 6. $x \geq 7$ 7. $y > -7$ 8. $y \leq 7$ 9. $x \geq -\dfrac{1}{12}$

10–3   Solve using both principles.

10. $2 + 6y > 14$ $y > 2$ **11.** $3 - 4x < 27$ $x > -6$
12. $7 - 3y \geq 27 + 2y$ **13.** $4 - 8x < 13 + 3x$ 12. $y \leq -4$ 13. $x > -\dfrac{9}{11}$

10–4   Solve by translating into inequalities.

14. Your quiz grades are 71, 75, 82, and 86. What is the lowest grade you can get on the last quiz and still have an average of at least 80? 86

10–5   Graph on a number line.

15. $y \leq 9$ **16.** $6x - 3 < x + 2$ **17.** $|x| \leq 2$ **18.** $|x - 1| > 3$

10–6   Determine whether the given point is a solution of the inequality $x - 2y > 1$.

19. $(0, 0)$ No   **20.** $(1, 3)$ No   **21.** $(4, -1)$ Yes

10–6   Graph on a plane.

22. $x < y$ **23.** $x + 2y \geq 4$

10–7   Solve by graphing.

24. $y \geq x$ **25.** $x > 1$
    $y < x + 1$ $y < -2$

CHAPTER 10   Test

Solve.

1. $x + 6 \leq 2$ 2. $14x + 9 > 13x - 4$ 3. $12x \leq 60$ $x \leq 5$
   $x \leq -4$ $x > -13$
4. $-2y \geq 26$ 5. $-4y \leq -32$ 6. $-5x \geq \frac{1}{4}$ $x \leq -\frac{1}{20}$
   $y \leq 13$
7. $4 - 6x > 40$ 8. $5 - 9x \geq 19 + 5x$ 7. $x < -6$ 8. $x \leq -1$

Solve by translating into an inequality.

9. The sum of three consecutive integers is greater than 29. What are the least possible values of these integers? 9, 10, 11

Graph on a number line.

10. $4x - 6 < x + 3$ $x < 3$ 11. $|x| > 5$ $x > 5$ or $x < -5$

Graph on a plane.

12. $y > x - 1$ 13. $2x - y \leq 3$

Solve by graphing.

14. $y \leq x$ 15. $y > -3$
    $y > x - 2$ $x < -2$

Challenge

16. Give all integer solutions for $|2x| \leq 5$. $-2, -1, 0, 1, 2$

CHAPTERS 1–10   Cumulative Review

1–1 Write an algebraic expression for each of the following.

1. the product of x and 4 less than y divided by the difference of x and 8 times y $\frac{x(y - 4)}{x - 8y}$

2. 19 more than the fifth power of a $a^5 + 19$

1–4 Evaluate.

3. $x - (x - 1) + (x^2 + 1)$ for $x = 10$ 102

4. $xy + (xy)^2 + x + y$ for $x = 5$ and $y = 2$ 117

1–5 Factor.

5. $121a + 88b$ **6.** $36x + 24y + 12z$
   $11(11a + 8b)$ $12(3x + 2y + z)$

2–3 Add.

7. $-12.1 + 100.6 - 18.5$ $_{117}$ **8.** $\frac{11}{9} - \frac{4}{18} + \frac{1}{6} - \frac{2}{3} + \frac{1}{2}$ $_1$

2–7 Factor.

9. $-21x - 28w$ **10.** $17x - 51y$ $_{17(x - 3y)}$ **11.** $144a^2 - 60b^2$ 9. $-7(3x + 4w)$ or
                                                                              $7(-3 + 4w)$
                                                                        11. $12(12a^2 - 5b^2)$

2–8 Simplify.

12. $-7(x - 1) + 2x$ **13.** $8[4 - (6x - 5)]$ **14.** $x - [x - (x - 1)]$ $_{x\ -\ 1}$
   $_{-5x\ +\ 7}$ $_{72\ -\ 48x}$

2–9 Translate to an equation and solve.

15. What percent of 1 is $\frac{1}{2}$? $_{50\%}$ **16.** 50 is 19% of what number? $_{38}$
17. 250% of what number is 6.25? $_{2.5}$

3–3, 3–4 Solve.

18. During the library marathon, Phil read twice as many books as Howard, but only half as many as Larry. If the three boys read 21 books, how many did Howard read? $_{2x\ +\ x\ +\ 4x\ =\ 21,\ \text{Howard read 3}}$

19. $5(a + 3) = 8a + 18$ $_{a\ =\ -1}$ **20.** $-3(m + 2) - 4 = -12 - (-2 + m)$ $_{m\ =\ 0}$

3–7 Solve.

21. The ratio of chocolate cookies to vanilla cookies sold in a local supermarket is 5 to 7. If 1320 packages of these cookies were sold one week, how many were vanilla? $_{770}$

4–2 Collect like terms.

22. $10a^2 + 6a - 8a^2 + 3a - 2a^2 - 8a$ $_a$
23. $(8m + 6n) - (12n + 7m) + 2(4m - 11n)$ $_{9m\ -\ 28n}$

4–6, 4–9 Multiply.

24. $(4 + 2b + c)(c - 1)$ **25.** $(2.5x - 0.3y)^2$ 24. $5c + 2bc + c^2 - 2b - 4$
26. $(5x - 6y)(x + 2y)$ **27.** $(a + 2c + 1)(a + 2c - 1)$ 25. $6.25x^2 - 1.5xy + 0.09y^2$
                                                                      26. $5x^2 + 4xy - 12y^2$
                                                                      27. $a^2 + 4ac + 4c^2 - 1$

5–1 to 5–7 Factor.

28. $x^3y^3 + x^2y^2 - 4xy$ **29.** $a^8 + a^7 - a^6$ **30.** $mx^2 + my^2$
31. $4 - 9m^4$ **32.** $-a^2 + 100$ **33.** $9x^2 - 9b^2$

28. $xy(x^2y^2 + xy - 4)$
29. $a^6(a^2 + a - 1)$
30. $m(x^2 + y^2)$
31. $(2 + 3m^2)(2 - 3m^2)$
32. $(10 + a)(10 - a)$
33. $9(x + b)(x - b)$

34. $x^2 - 4x - 12$ **35.** $s^2 - 16s + 15$ **36.** $t^3 - 5t^2 + 6t$

37. $7x^2 - 6x - 1$ **38.** $20y^2 + 19y + 3$ **39.** $6y^2 + 9y - 15$

6–2 Simplify.

40. $(h - 4k)^2$

41. $(2x + 7y)^2$

42. $(a + 3b)^2 - (2a - b)^2$

43. $(m + n)^2 - 5(m - n)^2$

44. $(2x + 10y)(x - 13y)$

45. $(14m - n)(m + 10n)$

6–3 Factor.

46. $5a^2 - 28am - 12m^2$ **47.** $15x^2 - 41xy + 14y^2$

48. $a^5 + a^4 - a^2 - a$ **49.** $x^2 + xy + 2x + 2y$

7–5 to 7–7   Write an equation for the line that satisfies each condition.

50. slope is 5, passes through the origin. $y = 5x$

51. passes through $(0, 3)$ and has x-intercept 6 $y = -\frac{1}{2}x + 3$

52. slope is -1, y-intercept is -12. $y = -x - 12$

53. x-intercept is 7, y-intercept is -6 $y = \frac{6}{7}x - 6$

54. contains the points $(-1, 2)$ and $(2, 11)$ $y = 3x + 5$

8–1   Find the indicated output for the function $g(x) = |x - 1| + x$.

55. $g(0)$ ₁   **56.** $g(1)$ ₁   **57.** $g(2)$ ₃   **58.** $g(-1)$ ₁

8–4   Find an equation of variation where y varies directly as x.

59. $y = 132$ when $x = 12$ **60.** $y = 100$ when $x = -5$
$y = 11x$ $y = -20x$

8–5   Find an equation of variation where y varies inversely as x.

61. $y = 1$ when $x = 15$ **62.** $y = \frac{1}{700}$ when $x = 35$ 61. $y = \frac{15}{x}$ 62. $y = \frac{0.05}{x}$

9–2   Solve these systems.

63. $6x + 3y = -6$ **64.** $2x + 3y = -3$ **65.** $x = 4$
$-2x + 5y = 14$ $y = 2x - 9$ $y = -2$
$(-2, 2)$ $(3, -3)$ $(4, -2)$

10–1, 10–2   Solve.

66. $8x - 2 \geq 7x + 5$ $x \geq 7$ **67.** $-4x \geq 24$ $x \leq -6$

68. $-3x < 30 + 2x$ $x > 6$ **69.** $5x + 3 \geq 6(x - 4) + 7$ $x \leq \frac{10}{3}$

34. $(x - 6)(x + 2)$
35. $(s - 1)(s - 15)$
36. $t(t - 2)(t - 3)$
37. $(7x + 1)(x - 1)$
38. $(4y + 3)(5y + 1)$
39. $3(y - 1)(2y + 5)$

40. $h^2 - 8hk + 16k^2$
41. $4x^2 + 28xy + 49y^2$
42. $-3a^2 + 10ab - 8b^2$
43. $16m^2 + 12mn - 4n^2$
44. $2x^2 - 16xy - 130y^2$
45. $14m^2 - 139mn - 10n^2$

46. $(a - 6m)(5a + 2m)$
47. $(3x - 7y)(5x - 2y)$
48. $a(a + 1)(a^3 - 1)$
49. $(x + y)(x + 2)$

10–5 Graph on a number line.

70. $5x - 1 < 24$ **71.** $|4x| \le 12$ **72.** $|x - 5| < 5$

10–6 Graph on a plane.

73. $y \le 5x$ **74.** $2y - 3x > 0$ **75.** $6y > 0$

10–7 Solve by graphing.

76. $2y < 5x$ **77.** $x > 1$
    $y > -x - 5$ $y \le 3$

Ready for Fractional Expressions and Equations?

4–4, 4–5 Add or subtract.

1. $(2x^2 + 3x - 7) + (x^2 + x - 8)$. $3x^2 + 4x - 15$
2. Subtract: $(x^2 + 6x + 8) - (x^2 - 3x - 4)$. $9x + 12$

4–6 to 4–8 Multiply.

3. $2x(3x + 2)$ $6x^2 + 4x$
4. $(x + 1)(x^2 - 2x + 1)$ $x^3 - x^2 - x + 1$
5. $(x - 2)(x + 2)$ $x^2 - 4$

5–2 to 5–4 Factor.

6. $x^2 - 1$ $(x - 1)(x + 1)$
7. $x^2 - 6x + 9$ $(x - 3)(x - 3)$
8. $x^2 + 3x + 2$ $(x + 2)(x + 1)$

5–8 Solve.

9. $3t + 2t = 12$ $\frac{12}{5}$
10. $x^2 - 5x + 6 = 0$ $2, 3$

5–9

11. One more than a number times one less than a number is 24.
    Find the number. 5 or -5

11

CHAPTER ELEVEN

Fractional Expressions and Equations

A fractional expression is a quotient of two polynomials. A fractional expression always indicates division. For example,

$$\frac{x^2 + 3x - 10}{3x + 2} \text{ means } (x^2 + 3x - 10) \div (3x + 2).$$

Multiplying

To multiply two fractional expressions multiply numerators and multiply denominators.

EXAMPLES
Multiply.

1. $\dfrac{x - 2}{3} \cdot \dfrac{x + 2}{x + 3} = \dfrac{(x - 2)(x + 2)}{3(x + 3)}$

$$= \frac{x^2 - 4}{3x + 9}$$

2. $\dfrac{-2}{2y + 3} \cdot \dfrac{3}{y - 5} = \dfrac{-2 \cdot 3}{(2y + 3)(y - 5)}$

$$= \frac{-6}{2y^2 - 7y - 15}$$

TRY THIS Multiply.

1. $\dfrac{x + 3}{5} \cdot \dfrac{x + 2}{x + 4}$
2. $\dfrac{-3}{2x + 1} \cdot \dfrac{4}{2x - 1}$
1. $\frac{x^2 + 5x + 6}{5x + 20}$
2. $\frac{-12}{4x^2 - 1}$

Recall from Chapter 1 that multiplying an expression by 1 gives an equivalent expression. This is also true for fractional expressions.

EXAMPLES.
Multiply.

3. $\dfrac{3x + 2}{x + 1} \cdot \dfrac{2x}{2x} = \dfrac{(3x + 2)2x}{(x + 1)2x}$
   $\dfrac{2x}{2x} = 1$

$$= \frac{6x^2 + 4x}{2x^2 + 2x}$$

4. $\dfrac{x+2}{x-1} \cdot \dfrac{x+1}{x+1} = \dfrac{(x+2)(x+1)}{(x-1)(x+1)}$ $\dfrac{x+1}{x+1} = 1$

$\qquad\qquad\qquad = \dfrac{x^2 + 3x + 2}{x^2 - 1}$

5. $\dfrac{2+x}{2-x} \cdot \dfrac{-1}{-1} = \dfrac{(2+x)(-1)}{(2-x)(-1)}$

$\qquad\qquad\quad = \dfrac{2(-1) + x(-1)}{2(-1) - x(-1)}$

$\qquad\qquad\quad = \dfrac{-2-x}{-2+x},\ \text{or}\ \dfrac{-2-x}{x-2}$

TRY THIS Multiply.

3. $\dfrac{2x+1}{3x-2} \cdot \dfrac{x}{x}$ **4.** $\dfrac{x+1}{x-2} \cdot \dfrac{x+2}{x+2}$ **5.** $\dfrac{x-8}{x-y} \cdot \dfrac{-1}{-1}$ 3. $\dfrac{2x^2+x}{3x^2-2x}$ 4. $\dfrac{x^2+3x+2}{x^2-4}$ 5. $\dfrac{8-x}{y-x}$

Simplifying

To simplify fractional expressions we do the reverse of multiplying.
We factor numerator and denominator and remove a factor of one.

EXAMPLES
Simplify.

6. $\dfrac{6x^2 + 4x}{2x^2 + 2x} = \dfrac{2x(3x+2)}{2x(x+1)}$ Factoring numerator and denominator

$\qquad\qquad\quad = \dfrac{2x}{2x} \cdot \dfrac{3x+2}{x+1}$ Factoring the fractional expression

$\qquad\qquad\quad = \dfrac{3x+2}{x+1}$ Removing a factor of 1

7. $\dfrac{x^2 + 3x + 2}{x^2 - 1} = \dfrac{(x+2)(x+1)}{(x+1)(x-1)}$

$\qquad\qquad\quad = \dfrac{x+1}{x+1} \cdot \dfrac{x+2}{x-1}$

$\qquad\qquad\quad = \dfrac{x+2}{x-1}$

TRY THIS Simplify.

6. $\dfrac{12y + 24}{48}$ **7.** $\dfrac{2x^2 + x}{3x^2 + 2x}$ **8.** $\dfrac{x^2 - 1}{2x^2 - x - 1}$ 6. $\dfrac{y+2}{4}$ 7. $\dfrac{2x+1}{3x+2}$ 8. $\dfrac{x+1}{2x+1}$

Multiplying and Simplifying

We usually simplify after multiplying fractional expressions. In the following examples we see why it is usually better not to multiply out numerators and denominators until after simplification.

EXAMPLES
Multiply and simplify.

8.
$$\frac{x^2 + 6x + 9}{x^2 - 4} \cdot \frac{x - 2}{x + 3} = \frac{(x^2 + 6x + 9)(x - 2)}{(x^2 - 4)(x + 3)}$$ Multiplying numerators and denominators

$$= \frac{(x + 3)(x + 3)(x - 2)}{(x + 2)(x - 2)(x + 3)}$$ Factoring numerator and denominator

$$= \frac{(x + 3)(x - 2)}{(x + 3)(x - 2)} \cdot \frac{x + 3}{x + 2}$$ Factoring the fractional expression

$$= \frac{x + 3}{x + 2}$$ Simplifying

9.
$$\frac{x^2 + x - 2}{15} \cdot \frac{5}{2x^2 - 3x + 1} = \frac{(x^2 + x - 2)5}{15(2x^2 - 3x + 1)}$$

$$= \frac{(x + 2)(x - 1)5}{5 \cdot 3(x - 1)(2x - 1)}$$

$$= \frac{(x - 1)5}{(x - 1)5} \cdot \frac{x + 2}{3(2x - 1)}$$ Factoring the fractional expression

$$= \frac{x + 2}{3(2x - 1)}$$

TRY THIS Multiply and simplify.

9. $\dfrac{a^2 - 4a + 4}{a^2 - 9} \cdot \dfrac{a + 3}{a - 2}$ **10.** $\dfrac{x^2 - 25}{6} \cdot \dfrac{3}{x + 5}$ 9. $\frac{a - 2}{a - 3}$ 10. $\frac{x - 5}{2}$

11–1

Exercises
Multiply.

1. $\frac{3x^2 + 12x}{2x - 2}$ 3. $\frac{x^2 - 1}{x^2 + 4x + 4}$ 5. $\frac{2x^2 + 5x + 3}{4x - 20}$

2. $\frac{4x^2 - 12x}{5x + 10}$ 4. $\frac{x^2 - 4x + 4}{x^2 - 25}$ 6. $\frac{30}{15x^2 - 2x - 24}$

1. $\dfrac{3x}{2} \cdot \dfrac{x + 4}{x - 1}$ **2.** $\dfrac{4x}{5} \cdot \dfrac{x - 3}{x + 2}$ **3.** $\dfrac{x - 1}{x + 2} \cdot \dfrac{x + 1}{x + 2}$

4. $\dfrac{x - 2}{x - 5} \cdot \dfrac{x - 2}{x + 5}$ **5.** $\dfrac{2x + 3}{4} \cdot \dfrac{x + 1}{x - 5}$ **6.** $\dfrac{-5}{3x - 4} \cdot \dfrac{-6}{5x + 6}$

7. $\frac{a^2 - 3a - 10}{a^4 - 1}$

8. $\frac{t^2 + 6t + 9}{t^4 - 4t^2 + 4}$

7. $\dfrac{a - 5}{a^2 + 1} \cdot \dfrac{a + 2}{a^2 - 1}$ **8.** $\dfrac{t + 3}{t^2 - 2} \cdot \dfrac{t + 3}{t^2 - 2}$ **9.** $\dfrac{x + 1}{2 + x} \cdot \dfrac{x - 1}{x + 1}$

9. $\frac{x^2 - 1}{x^2 + 3x + 2}$

10. $\dfrac{2x}{2x} \cdot \dfrac{x-1}{x+4}$

11. $\dfrac{3y-1}{2y+1} \cdot \dfrac{y}{y}$

12. $\dfrac{-1}{-1} \cdot \dfrac{3-x}{4-x}$

Simplify.

13. $\dfrac{a^2-9}{a^2+5a+6}$

14. $\dfrac{t^2-25}{t^2+t-20}$

15. $\dfrac{2t^2+6t+4}{4t^2-12t-16}$

16. $\dfrac{3a^2-9a-12}{6a^2+30a+24}$

17. $\dfrac{x^2-25}{x^2-10x+25}$

18. $\dfrac{x^2+8x+16}{x^2-16}$

19. $\dfrac{a^2-1}{a-1}$

20. $\dfrac{t^2-1}{t+1}$

21. $\dfrac{x^2+1}{x+1}$

22. $\dfrac{y^2+4}{y+2}$

23. $\dfrac{6x^2-54}{4x^2-36}$

24. $\dfrac{8x^2-32}{4x^2-16}$

25. $\dfrac{6t+12}{t^2-t-6}$

26. $\dfrac{5y+5}{y^2+7y+6}$

27. $\dfrac{a^2-10a+21}{a^2-11a+28}$

28. $\dfrac{y^2-3y-18}{y^2-2y-15}$

29. $\dfrac{t^2-4}{(t+2)^2}$

30. $\dfrac{(a-3)^2}{a^2-9}$

Multiply and simplify.

31. $\dfrac{x^2-3x-10}{(x-2)^2} \cdot \dfrac{x-2}{x-5}$

32. $\dfrac{t^2}{t^2-4} \cdot \dfrac{t^2-5t+6}{t^2-3t}$

33. $\dfrac{a^2-9}{a^2} \cdot \dfrac{a^2-3a}{a^2+a-12}$

34. $\dfrac{x^2+10x-11}{x^2-1} \cdot \dfrac{x+1}{x+11}$

35. $\dfrac{4a^2}{3a^2-12a+12} \cdot \dfrac{3a-6}{2a}$

36. $\dfrac{5v+5}{v-2} \cdot \dfrac{v^2-4v+4}{v^2-1}$

37. $\dfrac{x^4-16}{x^4-1} \cdot \dfrac{x^2+1}{x^2+4}$

38. $\dfrac{t^4-1}{t^4-81} \cdot \dfrac{t^2+9}{t^2+1}$

39. $\dfrac{(t-2)^3}{(t-1)^3} \cdot \dfrac{t^2-2t+1}{t^2-4t+4}$

40. $\dfrac{(y+4)^3}{(y+2)^3} \cdot \dfrac{y^2+4y+4}{y^2+8y+16}$

Extension

Simplify.

41. $\dfrac{x^4-16y^4}{(x^2+4y^2)(x-2y)}$

42. $\dfrac{(a-b)^2}{b^2-a^2}$

43. $\dfrac{t^4-1}{t^4-81} \cdot \dfrac{t^2-9}{t^2+1} \cdot \dfrac{(t-9)^2}{(t+1)^2}$

44. $\dfrac{(t-2)^3}{(t-1)^3} \cdot \dfrac{t^2-2t+1}{t^2-4t+4}$

45. $\dfrac{x^2-y^2}{(x-y)^2} \cdot \dfrac{x^2-2xy+y^2}{x^2-4xy-5y^2}$

46. $\dfrac{x-1}{x^2+1} \cdot \dfrac{x^4-1}{(x-1)^2} \cdot \dfrac{x^2-1}{x^4-2x^2+1}$

Challenge

Determine which replacements of x do not result in real numbers.

47. $\dfrac{x+1}{x^2+4x+4}$ -2

48. $\dfrac{x^2-16}{x^2+2x-3}$ $1, -3$

49. $\dfrac{x-7}{x^3-9x^2+14x}$ $0, 2, 7$

Answer column (right margin):

10. $\dfrac{2x^2-2x}{2x^2+8x}$

11. $\dfrac{3y^2-y}{2y^2+y}$

12. $\dfrac{x-3}{x-4}$

13. $\dfrac{a-3}{a+2}$

14. $\dfrac{t-5}{t-4}$

15. $\dfrac{t+2}{2(t-4)}$

16. $\dfrac{a-4}{2(a+4)}$

17. $\dfrac{x+5}{x-5}$

18. $\dfrac{x+4}{x-4}$

19. $a+1$

20. $t-1$

21. $\dfrac{x^2+1}{x+1}$

22. $\dfrac{y^2+4}{y+2}$

23. $\dfrac{3}{2}$

24. 2

25. $\dfrac{6}{t-3}$

26. $\dfrac{5}{y+6}$

27. $\dfrac{a-3}{a-4}$

28. $\dfrac{y-6}{y-5}$

29. $\dfrac{t-2}{t+2}$

30. $\dfrac{a-3}{a+3}$

31. $\dfrac{x+2}{x-2}$

32. $\dfrac{t}{t+2}$

33. $\dfrac{a^2-9}{a^2+4a}$

34. 1

35. $\dfrac{2a}{a-2}$

36. $\dfrac{5v-10}{v-1}$

37. $\dfrac{x^2-4}{x^2-1}$

38. $\dfrac{t^2-1}{t^2-9}$

39. $\dfrac{t-2}{t-1}$

40. $\dfrac{y+4}{y+2}$

41. $x+2y$

42. $\dfrac{b-a}{b+a}$

43. $\dfrac{(t-1)(t-9)^2}{(t^2+9)(t+1)}$

44. $\dfrac{t-2}{t-1}$

45. $\dfrac{x-y}{x-5y}$

46. 1

Division of Fractional Expressions

For any fractional expressions, we divide by multiplying by the reciprocal.

EXAMPLES
Divide and simplify.

1. $\dfrac{2x + 8}{3} \div \dfrac{x + 4}{9} = \dfrac{2(x + 4)}{3} \cdot \dfrac{9}{x + 4}$ Multiplying by the reciprocal

$\qquad\qquad\qquad = \dfrac{2(x + 4) \cdot 3 \cdot 3}{3(x + 4)}$

$\qquad\qquad\qquad = 2 \cdot 3 \cdot \dfrac{3(x + 4)}{3(x + 4)}$

$\qquad\qquad\qquad = 6$

2. $\dfrac{x + 1}{x + 2} \div \dfrac{x - 1}{x + 3} = \dfrac{x + 1}{x + 2} \cdot \dfrac{x + 3}{x - 1}$ Multiplying by the reciprocal

$\qquad\qquad\qquad = \dfrac{x^2 + 4x + 3}{x^2 + x - 2}$

TRY THIS Divide and simplify.   1. 8   2. $\dfrac{x^2 - 5x + 6}{x^2 + 10x + 25}$ 3. $\dfrac{3x - 3}{2x^2 - 8}$

1. $\dfrac{4x - 8}{5} \div \dfrac{x - 2}{10}$ 2. $\dfrac{x - 3}{x + 5} \div \dfrac{x + 5}{x - 2}$ 3. $\dfrac{3}{x^2 - 4} \div \dfrac{2}{x - 1}$

EXAMPLE 3
Divide and simplify.

$\dfrac{x + 1}{x^2 - 1} \div \dfrac{x + 1}{x^2 - 2x + 1} = \dfrac{x + 1}{x^2 - 1} \cdot \dfrac{x^2 - 2x + 1}{x + 1}$ Multiplying by the reciprocal

$\qquad\qquad\qquad\qquad = \dfrac{(x + 1)(x - 1)(x - 1)}{(x + 1)(x - 1)(x + 1)}$

$\qquad\qquad\qquad\qquad = \dfrac{(x + 1)(x - 1)}{(x + 1)(x - 1)} \cdot \dfrac{x - 1}{x + 1} = \dfrac{x - 1}{x + 1}$

TRY THIS Divide and simplify.

                                                     4. $\dfrac{x - 3}{x + 2}$

                                                     5. $x + 3$

4. $\dfrac{x - 3}{x + 5} \div \dfrac{x + 2}{x + 5}$ 5. $\dfrac{x^2 + 5x + 6}{x + 5} \div \dfrac{x + 2}{x + 5}$ 6. $\dfrac{y^2 - 1}{y + 1} \div \dfrac{y^2 - 2y + 1}{y + 1}$ 6. $\dfrac{y + 1}{y - 1}$

Exercises

Divide and simplify.

1. $\dfrac{5x - 5}{16} \div \dfrac{x - 1}{6}$ $\frac{15}{8}$

2. $\dfrac{-4 + 2x}{8} \div \dfrac{x - 2}{2}$ $\frac{1}{2}$

3. $\dfrac{-6 + 3x}{5} \div \dfrac{4x - 8}{25}$ $\frac{15}{4}$

4. $\dfrac{-12 + 4x}{4} \div \dfrac{-6 + 2x}{6}$ $\frac{8}{3}$

5. $\dfrac{a + 2}{a - 1} \div \dfrac{3a + 6}{a - 5}$

6. $\dfrac{t - 3}{t + 2} \div \dfrac{4t - 12}{t + 1}$

7. $\dfrac{x^2 - 4}{x} \div \dfrac{x - 2}{x + 2}$

8. $\dfrac{x^2 - 1}{x} \div \dfrac{x + 1}{x - 1}$

9. $\dfrac{x^2 - 9}{4x + 12} \div \dfrac{x - 3}{6}$

10. $\dfrac{4y - 8}{y + 2} \div \dfrac{y - 2}{y^2 - 4}$

11. $\dfrac{c^2 + 3c}{c^2 + 2c - 3} \div \dfrac{c}{c + 1}$

12. $\dfrac{x - 5}{2x} \div \dfrac{x^2 - 25}{4x^2}$

13. $\dfrac{2y^2 - 7y + 3}{2y^2 + 3y - 2} \div \dfrac{6y^2 - 5y + 1}{3y^2 + 5y - 2}$

14. $\dfrac{x^2 - x - 20}{x^2 + 7x + 12} \div \dfrac{x^2 - 10x + 25}{x^2 + 6x + 9}$

15. $\dfrac{c^2 + 10c + 21}{c^2 - 2c - 15} \div (c^2 + 2c - 35)$

16. $\dfrac{1 - z}{1 + 2z - z^2} \div (1 - z)$

17. $\dfrac{(t + 5)^3}{(t - 5)^3} \div \dfrac{(t + 5)^2}{(t - 5)^2}$

18. $\dfrac{(y - 3)^3}{(y + 3)^3} \div \dfrac{(y - 3)^2}{(y + 3)^2}$

5. $\dfrac{a - 5}{3a - 3}$

6. $\dfrac{t + 1}{4t + 8}$

7. $\dfrac{x^2 + 4x + 4}{x}$

8. $\dfrac{x^2 - 2x + 1}{x}$

9. $\frac{3}{2}$

10. $4y - 8$

11. $\dfrac{c + 1}{c - 1}$

12. $\dfrac{2x}{x + 5}$

13. $\dfrac{y - 3}{2y - 1}$

14. $\dfrac{x + 3}{x - 5}$

15. $\dfrac{1}{c^2 - 10c + 25}$

16. $\dfrac{1}{1 + 2z - z^2}$

17. $\dfrac{t + 5}{t - 5}$

18. $\dfrac{v - 3}{v + 3}$

Extension

Simplify.

19. $\dfrac{2a^2 - 5ab}{c - 3d} \div (4a^2 - 25b^2)$

20. $x - 2a \div \dfrac{a^2x^2 - 4a^4}{a^2x + 2a^3}$

21. $\dfrac{3a^2 - 5ab - 12b^2}{3ab + 4b^2} \div (3b^2 - ab)$

22. $\dfrac{3x^2 - 2xy - y^2}{x^2 - y^2} \div 3x^2 + 4xy + y^2$

23. $xy \cdot \dfrac{y^2 - 4xy}{y - x} \div \dfrac{16x^2y^2 - y^4}{4x^2 - 3xy - y^2}$

24. $\dfrac{z^2 - 8z + 16}{z^2 + 8z + 16} \div \dfrac{(z - 4)^5}{(z + 4)^5}$

19. $\dfrac{a}{(c - 3d)(2a + 5b)}$

20. 1

21. $\dfrac{-1}{b^2}$

22. $\dfrac{1}{(x + y)^2}$

23. x

24. $\dfrac{(z + 4)^3}{(z - 4)^3}$

Challenge

Simplify.

25. $\dfrac{x^2 - x + xy - y}{x^2 + 6x - 7} \div \dfrac{x^2 + 2xy + y^2}{4x + 4y}$ $\dfrac{4}{x + 7}$

26. $\dfrac{3x + 3y + 3}{9x} \div \dfrac{x^2 + 2xy + y^2 - 1}{x^4 + x^2}$ $\dfrac{x(x^2 + 1)}{3(x + y - 1)}$

27. $\left(\dfrac{y^2 + 5y + 6}{y^2} \cdot \dfrac{3y^3 + 6y^2}{y^2 - y - 12} \right) \div \dfrac{y^2 - y}{y^2 - 2y - 8}$ $\dfrac{3(y + 2)^3}{y(y - 1)}$

28. $\dfrac{a^4 - 81b^4}{a^2c - 6abc + 9b^2c} \cdot \dfrac{a + 3b}{a^2 + 9b^2} \div \dfrac{a^2 + 6ab + 9b^2}{(a - 3b)^2}$ $\dfrac{a - 3b}{c}$

Divisor a Monomial

Fractional expressions show division. To divide a polynomial by a monomial, divide each term by that monomial.

EXAMPLE

1. Divide $6x^2 + 3x - 2$ by 3.

$$\frac{6x^2 + 3x - 2}{3} = \frac{6x^2}{3} + \frac{3x}{3} - \frac{2}{3} \quad \text{Dividing each term by 3}$$

$$= 2x^2 + x - \frac{2}{3}$$

2. Divide $x^3 + 10x^2 + 8x$ by $2x$.

$$x^3 + 10x^2 + 8x - 2x = \frac{x^3 + 10x^2 + 8x}{2x}$$

$$= \frac{x^3}{2x} + \frac{10x^2}{2x} + \frac{8x}{2x} \quad \text{Dividing each term by } 2x$$

$$= \frac{1}{2}x^2 + 5x + 4$$

TRY THIS Divide.

1. $\dfrac{4x^3 + 6x - 5}{2}$ 2. $\dfrac{2x^3 + 6x^2 + 4x}{2x}$ 1. $2x^3 + 3x - \frac{5}{2}$ 2. $x^2 + 3x + 2$

Divisor Not a Monomial

When the divisor is not a monomial, we usually use long division.

EXAMPLE 3

Divide $x^2 + 5x + 6$ by $x + 2$.

$$
\begin{array}{r}
x \leftarrow \quad \text{Divide first term by first term to get } x. \\
x + 2 \overline{)x^2 + 5x + 6} \\
\underline{x^2 + 2x} \leftarrow \quad \text{Multiply } x \text{ by divisor } x + 2. \\
3x \leftarrow \quad \text{Subtract}
\end{array}
$$

We now "bring down" the next term of the dividend, 6.

$$
\begin{array}{r}
x + 3 \quad\longleftarrow\text{Divide first term by first term to get 3.} \\
x + 2\overline{\smash{)}x^2 + 5x + 6} \\
\underline{x^2 + 2x} \\
3x + 6 \\
\underline{3x + 6}\quad\longleftarrow\text{Multiply 3 by divisor }x + 2. \\
0\quad\longleftarrow\text{Subtract}
\end{array}
$$

The quotient is $x + 3$. To check, multiply quotient by divisor and add the remainder, if any, to see if you get the dividend.

$(x + 2)(x + 3) = x^2 + 5x + 6$. The division checks.

EXAMPLE 4
Divide $x^2 + 2x - 12$ by $x - 3$.

$$
\begin{array}{r}
x + 5 \quad\longleftarrow \\
x - 3\overline{\smash{)}x^2 + 2x - 12} \\
\underline{x^2 - 3x} \\
5x - 12 \\
\underline{5x - 15} \\
3\quad\longleftarrow\text{Remainder}
\end{array}
$$

Check:
$(x - 3)(x + 5) + 3 = x^2 + 2x - 15 + 3$
$\qquad\qquad\qquad\quad = x^2 + 2x - 12$

Quotient

The answer can be written as quotient plus remainder over divisor.

Quotient $\quad x + 5 + \dfrac{3\longleftarrow\text{Remainder}}{x - 3}\quad$ Divisor

TRY THIS Divide.

3. $(x^2 + x - 6) \div (x + 3)$ **4.** $x - 2\overline{\smash{)}x^2 + 2x - 9}$ 3. $x - 2$ 4. $x + 4 + \frac{-1}{x-2}$

When there are missing terms, we may write 0's or leave space.

EXAMPLES
Divide.

5. $(x^3 + 1) \div (x + 1)$

$$
\begin{array}{r}
x^2 - x \qquad\quad + 1 \\
x + 1\overline{\smash{)}x^3 + 0 \cdot x^2 + 0x + 1}\quad\text{Writing in the missing terms} \\
\underline{x^3 + \quad x^2} \\
- x^2 + 0x \\
\underline{- x^2 - \quad x} \\
x + 1 \\
\underline{x + 1}
\end{array}
$$

6. $(x^4 - 3x^2 + 1) \div (x - 4)$

$$
\begin{array}{r}
x^3 + 4x^2 + 13x + 52 \\
x - 4 \overline{\smash{)}\ x^4 \qquad\ -\ 3x^2 \qquad\ +\ 1} \\
\underline{x^4 - 4x^3} \\
4x^3 - 3x^2 \\
\underline{4x^3 - 16x^2} \\
13x^2 \\
\underline{13x^2 - 52x} \\
52x + 1 \\
\underline{52x - 208} \\
209
\end{array}
$$

Leaving space for missing terms

The answer is $x^3 + 4x^2 + 13x + 52 + \dfrac{209}{x - 4}$.

TRY THIS Divide.

5. $x + 3 \overline{\smash{)}\ x^3 - 7x + 10}$ **6.** $(x^3 - 1) \div (x - 1)$ 5. $x^2 - 3x + 2 + \frac{4}{x + 3}$ 6. $x^2 + x + 1$

11–3

Exercises

Divide.

1. $\dfrac{24x^4 - 4x^3 + x^2 - 16}{8}$

2. $\dfrac{12a^4 - 3a^2 + a - 6}{6}$

3. $\dfrac{u - 2u^2 - u^5}{u}$

4. $\dfrac{50x^5 - 7x^4 + x^2}{x}$

5. $(15t^3 + 24t^2 - 6t) \div 3t$

6. $(25t^3 + 15t^2 - 30t) \div 5t$

7. $(20x^6 - 20x^4 - 5x^2) \div (-5x^2)$

8. $(24x^6 + 32x^5 - 8x^2) \div (-8x^2)$

9. $(24x^5 - 40x^4 + 6x^3) \div (4x^3)$

10. $(18x^6 - 27x^5 - 3x^3) \div (9x^3)$

11. $\dfrac{9r^2s^2 + 3r^2s - 6rs^2}{-3rs}$

12. $\dfrac{4x^4y - 8x^6y^2 + 12x^8y^6}{4x^4y}$

Divide.

13. $(x^2 + 4x + 4) \div (x + 2)$

14. $(x^2 - 6x + 9) \div (x - 3)$

15. $(x^2 - 10x - 25) \div (x - 5)$

16. $(x^2 + 8x - 16) \div (x + 4)$

17. $(x^2 + 4x - 14) \div (x + 6)$

18. $(x^2 + 5x - 9) \div (x - 2)$

19. $\dfrac{x^2 - 9}{x + 3}$ **20.** $\dfrac{x^2 - 25}{x + 5}$ **21.** $\dfrac{x^5 + 1}{x + 1}$ **22.** $\dfrac{x^5 - 1}{x - 1}$

1. $3x^4 - x^3/2 + x^2/8 - 2$
2. $2a^4 - a^2/2 + a/6 - 1$
3. $1 - 2u - u^4$
4. $50x^4 - 7x^3 + x$
5. $5t^2 + 8t - 2$
6. $5t^2 + 3t - 6$
7. $-4x^4 + 4x^2 + 1$
8. $-3x^4 - 4x^3 + 1$
9. $6x^2 - 10x + 3/2$
10. $2x^3 - 3x^2 - 1/3$
11. $-3rs - r + 2s$
12. $1 - 2x^2y + 3x^4y^5$
13. $x + 2$
14. $x - 3$
15. $x - 5 + (-50)/(x - 5)$
16. $x + 4 + (-32)/(x + 4)$
17. $x - 2 + (-2)/(x + 6)$
18. $x + 7 + 5/(x - 2)$
19. $x - 3$
20. $x - 5$
21. $x^4 - x^3 + x^2 - x + 1$
22. $x^4 + x^3 + x^2 + x + 1$

23. $\dfrac{8x^3 - 22x^2 - 5x + 12}{4x + 3}$

24. $\dfrac{2x^3 - 9x^2 + 11x - 3}{2x - 3}$

25. $(x^6 - 13x^3 + 42) \div (x^3 - 7)$

26. $(x^6 + 5x^3 - 24) \div (x^3 - 3)$

27. $(x^4 - 16) \div (x - 2)$

28. $(x^4 - 81) \div (x - 3)$

29. $(t^3 - t^2 + t - 1) \div (t - 1)$

30. $(t^3 - t^2 + t - 1) \div (t + 1)$

23. $2x^2 - 7x + 4$
24. $x^2 - 3x + 1$
25. $x^3 - 6$
26. $x^3 + 8$
27. $x^3 + 2x^2 + 4x + 8$
28. $x^3 + 3x^2 + 9x + 27$
29. $t^2 + 1$
30. $t^2 - 2t + 3 + (-4)/(t + 1)$

Extension

Divide.

31. $(x^4 + 9x^2 + 20) \div (x^2 + 4)$ $x^2 + 5$

32. $(y^4 + a^2) \div (y + a)$ $y^3 - ay^2 + a^2y - a^3 + \dfrac{a^2(a^2 + 1)}{y + a}$

33. $(5a^3 + 8a^2 - 23a - 1) \div (5a^2 - 7a - 2)$ $a + 3 + \dfrac{5}{5a^2 - 7a - 2}$

34. $(15y^3 - 30y + 7 - 19y^2) \div (3y^2 - 2 - 5y)$ $5y + 2 + \dfrac{-10y + 11}{3y^2 - 5y - 2}$

35. $(6x^5 - 13x^3 + 5x + 3 - 4x^2 + 3x^4) \div (3x^3 - 2x - 1)$ $2x^2 + x - 3$

36. $(5x^7 - 3x^4 + 2x^2 - 10x + 2) \div (x^2 - x + 1)$ $5x^5 + 5x^4 - 8x^2 - 8x + 2$

37. $(a^6 - b^6) \div (a - b)$ $a^5 + a^4b + a^3b^2 + a^2b^3 + ab^4 + b^5$

38. $(x^5 + y^5) \div (x + y)$ $x^4 - x^3y + x^2y^2 - xy^3 + y^4$

Challenge

39. Divide $6a^{3h} + 13a^{2h} - 4a^h - 15$ by $2a^h + 3$. $3a^{2h} + 2a^h - 5$

If the remainder is 0 when one polynomial is divided by another, then the divisor is a factor of the dividend. Find the value(s) of c for which $x - 1$ is a factor of each polynomial.

40. $x^2 + 4x + c$ -5 **41.** $2x^2 + 3cx - 8$ 2 **42.** $c^2x^2 - 2cx + 1$ 1

COMPUTERS AND THE CENSUS

The 1890 United States census posed a crisis in data processing. Statistics from the 1880 census were still being analyzed in 1887. At that rate, the 1890 data would be obsolete before they could be completely analyzed.

Although the census as described in the Constitution had begun as a simple count of the number of citizens, over the years it had become a complex report that included information such as immigration, health, literacy, and employment statistics. Unless a fast, accurate way of processing the census data were found, the scope of the 1890 census would have to be narrowed. So, the Census Office held a competition to choose an efficient census-taking system.

Herman Hollerith, a graduate of the Columbia University School of Mines, won the competition with an electric tabulating system. His machine did the job in less than half the time required by either of two competing systems and used punched cards that did not require hand sorting and punching. Hollerith's machine is an early example of a computing machine used to process numerical data.

Addition and Subtraction

Using the Same Denominators

For any fractional expressions with the same denominator, we add or subtract the numerators and keep the denominator.

EXAMPLES
Add or subtract.

1. $\dfrac{2x^2 + 3x - 7}{2x + 1} + \dfrac{x^2 + x - 8}{2x + 1} = \dfrac{(2x^2 + 3x - 7) + (x^2 + x - 8)}{2x + 1}$

$= \dfrac{3x^2 + 4x - 15}{2x + 1}$

$= \dfrac{(x + 3)(3x - 5)}{2x + 1}$

2. $\dfrac{3x}{x + 2} - \dfrac{x - 2}{x + 2} = \dfrac{3x - (x - 2)}{x + 2}$ The parentheses are important to make sure you subtract the entire numerator.

$= \dfrac{3x - x + 2}{x + 2}$

$= \dfrac{2x + 2}{x + 2}$

$= \dfrac{2(x + 1)}{x + 2}$

TRY THIS Add or subtract.

1. $\dfrac{x^2 - 10x - 7}{2x + 1} + \dfrac{x^2 + x + 2}{2x + 1}$ **2.** $\dfrac{4x + 5}{x - 1} - \dfrac{2x - 1}{x - 1}$ 1. $x - 5$ 2. $\dfrac{2(x - 3)}{x - 1}$

Denominators as Additive Inverses

Sometimes we can make the denominators the same by multiplying by $\frac{-1}{-1}$.

EXAMPLES
Add or subtract.

3. $\dfrac{x}{5} - \dfrac{3x - 4}{-5} = \dfrac{x}{5} - \dfrac{-1}{-1} \cdot \dfrac{3x - 4}{-5}$ Multiplying by $\frac{-1}{-1}$

$$= \frac{x}{5} - \frac{4 - 3x}{5} \qquad -1(3x - 4) = 4 - 3x$$

$$= \frac{x - (4 - 3x)}{5} \qquad \text{Remember the parentheses.}$$

$$= \frac{x - 4 + 3x}{5}$$

$$= \frac{4x - 4}{5}$$

$$= \frac{4(x - 1)}{5}$$

4. $\dfrac{3x + 4}{x - 2} + \dfrac{x - 7}{2 - x} = \dfrac{3x + 4}{x - 2} + \dfrac{-1}{-1} \cdot \dfrac{x - 7}{2 - x}$

$$= \frac{3x + 4}{x - 2} + \frac{7 - x}{x - 2}$$

$$= \frac{3x + 4 + 7 - x}{x - 2}$$

$$= \frac{2x + 11}{x + 2}$$

5. $\dfrac{3x - 8}{(2x - 1)(x - 3)} - \dfrac{x + 5}{(1 - 2x)(x - 3)} = \dfrac{3x - 8}{(2x - 1)(x - 3)} - \dfrac{-1}{-1} \dfrac{x + 5}{(1 - 2x)(x - 3)}$

$$= \frac{3x - 8}{(2x - 1)(x - 3)} - \frac{-(x + 5)}{(2x - 1)(x - 3)}$$

$$= \frac{3x - 8 + x + 5}{(2x - 1)(x - 3)}$$

$$= \frac{4x - 3}{(2x - 1)(x - 3)}$$

TRY THIS Add or subtract.

3. $\dfrac{x}{4} + \dfrac{5}{-4}$ **4.** $\dfrac{2x + 1}{x - 3} - \dfrac{x + 2}{3 - x}$ **5.** $\dfrac{4y^2 - 4}{3x - 5} + \dfrac{3x^2 + 5}{5 - 3x}$ 3. $\frac{x - 5}{4}$ 4. $\frac{3(x + 1)}{x - 3}$

5. $\frac{4y^2 - 3x^2 - 9}{3x - 5}$

11–4

Exercises

Add or subtract.   1. $\frac{2(x - 2)(x - 1)}{2x - 1}$ 2. $\frac{x^2 + 4x + 1}{5x + 1}$ 3. $\frac{-2(x - 3)}{(x - 1)^2}$ 4. $\frac{3x + 4}{(x - 1)(x + 4)}$

1. $\dfrac{5x^2 - 3x + 2}{2x - 1} - \dfrac{3x^2 + 3x - 2}{2x - 1}$ **2.** $\dfrac{4x^2 + 2x - 3}{5x + 1} - \dfrac{3x^2 - 2x - 4}{5x + 1}$

3. $\dfrac{x + 1}{x^2 - 2x + 1} + \dfrac{5 - 3x}{x^2 - 2x + 1}$ **4.** $\dfrac{2x - 3}{x^2 + 3x - 4} + \dfrac{x - 7}{x^2 + 3x - 4}$

Add or subtract.

5. $\dfrac{11}{6} + \dfrac{5x}{-6}$ $\frac{11-5x}{6}$

6. $\dfrac{7}{8} + \dfrac{5x}{-8}$ $\frac{7-5x}{8}$

7. $\dfrac{5}{a} - \dfrac{8}{-a}$ $\frac{13}{a}$

8. $\dfrac{3}{t} - \dfrac{4}{-t}$ $\frac{7}{t}$

9. $\dfrac{x}{4} + \dfrac{3x-5}{-4}$ $\frac{-2x+5}{4}$

10. $\dfrac{x}{8} + \dfrac{2x-9}{-8}$ $\frac{-x+9}{8}$

11. $\dfrac{2}{x-1} + \dfrac{2}{1-x}$ 0

12. $\dfrac{x}{x-1} + \dfrac{1}{1-x}$ 1

13. $\dfrac{3-x}{x-7} - \dfrac{2x-5}{7-x}$ $\frac{x-2}{x-7}$

14. $\dfrac{4-x}{x-9} - \dfrac{3x-8}{9-x}$ $\frac{2x-4}{x-9}$

19. $\frac{-2(5x+4)}{2x-3}$

15. $\dfrac{t^2}{t-2} - \dfrac{4}{2-t}$ $\frac{t^2+4}{t-2}$

16. $\dfrac{y^2}{y-3} - \dfrac{9}{3-y}$ $\frac{y^2+9}{y-3}$

21. $\frac{4x}{x^2-5x-8}$

23. $\frac{3x^2+2x-3}{(x-2)(x-3)}$

17. $\dfrac{x-8}{x^2-16} + \dfrac{x-8}{16-x^2}$ 0

18. $\dfrac{x-2}{x^2-25} + \dfrac{x-2}{25-x^2}$ 0

27. $\frac{10x+2}{2x-3}$

19. $\dfrac{3(x-2)}{2x-3} - \dfrac{5(2x+1)}{2x-3} + \dfrac{3(x-1)}{3-2x}$

20. $\dfrac{2(x-1)}{2x-3} - \dfrac{3(x+2)}{2x-3} + \dfrac{x-1}{3-2x}$ $\frac{-2x-7}{2x-3}$

21. $\dfrac{x^2-2x}{x^2-5x-8} + \dfrac{x^2-6x}{8+5x-x^2}$

22. $\dfrac{5x-x^2}{x^2-4x-3} + \dfrac{3x-x^2}{3+4x-x^2}$ $\frac{2x}{(x-3)(x-1)}$

23. $\dfrac{(x+1)(2x-1)}{(x-2)(x-3)} - \dfrac{(x+2)(x-1)}{(x-2)(3-x)}$

24. $\dfrac{(x+2)(x-3)}{(x+1)(x-4)} - \dfrac{(x+5)(x-1)}{(x+1)(4-x)}$ $\frac{2x^2+3x-11}{(x+1)(x-4)}$

25. $\dfrac{x+3}{x-5} + \dfrac{2x-1}{5-x} - \dfrac{2(3x-1)}{x-5}$ $\frac{-7x+6}{x-5}$ **26.** $-\dfrac{2(4x+1)}{5x-7} - \dfrac{3(x-2)}{7-5x} + \dfrac{-10x+29}{5x-7}$ 3

27. $\dfrac{3(x-2)}{2x-3} + \dfrac{5(2x+1)}{2x-3} + \dfrac{3(x-1)}{3-2x}$

28. $\dfrac{5(x-2)}{3x-4} + \dfrac{2(x-3)}{4-3x} + \dfrac{3(5x+1)}{4-3x}$ $\frac{12x+7}{4-3x}$

29. $\dfrac{x+1}{(x+3)(x-3)} - \dfrac{4(x-3)}{(x-3)(x+3)} - \dfrac{(x-1)(x-3)}{(3-x)(x+3)}$ $\frac{x^2-7x+16}{(x+3)(x-3)}$

30. $\dfrac{2(x+5)}{(2x-3)(x-1)} - \dfrac{3x+4}{(2x-3)(1-x)} + \dfrac{x-5}{(3-2x)(x-1)}$ $\frac{4x+9}{(2x-3)(x-1)}$

Extension
Simplify.

31. $\dfrac{x}{(x-y)(y-z)} - \dfrac{x}{(y-x)(z-y)}$ 0 **32.** $\dfrac{x}{x-y} + \dfrac{y}{y-x} + \dfrac{x+y}{x-y} + \dfrac{x-y}{y-x}$ $\frac{x+y}{x-y}$

33. $\dfrac{b-c}{a-(b-c)} - \dfrac{b-a}{(b-a)-c}$ $\frac{2b-a-c}{a-b+c}$ **34.** $\dfrac{x+y+1}{y-(x+1)} + \dfrac{x+y-1}{x-(y-1)} - \dfrac{x-y-1}{1-(y-x)}$ -1

Challenge
Simplify.

35. $\dfrac{x^2}{3x^2-5x-2} - \dfrac{2x}{3x+1} \cdot \dfrac{1}{x-2}$ $\frac{x}{3x+1}$

36. $\dfrac{3}{x+4} \cdot \dfrac{2x+11}{x-3} - \dfrac{-1}{4+x} \cdot \dfrac{6x+3}{3-x}$ $\frac{-36}{(x+4)(x-3)}$

11-5 Using Different Denominators

LCM's of Algebraic Expressions

To add fractional expressions when denominators are different we begin by finding the least common multiple of the denominators.

> To find the LCM of two or more algebraic expressions we factor them. Then we use each factor the greatest number of times it occurs in any one expression.

EXAMPLES

1. Find the LCM of 12x, 16y, and 8xyz.

$$12x = 2 \cdot 2 \cdot 3 \cdot x$$
$$16y = 2 \cdot 2 \cdot 2 \cdot 2 \cdot y \qquad \text{LCM} = 2 \cdot 2 \cdot 2 \cdot 2 \cdot 3 \cdot x \cdot y \cdot z$$
$$8xyz = 2 \cdot 2 \cdot 2 \cdot x \cdot y \cdot z \qquad \qquad = 48xyz$$

2. Find the LCM of $x^2 + 5x - 6$ and $x^2 - 1$.

$$x^2 + 5x - 6 = (x + 6)(x - 1)$$
$$x^2 - 1 = (x + 1)(x - 1) \qquad \text{LCM} = (x + 6)(x + 1)(x - 1)$$

3. Find the LCM of $x^2 + 4$, $x + 1$, and 5.

These expressions are not factorable, so the LCM is their product, $5(x^2 + 4)(x + 1)$.

TRY THIS Find the LCM.   1. $60x^3y^2$ 2. $(y + 1)^2(y + 4)$ 3. $(t^2 + 16)(t - 2)$

1. $12xy^2, 15x^3y$ 2. $y^2 + 5y + 4, y^2 + 2y + 1$ 3. $t^2 + 16, t - 2$

EXAMPLES

4. Find the LCM of $x^2 - y^2$ and $2y - 2x$.

$$x^2 - y^2 = (x + y)(x - y)$$
$$2y - 2x = 2(y - x) = -2(x - y) \qquad \text{LCM} = -2(x + y)(x - y)$$

5. Find the LCM of $x^2 - 4y^2$, $x^2 - 4xy + 4y^2$, and $x - 2y$.

$$x^2 - 4y^2 = (x - 2y)(x + 2y)$$
$$x^2 - 4xy + 4y^2 = (x - 2y)(x - 2y) \qquad \text{LCM} = (x + 2y)(x - 2y)(x - 2y)$$
$$x - 2y = x - 2y$$

If an LCM is multiplied by -1, we still consider the answer to be an LCM. For example, the LCM of 7 and -7 is 7 or -7, the LCM of $x - 3$ and $3 - x$ is $x - 3$ or $3 - x$.

TRY THIS Find the LCM. 4. $3(a + b)(a - b)$ 5. $3x(x + 1)^2(x - 1)$

4. $a^2 - b^2, 3b - 3a$ 5. $x^2 + 2x + 1, 3x - 3x^2, x^2 - 1$

Addition with Different Denominators

Now that we know how to find LCM's, we can add fractional expressions with different denominators. We first find the LCM of the denominators (the least common denominator), multiply each fraction by 1 to get the same denominators, and then add numerators.

EXAMPLES
Add.

6. $\dfrac{5x^2}{8} + \dfrac{7x}{12} = \dfrac{5x^2}{2 \cdot 2 \cdot 2} + \dfrac{7x}{2 \cdot 2 \cdot 3}$ LCM of the denominator is $2 \cdot 2 \cdot 2 \cdot 3$, or 24

$$= \dfrac{5x^2}{2 \cdot 2 \cdot 2} \cdot \dfrac{3}{3} + \dfrac{7x}{2 \cdot 2 \cdot 3} \cdot \dfrac{2}{2}$$ Multiplying by 1 to get the same denominators

$$= \dfrac{15x^2 + 14x}{24}$$

7. $\dfrac{3}{x + 1} + \dfrac{5}{x - 1} = \dfrac{3}{x + 1} \cdot \dfrac{x - 1}{x - 1} + \dfrac{5}{x - 1} \cdot \dfrac{x + 1}{x + 1}$ LCM is $(x + 1)(x - 1)$

$$= \dfrac{3(x - 1) + 5(x + 1)}{(x - 1)(x + 1)}$$

$$= \dfrac{3x - 3 + 5x + 5}{(x + 1)(x + 1)}$$

$$= \dfrac{8x + 2}{(x - 1)(x + 1)}$$

$$= \dfrac{2(4x + 1)}{(x - 1)(x + 1)}$$

The numerator and denominator have no common factor, other than 1, so we cannot simplify further.

TRY THIS Add.

6. $\dfrac{7x^2}{6} + \dfrac{3x}{16}$ 7. $\dfrac{x}{x - 2} + \dfrac{4}{x + 2}$ 6. $\dfrac{56x^2 + 9x}{48}$ 7. $\dfrac{x^2 + 6x - 8}{(x - 2)(x + 2)}$

EXAMPLE 8

Add.

$$\frac{5}{x^2 + x} + \frac{4}{2x + 2} = \frac{5}{x(x + 1)} + \frac{4}{2(x + 1)} \quad \text{LCM} = 2x(x + 1)$$

$$= \frac{5}{x(x + 1)} \cdot \frac{2}{2} + \frac{4}{2(x + 1)} \cdot \frac{x}{x} \quad \text{Multiplying by 1}$$

$$= \frac{10}{2x(x + 1)} + \frac{4x}{2x(x + 1)}$$

$$= \frac{10 + 4x}{2x(x + 1)} \quad \text{Adding}$$

$$= \frac{2(5 + 2x)}{2x(x + 1)} \quad \text{Factoring numerator}$$

$$= \frac{2}{2} \cdot \frac{5 + 2x}{x(x + 1)}$$

$$= \frac{5 + 2x}{x(x + 1)}$$

$$= \frac{5 + 2x}{x^2 + x}$$

TRY THIS Add.

8. $\dfrac{3}{x^3 - x} + \dfrac{4}{x^2 + 2x + 1}$ **9.** $\dfrac{5}{x^2 + 17x + 16} + \dfrac{3}{x^2 + 9x + 8}$

8. $\dfrac{4x^2 - x + 3}{x(x - 1)(x + 1)^2}$

9. $\dfrac{8x + 88}{(x + 16)(x + 1)(x + 8)}$

Subtraction with Different Denominators

Subtraction of fractional expressions with different denominators is similar to addition. We first find the least common denominator, multiply each fraction by 1 to get the same denominators, and then subtract numerators.

EXAMPLE 9

Subtract.

$$\frac{x + 2}{x - 4} - \frac{x + 1}{x + 4} = \frac{x + 2}{x - 4} \cdot \frac{x + 4}{x + 4} - \frac{x + 1}{x + 4} \cdot \frac{x - 4}{x - 4} \quad \text{LCM} = (x - 4)(x + 4)$$

$$= \frac{(x + 2)(x + 4)}{(x - 4)(x + 4)} - \frac{(x + 1)(x - 4)}{(x - 4)(x + 4)}$$

$$= \frac{x^2 + 6x + 8 - (x^2 - 3x - 4)}{(x - 4)(x + 4)} \quad \text{Subtracting numerators} \\ \text{(don't forget parentheses)}$$

$$= \frac{x^2 + 6x + 8 - x^2 + 3x + 4}{(x - 4)(x + 4)}$$

$$= \frac{9x + 12}{(x - 4)(x + 4)}$$

$$= \frac{3(x + 4)}{(x - 4)(x + 4)}$$

$$= \frac{3}{x - 4} \cdot \frac{x + 4}{x + 4}$$

$$= \frac{3}{x - 4}$$

TRY THIS Subtract.

10. $\dfrac{-3x}{x^2 - 16} - \dfrac{x + 1}{x + 4}$ $\frac{-x^2 + 4}{x^2 - 16}$

11–5

Exercises

Find the LCM.

1. c^2d, cd^2, c^3d

3. $x - y$, $x + y$

5. $2(y - 3)$, $6(3 - y)$

7. t, $t + 2$, $t - 2$

9. $x^2 - 4$, $x^2 + 5x + 6$

11. $t^3 + 4t^2 + 4t$, $t^2 - 4t$

13. $a + 1$, $(a - 1)^2$, $a^2 - 1$

15. $m^2 - 5m + 6$, $m^2 - 4m + 4$

17. $2 + 3x$, $9x^2 - 4$, $2 - 3x$

19. $10v^2 + 30v$, $-5v^2 - 35v - 60$

21. $9x^3 - 9x^2 - 18x$, $6x^5 - 24x^4 + 24x^3$

23. $x^5 + 4x^4 + 4x^3$, $3x^2 - 12$, $2x + 4$

2. $2x^2$, $6xy$, $18y^2$

4. $a - 5$, $a + 5$

6. $4(x - 1)$, $8(1 - x)$

8. x, $x + 3$, $x - 3$

10. $x^2 + 3x + 2$, $x^2 - 4$

12. $y^3 - y^2$, $y^4 - y^2$

14. $x^2 - y^2$, $2x + 2y$, $x^2 + 2xy + y^2$

16. $2x^2 + 5x + 2$, $2x^2 - x - 1$

18. $3 - 2x$, $4x^2 - 9$, $3 + 2x$

20. $12a^2 + 24a$, $-4a^2 - 20a - 24$

22. $x^5 - 4x^3$, $x^3 + 4x^2 + 4x$

24. $x^5 + 2x^4 + x^3$, $2x^3 - 2x$, $5x - 5$

1. c^3d^2
2. $18x^2y^2$
3. $(x - y)(x + y)$
4. $(a - 5)(a + 5)$
5. $6(y - 3)$
6. $8(x - 1)$
7. $t(t + 2)(t - 2)$
8. $x(x + 3)(x - 3)$
9. $(x + 2)(x - 2)(x + 3)$
10. $(x + 1)(x - 2)(x + 2)$
11. $t(t + 2)^2(t - 4)$
12. $y^2(y + 1)(y - 1)$
13. $(a - 1)^2(a + 1)$
14. $2(x + y)^2(x - y)$
15. $(m - 2)^2(m - 3)$
16. $(x + 2)(x - 1)(2x + 1)$
17. $(3x + 2)(3x - 2)$
18. $(2x - 3)(2x + 3)$
19. $10v(v + 3)(v + 4)$
20. $12a(a + 2)(a + 3)$
21. $18x^3(x - 2)^2(x + 1)$
22. $x^3(x - 2)(x + 2)^2$
23. $6x^3(x + 2)^2(x - 2)$
24. $10x^3(x - 1)(x + 1)^2$

Add.

25. $\dfrac{2}{x} + \dfrac{5}{x^2}$

26. $\dfrac{4}{x} + \dfrac{8}{x^2}$

27. $\dfrac{5}{6r} + \dfrac{7}{8r}$

28. $\dfrac{2}{9t} + \dfrac{11}{6t}$

29. $\dfrac{x + y}{xy^2} + \dfrac{3x + y}{x^2y}$

30. $\dfrac{2c - d}{c^2d} + \dfrac{c + d}{cd^2}$

25. $\frac{2x + 5}{x^2}$

26. $\frac{4x + 8}{x^2}$

27. $\frac{41}{24r}$

28. $\frac{37}{18t}$

29. $\frac{x^2 + 4xy + y^2}{x^2y^2}$

30. $\frac{c^2 + 3cd - d^2}{c^2d^2}$

31. $\dfrac{3}{x-2} + \dfrac{3}{x+2}$

32. $\dfrac{2}{x-1} + \dfrac{2}{x+1}$

31. $\dfrac{6x}{(x-2)(x+2)}$

32. $\dfrac{4x}{(x-1)(x+1)}$

33. $\dfrac{3}{x+1} + \dfrac{2}{3x}$

34. $\dfrac{2}{x+5} + \dfrac{3}{4x}$

33. $\dfrac{11x+2}{3x(x+1)}$

34. $\dfrac{11x+15}{4x(x+5)}$

35. $\dfrac{2x}{x^2-16} + \dfrac{x}{x-4}$

36. $\dfrac{4x}{x^2-25} + \dfrac{x}{x+5}$

35. $\dfrac{x^2+6x}{(x-4)(x+4)}$

36. $\dfrac{x^2-x}{(x+5)(x-5)}$

37. $\dfrac{5}{z+4} + \dfrac{3}{3z+12}$

38. $\dfrac{t}{t-3} + \dfrac{5}{4t-12}$

37. $\dfrac{6}{z+4}$

38. $\dfrac{4t+5}{4(t-3)}$

39. $\dfrac{3}{x-1} + \dfrac{2}{(x-1)^2}$

40. $\dfrac{2}{x+3} + \dfrac{4}{(x+3)^2}$

39. $\dfrac{3x-1}{(x-1)^2}$

40. $\dfrac{2x+10}{(x+3)^2}$

41. $\dfrac{4a}{5a-10} + \dfrac{3a}{10a-20}$

42. $\dfrac{3a}{4a-20} + \dfrac{9a}{6a-30}$

41. $\dfrac{11a}{10(a-2)}$

42. $\dfrac{9a}{4(a-5)}$

43. $\dfrac{x+4}{x} + \dfrac{x}{x+4}$

44. $\dfrac{x}{x-5} + \dfrac{x-5}{x}$

43. $\dfrac{2x^2+8x+16}{x(x+4)}$

44. $\dfrac{2x^2-10x+25}{x(x-5)}$

45. $\dfrac{x}{x^2+2x+1} + \dfrac{1}{x^2+5x+4}$

46. $\dfrac{7}{a^2+a-2} + \dfrac{5}{a^2-4a+3}$

45. $\dfrac{x^2+5x+1}{(x+1)^2(x+4)}$

46. $\dfrac{12a-11}{(a+2)(a-1)(a-3)}$

47. $\dfrac{x+3}{x-5} + \dfrac{x-5}{x+3}$

48. $\dfrac{3x}{2y-3} + \dfrac{2x}{3y-2}$

47. $\dfrac{2x^2-4x+34}{(x-5)(x+3)}$

48. $\dfrac{13xy-12x}{(2y-3)(3y-2)}$

49. $\dfrac{a}{a^2-1} + \dfrac{2a}{a^2-a}$

50. $\dfrac{3x+2}{3x+6} + \dfrac{x-2}{x^2-4}$

49. $\dfrac{3a+2}{(a-1)(a+1)}$

50. $\dfrac{3x^2-x-10}{3(x+2)(x-2)}$

51. $\dfrac{6}{x-y} + \dfrac{4x}{y^2-x^2}$ $\quad \dfrac{2x+6y}{(x-y)(x+y)}$

52. $\dfrac{a-2}{3-a} + \dfrac{4-a^2}{a^2-9}$ $\quad \dfrac{-2a^2-a+10}{(a-3)(a+3)}$

53. $\dfrac{10}{x^2+x-6} + \dfrac{3x}{x^2-4x+4}$

54. $\dfrac{2}{z^2-z-6} + \dfrac{3}{z^2-9}$

53. $\dfrac{3x^2+19x-20}{(x+3)(x-2)^2}$

54. $\dfrac{5z+12}{(z-3)(z+3)(z+2)}$

Subtract.

55. $\dfrac{x-2}{6} - \dfrac{x+1}{3}$ $\quad \dfrac{-x-4}{6}$

56. $\dfrac{a+2}{2} - \dfrac{a-4}{4}$ $\quad \dfrac{a+8}{4}$

57. $\dfrac{y-5}{y} - \dfrac{3y-1}{4y}$ $\quad \dfrac{y-19}{4y}$

58. $\dfrac{x-1}{4x} - \dfrac{2x+3}{x}$

59. $\dfrac{4z-9}{3z} - \dfrac{3z-8}{4z}$

60. $\dfrac{3x-2}{4x} - \dfrac{3x+1}{6x}$ $\quad \dfrac{3x-8}{12x}$

61. $\dfrac{5x+3y}{2x^2y} - \dfrac{3x-4y}{xy^2}$

62. $\dfrac{4x+2t}{3xt^2} - \dfrac{5x-3t}{x^2t}$

63. $\dfrac{5}{x+5} - \dfrac{3}{x-5}$ $\quad \dfrac{2x-40}{(x+5)(x-5)}$

64. $\dfrac{2z}{z-1} - \dfrac{3z}{z+1}$

65. $\dfrac{5x}{x^2-9} - \dfrac{4}{x+3}$

66. $\dfrac{8x}{x^2-16} - \dfrac{5}{x+4}$ $\quad \dfrac{3x+20}{(x-4)(x+4)}$

67. $\dfrac{3}{2t^2-2t} - \dfrac{5}{2t-2}$

68. $\dfrac{4}{5b^2-5b} - \dfrac{3}{5b-5}$

69. $\dfrac{2s}{t^2-s^2} - \dfrac{s}{t-s}$ $\quad \dfrac{2s-st-s^2}{(t+s)(t-s)}$

58. $\dfrac{-7x-13}{4x}$

61. $\dfrac{-6x^2+13xy+3y^2}{2x^2y^2}$

64. $\dfrac{5z-z^2}{(z-1)(z+1)}$

67. $\dfrac{3-5t}{2t(t-1)}$

59. $\dfrac{7z-12}{12z}$

62. $\dfrac{4x^2-13xt+9t^2}{3x^2t^2}$

65. $\dfrac{x+12}{(x-3)(x+3)}$

68. $\dfrac{4-3b}{5b(b-1)}$

Extension

Simplify.

70. $\dfrac{x}{x^2+5x+6} - \dfrac{2}{x^2+3x+2}$

71. $\dfrac{x}{x^2+11x+30} - \dfrac{5}{x^2+9x+20}$

70. $\dfrac{x-3}{(x+1)(x+3)}$

71. $\dfrac{x-6}{(x+4)(x+6)}$

72. Find the LCM of $8x^2 - 8$, $6x^2 - 12x + 6$, and $10 - 10x$.

Find the perimeter and area of each figure.

73.

$$\frac{y+4}{3}$$

$$\frac{y-2}{5}$$

74.

$$\frac{3}{x+4}$$

$$\frac{2}{x-5}$$

73. $\frac{16y+28}{15}, \frac{y^2+2y-8}{15}$
74. $\frac{10x-14}{x^2-x-20}, \frac{6}{x^2-x-20}$

Add, and simplify if possible.

75. $\dfrac{5}{z+2} + \dfrac{4z}{z^2-4} + 2$

76. $\dfrac{-2}{y^2-9} + \dfrac{4y}{(y-3)^2} + \dfrac{6}{3-y}$

75. $\frac{(z+6)(2z-3)}{z^2-4}$

76. $\frac{-2(y^2-5y-30)}{(y-3)^2(y+3)}$

77. $\dfrac{3z^2}{z^4-4} + \dfrac{5z^2-3}{2z^4+z^2-6}$ $\frac{11z^4-22z^2+6}{(2z^2-3)(z^2+2)(z^2-2)}$

78. Write $\dfrac{a+b}{a-b}$ as the sum of two fractional expressions. $\frac{a}{a-b} + \frac{b}{a-b}$

79. Write $\dfrac{5x^2-2xy}{x^2+y^2}$ as the difference of two fractional expressions. $\frac{5x^2}{x^2+y^2} - \frac{2xy}{x^2+y^2}$

80. Two joggers leave the starting point of a circular course at the same time. One jogger completes one round in 6 minutes and the second jogger in 8 minutes. After how many minutes will they meet again at the starting place, assuming they continue to run at the same pace?   24 min

The planets Earth, Jupiter, Saturn, and Uranus revolve about the sun about once each 1, 12, 30, and 84 years, respectively.

81. How often will Jupiter and Saturn appear in the same direction in the night sky as seen from Earth?   Every 60 years

82. How often will Jupiter, Saturn, and Uranus all appear in the same direction in the night sky as seen from Earth?   Every 420 years

Combining Addition and Subtraction

Adding and Subtracting Fractional Expressions

When we have combined addition and subtraction operations, we find the LCM of the denominators and combine numerators.

EXAMPLE 1
Simplify.

$$\frac{1}{x} - \frac{1}{x^2} + \frac{2}{x+1} = \frac{1}{x} \cdot \frac{x(x+1)}{x(x+1)} - \frac{1}{x^2} \cdot \frac{x+1}{x+1} + \frac{2}{x+1} \cdot \frac{x^2}{x^2} \quad \text{LCM} = x^2(x+1)$$

$$= \frac{x(x+1)}{x^2(x+1)} - \frac{x+1}{x^2(x+1)} + \frac{2x^2}{x^2(x+1)}$$

$$= \frac{x(x+1) - (x+1) + 2x^2}{x^2(x+1)}$$

$$= \frac{x^2 + x - x - 1 + 2x^2}{x^2(x+1)}$$

$$= \frac{3x^2 - 1}{x^2(x+1)}$$

TRY THIS Simplify.

1. $\dfrac{1}{x} - \dfrac{5}{3x} + \dfrac{2x}{x+1}$ 2. $\dfrac{x}{x+2} - \dfrac{x}{x-1} + \dfrac{2-x}{3x^2+3x-6}$ 1. $\frac{6x^2 - 2x - 2}{3x(x+1)}$ 2. $\frac{-10x+2}{3(x+2)(x-1)}$

Complex Fractional Expressions (Optional)

A complex fractional expression is one that has a fractional expression in its numerator or denominator, or both. Here are some examples of complex fractional expressions.

$$\frac{1 + \dfrac{2}{x}}{3} \qquad \frac{\dfrac{x+y}{2}}{\dfrac{2x}{x+1}} \qquad \frac{\dfrac{1}{3} + \dfrac{1}{5}}{\dfrac{2}{x} - \dfrac{x}{y}}.$$

To simplify complex fractional expressions, we first add or subtract to get a single fractional expression in both numerator and denominator. Then we divide and simplify.

EXAMPLE 2
Simplify.

$$\frac{1 + \dfrac{2}{x}}{\dfrac{3}{4}} = \frac{1 \cdot \dfrac{x}{x} + \dfrac{2}{x}}{\dfrac{3}{4}} \qquad \text{Multiplying by } \dfrac{x}{x} \text{ to get a common denominator}$$

$$= \frac{\dfrac{x + 2}{x}}{\dfrac{3}{4}} \qquad \text{Adding in the numerator}$$

$$= \frac{x + 2}{x} \cdot \frac{4}{3} \qquad \text{Multiplying by the reciprocal of the denominator}$$

$$= \frac{4(x + 2)}{3x}$$

TRY THIS Simplify.

3. $\dfrac{\dfrac{2}{7} + \dfrac{3}{7}}{\dfrac{3}{4}}$ $\frac{20}{21}$ 4. $\dfrac{3 + \dfrac{x}{2}}{\dfrac{5}{4}}$ $\frac{2(x + 6)}{5}$

You can use one LCM for both the numerator and denominator.

EXAMPLE 3
Simplify.

$$\frac{1 - \dfrac{1}{x}}{1 - \dfrac{1}{x^2}} = \frac{1 - \dfrac{1}{x}}{1 - \dfrac{1}{x^3}} \cdot \frac{x^2}{x^2} \qquad \text{The LCM of expressions in numerator and denominator is } x^2. \text{ We multiply by } \dfrac{x^2}{x^2}.$$

$$= \frac{x^2 - x}{x^2 - 1}$$

$$= \frac{x(x - 1)}{(x + 1)(x - 1)}$$

$$= \frac{x}{x + 1}$$

TRY THIS Simplify.

5. $\dfrac{\dfrac{x}{2} + \dfrac{2x}{3}}{\dfrac{1}{x} - \dfrac{x}{2}}$ 6. $\dfrac{1 + \dfrac{1}{x}}{1 - \dfrac{1}{x^2}}$ 5. $\frac{7x^2}{3(2 - x^2)}$ 6. $\frac{x}{x - 1}$

Exercises

Simplify.

1. $\dfrac{4y}{y^2 - 1} - \dfrac{2}{y} - \dfrac{2}{y + 1}$

2. $\dfrac{x + 6}{4 - x^2} - \dfrac{x + 3}{x + 2} + \dfrac{x - 3}{2 - x}$

3. $\dfrac{2z}{1 - 2z} + \dfrac{3z}{2z + 1} - \dfrac{3}{4z^2 - 1}$

4. $\dfrac{4x}{1 - 3x} - \dfrac{5x}{3x + 1} + \dfrac{2}{9x^2 - 1}$

5. $\dfrac{5}{3 - 2x} + \dfrac{3}{2x - 3} - \dfrac{x - 3}{2x^2 - x - 3}$

6. $\dfrac{2r}{r^2 - s^2} + \dfrac{1}{r + s} - \dfrac{1}{r - s}$

7. $\dfrac{3}{2c - 1} - \dfrac{1}{c + 2} - \dfrac{5}{2c^2 + 3c - 2}$

8. $\dfrac{3y - 1}{2y^2 + y - 3} - \dfrac{2 - y}{y - 1} - \dfrac{1}{2y + 3}$

9. $\dfrac{1}{x + y} + \dfrac{1}{x - y} - \dfrac{2x}{x^2 - y^2}$

10. $\dfrac{1}{a - b} - \dfrac{1}{a + b} + \dfrac{2b}{a^2 - b^2}$

1. $\dfrac{2}{y(y - 1)}$

2. $\dfrac{2x - 3}{2 - x}$

3. $\dfrac{z - 3}{2z - 1}$

4. $\dfrac{-27x^2 + x + 2}{(3x - 1)(3x + 1)}$

5. $\dfrac{-3x + 1}{(2x - 3)(x + 1)}$

6. $\dfrac{2}{r + s}$

7. $\dfrac{1}{2c - 1}$

8. $\dfrac{2y^2 + y - 6}{(2y + 3)(y - 1)}$

9. 0

10. $\dfrac{4b}{(a + b)(a - b)}$

Simplify.

11. $\dfrac{1 + \dfrac{9}{16}}{1 - \dfrac{3}{4}}$ $\dfrac{25}{4}$

12. $\dfrac{\dfrac{5}{27} - 5}{\dfrac{1}{3} + 1}$ $\dfrac{-65}{18}$

13. $\dfrac{\dfrac{1}{x} + 3}{\dfrac{1}{x} - 5}$ $\dfrac{1 + 3x}{1 - 5x}$

14. $\dfrac{\dfrac{3}{s} + s}{\dfrac{s}{3} + s}$ $\dfrac{9 + 3s^2}{4s^2}$

15. $\dfrac{\dfrac{2}{y} + \dfrac{1}{2y}}{y + \dfrac{y}{2}}$ $\dfrac{5}{3y^2}$

16. $\dfrac{4 - \dfrac{1}{x^2}}{2 - \dfrac{1}{x}}$

16. $\dfrac{2x + 1}{x}$

17. $\dfrac{\dfrac{x}{x - y}}{\dfrac{x^2}{x^2 - y^2}}$

17. $\dfrac{x + y}{x}$

18. $\dfrac{\dfrac{x}{y} - \dfrac{y}{x}}{\dfrac{1}{y} + \dfrac{1}{x}}$ $x - y$

Extension

19. Find the reciprocal of $\dfrac{2}{x - 1} - \dfrac{1}{3x - 2}.$ $\dfrac{(x - 1)(3x - 2)}{5x - 3}$

Simplify.

20. $\dfrac{1 + \dfrac{a}{b - a}}{\dfrac{a}{a + b} - 1}$ $\dfrac{a + b}{a - b}$

21. $\dfrac{\dfrac{a}{b} + \dfrac{c}{d}}{\dfrac{b}{d} + \dfrac{d}{c}}$ $\dfrac{ac}{bd}$

22. $\dfrac{\dfrac{a}{b} - \dfrac{c}{d}}{\dfrac{b}{d} - \dfrac{d}{c}}$ $\dfrac{-ac}{bd}$

Challenge

Simplify.

23. $\left[\dfrac{\dfrac{x + 1}{x - 1} + 1}{\dfrac{x + 1}{x - 1} - 1}\right]^5$ x^5

24. $1 + \dfrac{1}{1 + \dfrac{1}{1 + \dfrac{1}{1 + \dfrac{1}{x}}}}$ $\dfrac{5x + 3}{3x + 2}$

25. $\dfrac{\dfrac{z}{1 - \dfrac{z}{2 + 2z}} - 2z}{\dfrac{2z}{5z - 2} - 3}$ $\dfrac{-2z(5z - 2)}{(z + 2)(-13z + 6)}$

Solving Fractional Equations

A fractional equation is an equation containing one or more fractional expressions. Here are some examples.

$$\frac{1}{x} = \frac{1}{4 - x} \qquad x + \frac{6}{x} = -5 \qquad \frac{x^2}{x - 1} = \frac{1}{x - 1}$$

To solve a fractional equation multiply on both sides by the LCM of all the denominators.

EXAMPLE 1
Solve.

$$\frac{1}{x} = \frac{1}{4 - x} \qquad \text{LCM is } x(4 - x)$$

$$x(4 - x) \cdot \frac{1}{x} = x(4 - x) \cdot \frac{1}{4 - x} \qquad \text{Multiplying on both sides by LCM}$$

$$4 - x = x$$
$$4 = 2x$$
$$2 = x$$

Check: $\dfrac{1}{x} = \dfrac{1}{4 - x}$

$$\begin{array}{c|c} \dfrac{1}{2} & \dfrac{1}{4 - 2} \\ & \dfrac{1}{2} \end{array}$$

The number checks, so 2 is the solution.

TRY THIS Solve.

1. $\dfrac{3}{4} + \dfrac{5}{8} = \dfrac{x}{12}$ $\frac{33}{8}$ 2. $\dfrac{1}{x} = \dfrac{1}{6 - x}$ 3

EXAMPLE 2
Solve.

$$x + \frac{6}{x} = -5$$

$$x\left(x + \frac{6}{x}\right) = -5x \qquad \text{LCM is } x$$

$$x^2 + x \cdot \frac{6}{x} = -5x$$

$$x^2 + 6 = -5x$$

$$x^2 + 5x + 6 = 0 \qquad \text{Getting 0 on one side}$$

$$(x + 3)(x + 2) = 0 \qquad \text{Factoring}$$

$$x = -3 \quad \text{or} \quad x = -2 \qquad \text{Using the principle of zero products}$$

Check:

$$x + \frac{6}{x} = -5 \qquad\qquad x + \frac{6}{x} = -5$$

$-3 + \frac{6}{-3}$	-5
$-3 - 2$	
-5	

$-2 + \frac{6}{-2}$	-5
$-2 - 3$	
-5	

Both numbers check, so there are two solutions, -3 and -2.

EXAMPLE 3
Solve.

$$\frac{x^2}{x - 1} = \frac{1}{x - 1}$$

$$(x - 1) \cdot \frac{x^2}{x - 1} = (x - 1) \cdot \frac{1}{x - 1} \qquad \text{LCM is } x - 1$$

$$x^2 = 1$$

$$x^2 - 1 = 0$$

$$(x - 1)(x + 1) = 0$$

$$x - 1 = 0 \quad \text{or} \quad x + 1 = 0$$

$$x = 1 \quad \text{or} \qquad x = -1$$

Check:

$$\frac{x^2}{x - 1} = \frac{1}{x - 1} \qquad\qquad \frac{x^2}{x - 1} = \frac{1}{x - 1}$$

$\frac{1^2}{1 - 1}$	$\frac{1}{1 - 1}$
$\frac{1}{0}$	$\frac{1}{0}$

$\frac{(-1)^2}{-1 - 1}$	$\frac{1}{-1 - 1}$
$-\frac{1}{2}$	$-\frac{1}{2}$

The number -1 is a solution, but 1 is not because it makes a denominator zero.

TRY THIS Solve.

3. $x + \frac{1}{x} = 2$ ₁
4. $\frac{x^2}{x + 2} = \frac{4}{x + 2}$ ₂
5. $\frac{1}{2x} + \frac{1}{x} = -12$ $-\frac{1}{8}$

11–7

Exercises
Solve.

1. $\frac{3}{8} + \frac{4}{5} = \frac{x}{20}$ $\frac{47}{2}$
2. $\frac{3}{5} + \frac{2}{3} = \frac{x}{9}$ $\frac{57}{8}$
3. $\frac{2}{3} - \frac{5}{6} = \frac{1}{x}$ -6

4. $\frac{1}{8} - \frac{3}{5} = \frac{1}{x}$ $-\frac{40}{19}$ **5.** $\frac{1}{6} + \frac{1}{8} = \frac{1}{t}$ $\frac{24}{7}$ **6.** $\frac{1}{8} + \frac{1}{10} = \frac{1}{t}$ $\frac{40}{9}$

7. $x + \frac{4}{x} = -5$ $-4; -1$ **8.** $x + \frac{3}{x} = -4$ $-3; -1$ **9.** $\frac{x}{4} - \frac{4}{x} = 0$ $4, -4$

10. $\frac{x}{5} - \frac{5}{x} = 0$ $5; -5$ **11.** $\frac{5}{x} = \frac{6}{x} - \frac{1}{3}$ 3 **12.** $\frac{4}{x} = \frac{5}{x} - \frac{1}{2}$ 2

13. $\frac{5}{3x} + \frac{3}{x} = 1$ $\frac{14}{3}$ **14.** $\frac{3}{4x} + \frac{5}{x} = 1$ $\frac{23}{4}$ **15.** $\frac{x-7}{x+2} = \frac{1}{4}$ 10

16. $\frac{a-2}{a+3} = \frac{3}{8}$ 5 **17.** $\frac{2}{x+1} = \frac{1}{x-2}$ 5 **18.** $\frac{5}{x-1} = \frac{3}{x+2}$ $-\frac{13}{2}$

19. $\frac{x}{6} - \frac{x}{10} = \frac{1}{6}$ $\frac{5}{2}$ **20.** $\frac{x}{8} - \frac{x}{12} = \frac{1}{8}$ 3 **21.** $\frac{x+1}{3} - \frac{x-1}{2} = 1$ -1

22. $\frac{x+2}{5} - \frac{x-2}{4} = 1$ -2 **23.** $\frac{a-3}{3a+2} = \frac{1}{5}$ $\frac{17}{2}$ **24.** $\frac{x-1}{2x+5} = \frac{1}{4}$ $\frac{9}{2}$

25. $\frac{x-1}{x-5} = \frac{4}{x-5}$ No solution   **26.** $\frac{x-7}{x-9} = \frac{2}{x-9}$ No solution **27.** $\frac{2}{x+3} = \frac{5}{x}$ -5

28. $\frac{3}{x+4} = \frac{4}{x}$ -16 **29.** $\frac{x-2}{x-3} = \frac{x-1}{x+1}$ $\frac{5}{3}$ **30.** $\frac{2b-3}{3b+2} = \frac{2b+1}{3b-2}$ $\frac{1}{5}$

Solve.

31. $\frac{1}{x+3} + \frac{1}{x-3} = \frac{1}{x^2-9}$ $\frac{1}{2}$ **32.** $\frac{4}{x-3} + \frac{2x}{x^2-9} = \frac{1}{x+3}$ No solution

33. $\frac{x}{x+4} - \frac{4}{x-4} = \frac{x^2+16}{x^2-16}$ No solution **34.** $\frac{5}{y-3} - \frac{30}{y^2-9} = 1$ $2, 3$

Extension
Solve.

35. $\frac{4}{y-2} - \frac{2y-3}{y^2-4} = \frac{5}{y+2}$ 7

36. $\frac{x}{x^2+3x-4} + \frac{x+1}{x^2+6x+8} = \frac{2x}{x^2+x-2}$ $-\frac{1}{6}$

37. $\frac{y}{y+0.2} - 1.2 = \frac{y-0.2}{y+0.2}$ $\frac{-1}{30}$ **38.** $\frac{x^2}{x^2-4} = \frac{x}{x+2} - \frac{2x}{2-x}$ $0, -1$

39. $4a - 3 = \frac{a+13}{a+1}$ $2, -2$ **40.** $\frac{3x-24}{x-3} = \frac{5x-4}{2}$ $\frac{1}{3}$

41. $\frac{y^2-4}{y+3} = 2 - \frac{y-2}{y+3}$ $4, -3$ **42.** $\frac{3a-5}{a^2+4a+3} + \frac{2a+2}{a+3} = \frac{a-3}{a+1}$ $-6, -1$

Challenge

43. Solve and check. $\dfrac{n}{n-\frac{4}{9}} - \dfrac{n}{n+\frac{4}{9}} = \dfrac{1}{n}$. $\frac{4}{3}, \frac{-4}{3}$

44. Suppose $x = \frac{ab}{a+b}$ and $y = \frac{ab}{a-b}$. Show that $\frac{y^2-x^2}{y^2+x^2} = \frac{2ab}{a^2+b^2}$.

11-8 Applied Problems

Work, Motion, and Reciprocal Problems

Suppose it takes a person 4 hours to do a certain job. Then in 1 hour, $\frac{1}{4}$ of the job gets done.

> In general, if a job can be done in t hours (or days, or some other unit of time), then $\frac{1}{t}$ of it can be done in 1 hour (or day).

EXAMPLE 1
Solve.

Team A can set up chairs in the gym in 10 minutes and Team B can set up the chairs in 15 minutes. How long would it take them, working together, to set up the same chairs?

It takes Team A 10 min, then in 1 min Team A does $\frac{1}{10}$ of the job. In 1 min Team B does $\frac{1}{15}$ of the job. Working together, they can do

$$\frac{1}{10} + \frac{1}{15}$$

of the job in 1 min. Let $t =$ the time it takes to set up the chairs, if they work together. Then in 1 min they can set up $\frac{1}{t}$ of the chairs.

$$\frac{1}{10} + \frac{1}{15} = \frac{1}{t}.$$
$$30t\left(\frac{1}{10} + \frac{1}{15}\right) = 30t \cdot \frac{1}{t}$$
$$3t + 2t = 30$$
$$5t = 30$$
$$t = 6$$

It takes 6 minutes.

TRY THIS Solve.

1. By checking work records a contractor finds that it takes crew A 6 hr to construct a wall of a certain size. It takes crew B 8 hr to construct the same wall. How long would it take if they worked together? $3\frac{3}{7}$ hr

EXAMPLE 2

Solve.

One car travels 20 km/h faster than another. While one of them travels 240 km, the other travels 180 km. Find their speeds.

Let r represent the speed of the slower car. Then $r + 20$ is the speed of the faster car. The cars travel the same time so we can use t for time. We organize the information in a chart, keeping in mind the formula $d = rt$.

	distance	rate	time
slower car	180	r	t
faster car	240	$r + 20$	t

If we solve the formula $d = rt$ for t, we get $t = \frac{d}{r}$. Then from the rows of the table, we get

$$t = \frac{180}{r}$$

and

$$t = \frac{240}{r + 20}.$$

Since these times are the same, we have the following equation.

$$\frac{180}{r} = \frac{240}{r + 20}$$

$$\frac{180 \cdot r(r + 20)}{r} = \frac{240 \cdot r(r + 20)}{r + 20} \quad \text{Multiplying on both sides by the LCM, } r(r + 20)$$

$$180(r + 20) = 240r$$

$$180r + 3600 = 240r$$

$$\frac{3600}{60} = r$$

$$60 = r$$

$$80 = r + 20$$

The speeds of 60 km/h for the slower car and 80 km/h for the faster car check in the problem.

TRY THIS

2. One boat travels 10 km/h faster than another. While one boat travels 120 km, the other travels 155 km. Find their speeds. $34\frac{2}{7}$ km/h, $44\frac{2}{7}$ km/h

EXAMPLE 3

Solve.

The reciprocal of 2 less than a certain number is twice the reciprocal of the number itself. What is the number?

Let x = the number. Then 2 less than the number is $x - 2$ and the reciprocal of the number is $1/x$.

$$\left(\begin{array}{c}\text{Reciprocal of 2 less} \\ \text{than the number}\end{array}\right) \text{ is } \left(\begin{array}{c}\text{twice the reciprocal} \\ \text{of the number.}\end{array}\right)$$

$$\frac{1}{x - 2} \quad = \quad 2 \cdot \frac{1}{x} \qquad \text{Translating}$$

$$\frac{1}{x - 2} = \frac{2}{x} \qquad \text{LCM is } x(x - 2)$$

$$\frac{x(x - 2)}{x - 2} = \frac{2x(x - 2)}{x} \qquad \text{Multiplying by LCM}$$

$$x = 2(x - 2) \qquad \text{Simplifying}$$
$$x = 2x - 4$$
$$x = 4$$

Check: Go to the original problem. The number to be checked is 4. Two less than 4 is 2. The reciprocal of 2 is $\frac{1}{2}$. The reciprocal of the number itself is $\frac{1}{4}$. Now $\frac{1}{2}$ is twice $\frac{1}{4}$, so the conditions are satisfied. Thus, the solution is 4.

TRY THIS Solve.

3. The reciprocal of two more than a number is three times the reciprocal of the number. Find the number. -3

Proportion Problems

We know from Chapter 3 that an equality of ratios, $\frac{A}{B} = \frac{C}{D}$ is called a proportion. A useful property for solving a proportion is the following.

If $\frac{A}{B} = \frac{C}{D}$, then $AD = BC$ $(B, D \neq 0)$

The property can be proved using the multiplication principle. You may be asked to do so in Section 11-9.

EXAMPLES

4. *Estimating Wildlife Populations.* To determine the number of fish in a lake, a conservationist catches 225 fish, tags them, and throws them back into the lake. Later 108 fish are caught. 15 of them are found to be tagged. About how many fish are in the lake?

Let f = number of fish in the lake.

Tagged fish originally → $\dfrac{225}{f}$ = $\dfrac{15}{108}$ ← Tagged fish caught later

Fish in lake →   ← Fish caught later

$$108 \cdot 225 = f \cdot 15 \quad \text{Using the property of proportions}$$

$$\frac{108 \cdot 225}{15} = f$$

$$1620 = f$$

Thus there are about 1620 fish in the lake.

5. *An Ecology Problem.* Five people produce 13 kilograms of refuse in one day. A certain city has about 900,000 people. About how many kilograms of refuse are produced there in one day.

Let x = the number of kilograms of refuse produced in one day.

People → $\dfrac{5}{13}$ = $\dfrac{900,000}{x}$ ← People

Refuse →   ← Refuse

$$5x = 13 \cdot 900,000 \quad \text{Using the property of proportions}$$

$$x = 2,340,000$$

Thus, about 2,340,000 kilograms of refuse are produced in one day.

TRY THIS Solve.

4. To determine the number of deer in a forest a conservationist catches 612 deer, tags them, and lets them loose. Later, 244 deer are caught and 72 of them are tagged. About how many deer are in the forest? 2074

5. In one day a certain city produced 2,000,000 kg of refuse. Using a ratio of 5 people for 13 kg of refuse, estimate the number of people in the city. 769,231

6. The ratio of the weight of an object on Mars to the weight of an object on earth is 0.379 to 1. How much would a 14-ton spacecraft weigh on Mars? 5.306 tons

Exercises

Solve.

1. It takes painter A 3 hours to paint a certain area of a house. It takes painter B 5 hours to do the same job. How long would it take them, working together, to do the painting job? $1\frac{7}{8}$ hr

2. By checking work records a plumber finds that worker A can do a certain job in 12 hours. Worker B can do the same job in 9 hours. How long would it take if they worked together? $5\frac{1}{7}$ hr

3. A tank can be filled in 18 hours by pipe A or in 24 hours by pipe B. How long would it take both pipes to fill the tank? $10\frac{2}{7}$ hr

4. Team A can set up chairs in the gym in 15 minutes and Team B can set up the chairs in 20 minutes. How long would it take them, working together, to set up the same chairs? $8\frac{4}{7}$ min

5. One car travels 40 km/h faster than another. While one travels 150 km, the other goes 350 km. Find their speeds. 30 km/h, 70 km/h

6. A person traveled 120 mi in one direction. The return trip was accomplished at double the speed, and took 3 hr less time. Find the speed going. 20 mi/h

7. The speed of a freight train is 14 km/h slower than the speed of a passenger train. The freight train travels 330 km in the same time that it takes the passenger train to travel 400 km. Find the speed of each train. p: 80 km/h, f: 66 km/h

8. The reciprocal of 4 plus the reciprocal of 5 is the reciprocal of what number? $\frac{20}{9}$, or $2\frac{2}{9}$

9. The sum of half a number and its reciprocal is the same as 51 divided by the number. Find the number. $\frac{1}{2}x + \frac{1}{x} = \frac{51}{x}, x = 10$

10. The inverse of a number divided by twelve is the same as one less than three times its reciprocal. Find the number. $\frac{-x}{12} = \frac{3}{x} - 1, x = 6$

11. Last season a fast-pitch softball player got 238 hits in 595 times at bat. This season her ratio of hits to number of times at bat is the same. She batted 510 times. How many hits has she had? 204

12. The coffee beans from 14 trees are required to produce 7.7 kilograms of coffee. How many trees are required to produce 320 kilograms of coffee? $581\frac{9}{11}$

13. A sample of 184 light bulbs contained 6 defective bulbs. How many would you expect in 12,880 bulbs? 420

14. 10 cm³ of a specimen of blood contains 1.2 g of hemoglobin. How many grams would 16 cm³ of the same blood contain? 1.92

15. The ratio of the weight of an object on the moon to the weight of an object on earth is 0.166 to 1.
    a. How much would a 12-ton rocket weight on the moon?
    b. How much would a 90-kg astronaut weight on the moon?   a) 1.992 tons
       b) 14.94 kg

16. To determine the number of trout in a lake, a conservationist catches 112 trout, tags them, and throws them back into the lake. Later 82 trout are caught. 32 of them are found to be tagged. How many trout are in the lake? 287

17. A tree 92 feet high casts a shadow which is 54 feet long. How long a shadow will a 24 foot high telephone pole cast at the same time? $\frac{92}{54} = \frac{24}{x}, x = 14\frac{2}{23}$ ft

18. In 17 innings a baseball pitcher allowed 6 earned runs. How many runs would be allowed in 9 innings? $\frac{17}{6} = \frac{9}{x}, x = 3.18$

19. Simplest fractional notation for a rational number is $\frac{9}{17}$. Find an equal ratio where the sum of the numerator and denominator is 104. $9x + 17x = 104, x = 4, \frac{36}{68}$

20. A baseball team has 12 more games to play. They have won 25 out of the 36 games they have played. How many more games must they win to finish with a 0.750 record? $\frac{25 + x}{48} = .75, x = 11$

Extension

21. In a proportion $\frac{A}{B} = \frac{C}{D}$, the numbers A and D are often called extremes while the numbers B and C are called the means. Write four true proportions. Compare the product of the means with the product of the extremes. Ex. $\frac{B}{A} = \frac{D}{C}, \frac{A}{C} = \frac{B}{D}, \frac{C}{A} = \frac{D}{B}, \frac{D}{C} = \frac{B}{A}$, equal

22. Compare $\frac{A + B}{B} = \frac{C + D}{D}$ with the proportion $\frac{A}{B} = \frac{C}{D}$.

23. A number B is said to be the geometric mean between A and C if the proportion $\frac{A}{B} = \frac{B}{C}$ is true. Find the geometric mean between 4 and 9, between 2 and 32. 6, 8

22. $\frac{A + B}{B} = \frac{C + D}{D}$,
    $\frac{A}{B} + \frac{B}{B} = \frac{C}{D} + \frac{D}{D}$,
    $\frac{A}{B} + 1 = \frac{C}{D} + 1, \frac{A}{B} = \frac{C}{D}$

24. Rosina, Ng, and Oscar can complete a certain job in three days. Rosina can do the job in 8 days and Ng can do it in 10 days. How many days will it take Oscar to complete the job. $\frac{1}{8} + \frac{1}{10} + \frac{1}{x} = \frac{1}{3}, 9\frac{3}{13}$ days

Challenge

25. How soon after 5 o'clock will the hands first be together? $27\frac{3}{11}$ min or $\frac{5}{11}$ hr

26. To reach an appointment 50 miles away Dr. Wright allowed one hour. After driving thirty miles she realized that her speed would have to be increased 15 mi/h for the remainder of the trip. What was her speed for the first 30 miles? $\frac{30}{r} + \frac{20}{r + 15} = 1, 45$

27. Together, Michelle, Sal, and Kristen can do a job in 1 hour and 20 minutes. To do the job alone, Michelle needs twice the time that Sal needs and two hours more than Kristen. How long would it take each to complete the job working alone? Michelle 6hr, Sal 3 hr, Kristen 4 hr

In our work with division of rational numbers and division of fraction expressions we used the division rule of multiplying by the reciprocal of the divisor. We can prove this rule.

THEOREM

The Division Theorem

For any number a and any nonzero number b,

$$\frac{a}{b} = a \cdot \frac{1}{b}.$$

To prove this theorem we will use the definition of division. That is, $\frac{a}{b} = c$ if $c \cdot b = a$. Thus, to show that $a \cdot \frac{1}{b}$ is the quotient $\frac{a}{b}$ we will need to show that when b is multiplied by $a \cdot \frac{1}{b}$ the result is a.

1. $\left(a \cdot \frac{1}{b}\right) \cdot b = a \cdot \left(\frac{1}{b} \cdot b\right)$	1. Associative property
2. $\qquad\qquad = a \cdot (1)$	2. Definition of reciprocal
3. $\qquad\qquad = a$	3. Property of 1
4. $\left(a \cdot \frac{1}{b}\right) \cdot b = a$	4. Transitive property of equality

Thus, $a \cdot \frac{1}{b}$ is the quotient $\frac{a}{b}$.

Another theorem related to reciprocals concerns the reciprocal of a product. The reciprocal $\frac{1}{ab}$ of a product ab is the product of the reciprocal $\frac{1}{a} \cdot \frac{1}{b}$.

The strategy for proving this theorem is to apply the definition of reciprocal. We must show that $(ab) \cdot \left(\frac{1}{a} \cdot \frac{1}{b}\right)$ is 1.

TRY THIS

1. Write a proof of the theorem concerning the reciprocal of a product. (Hint: Multiply and use the commutative and associative properties.)

We know that fractional expressions can be multiplied by multiplying numerators and multiplying denominators. We prove this as our next theorem.

THEOREM

For any numbers a, c, and any nonzero numbers b, d,

$$\frac{a}{b} \cdot \frac{c}{d} = \frac{ac}{bd}.$$

---

1. $\frac{a}{b} = a \cdot \frac{1}{b}$ and $\frac{c}{d} = c \cdot \frac{1}{d}$ 1. Division theorem

2. $\frac{a}{b} \cdot \frac{c}{d} = \left(a \cdot \frac{1}{b}\right)\left(c \cdot \frac{1}{d}\right)$ 2. Substituting $a \cdot \frac{1}{b}$ for $\frac{a}{b}$ and $c \cdot \frac{1}{d}$ for $\frac{c}{d}$

3. $\qquad = (a \cdot c)\left(\frac{1}{b} \cdot \frac{1}{d}\right)$ 3. Associate property

4. $\qquad = ac\left(\frac{1}{bd}\right)$ 4. Multiplication of fractions

5. $\qquad = \frac{ac}{bd}$ 5. Division theorem

6. $\frac{a}{b} \cdot \frac{c}{d} = \frac{ac}{bd}$ 6. Transitive property of equality

TRY THIS

2. Complete the proof of the theorem above by supplying the missing reasons.

11–9

Exercises

1. Complete the proof of the following theorem by supplying the reasons.

For any numbers a, b and any non-zero number c, $\frac{a}{c} + \frac{b}{c} = \frac{a + c}{c}$.

1. $\frac{a}{c} = a \cdot \frac{1}{c}$ and $\frac{b}{c} = b \cdot \frac{1}{c}$	1. Division theorem
2. $\frac{a}{c} + \frac{b}{c} = a \cdot \frac{1}{c} + b \cdot \frac{1}{c}$	2. Substituting $a \cdot \frac{1}{c}$ for $\frac{a}{c}$ and $b \cdot \frac{1}{c}$ for $\frac{b}{c}$
3. $\qquad = (a + b)\frac{1}{c}$	3. Distribution law
4. $\qquad = \frac{a + b}{c}$	4. Division theorem
5. $\frac{a}{c} + \frac{b}{c} = \frac{a + b}{c}$	5. Transitive property of equality

2. Write a column proof of the following theorem. For any numbers a, b and any nonzero number

$$c, \frac{a}{c} - \frac{b}{c} = \frac{a - b}{c}.$$

(Hint: Use Exercise 1 as a model for your proof.)

3. Prove that if $\frac{a}{b}$ is any nonzero rational number, then its reciprocal is $\frac{b}{a}$. (Hint: Show that $\frac{b}{a}$ satisfies the definition of reciprocal.)

4. Prove the property of proportion:

$$\text{if } \frac{a}{b} = \frac{c}{d}, \text{ then } ad = bc.$$

THE RULE OF FALSE POSITION

Suppose you know that a number plus a seventh of the number is nineteen. How can you find the number? One way is to write a linear equation, $x + \frac{1}{7}x = 19$, and solve it for x. Another way is to use the *rule of false position*.

To use the rule of false position, choose any value for x. Then try it in the equation. Suppose $x = 7$. Then $x + \frac{1}{7}x = 8$, not 19. But you can use your false answer to find the true answer. The ratio of the true value of x is to 7 as 19 is to 8. So, the following proportion can be solved for x.

$$\frac{x}{7} = \frac{19}{8} \qquad x = \frac{7 \cdot 19}{8} \qquad x = 16\frac{5}{8}$$

The solution to $x + \frac{1}{7}x = 19$ is $16\frac{5}{8}$.

The rule of false position only works for linear equations with no constant terms on the left. Here is another example.

$$28x + 6(4x - 9x) - \frac{x}{2} = 10$$

When x is 1, the left side equals -2.5. So the true value of x is the solution of $\frac{x}{1} = \frac{10}{-2.5}$. Find the true value of x. -4

The rule of false position was known to mathematicians in both ancient Egypt and ancient China. It appears in the Rhind Papyrus, a role of paper-like material about 1 foot high and 18 feet long that is now in the British Museum. Although the Rhind Papyrus was written about 1650 B.C., its contents were copied from another document that was written between 2000 and 1800 B.C.

USING A CALCULATOR

Fractional Expressions

A calculator with a memory can be used to solve problems with fractional expressions. Denominators are usually computed first.

EXAMPLE 1

Problem: Evaluate the following expression for $x = -0.48$.

$$\frac{2x^2 + x}{3x^2 + 2x}$$

Enter: 0.48 [+/−]   [Min] 3 [×]   [MR]   [x^2]   [+]

Display: 0.48 −0.48   3   −0.48 0.2304 0.6912

Enter: 2 [×]   [MR]   [=]   [Min]

Display: 2   −0.48 −0.2688

The value of the denominator is now stored in the memory.

Enter: 0.48 [+/−]   [x^2]   [×] 2 [+]   0.48 [+/−]

Display: 0.48 −0.48 0.2304   2 0.4608 0.48 −0.48

Enter: [=]   [÷]   [MR]   [=]

Display: −0.0192   −0.2688 0.0714285

Practice Problem: Evaluate the expression in Example 1 for $x = -16$. 0.673913

EXAMPLE 2

Recall that a display such as $3.02-05$ stands for a number in scientific notation. So, $3.02-05 = 3.02 \times 10^{-5} = 0.0000302$.

Problem: What happens to the expression $\frac{x+1}{x^2}$ as x becomes very large?

Enter: 175 [+] 1 [=]   [÷]   175 [x^2]   [=]

Display: 175   1 176   175 30625 5.74693−03

Answer: 0.00574693

Practice Problem: Evaluate the expression in Example 2 for
$x = 50, 100, 150,$ and 200. 0.0204, 0.0101, 0.0067111, 0.005025

EXAMPLE 3

In this problem, the divisor must be evaluated first.

Problem: Find the value of the following expression for $x = 3.2$
and $y = 0.8$.

$$\left(\frac{x}{y} - \frac{y}{x}\right) \div \left(\frac{1}{y} + \frac{1}{x}\right)$$

Substitute the values for x and y: $\left(\dfrac{3.2}{0.8} - \dfrac{0.8}{3.2}\right) \div \left(\dfrac{1}{0.8} + \dfrac{1}{3.2}\right)$

Enter: 1 ⟨÷⟩ 0.8 ⟨+⟩ 1 ⟨÷⟩ 3.2 ⟨=⟩ ⟨Min⟩

Display: 1   0.8 1.25 1   3.2 1.5625 1.5625

Enter: 3.2 ⟨÷⟩ 0.8 ⟨−⟩ 0.8 ⟨÷⟩ 3.2 ⟨=⟩ ⟨÷⟩

Display: 3.2   0.8   4   0.8   3.2 3.75

Enter: ⟨MR⟩ ⟨=⟩

Display: 1.5625   2.4

Practice Problem: Evaluate the expression in Example 3 for $x =$ 0.05 and $y = 3.65.$ −3.6

EXAMPLE 4

In this problem, you must compute each side of the equation separately.

Problem: Check that -3.7 is a solution of the following equation.

$$\frac{x^2}{x - 3.7} = \frac{13.69}{x - 3.7}$$

Enter: 3.7 ⟨+/−⟩ ⟨−⟩ 3.7 ⟨=⟩ ⟨Min⟩ 3.7 ⟨+/−⟩ ⟨x²⟩

Display: 3.7 −3.7   3.7 −7.4   3.7 −3.7 13.69

Enter: ⟨÷⟩ ⟨MR⟩ ⟨=⟩

Display: −7.4 −1.85

Enter: 3.7 ⟨+/−⟩ ⟨−⟩ 3.7 ⟨=⟩ ⟨Min⟩ 13.69 ⟨÷⟩

Display: 3.7 −3.7   3.7 −7.4   13.69

Enter: ⟨MR⟩ ⟨=⟩

Display: −7.4 −1.85

Practice Problem: Is $\frac{4}{3}$ a solution of the following equation? Yes

$$\frac{n}{n - \dfrac{4}{9}} - \frac{n}{n + \dfrac{4}{9}} = \frac{1}{n}$$

Nested Form

If your calculator does not have a square or power key, you can still use it to help you evaluate higher-degree expressions. To do so, you must first write an expression in *nested form* so that there are no exponents greater than one.

EXAMPLE 5

Problem: Evaluate $3x^2 + 2x - 9$ for $x = 3.8.$

Nested Polynomial: $(3x + 2)x - 9$

Enter: 3.8 [Min] 3 [×] [MR] [+] 2 [=] [×]

Display: 3.8   3.8   3   3.8 11.4 2 13.4

Enter: [MR] [−] 9 [=]

Display: 3.8 50.52 9 41.92

Practice Problem: Evaluate $7x^2 - 5x + 3$ for $x = 0.37$. ~2.1083

EXAMPLE 6

This time, the memory is used to store the value of the denominator. So, the value 33 must be entered each time for x.

Problem: Evaluate $\dfrac{3x + 4}{5x^2 - 2x}$ for $x = 33$.

Nested Form: $\dfrac{3x + 4}{(5x - 2)x}$

Enter: 5 [×] 33 [−] 2 [=] [×] 33 [=] [Min]

Display: 5   33 165 2 163   33 5379 5379

Enter: 3 [×] 33 [+] 4 [=] [÷] [MR]   [=]

Display: 3   33 99 4 103   5379 0.0191485

Practice Problem: Evaluate $\dfrac{5x^2 + x - 3}{4x^2 - 7}$ for $x = 0.6$. ~0.1079136

EXAMPLE 7

Problem: Evaluate $4x^3 - 5x^2 + 7x - 9$ for $x = 14$.

Nested Polynomial: $((4x - 5)x + 7)x - 9$

Enter: 14 [Min] [×] 4 [−] 5 [=] [×] [MR]

Display: 14   14   4 56 5 51   14

Enter: [+] 7 [=] [×] [MR] [−] 9 [=]

Display: 714 7 721   14 10094 9 10085

Practice Problem: Evaluate the polynomial in Example 7 for $x = 8.3$. ~1991.798

The Square Root Key

Many calculators have a square root key. This key acts directly on the number in the display. Pressing the key replaces the displayed number with its positive square root.

EXAMPLE 8

Problem: Find $\sqrt{458}$.

Enter: 458 [√]

Display: 458 21.400935

Practice Problem: Find $\sqrt{318,096}$. ₅₆₄

EXAMPLE 9

Problem: Find $8 + \sqrt{17}$.

Enter: 8 [+] 17   [√]   [=]

Display: 8   17 4.1231056 12.123106

Practice Problem: Find $42 - \sqrt{23}$. ~37.204168

CAREERS/Agriculture

America's farms are the most productive in the world. Favorable climate and fertile soil account for part of the abundance. Development of high-yielding crop varieties has been important, too, as have advances in pest control and mechanical harvesting.

The majority of the credit for America's excellence in agricultural production, however, must go to individual farmers and the workers who help them. Through hard work and intelligent decision-making, farmers and agricultural workers have consistently boosted the quantity and quality of produce harvested from our fields.

Most of America's farmers are as handy with a calculator and a computer as they are with a pitchfork and spade. It is not easy to make money farming nowadays, no matter how large a harvest may be. It is not uncommon for a farmer to invest half a million dollars in a year's crop. Costs for rental of land, purchase of seed, treatment of land with pesticides, leasing of farm equipment, and wages for workers must be predicted and controlled if a farm is to show any profit at all at the end of a year.

Sad to say, even when a farmer does keep costs to a minimum, he or she can end up with a record harvest and still lose money. This is because a farmer's income is largely dependent on the price being paid for the crop in a given year. For example, a cotton farmer may wind up with a profit if buyers are willing to pay 71¢ a pound, but may lose money if the price drops to 67¢ a pound.

A knowledge of mathematics cannot take all the risk out of farming, but it can help the farmer make wise decisions and thus keep risk to a minimum.

The exercises that follow are similar to those that must be solved by farmers and other agricultural workers.

Exercises

1. A strawberry grower has obtained the following quantities of berries from 5 plots of land: 63 pounds, 77 pounds, 68 pounds, 49 pounds, 55 pounds. How many pounds must the sixth plot yield if the grower is to achieve an overall average of 62 pounds per plot? (See Section 10–4.) 60 pounds

2. The length of a certain field is 216 yards. Its owner wants to cultivate 20,000 square yards of this field. To what width should this field be planted in order to achieve the owner's objective? (The owner will be cultivating the entire length of the field.) (See Section 10–4.) ≈93 yds

3. Freida has a budget of $675 for seed and fertilizer. If the seed costs $92.65, how much can she spend on fertilizer? (See Section 10–4.) $582.35

4. Lee picked plums from 125 trees this week (working 5 days). His goal is to average picking 20 trees a day. How many trees must he pick next week (working 5 days) to bring his average to his goal by the end of next week? (See Section 10–4.) 15

5. In checking records a farmer finds that crew A can harvest a certain area of field in 5 hours. Crew B can do the same job in 7 hours. How long would it take to harvest the same area if crew A and crew B worked together? (See Section 11–8.) $2\frac{11}{12}$ hours

Review the material in the chapter. Then see how you have done by trying these review exercises. If you miss an exercise, restudy the indicated lesson.

11–1 Multiply.

1. $\dfrac{t-1}{t+4} \cdot \dfrac{3t}{5}$ $\dfrac{3t^2 - 3t}{5t + 20}$ **2.** $\dfrac{y+3}{y-5} \cdot \dfrac{2y}{2y}$ $\dfrac{2y^2 + 6y}{2y^2 - 10y}$

11–1 Simplify.

3. $\dfrac{4x^2 - 8x}{4x^2 + 4x}$ $\dfrac{x-2}{x+1}$ **4.** $\dfrac{14x^2 - x - 3}{2x^2 - 7x + 3}$ $\dfrac{7x+3}{x-3}$

11–1 Multiply and simplify.

5. $\dfrac{a^2 - 36}{10a} \cdot \dfrac{2a}{a+6}$ $\dfrac{a-6}{5}$ **6.** $\dfrac{6t-6}{2t^2 + t - 1} \cdot \dfrac{t^2 - 1}{t^2 - 2t + 1}$ $\dfrac{6}{2t-1}$

11–2 Divide and simplify.

7. $\dfrac{10 - 5t}{3} \div \dfrac{t-2}{12t}$ $-20t$ **8.** $\dfrac{4x^4}{x^2 - 1} \div \dfrac{2x^3}{x^2 - 2x + 1}$ $\dfrac{2x^2 - 2x}{x+1}$

11–3 Divide.

9. $(10x^3 - x^2 + 6x) \div 2x$ **10.** $(6x^3 - 5x^2 - 13x + 13) \div (2x + 3)$

11–4 Add or subtract.

11. $\dfrac{x+8}{x+7} + \dfrac{10 - 4x}{x+7}$ **12.** $\dfrac{8x}{x-2} - \dfrac{9x}{x-2}$ 11. $\dfrac{-3x + 18}{x+7}$ 12. $\dfrac{-x}{x-2}$

13. $\dfrac{x+3}{x-2} + \dfrac{x}{2-x}$ **14.** $\dfrac{x+3}{x-2} - \dfrac{x}{2-x}$ 13. $\dfrac{3}{x-2}$ 14. $\dfrac{2x+3}{x-2}$

11–5 Find the LCM.

15. $3x^2, 10xy, 15y^2$ **16.** $(a-2), 4(2-a)$ **17.** $(y-2)(y^2 - 4)(y+1)$
$\quad 30x^2 y^2$ $\qquad\qquad 4(a-2)$ $\qquad\qquad (y^2 - 4)(y+1)$

11–5 Add and simplify if possible.

18. $\dfrac{3}{3x - 9} + \dfrac{x-2}{3-x}$ -1 **19.** $\dfrac{2a}{a+1} + \dfrac{4a}{a^2 - 1}$ $\dfrac{2a}{a-1}$

11–5 Subtract and simplify if possible.

20. $\dfrac{3x-1}{2x} - \dfrac{x-3}{x}$ **21.** $\dfrac{1}{x^2 - 25} - \dfrac{x-5}{x^2 - 4x - 5}$ 20. $\dfrac{x+5}{2x}$ 21. $\dfrac{-x^2 + x + 26}{(x-5)(x+5)(x+1)}$

11–6 Simplify.

22. $\dfrac{3x}{x+2} - \dfrac{x}{x-2} + \dfrac{8}{x^2 - 4}$ **23.** $\dfrac{\dfrac{1}{z} + 1}{\dfrac{1}{z^2} - 1}$ 22. $\dfrac{2(x-2)}{x+2}$ 23. $\dfrac{z}{1-z}$

11–7 Solve.

24. $\dfrac{3}{y} - \dfrac{1}{4} = \dfrac{1}{y}$ $\quad$ 8 $\quad$ **25.** $\dfrac{15}{x} - \dfrac{15}{x+2} = 2$ $\quad$ 3, 5

11–8 Solve.

26. In checking records a contractor finds that crew A can pave a certain length of highway in 9 hours. Crew B can do the same job in 12 hours. How long would it take if they worked together? $5\frac{1}{7}$ hours

27. A lab is testing two high-speed trains. One train travels 40 *km/h* faster than the other. While one train travels 70 *km*, the other travels 60 *km*. Find their speeds. 240 km/h, 280 km/h

28. The reciprocal of one more than a number is twice the reciprocal of the number itself. What is the number? -2

29. A sample of 250 batteries contained 8 defective batteries. How many defective batteries would you expect in 5000 batteries? 160

CHAPTER 11 Test

Simplify.

1. $\dfrac{6x^2 + 17x + 7}{2x^2 + 7x + 3}$ $\quad \frac{3x+7}{x+3}$

Multiply and simplify.

2. $\dfrac{a^2 - 25}{6a} \cdot \dfrac{3a}{a - 5}$ $\quad \frac{a+5}{2}$

Divide and simplify.

3. $\dfrac{25x^2 - 1}{9x^2 - 6x} \div \dfrac{5x^2 + 9x - 2}{3x^2 + x - 2}$ $\quad \frac{(5x+1)(x+1)}{3x(x-2)}$

Divide.

4. $(12x^4 + 9x^3 - 15x^2) \div 3x^2$ $\quad 4x^2 + 3x - 5$

5. $(6x^3 - 8x^2 - 14x + 13) \div (3x + 2)$ $\quad 2x^2 - 4x + 2 + \frac{9}{3x+2}$

Add or subtract. Simplify if possible.

6. $\dfrac{16 + x}{x^3} + \dfrac{7 - 4x}{x^3}$ $\quad$ **7.** $\dfrac{5 - t}{t^2 + 1} - \dfrac{t - 3}{t^2 + 1}$ $\quad$ 6. $\frac{23 - 3x}{x^3}$ $\quad$ 7. $\frac{8 - 2t}{t^2 + 1}$

8. $\dfrac{x - 4}{x - 3} + \dfrac{x - 1}{3 - x}$ $\quad \frac{-3}{x-3}$ $\quad$ **9.** $\dfrac{x - 4}{x - 3} - \dfrac{x - 1}{3 - x}$ $\quad \frac{2x-5}{x-3}$

10. $\dfrac{5}{t - 1} + \dfrac{3}{t}$ $\quad \frac{8t - 1}{t(t-1)}$ $\quad$ **11.** $\dfrac{1}{x^2 - 16} - \dfrac{x + 4}{x^2 - 3x - 4}$ $\quad \frac{-x^2 - 7x - 15}{(x+4)(x-4)(x+1)}$

12. $\dfrac{1}{x - 1} + \dfrac{4}{x^2 - 1} - \dfrac{2}{x^2 - 2x + 1}$ $\quad \frac{x^2 + 2x - 7}{(x-1)^2(x-1)}$

Solve.

13. $\dfrac{7}{y} - \dfrac{1}{3} = \dfrac{1}{4}$ ₁₂   **14.** $\dfrac{15}{x} - \dfrac{15}{x-2} = -2$ _{5, −3}

15. The reciprocal of three less than a number is four times the reciprocal of the number itself. What is the number? ₄

16. A sample of 125 spark plugs contained 4 defective spark plugs. How many defective spark plugs would you expect in 500 spark plugs? ₁₆

Challenge

17. Find the value of c for which $x + 1$ is a factor of $3cx^2 + 5cx + 2$. ₁

Ready for Real Numbers and Radical Expressions?

1–2   Simplify.

1. $\dfrac{18}{50}$ _{9/25} **2.** $\dfrac{18}{66}$ _{3/11} **3.** $\dfrac{81}{27}$ ₃ **4.** $\dfrac{100}{50}$ ₂

1–3   What is the meaning of each?

5. 5^2 **6.** 4^3 **7.** 7^6 **8.** x^5

5. 5×5
6. $4 \times 4 \times 4$
7. $7 \times 7 \times 7 \times 7 \times 7 \times 7$
8. $x \times x \times x \times x \times x$

2–1   Simplify.

9. $|-8|$ ₈   **10.** $1 - 15|$ ₁₅ **11.** $|0|$ ₀

2–5   Multiply.

12. $\dfrac{5}{3} \cdot \dfrac{5}{3}$ _{25/9}   **13.** $\left(-\dfrac{2}{9}\right) \cdot \dfrac{2}{9}$ _{−4/81}   **14.** $\left(-\dfrac{3}{16}\right) \cdot \left(-\dfrac{3}{16}\right)$ _{9/256} **15.** $\dfrac{11}{4} \cdot \left(-\dfrac{11}{4}\right)$ _{−121/16}

16. $(-5)(-5)$ ₂₅ **17.** $(-6)(-6)(-6)$ _{−216} **18.** $\left(-\dfrac{3}{4}\right)\left(-\dfrac{3}{4}\right)$ _{9/16}   **19.** $\left(-\dfrac{1}{5}\right)\left(-\dfrac{1}{5}\right)\left(-\dfrac{1}{5}\right)$ _{−1/125}

2–6   Write decimal notation.

20. $\dfrac{7}{8}$ **21.** $\dfrac{5}{11}$ **22.** $\dfrac{5}{12}$ **23.** $\dfrac{4}{9}$

20. 0.875
21. 0.4545
22. 0.4166
23. 0.44

4–1

24. Multiply and simplify: $x^3 \cdot x^3$. _{x^6}

5–1, 5–5   Factor.

25. $x^3 - x^2$ _{$x^2(x - 1)$} **26.** $5x - 30x^2$ _{$5x(1 - 6x)$}

27. $x^2 + 2x + 1$ **28.** $x^2 - 14x + 49$ _{$(x - 7)(x - 7)$}
_{$(x + 1)(x + 1)$}

12

CHAPTER TWELVE

Real Numbers
and Radical Expressions

12-1 Real Numbers

In this section we will learn about square roots, irrational numbers, and real numbers.

Square Roots

When we raise a number to the second power we have squared the number. Sometimes we may need to find the number which was squared. We call this process finding a square root of a number.

> The number c is a *square root* of a if $c^2 = a$.

Every positive number has two square roots. For example, the square roots of 25 are 5 and -5 because $5^2 = 25$ and $(-5)^2 = 25$. The positive square root is also called the principal square root. The symbol $\sqrt{}$ is called a radical symbol. The radical symbol refers only to the principal root. Thus, $\sqrt{25} = 5$. To name the negative square root of a number, we use $-\sqrt{}$. The number 0 has only one square root, 0.

EXAMPLES

1. Find the square roots of 81.   9 and -9 are square roots.

2. Find $\sqrt{225}$. $\sqrt{225} = 15$, taking the principal root.

3. Find $-\sqrt{64}$. $\sqrt{64} = 8$, so $-\sqrt{64} = -8$.

TRY THIS Find the following.
1. The square roots of 169   2. $-\sqrt{100}$ 3. $\sqrt{256}$

1. 13, -13
2. -10
3. 16

Irrational Numbers

Recall that all rational numbers can be named by fractional notation $\frac{a}{b}$, where a and b are integers and $b \neq 0$. Rational numbers can be named in other ways, such as with decimal notation, but they can all be named with fractional notation. Suppose we try to find a rational number for $\sqrt{2}$. We look for a number $\frac{a}{b}$ for which $\left(\frac{a}{b}\right)^2 = 2$.

We can find rational numbers whose squares are quite close to 2.

$$\left(\frac{14}{10}\right)^2 = (1.4)^2 = 1.96 \qquad \left(\frac{14142}{10000}\right)^2 = (1.4142)^2 = 1.99996164$$

$$\left(\frac{141}{100}\right)^2 = (1.41)^2 = 1.9881 \qquad \left(\frac{141421}{100000}\right)^2 = (1.41421)^2 = 1.99998992$$

$$\left(\frac{1414}{1000}\right)^2 = (1.414)^2 = 1.999396$$

Actually, we can never find one whose square is exactly 2. This can be proved but we will not do so here. Since $\sqrt{2}$ is not a rational number, we call it an irrational number

An *irrational number* is a number that cannot be named by fractional notation $\frac{a}{b}$, where a and b are integers and $b \neq 0$.

The square roots of most whole numbers are irrational. Only the perfect squares 1, 4, 9, 16, 25, 36, etc. have rational square roots.

EXAMPLES

Identify the rational numbers and the irrational numbers.

4. $\sqrt{3}$ $\sqrt{3}$ is irrational, since 3 is not a perfect square.

5. $\sqrt{25}$ $\sqrt{25}$ is rational, since 25 is a perfect square.

6. $\sqrt{35}$ $\sqrt{35}$ is irrational, since 35 is not a perfect square.

TRY THIS Identify the rational numbers and the irrational numbers.

4. $\sqrt{5}$ 5. $-\sqrt{36}$ 6. $-\sqrt{32}$ 7. $\sqrt{101}$

4. Irrational
5. Rational
6. Irrational
7. Irrational

Real Numbers

The rational numbers are very close together on the number line. Yet no matter how close together two rational numbers are, we can find infinitely many rational numbers between them. By averaging, we can find the number halfway between. This process can be repeated indefinitely. For instance, the number halfway between $\frac{1}{32}$ and $\frac{2}{32}$ is $\frac{3}{64}$, the average of $\frac{1}{32}$ and $\frac{2}{32}$. In turn, $\frac{5}{128}$ is halfway between $\frac{1}{32}$ and $\frac{3}{64}$. It looks like the rational numbers fill up the number line, but they do not. There are many points on the line for which there are no rational numbers. These points correspond to irrational numbers.

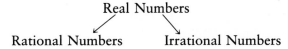

DEFINITION

The *real numbers* consist of the rational numbers and the irrational numbers. There is a real number for each point on a number line.

We know that decimal notation for a rational number either ends or continues to repeat the same group of digits. For example,

$\frac{1}{4} = 0.25$ The decimal ends.

$\frac{1}{3} = 0.3333\ldots$ The 3 repeats.

$\frac{5}{11} = 0.45\overline{45}$ The bar indicates that "45" repeats.

Decimal notation for an irrational number never ends and does not repeat any group of digits. The number π is an example.

$\pi = 3.1415926535\ldots$

Decimal notation for π never ends and never repeats. The numbers 3.1416, 3.14, or $\frac{22}{7}$ are only rational number approximations for π.

Here are some other examples of irrational numbers.

2.818118111811118111118 . . .   No group of digits repeats.
0.0350355035550355550 . . .   No group of digits repeats.

Decimal notation for an irrational number is nonrepeating and nonending.

EXAMPLES

Identify the rational numbers and the irrational numbers.

7. $\frac{18}{37}$ Rational, since it is the ratio of two integers.

8. $2.565656\ldots$ Rational, since the digits "56" repeat.

9. $4.020020002\ldots$ Irrational, since the decimal notation neither ends nor has repeating digits.

TRY THIS Identify the rational numbers and the irrational numbers.

8. $-\frac{95}{37}$ 9. 612 10. $0.353535\ldots$ 11. $3.01001000100001\ldots$

Approximating Irrational Numbers

We may need to use rational numbers to approximate irrational numbers. Table 1 in the Appendix contains rational approximations for square roots.

EXAMPLE 10

Use Table 1 to approximate $\sqrt{10}$.

We find 10 in the first column headed N. We look in the third column headed $\sqrt{N}$ opposite 10. So, $\sqrt{10} \approx 3.162$. The symbol $\approx$ means "is approximately equal to."

TRY THIS Use Table 1 to approximate these square roots.

12. $\sqrt{7}$ 13. $\sqrt{72}$ 12. 2.236   13. 8.485

12–1	

Exercises

Find the square roots of each number.

1. 1 2. 4 3. 16 4. 9

5. 100 6. 121 7. 169 8. 144

Simplify.

9. $\sqrt{4}$ 10. $\sqrt{1}$ 11. $-\sqrt{9}$ 12. $-\sqrt{25}$ 13. $-\sqrt{64}$

14. $-\sqrt{81}$ 15. $-\sqrt{225}$ 16. $\sqrt{400}$ 17. $\sqrt{361}$ 18. $\sqrt{441}$

Identify each square root as rational or irrational.

19. $\sqrt{2}$ **20.** $\sqrt{6}$ **21.** $\sqrt{8}$ **22.** $\sqrt{10}$ **23.** $\sqrt{49}$ **24.** $\sqrt{100}$

25. $\sqrt{98}$ **26.** $\sqrt{75}$ **27.** $-\sqrt{4}$ **28.** $-\sqrt{1}$ **29.** $-\sqrt{12}$ **30.** $-\sqrt{14}$

Identify each fraction or decimal as rational or irrational.

31. 4.23   **32.** 0.03   **33.** 23   **34.** -19 **35.** $-\frac{2}{3}$ **36.** 0   **37.** $\frac{2.3}{0.01}$

38. 0.424242...   **39.** 0.156156156...   **40.** 4.282282228...

41. 7.767767776...   **42.** $-34.69191191119...$ **43.** $-63.030030003...$

Use Table 1 to approximate these square roots.

44. $\sqrt{5}$ **45.** $\sqrt{6}$ **46.** $\sqrt{17}$ **47.** $\sqrt{19}$ **48.** $\sqrt{93}$ **49.** $\sqrt{43}$ **50.** $\sqrt{40}$

Extension

51. Simplify $\sqrt{\sqrt{16}}$ **52.** Simplify $\sqrt{3^2 + 4^2}$

53. Between what two consecutive integers is $-\sqrt{33}$?

54. Use Table 1 to find the irrational numbers approximated by the following square roots.

   a. 8.544   **b.** 4.123   **c.** 7.681   **d.** 5.099   **e.** 1.732

55. 10.63 is an approximation for what square root?

56. What number is halfway between x and y?

57. Find a number which is the square of an integer and the cube of a different integer.

31. Rational		41. Irrational	
32. Rational		42. Irrational	
33. Rational		43. Irrational	
34. Rational		44. 2.236	
35. Rational		45. 2.450	
36. Rational		46. 4.123	
37. Rational		47. 4.359	
38. Rational		48. 9.644	
39. Irrational		49. 6.557	
40. Irrational		50. 6.325	

Challenge

How can we find fractional notation for repeating decimals?
Find fractional notation for $0.3\overline{26}$.

We let N = the number. Then we multiply N by 10^n, where n is the number of digits in the repeating part of the decimal notation. Since there are 2 digits in 26 we multiply by 10^2 or 100.

$$
\begin{aligned}
100N &= 32.6\overline{26} \quad \text{Multiplying by 100 on both sides} \\
N &= 0.3\overline{26} \quad \text{Subtracting} \\
\hline
99N &= 32.3 \\
N &= \frac{32.3}{99} \\
N &= \frac{323}{990}
\end{aligned}
$$

Find fractional notation for each.

58. $0.\overline{81}$ $\frac{9}{11}$ **59.** $1.\overline{714285}$ $\frac{12}{7}$ **60.** $0.2\overline{3}$ $\frac{7}{30}$

Nonnegative Radicands

When an expression is written under a radical, we have a radical expression. These are radical expressions.

$$\sqrt{14} \qquad \sqrt{x} \qquad \sqrt{x^2 + 4} \qquad \sqrt{\frac{x^2 - 5}{2}}$$

The expression written under the radical is called the radicand.

The square of any number is always positive. For example, $8^2 = 64$ and $(-11)^2 = 121$. So there are no numbers that can be squared to get negative numbers.

> Radical expressions with negative radicands have no meaning in the real number system.

Thus, the following expressions do not represent real numbers.

$$\sqrt{-100} \qquad \sqrt{-49} \qquad -\sqrt{-3}$$

EXAMPLE 1
Determine whether 6 is a sensible replacement in the expression $\sqrt{1 - y}$.

If we replace y by 6, we get $\sqrt{1 - 6} = \sqrt{-5}$, which has no meaning because the radicand is negative.

TRY THIS
1. Determine whether 8 is a sensible replacement in $\sqrt{15 - 2x}$. No
2. Determine whether -10 is a sensible replacement in $\sqrt{4 - x}$. Yes

EXAMPLES
Determine the sensible replacements in each expression.

2. $\sqrt{x}$ Any number greater than or equal to 0 is sensible.

3. $\sqrt{x + 2}$ We solve the inequality $x + 2 \geq 0$. Any number greater than or equal to -2 is sensible.

4. $\sqrt{x^2}$ Squares of numbers are never negative. All replacements are sensible.

5. $\sqrt{x^2 + 1}$ Since x^2 is never negative, then $x^2 + 1$ is never negative. All replacements are sensible.

TRY THIS Determine the sensible replacements in each expression.
3. $\sqrt{a}$ **4.** $\sqrt{x - 3}$ **5.** $\sqrt{2x - 5}$ **6.** $\sqrt{x^2 + 3}$

3. $a \geq 0$
4. $x \geq 3$
5. $x \geq \frac{5}{2}$
6. All replacements

Perfect Square Radicands

We know the square of any number is never negative. Thus, in the expression $\sqrt{x^2}$, the radicand x^2 is never negative. It would seem that $\sqrt{x^2}$ is x. However, we must remember that $\sqrt{}$ means the principal square root (positive or zero). Thus, if x is negative, x^2 is positive, and $\sqrt{x^2}$ must represent a positive number.

Suppose $x = 3$. Then $\sqrt{x^2} = \sqrt{3^2}$, which is $\sqrt{9}$, or 3.
Suppose $x = -3$. Then $\sqrt{x^2} = \sqrt{(-3)^2}$,
which is $\sqrt{9}$ or 3, the absolute value of -3.

In either case we have $\sqrt{x^2} = |x|$.

> Any radical expression $\sqrt{A^2}$ can be simplified to $|A|$.

EXAMPLES
Simplify.

6. $\sqrt{(3x)^2} = |3x|$ Absolute value notation is necessary.

7. $\sqrt{a^2b^2} = \sqrt{(ab)^2} = |ab|$

8. $\sqrt{x^2 + 2x + 1} = \sqrt{(x + 1)^2} = |x + 1|$

We sometimes simplify absolute value notation. In Example 6, $|3x|$ simplifies to $|3| \cdot |x|$ or $3|x|$.

TRY THIS Simplify.
7. $\sqrt{(xy)^2}$ **8.** $\sqrt{x^2y^2}$ **9.** $\sqrt{(x - 1)^2}$

10. $\sqrt{x^2 + 8x + 16}$ **11.** $\sqrt{25y^2}$ **12.** $\sqrt{\frac{1}{4}t^2}$

7. $|xy|$
8. $|xy|$
9. $|x - 1|$
10. $|x + 4|$
11. $5|y|$
12. $\frac{1}{2}|t|$

Exercises

Determine the sensible replacements in each expression.

1. $\sqrt{5x}$
2. $\sqrt{3y}$
3. $\sqrt{t-5}$
4. $\sqrt{y-8}$
5. $\sqrt{y+8}$
6. $\sqrt{x+6}$
7. $\sqrt{x+20}$
8. $\sqrt{m-18}$
9. $\sqrt{2y-7}$
10. $\sqrt{3x+8}$
11. $\sqrt{t^2+5}$
12. $\sqrt{y^2+1}$

Simplify.

13. $\sqrt{t^2}$
14. $\sqrt{x^2}$
15. $\sqrt{9x^2}$
16. $\sqrt{4a^2}$
17. $\sqrt{(-7)^2}$
18. $\sqrt{(-5)^2}$
19. $\sqrt{(-4d)^2}$
20. $\sqrt{(-3b)^2}$
21. $\sqrt{(x+3)^2}$
22. $\sqrt{(x-7)^2}$
23. $\sqrt{a^2-10a+25}$
24. $\sqrt{x^2+2x+1}$

Extension

Solve.

25. $\sqrt{x^2}=6$
26. $\sqrt{y^2}=-7$
27. $-\sqrt{x^2}=-3$
28. $t^2=49$

Simplify.

29. $\sqrt{(3a)^2}$
30. $(\sqrt{3a})^2$
31. $\sqrt{\dfrac{144x^8}{36y^6}}$
32. $\sqrt{\dfrac{y^{12}}{8100}}$
33. $\sqrt{\dfrac{169}{m^{16}}}$
34. $\sqrt{\dfrac{p^2}{3600}}$

Determine the sensible replacements in each expression.

35. $\sqrt{m(m+3)}$ $_{m \geq 0 \text{ and } m \leq -3}$
36. $\sqrt{x^2(x-3)}$ $_{x \geq 3}$

Challenge

Determine the sensible replacements in each expression.

37. $\sqrt{(x+3)(x-2)}$ $_{37. \; x \geq 2 \text{ and } x \leq -3}$
38. $\sqrt{x^2+7x+12}$ $_{38. \; x \leq -4 \text{ and } x \geq -3}$
39. $\sqrt{x^2-4}$ $_{39. \; x \geq 2 \text{ and } x \leq -2}$
40. $\sqrt{4x^2-1}$ $_{40. \; x \geq \frac{1}{2} \text{ and } x \leq -\frac{1}{2}}$

41. For a polynomial of the form $ax^2+bx+c=0$ to have real solutions, $\sqrt{b^2-4ac}$ must be sensible. Which of the following polynomials have real solutions?
   a. $x^2-12x+3=0$
   b. $x^2+2x-50=0$
   c. $x^2+5x+7=0$
   d. $5x^2+2x+1=0$
   e. $-x^2+x+1=0$
   f. $-x^2+x-1=0$
   $_{a,b,e}$

Answers (right margin):
1. $x \geq 0$
2. $x \geq 0$
3. $t \geq 5$
4. $y \geq 8$
5. $y \geq -8$
6. $x \geq -6$
7. $x \geq -20$
8. $m \geq 18$
9. $y \geq \frac{7}{2}$
10. $x \geq -\frac{8}{3}$
11. any value
12. any value
13. $|t|$
14. $|x|$
15. $3|x|$
16. $2|a|$
17. 7
18. 5
19. $4|d|$
20. $3|b|$
21. $|x+3|$
22. $|x-7|$
23. $|a-5|$
24. $|x+1|$
25. 6, -6
26. No value
27. 3, -3
28. 7, -7
29. $3|a|$
30. $3|a|$
31. $2\left|\dfrac{x^4}{y^3}\right|$
32. $\dfrac{y^6}{90}$
33. $\dfrac{13}{m^8}$
34. $\dfrac{|P|}{60}$

Multiplying Radical Expressions

To see how we can multiply with radical notation, look at the following examples.

EXAMPLES
Simplify.

1. $\sqrt{9} \cdot \sqrt{4} = 3 \cdot 2 = 6$ The product of square roots
$\sqrt{9 \cdot 4} = \sqrt{36} = 6$ The square root of a product

2. $\sqrt{4} \cdot \sqrt{25} = 2 \cdot 5 = 10$
$\sqrt{4 \cdot 25} = \sqrt{100} = 10$

TRY THIS Multiply.
1. $\sqrt{49}\sqrt{64}$ 56   2. $\sqrt{16}\sqrt{121}$ 44

We can multiply radical expressions by multiplying the radicands, provided the radicands are not negative.

For any nonnegative radicands A and B, $\sqrt{A} \cdot \sqrt{B} = \sqrt{A \cdot B}$. (The product of square roots, provided they exist, is the square root of the product of the radicands.)

EXAMPLES
Multiply. Assume all radicands are nonnegative.

3. $\sqrt{5}\sqrt{7} = \sqrt{5 \cdot 7} = \sqrt{35}$

4. $\sqrt{8}\sqrt{8} = \sqrt{8 \cdot 8} = \sqrt{64} = 8$

5. $\sqrt{\dfrac{2}{3}}\sqrt{\dfrac{4}{5}} = \sqrt{\dfrac{2}{3} \cdot \dfrac{4}{5}} = \sqrt{\dfrac{8}{15}}$

6. $\sqrt{2x}\sqrt{3x - 1} = \sqrt{2x(3x - 1)} = \sqrt{6x^2 - 2x}$

TRY THIS Multiply. Assume all radicands are nonnegative.
3. $\sqrt{3}\sqrt{7}$ 4. $\sqrt{5}\sqrt{5}$ 5. $\sqrt{x}\sqrt{x + 1}$ 6. $\sqrt{x + 1}\sqrt{x - 1}$
    $\sqrt{21}$ 5 $\sqrt{x^2 + x}$ $\sqrt{x^2 - 1}$

Factoring Radical Expressions

We know that for nonnegative radicands,
$$\sqrt{A}\,\sqrt{B} = \sqrt{AB}.$$

To factor radical expressions we can think of this equation in reverse.
$$\sqrt{AB} = \sqrt{A}\,\sqrt{B}$$

In some cases we can simplify after factoring.

A radical expression is simplified when its radicand has no factors which are perfect squares.

EXAMPLES

Factor. Simplify where possible.

7. $\sqrt{18} = \sqrt{9 \cdot 2}$ Factoring the radicand as a perfect square factor

$\quad = \sqrt{9} \cdot \sqrt{2}$ Factoring the radical expression

$\quad = 3\sqrt{2}$ The radicand has no factors which are perfect squares.

8. $\sqrt{25x} = \sqrt{25} \cdot \sqrt{x} = 5\sqrt{x}$

9. $\sqrt{36x^2} = \sqrt{36}\,\sqrt{x^2} = 6|x|$

TRY THIS Factor. Simplify where possible.

7. $\sqrt{32}$ 8. $\sqrt{25x^2}$ 9. $\sqrt{64t}$ 10. $\sqrt{76a^2}$

7. $4\sqrt{2}$
8. $5|x|$
9. $8\sqrt{t}$
10. $2a\sqrt{19}$

Approximating Square Roots

Table 1 lists square roots only to 100. We can use it to find approximate square roots for other numbers. First we factor out the largest perfect square, if there is one. If there is none, we use any factorization which will give smaller factors.

EXAMPLES

Approximate these square roots by factoring and using Table 1.

10. $\sqrt{160} = \sqrt{16 \cdot 10}$ Choosing a factor of the radicand as

$\quad = \sqrt{16}\,\sqrt{10}$ a perfect square.

$\quad = 4\sqrt{10}$

$\quad \approx 4(3.162)$ Using Table 1, $\sqrt{10} \approx 3.162$

$\quad \approx 12.648$

11. $\sqrt{341} = \sqrt{11 \cdot 31}$ There is no perfect square factor.

$\qquad = \sqrt{11}\sqrt{31}$

$\qquad \approx 3.317 \times 5.568$

$\qquad \approx 18.469$ Rounded to 3 decimal places

TRY THIS Approximate these square roots. Round to three decimal places.

11. $\sqrt{275}$ **12.** $\sqrt{102}$ 10.099

16.585

| **12–3** | |

Exercises

Multiply.

1. $\sqrt{2}\sqrt{3}$ $\sqrt{6}$

2. $\sqrt{3}\sqrt{5}$ $\sqrt{15}$

3. $\sqrt{4}\sqrt{3}$ $\sqrt{12} = 2\sqrt{3}$

4. $\sqrt{2}\sqrt{9}$ $\sqrt{18} = 3\sqrt{2}$

5. $\sqrt{\frac{2}{5}}\sqrt{\frac{3}{4}}$ $\sqrt{\frac{3}{10}}$

6. $\sqrt{\frac{3}{8}}\sqrt{\frac{1}{5}}$ $\sqrt{\frac{3}{40}}$

7. $\sqrt{17}\sqrt{17}$ 17

8. $\sqrt{18}\sqrt{18}$ 18

9. $\sqrt{25}\sqrt{3}$ $\sqrt{75} = 5\sqrt{3}$

10. $\sqrt{36}\sqrt{2}$ $\sqrt{72} = 6\sqrt{2}$

11. $\sqrt{2}\sqrt{x}$ $\sqrt{2x}$

12. $\sqrt{3}\sqrt{a}$ $\sqrt{3a}$

13. $\sqrt{0.24}\sqrt{3}$ $\sqrt{0.72}$

14. $\sqrt{2}\sqrt{0.56}$ $\sqrt{1.12}$

15. $\sqrt{x}\sqrt{t}$ $\sqrt{xt}$

16. $\sqrt{a}\sqrt{y}$ $\sqrt{ay}$

17. $\sqrt{x}\sqrt{x-3}$ $\sqrt{x^2-3x}$

18. $\sqrt{x}\sqrt{x+1}$ $\sqrt{x^2+x}$

19. $\sqrt{5}\sqrt{2x-1}$

20. $\sqrt{3}\sqrt{4x+2}$ $\sqrt{12x+6}$

21. $\sqrt{x+2}\sqrt{x+1}$ $\sqrt{x^2+3x+2}$

22. $\sqrt{x-3}\sqrt{x+4}$

23. $\sqrt{x-3}\sqrt{2x+4}$

24. $\sqrt{2x+5}\sqrt{x-4}$ $\sqrt{2x^2-3x-20}$

25. $\sqrt{x+4}\sqrt{x-4}$

26. $\sqrt{x-2}\sqrt{x+2}$

27. $\sqrt{x+y}\sqrt{x-y}$ $\sqrt{x^2-y^2}$

28. $\sqrt{a-b}\sqrt{a+b}$

29. $\sqrt{-3}\sqrt{2x}$ No real value

30. $\sqrt{-5}\sqrt{-4x}$ No real value

Factor. Simplify where possible.

31. $\sqrt{12}$ $2\sqrt{3}$ **32.** $\sqrt{8}$ $2\sqrt{2}$ **33.** $\sqrt{75}$ $5\sqrt{3}$ **34.** $\sqrt{50}$ $5\sqrt{2}$

35. $\sqrt{20}$ $2\sqrt{5}$ **36.** $\sqrt{45}$ $3\sqrt{5}$ **37.** $\sqrt{200}$ $10\sqrt{2}$ **38.** $\sqrt{300}$ $10\sqrt{3}$

39. $\sqrt{3x}$ $\sqrt{3}\sqrt{x}$ **40.** $\sqrt{5y}$ $\sqrt{5}\sqrt{y}$ **41.** $\sqrt{9x}$ $3\sqrt{x}$ **42.** $\sqrt{4y}$ $2\sqrt{y}$

43. $\sqrt{16a}$ $4\sqrt{a}$ **44.** $\sqrt{49b}$ $7\sqrt{b}$ **45.** $\sqrt{64y^2}$ $8|y|$ **46.** $\sqrt{9x^2}$ $3|x|$

47. $\sqrt{13x^2}$ **48.** $\sqrt{29t^2}$ **49.** $\sqrt{8t^2}$ $2|t|\sqrt{2}$ **50.** $\sqrt{125a^2}$ $5|a|\sqrt{5}$

Approximate these square roots. Round to three decimal places.

51. $\sqrt{125}$ **52.** $\sqrt{124}$ **53.** $\sqrt{180}$ **54.** $\sqrt{150}$

55. $\sqrt{360}$ **56.** $\sqrt{250}$ **57.** $\sqrt{105}$ **58.** $\sqrt{115}$

19. $\sqrt{10x-5}$
22. $\sqrt{x^2+x-12}$
23. $\sqrt{2x^2-2x-12}$
25. $\sqrt{x^2-16}$
26. $\sqrt{x^2-4}$
28. $\sqrt{a^2-b^2}$

47. $|x|\sqrt{13}$
48. $|x|\sqrt{29}$
51. 11.180

52. 11.136
53. 13.416
54. 12.250
55. 18.972
56. 15.810
57. 10.248
58. 10.724

59. $\sqrt{300}$ **60.** $\sqrt{200}$ **61.** $\sqrt{143}$ **62.** $\sqrt{187}$

63. $\sqrt{2000}$ **64.** $\sqrt{1000}$ **65.** $\sqrt{768}$ **66.** $\sqrt{867}$

59. 17.320
60. 14.140
61. 11.961
62. 13.676
63. 44.720
64. 31.620
65. 27.712
66. 29.444

Extension

Factor.

67. $\sqrt{3x-3}$ $\sqrt{3}\sqrt{x-1}$ **68.** $\sqrt{x^2-x-2}$ **69.** $\sqrt{x^2-4}$ $\sqrt{x+2}\sqrt{x-2}$

70. $\sqrt{2x^2-5x-12}$ **71.** $\sqrt{x^3-2x^2}$ **72.** $\sqrt{a^2-b^2}$ $\sqrt{a+b}\sqrt{a-b}$

Simplify.

68. $\sqrt{x-2}\sqrt{x+1}$
70. $\sqrt{x-4}\sqrt{2x+3}$
71. $x\sqrt{x-2}$

73. $\sqrt{0.01}$ 0.1   **74.** $\sqrt{0.25}$ 0.5   **75.** $\sqrt{x^4}$ x^2 **76.** $\sqrt{9a^6}$ $3|a^3|$

77. Find $\sqrt{49}$, $\sqrt{490}$, $\sqrt{4900}$, $\sqrt{49,000}$ and $\sqrt{490,000}$. What
pattern do you see? 7, $7\sqrt{10}$, 70, $70\sqrt{10}$, 700; Each is $\sqrt{10}$ times the last.

Challenge

Use the proper symbol ($>$, $<$, or $=$) between each pair of values.
Assume x is positive.

78. 15 $4\sqrt{14}$ $>$ **79.** $15\sqrt{2}$ $\sqrt{450}$ $=$ **80.** 16 $\sqrt{15}\sqrt{17}$ $>$

81. $3\sqrt{11}$ $7\sqrt{2}$ $>$ **82.** $5\sqrt{7}$ $4\sqrt{11}$ $<$ **83.** 8 $\sqrt{15}+\sqrt{17}$ $>$

84. $3\sqrt{x}$ $2\sqrt{2.5x}$ $<$ **85.** $4\sqrt{x}$ $5\sqrt{0.64x}$ $=$ **86.** $90\sqrt{100x}$ $100\sqrt{90x}$ $<$

87. Speed of a skidding car. How do police determine the speed of a
car after an accident? The formula

$$r = 2\sqrt{5L}$$

can be used to approximate the speed r, in mi/h, of a car that
has left a skid mark of length L, in feet. What was the speed of a
car that left skid marks of lengths 20 ft? 70 ft? 150 ft? 20, 37.4, 54.8

Simplest Form

In many formulas and problems involving radical notation, variables do not represent negative numbers. Thus absolute value is not necessary. From now on we shall assume that all radicands are nonnegative.

To simplify radical expressions we usually try to factor out as many perfect square factors as possible. Compare the following.

$$\sqrt{50} = \sqrt{10 \cdot 5} = \sqrt{10}\sqrt{5} \qquad \sqrt{50} = \sqrt{25 \cdot 2} = 5\sqrt{2}$$

In the case on the right, we factored out the perfect square 25. If you do not recognize perfect squares, try factoring the radicand into its prime factors.

$$\sqrt{50} = \sqrt{2 \cdot 5 \cdot 5} = 5\sqrt{2}$$

The radical expression $5\sqrt{2}$ is considered to be in simplest form.

EXAMPLES

1. $\sqrt{48t} = \sqrt{16 \cdot 3t}$ Identifying perfect square factors
$\phantom{\sqrt{48t}} = \sqrt{16}\sqrt{3t}$ Factoring into radicals
$\phantom{\sqrt{48t}} = 4\sqrt{3t}$

2. $\sqrt{20t^2} = \sqrt{4 \cdot t^2 \cdot 5}$
$\phantom{\sqrt{20t^2}} = \sqrt{4} \cdot \sqrt{t^2} \cdot \sqrt{5}$ Factoring into several radicals
$\phantom{\sqrt{20t^2}} = 2t\sqrt{5}$

3. $\sqrt{3x^2 + 6x + 3} = \sqrt{3(x^2 + 2x + 1)}$
$\phantom{\sqrt{3x^2 + 6x + 3}} = \sqrt{3}\sqrt{x^2 + 2x + 1}$ Factoring into radicals
$\phantom{\sqrt{3x^2 + 6x + 3}} = \sqrt{3}\sqrt{(x + 1)^2}$
$\phantom{\sqrt{3x^2 + 6x + 3}} = \sqrt{3}(x + 1)$

TRY THIS Simplify.

1. $\sqrt{60x}$ 2. $\sqrt{45x^2}$ 3. $\sqrt{3x^2 - 6x + 3}$

1. $2\sqrt{15x}$
2. $3x\sqrt{5}$
3. $\sqrt{3}(x - 1)$

Simplifying Square Roots of Powers

To take a square root of a power such as x^8, the exponent must be even. We then take half the exponent. Recall that $(x^4)^2 = x^8$.

EXAMPLES

4. $x^3 \cdot x^3 = x^6$, so $\sqrt{x^6} = x^3$ 5. $(x^5)^2 = x^{10}$, so $\sqrt{x^{10}} = x^5$ 6. $\sqrt{x^{22}} = x^{11}$

When odd powers occur, express the power in terms of the nearest
even power. Then simplify the even power.

EXAMPLE 7
Simplify by factoring.

$$\sqrt{x^9} = \sqrt{x^8 x}$$
$$= \sqrt{x^8}\sqrt{x}$$
$$= x^4\sqrt{x}$$

TRY THIS Simplify.

4. $\sqrt{y^8}$ 5. $\sqrt{(x + y)^{14}}$ 6. $\sqrt{t^{15}}$

4. y^4
5. $(x + y)^7$
6. $t^7\sqrt{t}$

Sometimes we can simplify after multiplying. Perfect square factors
may then be found.

EXAMPLES
Multiply and then simplify by factoring.

8. $\sqrt{2}\sqrt{14} = \sqrt{2 \cdot 14}$ Multiplying
   $\qquad = \sqrt{2 \cdot 2 \cdot 7}$ Factoring to find perfect square factors
   $\qquad = \sqrt{2 \cdot 2} \cdot \sqrt{7}$
   $\qquad = 2\sqrt{7}$

9. $\sqrt{3x^2}\sqrt{9x^3} = \sqrt{3 \cdot 9x^5}$ Multiplying
   $\qquad = \sqrt{3 \cdot 9 \cdot x^4 \cdot x}$ Factoring to find perfect square factors
   $\qquad = \sqrt{9 \cdot x^4 \cdot 3 \cdot x}$ Perfect squares
   $\qquad = \sqrt{9}\sqrt{x^4}\sqrt{3x}$
   $\qquad = 3x^2\sqrt{3x}$

TRY THIS Multiply and simplify.

7. $\sqrt{3y}\sqrt{6}$ 8. $\sqrt{2x}\sqrt{50x}$ 9. $\sqrt{2x^3}\sqrt{8x^3y^4}$ 10. $\sqrt{10xy^2}\sqrt{5x^2y^3}$

7. $3\sqrt{2y}$
8. $10x$
9. $4x^3y^2$
10. $5xy^2\sqrt{2xy}$

| **12–4** | |

Exercises
Simplify.

1. $\sqrt{180}$ $6\sqrt{5}$

2. $\sqrt{448}$ $8\sqrt{7}$

3. $\sqrt{48x}$ $4\sqrt{3x}$

4. $\sqrt{40m}$ $2\sqrt{10m}$

5. $\sqrt{288y}$ $12\sqrt{2y}$

6. $\sqrt{363p}$ $11\sqrt{3p}$

7. $\sqrt{20x^2}$ $2x\sqrt{5}$ 8. $\sqrt{28x^2}$ $2x\sqrt{7}$ 9. $\sqrt{8x^2 + 8x + 2}$ $\sqrt{2}(2x + 1)$

10. $\sqrt{27x^2 - 36x + 12}$ 11. $\sqrt{36y + 12y^2 + y^3}$ 12. $\sqrt{x - 2x^2 + x^3}$

10. $\sqrt{3}(3x - 2)$
11. $\sqrt{y}(6 + y)$
12. $\sqrt{x}(1 - x)$

Simplify.

13. $\sqrt{x^6}$ x^3 14. $\sqrt{x^{10}}$ x^5 15. $\sqrt{x^{12}}$ x^6

16. $\sqrt{x^{16}}$ x^8 17. $\sqrt{x^5}$ $x^2\sqrt{x}$ 18. $\sqrt{x^3}$ $x\sqrt{x}$

19. $\sqrt{t^{19}}$ $t^9\sqrt{t}$ 20. $\sqrt{p^{17}}$ $p^8\sqrt{p}$ 21. $\sqrt{(y - 2)^8}$ $(y - 2)^4$

22. $\sqrt{(x + 3)^6}$ $(x + 3)^3$ 23. $\sqrt{4(x + 5)^{10}}$ $2(x + 5)^5$ 24. $\sqrt{16(a - 7)^4}$ $4(a - 7)^2$

25. $\sqrt{36m^3}$ $6m\sqrt{m}$ 26. $\sqrt{250y^3}$ $5y\sqrt{10y}$ 27. $\sqrt{8a^5}$ $2a^2\sqrt{2a}$

28. $\sqrt{12b^7}$ $2b^3\sqrt{3b}$ 29. $\sqrt{448x^6y^3}$ $8x^3y\sqrt{7y}$ 30. $\sqrt{243x^5y^4}$ $9x^2y^2\sqrt{3x}$

Multiply and simplify.

31. $\sqrt{3}\sqrt{18}$ $3\sqrt{6}$ 32. $\sqrt{5}\sqrt{10}$ $5\sqrt{2}$ 33. $\sqrt{15}\sqrt{6}$ $3\sqrt{10}$

34. $\sqrt{3}\sqrt{27}$ 9 35. $\sqrt{18}\sqrt{14x}$ $6\sqrt{7x}$ 36. $\sqrt{12}\sqrt{18x}$ $6\sqrt{6x}$

37. $\sqrt{3x}\sqrt{12y}$ $6\sqrt{xy}$ 38. $\sqrt{7x}\sqrt{21y}$ $7\sqrt{3xy}$ 39. $\sqrt{10}\sqrt{10}$ 10

40. $\sqrt{11}\sqrt{11x}$ $11\sqrt{x}$ 41. $\sqrt{5b}\sqrt{15b}$ $5b\sqrt{3}$ 42. $\sqrt{6a}\sqrt{18a}$ $6a\sqrt{3}$

43. $\sqrt{2t}\sqrt{2t}$ $2t$ 44. $\sqrt{3a}\sqrt{3a}$ $3a$ 45. $\sqrt{ab}\sqrt{ac}$ $a\sqrt{bc}$

46. $\sqrt{xy}\sqrt{xz}$ $x\sqrt{yz}$ 47. $\sqrt{2x^2y}\sqrt{4xy^2}$ $2xy\sqrt{2xy}$ 48. $\sqrt{15mn^2}\sqrt{5m^2n}$ $5mn\sqrt{3mn}$

49. $\sqrt{18x^2y^3}\sqrt{6xy^4}$ $6xy^3\sqrt{3xy}$ 50. $\sqrt{12x^3y^2}\sqrt{8xy}$ $4x^2y\sqrt{6y}$ 51. $\sqrt{50ab}\sqrt{10a^2b^4}$ $10ab^2\sqrt{5ab}$

Extension

52. $(\sqrt{2y})(\sqrt{3})(\sqrt{8y})$ $4y\sqrt{3}$ 53. $\sqrt{a}(\sqrt{a^3} - 5)$ $a^2 - 5\sqrt{a}$

54. $\sqrt{27(x + 1)}\sqrt{12y(x + 1)^2}$ 55. $\sqrt{18(x - 2)}\sqrt{20(x - 2)^3}$ $6(x - 2)^2\sqrt{10}$

56. $\sqrt{x}\sqrt{2x}\sqrt{10x^3}$ $2x^3\sqrt{5x}$ 57. $\sqrt{0.04x^{4n}}$ $0.2x^{2n}$

54. $18(x + 1)\sqrt{x + 1}$

58. $\sqrt{2^{109}}\sqrt{x^{306}}\sqrt{x^{11}}$ $2^{54}x^{158}\sqrt{2x}$ 59. $\sqrt{147}\sqrt{y^{27}}\sqrt{x^{315}}$ $7y^{13}x^{157}\sqrt{3xy}$

Challenge

60. We know that $\sqrt{A} \cdot \sqrt{B} = \sqrt{AB}$. Is it true that $\sqrt{A} + \sqrt{B}$ $= \sqrt{A + B}$? Only if A or $B = 0$

61. Is it true that $\sqrt{A} - \sqrt{B} = \sqrt{A - B}$? Only if $B = 0$

62. Simplify $\sqrt{y^n}$, given n is an even whole number ≥ 2. $y^{(n/2)}$

63. Simplify $\sqrt{y^n}$, given n is an odd whole number ≥ 3. $y^{[(n - 1)/2]}\sqrt{y}$

64. Multiply $(x^2 + \sqrt{2}xy + y^2)$ by $(x^2 - \sqrt{2}xy + y^2)$. Use your result to factor $x^8 + y^8$. $x^4 + y^4$; $(x^4 + \sqrt{2} x^2y^2 + y^4)(x^4 - \sqrt{2}x^2y^2 + y^4)$

The number c is called the cube root of a if $c^3 = a$. We write it as $c = \sqrt[3]{a}$.

65. Find $\sqrt[3]{8}$. 2

66. Does $\sqrt[3]{-8}$ have any real number solutions? Yes, -2

Fractional Radicands

Perfect Square Radicands

Fractional radicands with a perfect square numerator and denominator can be simplified by taking the square root of the numerator and denominator separately.

EXAMPLES
Simplify.

1. $\sqrt{\dfrac{25}{9}} = \dfrac{5}{3}$ since $\dfrac{5}{3} \cdot \dfrac{5}{3} = \dfrac{25}{9}$.   2. $\sqrt{\dfrac{1}{16}} = \dfrac{1}{4}$ since $\dfrac{1}{4} \cdot \dfrac{1}{4} = \dfrac{1}{16}$.

Sometimes a fractional radicand can be simplified to one that has a perfect square numerator and denominator.

EXAMPLE 3
Simplify.

$$\sqrt{\dfrac{18}{50}} = \sqrt{\dfrac{9 \cdot 2}{25 \cdot 2}}$$

$$= \sqrt{\dfrac{9}{25} \cdot \dfrac{2}{2}}$$

$$= \sqrt{\dfrac{9}{25} \cdot 1}$$

$$= \sqrt{\dfrac{9}{25}}$$

$$= \dfrac{3}{5} \text{ since } \dfrac{3}{5} \cdot \dfrac{3}{5} = \dfrac{9}{25}.$$

TRY THIS Simplify.

1. $\sqrt{\dfrac{16}{9}}$ $\frac{4}{3}$ 2. $\sqrt{\dfrac{1}{25}}$ $\frac{1}{5}$ 3. $\sqrt{\dfrac{1}{9}}$ $\frac{1}{3}$ 4. $\sqrt{\dfrac{18}{32}}$ $\frac{3}{4}$ 5. $\sqrt{\dfrac{2250}{2560}}$ $\frac{15}{16}$

Making the Denominator a Perfect Square

When neither the numerator nor denominator is a perfect square, we can simplify to an expression that has a whole number radicand. A simplified expression is then in the form $a\sqrt{b}$ where b is a whole number with no perfect square factors.

EXAMPLE 4

Simplify $\sqrt{\dfrac{2}{3}}$.

We multiply the radicand by 1 under the radical sign, choosing $\frac{3}{3}$ for 1. This makes the denominator a perfect square.

$$\sqrt{\dfrac{2}{3}} = \sqrt{\dfrac{2}{3} \cdot \dfrac{3}{3}} \qquad \text{Multiplying by 1 to make the denominator 9}$$

$$= \sqrt{\dfrac{6}{9}}$$

$$= \sqrt{\dfrac{1}{9} \cdot 6} \qquad \text{Factoring to get a perfect square factor}$$

$$= \dfrac{1}{3}\sqrt{6}$$

We can always multiply by 1 under the radical sign to make a denominator a perfect square. This is called rationalizing the denominator.

EXAMPLE 5

Rationalize the denominator.

$$\sqrt{\dfrac{5}{12}} = \sqrt{\dfrac{5}{12} \cdot \dfrac{3}{3}} = \sqrt{\dfrac{15}{36}} = \sqrt{\dfrac{1}{36} \cdot 15} = \dfrac{1}{6}\sqrt{15}$$

In Example 5 we chose $\frac{3}{3}$ to make the denominator the smallest multiple of 12 that is a perfect square.

TRY THIS Rationalize the denominator.

6. $\sqrt{\dfrac{3}{7}}$ 7. $\sqrt{\dfrac{5}{8}}$ 8. $\sqrt{\dfrac{2}{27}}$ 6. $\frac{1}{7}\sqrt{21}$ 7. $\sqrt{\frac{10}{16}} = \frac{1}{4}\sqrt{10}$ 8. $\frac{1}{9}\sqrt{6}$

Approximating Square Roots of Fractions

Now we can use the square root table to find square roots of fractions. Begin by rationalizing the denominator.

EXAMPLE 6

Approximate $\sqrt{\dfrac{3}{5}}$ to three decimal places.

$$\sqrt{\dfrac{3}{5}} = \sqrt{\dfrac{3}{5} \cdot \dfrac{5}{5}} = \sqrt{\dfrac{15}{25}} = \sqrt{\dfrac{1}{25} \cdot 15} = \dfrac{1}{5}\sqrt{15}$$

From Table 1, $\sqrt{15} \approx 3.873$, $\frac{1}{5}(3.873) = 0.7746$

9. $\sqrt{\dfrac{2}{7}}$ 0.534 **10.** $\sqrt{\dfrac{5}{8}}$ 0.791 **11.** $\sqrt{\dfrac{7}{18}}$ 0.624

12–5

Exercises

Simplify.

1. $\sqrt{\dfrac{9}{49}}$ $\dfrac{3}{7}$ **2.** $\sqrt{\dfrac{16}{25}}$ $\dfrac{4}{5}$ **3.** $\sqrt{\dfrac{1}{36}}$ $\dfrac{1}{6}$ **4.** $\sqrt{\dfrac{1}{4}}$ $\dfrac{1}{2}$

5. $-\sqrt{\dfrac{16}{81}}$ $-\dfrac{4}{9}$ **6.** $-\sqrt{\dfrac{25}{49}}$ $\dfrac{-5}{7}$ **7.** $\sqrt{\dfrac{64}{289}}$ $\dfrac{8}{17}$ **8.** $\sqrt{\dfrac{81}{361}}$ $\dfrac{9}{19}$

9. $-\sqrt{\dfrac{9}{100}}$ $-\dfrac{3}{10}$ **10.** $-\sqrt{\dfrac{49}{100}}$ $-\dfrac{7}{10}$ **11.** $\sqrt{\dfrac{27}{75}}$ $\dfrac{3}{5}$ **12.** $\sqrt{\dfrac{50}{18}}$ $\dfrac{5}{3}$

Rationalize the denominator.

13. $\sqrt{\dfrac{2}{5}}$ **14.** $\sqrt{\dfrac{2}{7}}$ **15.** $\sqrt{\dfrac{3}{8}}$ **16.** $\sqrt{\dfrac{7}{8}}$ **17.** $\sqrt{\dfrac{7}{12}}$ **18.** $\sqrt{\dfrac{1}{12}}$

19. $\sqrt{\dfrac{1}{18}}$ **20.** $\sqrt{\dfrac{5}{18}}$ **21.** $\sqrt{\dfrac{1}{2}}$ **22.** $\sqrt{\dfrac{1}{3}}$ **23.** $\sqrt{\dfrac{8}{3}}$ **24.** $\sqrt{\dfrac{12}{5}}$

25. $\sqrt{\dfrac{3}{x}}$ **26.** $\sqrt{\dfrac{2}{x}}$ **27.** $\sqrt{\dfrac{x}{y}}$ **28.** $\sqrt{\dfrac{a}{b}}$ **29.** $\sqrt{\dfrac{x^2}{18}}$ **30.** $\sqrt{\dfrac{x^2}{20}}$

Approximate to three decimal places.

31. $\sqrt{\dfrac{1}{3}}$ 0.577   **32.** $\sqrt{\dfrac{3}{2}}$ 1.225   **33.** $\sqrt{\dfrac{7}{8}}$ 0.935 **34.** $\sqrt{\dfrac{3}{8}}$ 0.612

35. $\sqrt{\dfrac{1}{12}}$ 0.289   **36.** $\sqrt{\dfrac{5}{12}}$ 0.646   **37.** $\sqrt{\dfrac{1}{2}}$ 0.707 **38.** $\sqrt{\dfrac{1}{7}}$ 0.378

39. $\sqrt{\dfrac{7}{20}}$ 0.592   **40.** $\sqrt{\dfrac{3}{20}}$ 0.387   **41.** $\sqrt{\dfrac{13}{18}}$ 0.850 **42.** $\sqrt{\dfrac{11}{18}}$ 0.782

13. $\dfrac{1}{5}\sqrt{10}$

14. $\dfrac{1}{7}\sqrt{14}$

15. $\dfrac{1}{4}\sqrt{6}$

16. $\dfrac{1}{4}\sqrt{14}$

17. $\dfrac{1}{6}\sqrt{21}$

18. $\dfrac{1}{6}\sqrt{3}$

19. $\dfrac{1}{6}\sqrt{2}$

20. $\dfrac{1}{6}\sqrt{10}$

21. $\dfrac{1}{2}\sqrt{2}$

22. $\dfrac{1}{3}\sqrt{3}$

23. $\dfrac{2}{3}\sqrt{6}$

24. $\dfrac{2}{5}\sqrt{15}$

25. $\dfrac{1}{x}\sqrt{3x}$

26. $\dfrac{1}{x}\sqrt{2x}$

27. $\dfrac{1}{y}\sqrt{xy}$

28. $\dfrac{1}{b}\sqrt{ab}$

29. $\dfrac{x\sqrt{2}}{6}$

30. $\dfrac{x\sqrt{5}}{10}$

Extension

Simplify.

43. $\sqrt{\dfrac{36}{x^2}}$ **44.** $\sqrt{\dfrac{25}{a^2}}$ **45.** $\sqrt{\dfrac{9a^2}{625}}$ **46.** $\sqrt{\dfrac{x^2y^2}{256}}$

$\frac{6}{x}$ $\frac{5}{a}$ $\frac{3a}{25}$ $\frac{xy}{16}$

Rationalize the denominator.

47. $\sqrt{\dfrac{5}{16}}$ **48.** $\sqrt{\dfrac{3}{1000}}$ **49.** $\sqrt{\dfrac{1}{5x^3}}$ **50.** $\sqrt{\dfrac{3x^2y}{a^2x^5}}$

51. $\sqrt{\dfrac{3a}{b}}$ **52.** $\sqrt{\dfrac{1}{5zw^2}}$ **53.** $\sqrt{0.007}$ **54.** $\sqrt{0.012}$

47. $\frac{\sqrt{5}}{4}$

48. $\frac{\sqrt{30}}{100}$

49. $\frac{\sqrt{5x}}{5x^2}$

50. $\frac{\sqrt{3yx}}{ax^2}$

51. $\frac{\sqrt{3ab}}{b}$

52. $\frac{\sqrt{5z}}{5zw}$

53. $\frac{\sqrt{70}}{100}$

54. $\frac{\sqrt{30}}{50}$

Challenge

The period T of a pendulum is the time it takes to move from one side to the other and back. A formula for the period is

$$T = 2\pi\sqrt{\dfrac{L}{32}}$$ where T is in seconds and L is in feet. Use 3.14 for π.

55. Find the periods of pendulums of lengths 2 ft, 8 ft, 64 ft, and 100 ft.   1.57, 3.14, 8.88, 11.10

56. Find the period of a pendulum of length $\frac{2}{3}$ in.   0.262 sec

57. The pendulum of a grandfather clock is $\frac{32}{\pi^2}$ feet long. How long does it take to swing from one side to the other?   1 second

12–6 Division

Dividing with Radicals

To multiply with radical notation, we multiply radicands. To divide, we divide the radicands.

> In general, for any nonnegative radicands A and B,
> $$\frac{\sqrt{A}}{\sqrt{B}} = \sqrt{\frac{A}{B}}.$$
> (The quotient of square roots, provided they exist, is the square root of the quotient of the radicands.)

EXAMPLES

Divide and simplify by using fractional radicands.

1. $\dfrac{\sqrt{27}}{\sqrt{3}} = \sqrt{\dfrac{27}{3}} = \sqrt{9} = 3$

2. $\dfrac{\sqrt{7}}{\sqrt{14}} = \sqrt{\dfrac{7}{14}} = \sqrt{\dfrac{1}{2}} = \sqrt{\dfrac{1}{2} \cdot \dfrac{2}{2}} = \sqrt{\dfrac{2}{4}} = \sqrt{\dfrac{1}{4} \cdot 2} = \dfrac{1}{2}\sqrt{2}$

3. $\dfrac{\sqrt{30a^3}}{\sqrt{6a^2}} = \sqrt{\dfrac{30a^3}{6a^2}} = \sqrt{5a}$

TRY THIS Divide and simplify.

1. $\dfrac{\sqrt{5}}{\sqrt{5}}$ ^{1} 2. $\dfrac{\sqrt{2}}{\sqrt{6}}$ $\frac{1}{3}\sqrt{3}$ 3. $\dfrac{\sqrt{42x^4}}{\sqrt{7x^2}}$ $_{x\sqrt{6}}$

Rationalizing Denominators

Sometimes we can simplify a division problem by rationalizing the denominator. We again multiply by 1, but this time we choose a fraction of the form $\dfrac{\sqrt{a}}{\sqrt{a}}$.

EXAMPLES

Rationalize the denominator.

4. $\dfrac{\sqrt{2}}{\sqrt{3}} = \dfrac{\sqrt{2}}{\sqrt{3}} \cdot \dfrac{\sqrt{3}}{\sqrt{3}} = \dfrac{\sqrt{2}\sqrt{3}}{\sqrt{3}\sqrt{3}} = \dfrac{\sqrt{6}}{3}$, or $\dfrac{1}{3}\sqrt{6}$

5. $\dfrac{\sqrt{5}}{\sqrt{x}} = \dfrac{\sqrt{5}}{\sqrt{x}} \cdot \dfrac{\sqrt{x}}{\sqrt{x}}$ Multiplying by 1

$\qquad = \dfrac{\sqrt{5}\sqrt{x}}{\sqrt{x}\sqrt{x}}$

$\qquad = \dfrac{\sqrt{5x}}{x}$

6. $\dfrac{\sqrt{49a^5}}{\sqrt{12}} = \dfrac{\sqrt{49a^5}}{\sqrt{12}} \cdot \dfrac{\sqrt{3}}{\sqrt{3}}$ Multiplying by 1

$\qquad = \dfrac{\sqrt{49a^5}\sqrt{3}}{\sqrt{36}}$

$\qquad = \dfrac{\sqrt{49a^4 \cdot 3a}}{\sqrt{36}}$ Identifying perfect square factors

$\qquad = \dfrac{7a^2\sqrt{3a}}{6}$

TRY THIS Rationalize the denominator.

4. $\dfrac{\sqrt{5}}{\sqrt{7}}$ **5.** $\dfrac{\sqrt{x}}{\sqrt{y}}$ **6.** $\dfrac{\sqrt{16x^7}}{\sqrt{27}}$ 4. $\frac{\sqrt{35}}{7}$ 5. $\frac{\sqrt{xy}}{y}$ 6. $\frac{4x^3\sqrt{3x}}{9}$

12–6

Exercises

Divide and simplify.

1. $\dfrac{\sqrt{18}}{\sqrt{2}}$ 3   **2.** $\dfrac{\sqrt{20}}{\sqrt{5}}$ 2   **3.** $\dfrac{\sqrt{60}}{\sqrt{15}}$ 2   **4.** $\dfrac{\sqrt{108}}{\sqrt{3}}$ 6

5. $\dfrac{\sqrt{75}}{\sqrt{15}}$ $\sqrt{5}$ **6.** $\dfrac{\sqrt{18}}{\sqrt{3}}$ $\sqrt{6}$ **7.** $\dfrac{\sqrt{3}}{\sqrt{75}}$ $\frac{1}{5}$ **8.** $\dfrac{\sqrt{3}}{\sqrt{48}}$ $\frac{1}{4}$

9. $\dfrac{\sqrt{12}}{\sqrt{75}}$ $\frac{2}{5}$ **10.** $\dfrac{\sqrt{18}}{\sqrt{32}}$ $\frac{3}{4}$ **11.** $\dfrac{\sqrt{8x}}{\sqrt{2x}}$ 2   **12.** $\dfrac{\sqrt{18b}}{\sqrt{2b}}$ 3

13. $\dfrac{\sqrt{63y^3}}{\sqrt{7y}}$ $3y$ **14.** $\dfrac{\sqrt{48x^3}}{\sqrt{3x}}$ $4x$ **15.** $\dfrac{\sqrt{15x^5}}{\sqrt{3x}}$ $x^2\sqrt{5}$ **16.** $\dfrac{\sqrt{30a^5}}{\sqrt{5a}}$ $a^2\sqrt{6}$

17. $\dfrac{\sqrt{7}}{\sqrt{3}}$ $\frac{1}{3}\sqrt{21}$ **18.** $\dfrac{\sqrt{2}}{\sqrt{5}}$ $\frac{1}{5}\sqrt{10}$ **19.** $\dfrac{\sqrt{9}}{\sqrt{8}}$ $\frac{3}{4}\sqrt{2}$ **20.** $\dfrac{\sqrt{4}}{\sqrt{27}}$ $\frac{2}{9}\sqrt{3}$

21. $\dfrac{\sqrt{3x}}{\sqrt{\frac{3x}{4}}}$ 2   **22.** $\dfrac{\sqrt{5x}}{\sqrt{\frac{5x}{9}}}$ 3   **23.** $\dfrac{\sqrt{\frac{5}{6}}}{\sqrt{\frac{2}{3}}}$ $\frac{1}{2}\sqrt{5}$ **24.** $\dfrac{\sqrt{\frac{3}{7}}}{\sqrt{\frac{3}{14}}}$ $\sqrt{2}$

Rationalize the denominator.

25. $\dfrac{\sqrt{2}}{\sqrt{5}}$ $\frac{\sqrt{10}}{5}$ **26.** $\dfrac{\sqrt{3}}{\sqrt{2}}$ $\frac{\sqrt{6}}{2}$ **27.** $\dfrac{2}{\sqrt{2}}$ $\sqrt{2}$ **28.** $\dfrac{3}{\sqrt{3}}$ $\sqrt{3}$

29. $\dfrac{\sqrt{5}}{\sqrt{11}}$ $\frac{\sqrt{55}}{11}$ **30.** $\dfrac{\sqrt{7}}{\sqrt{27}}$ $\frac{\sqrt{21}}{9}$ **31.** $\dfrac{\sqrt{7}}{\sqrt{12}}$ $\frac{\sqrt{21}}{6}$ **32.** $\dfrac{\sqrt{5}}{\sqrt{18}}$ $\frac{\sqrt{10}}{6}$

33. $\dfrac{\sqrt{48}}{\sqrt{32}}$ $\frac{\sqrt{6}}{2}$ **34.** $\dfrac{\sqrt{56}}{\sqrt{40}}$ $\frac{\sqrt{35}}{5}$ **35.** $\dfrac{\sqrt{450}}{\sqrt{18}}$ 5   **36.** $\dfrac{\sqrt{224}}{\sqrt{14}}$ 4

37. $\dfrac{\sqrt{3}}{\sqrt{x}}$ $\frac{\sqrt{3x}}{x}$ **38.** $\dfrac{\sqrt{2}}{\sqrt{y}}$ $\frac{\sqrt{2y}}{y}$ **39.** $\dfrac{4y}{\sqrt{3}}$ $\frac{4y\sqrt{3}}{3}$ **40.** $\dfrac{8x}{\sqrt{5}}$ $\frac{8x\sqrt{5}}{5}$

41. $\dfrac{\sqrt{a^3}}{\sqrt{8}}$ $\frac{a\sqrt{2a}}{4}$ **42.** $\dfrac{\sqrt{x^3}}{\sqrt{27}}$ $\frac{x\sqrt{3x}}{9}$ **43.** $\dfrac{\sqrt{56}}{\sqrt{12x}}$ $\frac{\sqrt{42x}}{3x}$ **44.** $\dfrac{\sqrt{45}}{\sqrt{8a}}$ $\frac{3\sqrt{10a}}{4a}$

45. $\dfrac{\sqrt{27c}}{\sqrt{32c^3}}$ $\frac{3\sqrt{6}}{8c}$ **46.** $\dfrac{\sqrt{7x^3}}{\sqrt{12x}}$ $\frac{x\sqrt{21}}{6}$ **47.** $\dfrac{\sqrt{y^5}}{\sqrt{xy^2}}$ $\frac{y\sqrt{xy}}{x}$ **48.** $\dfrac{\sqrt{x^3}}{\sqrt{xy}}$ $\frac{x\sqrt{y}}{y}$

49. $\dfrac{\sqrt{16a^4b^6}}{\sqrt{128a^6b^6}}$ $\frac{\sqrt{2}}{4a}$ **50.** $\dfrac{\sqrt{45mn^2}}{\sqrt{32m}}$ $\frac{3n\sqrt{10}}{8}$

Extension

Rationalize the denominator.

51. $\dfrac{\sqrt{2}}{3\sqrt{3}}$ $\frac{\sqrt{6}}{9}$ **52.** $\dfrac{3\sqrt{6}}{6\sqrt{2}}$ $\frac{\sqrt{3}}{2}$ **53.** $\dfrac{5\sqrt{2}}{3\sqrt{5}}$ $\frac{\sqrt{10}}{3}$

54. $\dfrac{3\sqrt{15}}{5\sqrt{32}}$ $\frac{3\sqrt{30}}{40}$ **55.** $\dfrac{4\sqrt{\frac{6}{7}}}{\sqrt{\frac{12}{63}}}$ $\frac{8\sqrt{2}}{21}$ **56.** $\dfrac{\sqrt{\frac{2}{3}}}{\sqrt{\frac{3}{2}}}$ $\frac{2}{3}$

Challenge

Multiply.

57. $(\sqrt{5}+7)(\sqrt{5}-7)$ –44 **58.** $(1+\sqrt{5})(1-\sqrt{5})$ –4 **59.** $(\sqrt{6}-\sqrt{3})(\sqrt{6}+\sqrt{3})$ 3

Rationalize the denominator.

60. $\dfrac{a\sqrt{b}}{b\sqrt{a}}$ $\frac{\sqrt{ab}}{b}$

We can add any two real numbers. The following are sums of real numbers.

$$5 + \sqrt{2} \qquad \sqrt{3} - \sqrt{5} \qquad 2\sqrt{2} + 5\sqrt{3} \qquad \sqrt{5} - 5$$

When we have radical expressions with the same radicands we can simplify using the distributive law.

EXAMPLE 1
Add

$$3\sqrt{5} + 4\sqrt{5} = (3 + 4)\sqrt{5} \quad \text{Using the distributive law}$$
$$= 7\sqrt{5}$$

Remember, to combine like this, the radicands must be the same. Sometimes we can make them the same by simplifying the radicands.

EXAMPLES
2. Subtract $\sqrt{8}$ from $\sqrt{2}$.

$$\sqrt{2} - \sqrt{8} = \sqrt{2} - \sqrt{4 \cdot 2}$$
$$= \sqrt{2} - 2\sqrt{2}$$
$$= 1\sqrt{2} - 2\sqrt{2}$$
$$= (1 - 2)\sqrt{2} \quad \text{Using the distributive law}$$
$$= -\sqrt{2}$$

3. Add $\sqrt{x}$ to $\sqrt{4x}$.

$$\sqrt{x} + \sqrt{4x} = \sqrt{x} + 2\sqrt{x}$$
$$= (1 + 2)\sqrt{x} = 3\sqrt{x}$$

4. Add $\sqrt{x^3 - x^2}$ to $\sqrt{4x - 4}$.

$$\sqrt{x^3 - x^2} + \sqrt{4x - 4} = \sqrt{x^2(x - 1)} + \sqrt{4(x - 1)} \quad \text{Factoring radicands}$$
$$= \sqrt{x^2}\sqrt{x - 1} + \sqrt{4}\sqrt{x - 1}$$
$$= x\sqrt{x - 1} + 2\sqrt{x - 1}$$
$$= (x + 2)\sqrt{x - 1} \quad \text{Using the distributive law}$$

TRY THIS Add or subtract.

1. $3\sqrt{2} + 9\sqrt{2}$ 2. $8\sqrt{5} - 3\sqrt{5}$ 3. $2\sqrt{10} - 7\sqrt{40}$

4. $\sqrt{24y} + \sqrt{54y}$ 5. $\sqrt{9x + 9} - \sqrt{4x + 4}$

1. $12\sqrt{2}$
2. $5\sqrt{5}$
3. $-12\sqrt{10}$
4. $5\sqrt{6y}$
5. $\sqrt{x + 1}$

Sometimes after rationalizing denominators, we can factor and combine expressions.

EXAMPLE 5
Add.

$$\sqrt{3} + \sqrt{\frac{1}{3}} = \sqrt{3} + \sqrt{\frac{1}{3}\cdot\frac{3}{3}} \quad \text{Multiplying by 1}$$

$$= \sqrt{3} + \sqrt{\frac{3}{9}}$$

$$= \sqrt{3} + \sqrt{\frac{1}{9}\cdot 3}$$

$$= \sqrt{3} + \frac{1}{3}\sqrt{3}$$

$$= \left(1 + \frac{1}{3}\right)\sqrt{3} \quad \text{Using the distributive law}$$

$$= \frac{4}{3}\sqrt{3}$$

TRY THIS Add or subtract.

6. $\sqrt{2} + \sqrt{\frac{1}{2}}$ **7.** $\sqrt{\frac{5}{3}} - \sqrt{\frac{3}{5}}$ **8.** $\frac{x}{\sqrt{x}} + \sqrt{x}$

6. $\frac{3}{2}\sqrt{2}$

7. $\frac{2\sqrt{15}}{15}$

8. $2\sqrt{x}$

12–7

Exercises
Add or subtract.

1. $3\sqrt{2} + 4\sqrt{2}$ $\ _{7\sqrt{2}}$ **2.** $8\sqrt{3} + 3\sqrt{3}$ $\ _{11\sqrt{3}}$

3. $7\sqrt{5} - 3\sqrt{5}$ $\ _{4\sqrt{5}}$ **4.** $8\sqrt{2} - 5\sqrt{2}$ $\ _{3\sqrt{2}}$

5. $6\sqrt{x} + 7\sqrt{x}$ $\ _{13\sqrt{x}}$ **6.** $9\sqrt{y} + 3\sqrt{y}$ $\ _{12\sqrt{y}}$

7. $9\sqrt{x} - 11\sqrt{x}$ $\ _{-2\sqrt{x}}$ **8.** $6\sqrt{a} - 14\sqrt{a}$ $\ _{-8\sqrt{a}}$

9. $5\sqrt{8} + 15\sqrt{2}$ $\ _{25\sqrt{2}}$ **10.** $3\sqrt{12} + 2\sqrt{3}$ $\ _{8\sqrt{3}}$

11. $\sqrt{27} - 2\sqrt{3}$ $\ _{\sqrt{3}}$ **12.** $7\sqrt{50} - 3\sqrt{2}$ $\ _{32\sqrt{2}}$

13. $\sqrt{45} - \sqrt{20}$ $\ _{\sqrt{5}}$ **14.** $\sqrt{27} - \sqrt{12}$ $\ _{\sqrt{3}}$

15. $\sqrt{72} + \sqrt{98}$ $\ _{13\sqrt{2}}$ **16.** $\sqrt{45} + \sqrt{80}$ $\ _{7\sqrt{5}}$

17. $2\sqrt{12} + \sqrt{27} - \sqrt{48}$ $\ _{3\sqrt{3}}$ **18.** $9\sqrt{8} - \sqrt{72} + \sqrt{98}$ $\ _{19\sqrt{2}}$

19. $3\sqrt{18} - 2\sqrt{32} - 5\sqrt{50}$ $\ _{-24\sqrt{2}}$ **20.** $\sqrt{18} - 3\sqrt{8} + \sqrt{50}$ $\ _{2\sqrt{2}}$

21. $2\sqrt{27} - 3\sqrt{48} + 2\sqrt{18}$ $\ _{6\sqrt{2}\,-\,6\sqrt{3}}$ **22.** $3\sqrt{48} - 2\sqrt{27} - 2\sqrt{18}$ $\ _{6\sqrt{3}\,-\,6\sqrt{2}}$

23. $\sqrt{4x} + \sqrt{81x^3}$ $(2 + 9x)\sqrt{x}$

24. $\sqrt{12x^2} + \sqrt{27}$ $(2x + 3)\sqrt{3}$

25. $\sqrt{27} - \sqrt{12x^2}$ $(3 - 2x)\sqrt{3}$

26. $\sqrt{81x^3} - \sqrt{4x}$ $(9x - 2)\sqrt{x}$

27. $\sqrt{8x + 8} + \sqrt{2x + 2}$ $3\sqrt{2x + 2}$

28. $\sqrt{12x + 12} + \sqrt{3x + 3}$ $3\sqrt{3x + 3}$

29. $\sqrt{x^5 - x^2} + \sqrt{9x^3 - 9}$

30. $\sqrt{16x - 16} + \sqrt{25x^3 - 25x^2}$ $(4 + 5x)\sqrt{x - 1}$

31. $3x\sqrt{y^3x} - x\sqrt{yx^3} + y\sqrt{y^3x}$

32. $4a\sqrt{a^2b} + a\sqrt{a^2b^3} - 5\sqrt{b^3}$ $(4a^2 + a^2b - 5b)\sqrt{b}$

33. $\sqrt{8(a + b)^3} - \sqrt{32(a + b)^3}$

34. $\sqrt{x^2y + 6xy + 9y} + \sqrt{y^3}$ $(x + y + 3)\sqrt{y}$

35. $\sqrt{3} - \sqrt{\frac{1}{3}}$ $\frac{2\sqrt{3}}{3}$

36. $\sqrt{2} - \sqrt{\frac{1}{2}}$ $\frac{\sqrt{2}}{2}$

29. $(x + 3)\sqrt{x^3 - 1}$
31. $(-x^2 + 3xy + y^2)\sqrt{xy}$
33. $-2(a + b)\sqrt{2(a + b)}$

37. $5\sqrt{2} + 3\sqrt{\frac{1}{2}}$ $\frac{13\sqrt{2}}{2}$

38. $4\sqrt{3} + 2\sqrt{\frac{1}{3}}$ $\frac{14\sqrt{3}}{3}$

39. $\sqrt{\frac{2}{3}} - \sqrt{\frac{1}{6}}$ $\frac{\sqrt{6}}{6}$

40. $\sqrt{\frac{1}{2}} - \sqrt{\frac{1}{8}}$ $\frac{\sqrt{2}}{4}$

41. $\sqrt{\frac{1}{12}} - \sqrt{\frac{1}{27}}$ $\frac{-\sqrt{3}}{18}$

42. $\sqrt{\frac{5}{6}} - \sqrt{\frac{6}{5}}$ $\frac{-\sqrt{30}}{30}$

Extension

43. Three students were asked to simplify $\sqrt{10} + \sqrt{50}$. Their answers were $\sqrt{10}(1 + \sqrt{5})$, $\sqrt{10} + 5\sqrt{2}$, and $\sqrt{2}(5 + \sqrt{5})$.
  a. Which, if any, is incorrect? None
  b. Which is in simplest form? $\sqrt{10} + 5\sqrt{2}$

Add or subtract.

44. $\sqrt{125} - \sqrt{45} + 2\sqrt{5}$ $4\sqrt{5}$

45. $3\sqrt{\frac{1}{2}} + \frac{5}{2}\sqrt{18} + \sqrt{98}$ $16\sqrt{2}$

46. $\frac{3}{5}\sqrt{24} + \frac{2}{5}\sqrt{150} - \sqrt{96}$ $\frac{-4\sqrt{6}}{5}$

47. $\frac{1}{3}\sqrt{27} + \sqrt{8} + \sqrt{300} - \sqrt{18} - \sqrt{162}$ $11\sqrt{3} - 10\sqrt{2}$

48. $\sqrt{ab^6} + b\sqrt{a^3} + a\sqrt{a}$ $(b^3 + ab + a)\sqrt{a}$

49. $x\sqrt{2y} - \sqrt{8x^2y} + \frac{x}{3}\sqrt{18y}$ 0

50. $7x\sqrt{12xy^2} - 9y\sqrt{27x^3} + 5\sqrt{300x^3y^2}$ $37xy\sqrt{3x}$

51. $\sqrt{x} + \sqrt{\frac{1}{x}}$ $\frac{x + 1}{x}\sqrt{x}$

Challenge

Add or subtract. Simplify when possible.

52. $5\sqrt{\frac{3}{10}} + 2\sqrt{\frac{5}{6}} - 6\sqrt{\frac{15}{32}}$ $\frac{\sqrt{30}}{12}$ **53.** $2\sqrt{\frac{2a}{b}} - 4\sqrt{\frac{b}{2a^3}} + 5\sqrt{\frac{1}{8}a^3b}$ $\left(2 - \frac{2}{a^2} + \frac{5a}{4}\right)\sqrt{2ab}$

54. Evaluate for $a = 1$, $b = 3$, $c = 2$, $d = 4$.

   a. $\sqrt{a^2 + c^2}$, $\sqrt{a^2} + \sqrt{c^2}$ $\sqrt{5}, 3$ **b.** $\sqrt{b^2 + c^2}$, $\sqrt{b^2} + \sqrt{c^2}$ $\sqrt{13}, 5$

   c. $\sqrt{a^2 + d^2}$, $\sqrt{a^2} + \sqrt{d^2}$ $\sqrt{17}, 5$ **d.** $\sqrt{b^2 + d^2}$, $\sqrt{b^2} + \sqrt{d^2}$ $5, 7$

   e. $\sqrt{a^2 + b^2}$, $\sqrt{a^2} + \sqrt{b^2}$ $\sqrt{10}, 4$ **f.** $\sqrt{c^2 + d^2}$, $\sqrt{c^2} + \sqrt{d^2}$ $2\sqrt{5}, 6$

55. Can you find any numbers that would make the following true?
$\sqrt{x^2 + y^2} = \sqrt{x^2} + \sqrt{y^2}$ x or y is 0, the other can be any number

Binomial pairs such as $1 + \sqrt{2}$ and $1 - \sqrt{2}$ are called conjugates. We can use conjugates to rationalize binomial denominators containing radicals. Rationalize each denominator.

56. $\dfrac{5}{1 - \sqrt{2}}$ **57.** $\dfrac{8 + \sqrt{3}}{3 - \sqrt{2}}$ 56. $-5 - 5\sqrt{2}$ 57. $\dfrac{24 + 3\sqrt{3} + 8\sqrt{2} + \sqrt{6}}{7}$

USING A CALCULATOR/Evaluating Radical Expressions

A calculator with a square root key can be used to compute with radicals and evaluate radical expressions. Remember that the square root key acts only on the number in the display. In the examples below, displays are shown to three decimal places.

EXAMPLE 1
Problem: Find $\sqrt{x^2} + \sqrt{y^2}$ for $x = 7$ and $y = 8$.

Enter: 7 $\boxed{x^2}$ $\boxed{\sqrt{}}$ $\boxed{+}$ 8 $\boxed{x^2}$

Display: 7   49   7   8   64

Enter: $\boxed{\sqrt{}}$ $\boxed{=}$

Display: 8   15

EXAMPLE 2
Problem: Find $\sqrt{x^2 + y^2}$ for $x = 7$ and $y = 8$.

Enter: 7 $\boxed{x^2}$ $+$ 8 $\boxed{x^2}$

Display: 7 49   8   64

Enter: $\boxed{=}$ $\boxed{\sqrt{}}$

Display: 113   10.630

EXAMPLE 3
Problem: Find $x^2 + \sqrt{y^2}$ for $x = 7$ and $y = 8$.

Enter: 7 $\boxed{x^2}$ $+$ 8 $\boxed{x^2}$ $\boxed{\sqrt{}}$ $\boxed{=}$

Display: 7   49   8   64   8   57

Notice that Examples 2 and 3 are very much alike.

The only difference is that, in Example 2, you press the equals key and then the square root key. In Example 3, you press the square root key and then the equals key. for $c = 15$ and $b = 10$, find $\sqrt{c^2 - b^2}$, $\sqrt{c^2} - b^2$, and $c^2 - \sqrt{b^2}$.

If you are not certain what order of operations to use on your calculator, you can experiment with a problem for which you already know the answer. In Example 4, you might try $h = 100$ before solving the problem.

EXAMPLE 4
Problem: Let $V = 3.5\sqrt{h}$. Find V for $h = 207.36$.

Enter: 3.5 $\boxed{\times}$ 207.36 $\boxed{\sqrt{}}$ $\boxed{=}$

Display: 3.5   207.36 14.4   50.4

EXAMPLE 5
Problem: Find $5\sqrt{2} + 3\sqrt{\frac{1}{2}}$.

Enter: 1 $\boxed{\div}$ 2 $\boxed{=}$ $\boxed{\sqrt{}}$ $\boxed{\times}$

Display: 1   2   0.5   0.707

Enter: 3 $\boxed{\div}$ 5 $\boxed{\times}$ 2 $\boxed{\sqrt{}}$

Display: 3 2.121 5   2 1.414

Enter: $\boxed{=}$

Display: 9.192

Right Triangles

In a right triangle, the longest side is called the hypotenuse. The other two sides are called legs. We usually use the letters a and b for the lengths of the legs and c for the length of the hypotenuse. They are related as follows.

> **The Pythagorean Property of Right Triangles**
>
> In any right triangle if a and b are the lengths of the legs and c is the length of the hypotenuse, then
>
> $$a^2 + b^2 = c^2.$$

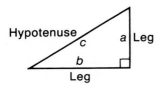

If we know the lengths of any two sides, we can find the length of the third side.

EXAMPLE 1
Find the length of the hypotenuse of this right triangle.

$$4^2 + 5^2 = c^2$$
$$16 + 25 = c^2$$
$$41 = c^2$$
$$c = \sqrt{41}$$
$$c \approx 6.403 \quad \text{From Table 1}$$

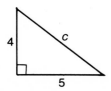

EXAMPLE 2

Find the length of the leg of this right triangle.

$$10^2 + b^2 = 12^2$$
$$100 + b^2 = 144$$
$$b^2 = 144 - 100$$
$$b^2 = 44$$
$$b^2 = \sqrt{44}$$
$$b = 6.633 \quad \text{From Table 1}$$

TRY THIS

1. Find the length of the hypotenuse in this right triangle. $\sqrt{65} = 8.062$

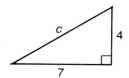

2. Find the length of the leg of this right triangle. $\sqrt{75} = 8.660$

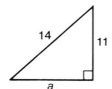

EXAMPLES

Find the length of the leg of each right triangle.

3.
$$1^2 + b^2 = (\sqrt{7})^2$$
$$1 + b^2 = 7$$
$$b^2 = 7 - 1$$
$$b^2 = 6$$
$$b = \sqrt{6}$$
$$b \approx 2.449$$

Find the length of the leg of this right triangle.

4.
$$a^2 + 10^2 = 15^2$$
$$a^2 + 100 = 225$$
$$a^2 = 225 - 100$$
$$a^2 = 125$$
$$a = \sqrt{125}$$
$$a = \sqrt{25 \cdot 5}$$
$$a = \sqrt{25} \cdot \sqrt{5}$$
$$a = 5\sqrt{5}$$
$$a \approx 5 \times 2.236$$
$$a \approx 11.18$$

TRY THIS Find the length of the leg of each right triangle.

$\sqrt{10} = 3.162$

4.

$\sqrt{175} = 5\sqrt{7} = 13.229$

Applications

The Pythagorean Property can help solve certain problems.

EXAMPLE 5

A 12-foot ladder is leaning against a building. The bottom of the ladder is 7 ft from the building. How high is the top of the ladder?

We first make a drawing. In it we see a right triangle.

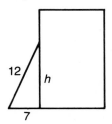

Now $7^2 + h^2 = 12^2$. We solve this equation.

$$49 + h^2 = 144$$
$$h^2 = 144 - 49$$
$$h^2 = 95$$
$$h = \sqrt{95}$$
$$h \approx 9.747 \text{ ft}$$

EXAMPLE 6

On a little league baseball diamond, the distance between the bases is 60 feet. Find the distance from home plate to second base. First we make a drawing. In it we see a right triangle.

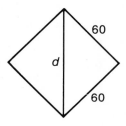

We have $60^2 + 60^2 = d^2$.

$$3600 + 3600 = d^2$$
$$7200 = d^2$$
$$\sqrt{7200} = d$$
$$\sqrt{36 \cdot 2 \cdot 100} = d$$
$$6 \cdot 10\sqrt{2} = d$$
$$60\sqrt{2} = d$$
$$60 \cdot (1.414) \approx d \quad \text{From Table 1}$$
$$84.8 \approx d$$

The distance from home plate to second base is about 84.8 feet.

5. How long is a guy wire that reaches from the top of a 15-ft pole to a point on the ground 10 ft from the pole? $5\sqrt{13} = 18.028$ ft

12–8

Exercises

Find the length of the third side of each right triangle.

1. ₁₇

2.

3. $4\sqrt{2}$

4. $7\sqrt{2}$

5. ₁₂

6.

7. ₄

8.

In a right triangle, find the length of the side not given.

9. $a = 10, b = 24$ ₂₆   10. $a = 5, b = 12$ ₁₃

11. $a = 9, c = 15$ ₁₂   12. $a = 18, c = 30$ ₂₄

13. $b = 1, c = \sqrt{5}$ ₂   14. $b = 1, c = \sqrt{2}$ ₁

15. $a = 1, c = \sqrt{3}$ $\sqrt{2}$ 16. $a = \sqrt{3}, b = \sqrt{5}$ $2\sqrt{2}$

17. $c = 10, b = 5\sqrt{3}$ ₅

Solve. Don't forget to make drawings.

18. A 10-meter ladder is leaning against a building. The bottom of the ladder is 5 m from the building. How high is the top of the ladder? $5\sqrt{3}$ or 8.66 m

19. Find the length of a diagonal of a square whose sides are 3 cm long. $3\sqrt{2}$ or 4.24 cm

20. How long is a guy wire reaching from the top of a 12-ft pole to a point 8 ft from the pole? $4\sqrt{13}$ or 14.42 ft

21. How long must a wire be to reach from the top of a 13-m telephone pole to a point on the ground 9 m from the foot of the pole? $5\sqrt{10}$ or 15.81 m

22. A slow-pitch softball diamond is actually a square 65 ft on a side. How far is it from home to second base? $65\sqrt{2}$ or 91.92 ft

23. A baseball diamond is actually a square 90 ft on a side. How far is it from first to third base? $90\sqrt{2}$ or 127.28 ft

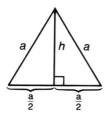

Extension

An equilateral triangle is shown below.

24. Find an expression for its height h in terms of a. $\frac{a}{2}\sqrt{3}$

25. Find an expression for its area A in terms of a. $\frac{a^2}{4}\sqrt{3}$

26. Figure $ABCD$ is a square. Find AC. $\frac{2}{3}$

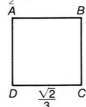

27. Suppose an outfielder catches the ball on the third base line about 40 feet behind third base. About how far would the outfielder have to throw the ball to first base? (Be sure to make a drawing.) $50\sqrt{10} \approx 158$ ft

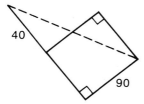

28. The diagonal of a square has length $8\sqrt{2}$ ft. Find the length of a side of the square. 8

29. Find the length of the diagonal of a rectangle whose length is 12 inches and whose width is 7 inches. $\sqrt{193} \approx 13.89$ in.

Challenge

30. A right triangle has sides whose lengths are consecutive integers. Find the lengths of the sides. 3, 4, 5

31. Find the length of the diagonal of a 10 cm cube. $10\sqrt{3}$

32. Any three positive integers which can be the lengths of sides of a right triangle are called a Pythagorean Triple. For instance, 3, 4 and 5 are a Pythagorean Triple. Find two other sets of Pythagorean Triples. Any multiple of 3, 4, 5; 5, 12, 13; 7, 24, 25 etc.

33. Two cars leave a service station at the same time. One car travels east at a speed of 50 mph, and the other travels south at a speed of 60 mph. After one-half hour, how far apart are they? When will they be 100 miles apart? $\sqrt{1525} = 5\sqrt{61} \approx 39.05$ mi, 1.28 hr

Find x.

34.

35.

36.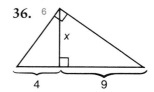

Solving Equations with Radicals

To solve equations with radicals we first convert them to equations without radicals. We do this by squaring both sides of the equation. The following new principle is used.

> **The Principle of Squaring**
>
> If an equation $a = b$ is true, then the equation $a^2 = b^2$ is true.

EXAMPLE 1

Solve.

$$\sqrt{2x} - 4 = 7$$
$$\sqrt{2x} = 11 \quad \text{Getting the radical alone on one side}$$
$$(\sqrt{2x})^2 = 11^2 \quad \text{Squaring both sides}$$
$$2x = 121$$
$$x = \frac{121}{2}$$

Check:

$$\sqrt{2x} - 4 = 7$$
$$\sqrt{2 \cdot \frac{121}{2}} - 4 \quad \Big| \quad 7$$
$$\sqrt{121} - 4$$
$$11 - 4$$
$$7 \quad \Big|$$

It is important to check. When we square both sides of an equation, the new equation may have solutions that the first one does not. For example, the equation $x = 1$ has just one solution, the number 1. When we square both sides we get

$$x^2 = 1,$$

which has two solutions, 1 and -1.

TRY THIS Solve.

1. $\sqrt{3x} - 5 = 3$ **2.** $2\sqrt{5x} + 3 = 16$

EXAMPLE 2

Solve.

$$\sqrt{x + 1} = \sqrt{2x - 5}.$$
$$(\sqrt{x + 1})^2 = (\sqrt{2x - 5})^2 \quad \text{Squaring both sides}$$
$$x + 1 = 2x - 5$$
$$x = 6$$

6 checks, so it is the solution.

TRY THIS Solve.

3. $\sqrt{3x + 1} = \sqrt{2x + 3}$ ₂   **4.** $\sqrt{x - 2} - 5 = 3$ ₆₆

Applications

How far can you see from a given height? There is a formula for this. At a height of h meters you can see V kilometers to the horizon. These numbers are related as follows.

$$V = 3.5\sqrt{h}$$

Earth

EXAMPLE 3

How far to the horizon can you see through an airplane window at a height, or altitude, of 9000 meters?

We substitute 9000 for h and simplify.

$$V = 3.5\sqrt{9000}$$
$$V = 3.5\sqrt{900 \cdot 10}$$
$$V = 3.5 \times 30 \times \sqrt{10}$$
$$V \approx 3.5 \times 30 \times 3.162 \quad \text{From Table 1}$$
$$V \approx 332.010 \text{ km}$$

TRY THIS

5. How far can you see to the horizon through an airplane window at a height of 8000 m? 313.05 km

6. How far can a sailor see to the horizon from the top of a 20-m mast? 15.652 km

EXAMPLE 4

A person can see 50.4 kilometers to the horizon from the top of a cliff. How high is the cliff? Use $V = 3.5\sqrt{h}$.

We substitute 50.4 for V and solve.

$$50.4 = 3.5\sqrt{h}$$
$$\frac{50.4}{3.5} = \sqrt{h}$$
$$14.4 = \sqrt{h}$$
$$(14.4)^2 = (\sqrt{h})^2$$
$$(14.4)^2 = h$$
$$207.36 \text{ m} = h \quad \text{The cliff is 207.36 meters high.}$$

TRY THIS

7. A person can see 61 km to the horizon from the roof of a building. How high is the rooftop? 303.76 m

---

| **12–9** | |

Exercises

Solve.

1. $\sqrt{x} = 5$ 25
2. $\sqrt{x} = 7$ 49
3. $\sqrt{x} = 6.2$ 38.44
4. $\sqrt{x} = 4.3$ 18.49
5. $\sqrt{x + 3} = 20$ 397
6. $\sqrt{x + 4} = 11$ 117
7. $\sqrt{2x + 4} = 25$ 310.5
8. $\sqrt{2x + 1} = 13$ 84
9. $3 + \sqrt{x - 1} = 5$ 3
10. $4 + \sqrt{y - 3} = 11$ 52
11. $6 - 2\sqrt{3n} = 0$ 3
12. $8 - 4\sqrt{5n} = 0$ $\frac{4}{5}$
13. $\sqrt{5x - 7} = \sqrt{x + 10}$ $\frac{17}{4}$
14. $\sqrt{4x - 5} = \sqrt{x + 9}$ $\frac{14}{3}$
15. $\sqrt{x} = -7$ No value
16. $-\sqrt{x} = 5$ No value
17. $\sqrt{2y + 6} = \sqrt{2y - 5}$ No value
18. $2\sqrt{x - 2} = \sqrt{7 - x}$ 3

Solve. Using $V = 3.5\sqrt{h}$ for Exercises 19–22.

19. How far can you see to the horizon through an airplane window at a height of 9800 m? 346.48 km

20. How far can a sailor see to the horizon from the top of a 24-m mast? 17.15 km

21. A person can see 371 km to the horizon from an airplane window. How high is the airplane? 11,236 m

22. A person can see 99.4 km to the horizon from the top of a hill. How high is the hill? 806.56 m

The formula $r = 2\sqrt{5L}$ can be used to approximate the speed r, in mi/h, of a car that has left a skid mark of length L, in feet. Note: $L = \frac{r^2}{20}$

23. How far will a car skid at 50 mi/h? at 70 mi/h? 125,245

24. How far will a car skid at 60 mi/h? at 100 mi/h? 180,500

Extension

Solve.

25. $\sqrt{5x^2 + 5} = 5$ 26. $\sqrt{x} = -x$ Zero

2 or −2

27. Find a number such that twice its square root is 14. 49

28. Find a number such that the inverse of three times its square root is -33. 121

29. Find a number such that the square root of four more than 5 times the number is 8. 12

The formula $T = 2\pi\sqrt{\dfrac{L}{32}}$ can be used to find the period T, in seconds, of a pendulum of length L, in feet. Note: $L = 8\left(\dfrac{T}{\pi}\right)^2$

30. What is the length of a pendulum that has a period of 1.6 sec? Use 3.14 for π. 2.08 ft

31. What is the length of a pendulum that has a period of 3 sec? Use 3.14 for π. 7.30 ft

Challenge

Solve.

32. $x - 1 = \sqrt{x + 5}$ 4   33. $\sqrt{y^2 + 6} + y - 3 = 0$ $\frac{1}{2}$

34. $\sqrt{x - 5} + \sqrt{x} = 5$ (Use the principle of squaring twice.) 9

35. $\sqrt{3x + 1} = 1 + \sqrt{x + 4}$ 5

36. $4 + \sqrt{10 - x} = 6 + \sqrt{4 - x}$ $\frac{15}{4}$ 37. $x = (x - 2)\sqrt{x}$ 0 or 4. −1 is not a solution.

38. Solve $A = \sqrt{1 + \dfrac{a^2}{b^2}}$ for b. $\sqrt{\dfrac{a^2}{A^2 - 1}}$

The formula $t = \sqrt{\dfrac{2s}{g}}$ gives the time in seconds for an object, initially at rest, to fall s feet.

39. Solve the formula for s. $\frac{t^2 g}{2}$

40. If $g = 32.2$, find the distance an object falls in the first 5 seconds. 402.5 ft

41. Find the distance an object falls in the first 10 seconds. 50 g or 1610 ft

Use the formula $V = 3.5\sqrt{h}$ for Exercise 42.

42. A person can see 20 km further after climbing 100 m. At what height was the person originally? (Use a system of equations.) 34.725 m ($V = 20.625$ km)

Stores frequently sell products at a reduced, or sale price. Usually the sale price is a percent of the regular price.

This week only, calculators Reg. $25, now 20% off.

To determine the sale price, we must subtract 20% of the regular price from the regular price.

$$\text{Sale price} = \$25.00 - (0.20 \times \$25.00)$$
$$= \$25.00 - \$5.00$$
$$= \$20.00$$

Tennis outfits, regularly $36.95, now $26.

To determine the rate of discount, we must find the discount (markdown) and determine its percent of the regular price.

$$\text{Discount} = \$36.95 - \$26.00$$
$$= \$10.95$$
$$\text{Rate of discount} = \$10.95 \div \$36.95$$
$$= 0.30$$
$$= 30\%$$

Skis $\frac{1}{3}$ off. Regularly $230

To determine the sale price, we must find $\frac{1}{3}$ of the regular price and subtract it.

$$\text{Sale price} = \$230.00 - (\tfrac{1}{3} \times \$230.00)$$
$$= \$230.00 = \$76.67$$
$$= \$153.33$$

2 for 1. Buy 1 tape, get 1 free ($9.98 tapes only)

To determine the price per tape, we must divide the price we pay by the number of items we get.

$$\text{Sale price} = \$9.98 \div 2$$
$$= \$4.99$$

Exercises
Find the sale price.

1. Vitamins $7.50, discount rate 15% $6.38
2. Jogging suits $39.99, discount rate 40% $23.99

3. Baseball gloves $32.00, discount rate 30% _{$22.40}

4. Cassette recorders $25.98, discount rate 25% _{$19.49}

5. Suitcases $43.75, discount rate 20% _{$35.00}

6. Chain saws $249.50, discount rate 10% _{$224.55}

Find the discount rate. Round to the nearest percent.

7. Soap $1.59, now $1.00 _{37%}

8. School notebooks $5.00, now $4.00 _{20%}

9. Metric wrenches $17.95, now $14.95 _{17%}

10. Electronic football $32.00, now $25.00 _{22%}

11. Clock-radio $29.99, now $20.00 _{33%}

12. Calendars $3.45, now $1.75 _{49%}

Find the sale price.

13. 35 mm cameras $110.00, now $\frac{1}{2}$ off _{$55.00}

14. Leather briefcases $49.00, now $\frac{1}{3}$ off _{$32.67}

15. Winter coats $160.00, now $\frac{1}{4}$ off _{$120.00}

16. Holiday wrapping paper $1.29, now $\frac{1}{2}$ off _{$0.65}

17. Stereo system $365.00, now $\frac{1}{3}$ off _{$243.33}

Find the sale price per item.

18. Toothpaste $1.09, buy 1 and get 1 free _{$0.55}

19. Sport socks $2.39, buy 2 and get 1 free _{$1.59}

20. Paperback books $2.95, buy 2 and get 1 free _{$1.97}

21. Records $5.95, buy 1 and get 1 free _{$2.98}

22. Soup $0.99, buy 3 and get 1 free _{$0.74}

CHAPTER 12   Review

Review the material in the chapter. Then see how you have done by trying these review exercises. If you miss an exercise, restudy the indicated lesson.

12–1   Simplify.

1. $\sqrt{36}$ ₆   2. $-\sqrt{81}$ _{–9}   3. $\sqrt{49}$ ₇   4. $-\sqrt{169}$ _{–13}

12–1   Identify each number as rational or irrational.

5. $\sqrt{3}$ **6.** $\sqrt{36}$ **7.** $-\sqrt{12}$ **8.** $-\sqrt{4}$
Irrational   Rational   Irrational   Rational   9. Rational

9. $0.272727\ldots$ **10.** $0.313313331\ldots$ 10. Irrational

12–1   Use Table 1 to approximate these square roots.

11. $\sqrt{3}$ **12.** $\sqrt{99}$ 11. 1.732
12. 9.950

12–2   Determine the sensible replacements in each expression.

13. $\sqrt{x+7}$ **14.** $\sqrt{x-10}$ 13. $x \geq -7$
14. $x \geq 10$

12–2   Simplify.

15. $\sqrt{m^2}$ m **16.** $\sqrt{49t^2}$ $7t$ **17.** $\sqrt{p^2}$ p **18.** $\sqrt{(x-4)^2}$ $x-4$

12–3   Multiply.

19. $\sqrt{3}\sqrt{7}$ $\sqrt{21}$ **20.** $\sqrt{a}\sqrt{t}$ $\sqrt{at}$
21. $\sqrt{x-3}\sqrt{x+3}$ **22.** $\sqrt{2x}\sqrt{3y}$ 21. $\sqrt{x^2-9}$ 22. $\sqrt{6xy}$

12–3   Factor.

23. $-\sqrt{48}$ $-4\sqrt{3}$ **24.** $\sqrt{x^2-49}$ $\sqrt{x-7}\sqrt{x+7}$

12–3   Approximate to three decimal places. Use Table 1.

25. $\sqrt{108}$ 10.392   **26.** $\sqrt{320}$ 17.888

12–4   Multiply and simplify.

27. $\sqrt{5x}\sqrt{8x}$ **28.** $\sqrt{5x}\sqrt{10xy^2}$ 27. $2x\sqrt{10}$ 28. $5xy\sqrt{2}$

12–5   Simplify.

29. $\sqrt{\dfrac{25}{64}}$ $\frac{5}{8}$ **30.** $\sqrt{\dfrac{20}{45}}$ $\frac{2}{3}$ **31.** $\sqrt{\dfrac{49}{t^2}}$ $\frac{7}{t}$

12–5   Rationalize the denominator.

32. $\sqrt{\dfrac{1}{2}}$ $\frac{1}{2}\sqrt{2}$ **33.** $\sqrt{\dfrac{1}{8}}$ $\frac{1}{4}\sqrt{2}$ **34.** $\sqrt{\dfrac{5}{y}}$ $\frac{1}{y}\sqrt{5y}$

12–5   Approximate to three decimal places. Use Table 1.

35. $\sqrt{\dfrac{1}{8}}$ **36.** $\sqrt{\dfrac{11}{20}}$ 35. 0.354   36. 0.742

12–6   Divide and simplify.

37. $\dfrac{\sqrt{27}}{\sqrt{45}}$ **38.** $\dfrac{\sqrt{45x^2y}}{\sqrt{54y}}$ 37. $\frac{1}{5}\sqrt{15}$ 38. $\frac{x}{6}\sqrt{30}$ or $\frac{1}{6}c\sqrt{30}$

12–6 Rationalize the denominator.

39. $\dfrac{2}{\sqrt{3}}$ $\frac{2}{3}\sqrt{3}$

12–7 Add or subtract.

40. $10\sqrt{5} + 3\sqrt{5}$ $13\sqrt{5}$ **41.** $\sqrt{80} - \sqrt{45}$ $\sqrt{5}$ **42.** $3\sqrt{2} - 5\sqrt{\dfrac{1}{2}}$ $\frac{1}{2}\sqrt{2}$

12–8

43. In a right triangle, $a = 15$ and $b = 20$. Find the length of c. 25

12–9

44. Solve $\sqrt{x - 3} = 7$. 52

45. How far can you see to the horizon through an airplane window at a height of 5000 m? Use $V = 3.5\sqrt{h}$. 247.49 km

---

CHAPTER 12   Test

Simplify.

1. $\sqrt{64}$ 8 ****2.** $-\sqrt{25}$ –5

Identify each number as rational or irrational.

3. $\sqrt{16}$ Rational **4.** $-\sqrt{10}$ Irrational

5. $0.136136136 \ldots$ Rational **6.** $0.4324432444 \ldots$ Irrational

Simplify.

7. $\sqrt{a^2}$ $|a|$ **8.** $\sqrt{36y^2}$ $6|y|$

Multiply.

9. $\sqrt{5}\sqrt{6}$ $\sqrt{30}$ **10.** $\sqrt{x + 5}\sqrt{x - 5}$ $\sqrt{x^2 - 25}$

Factor. Simplify where possible.

11. $\sqrt{27}$ $3\sqrt{3}$ **12.** $\sqrt{25x - 25}$ $5\sqrt{x - 1}$

Multiply and simplify.

13. $\sqrt{5}\sqrt{10}$ $5\sqrt{2}$ **14.** $\sqrt{3ab}\sqrt{6ab^3}$ $3ab^2\sqrt{2}$

Simplify.

15. $\sqrt{\dfrac{27}{12}}$ $\frac{3}{2}$ **16.** $\sqrt{\dfrac{144}{a^2}}$ $\frac{12}{a}$

Rationalize the denominator.

17. $\sqrt{\dfrac{2}{5}}$ $\frac{1}{5}\sqrt{10}$

18. $\sqrt{\dfrac{2x}{y}}$ $\frac{1}{y}\sqrt{2xy}$

Divide and simplify.

19. $\dfrac{\sqrt{27}}{\sqrt{32}}$ $\frac{3}{8}\sqrt{6}$

20. $\dfrac{\sqrt{35x}}{\sqrt{80xy^2}}$ $\frac{1}{4y}\sqrt{7}$

Add or subtract.

21. $3\sqrt{18} - 5\sqrt{18}$ **22.** $\sqrt{5} + \sqrt{\dfrac{1}{5}}$ 21. $-2\sqrt{18}$ 22. $\frac{6}{5}\sqrt{5}$

23. In a right triangle, $a = 8$ and $b = 4$. Find the length of c. $4\sqrt{5}$

24. Solve $\sqrt{3x} + 2 = 14$. 48

Challenge

25. Solve $\sqrt{1 - x} + 1 = \sqrt{6 - x}$. $x = -3$

Ready for Quadratic Equations and Functions?

4–8 Multiply.

1. $(x - 5)^2$ **2.** $(3x + 1)^2$ 1. $x^2 - 10x + 25$ 2. $9x^2 + 6x + 1$

5–8 What constant term must be added to each expression to make it the square of a binomial?

3. $x^2 - 8x$ 16 **4.** $m^2 + 20m$ 100 **5.** $y^2 - 14y$ 49 **6.** $x^2 + 2x$ 1

5–8 Solve.

7. $x^2 - 6x = 0$ 0, 6 **8.** $x^2 - 5x + 6 = 0$ 2, 3

12–1 Approximate. Round to the nearest hundredth.

9. $\sqrt{88}$ 9.38 **10.** $\sqrt{17}$ 4.12 **11.** $\sqrt{11}$ 3.32 **12.** $\sqrt{20}$ 4.47

12–4 Simplify.

13. $\sqrt{88}$ $2\sqrt{22}$ **14.** $\sqrt{20}$ $2\sqrt{5}$ **15.** $\sqrt{44}$ $2\sqrt{11}$ **16.** $\sqrt{32}$ $4\sqrt{2}$

12–5 Simplify.

17. $\sqrt{\dfrac{2890}{2560}}$ $\frac{17}{16}$ **18.** $\sqrt{\dfrac{6760}{6250}}$ $\frac{26}{25}$

12–6 Rationalize the denominator.

19. $\sqrt{\dfrac{7}{3}}$ $\frac{\sqrt{21}}{3}$ **20.** $\sqrt{\dfrac{5}{2}}$ $\frac{\sqrt{10}}{2}$ **21.** $\sqrt{\dfrac{1}{5}}$ $\frac{\sqrt{5}}{5}$ **22.** $\sqrt{\dfrac{7}{8}}$ $\frac{\sqrt{14}}{4}$

CHAPTER THIRTEEN

Quadratic Equations and Functions

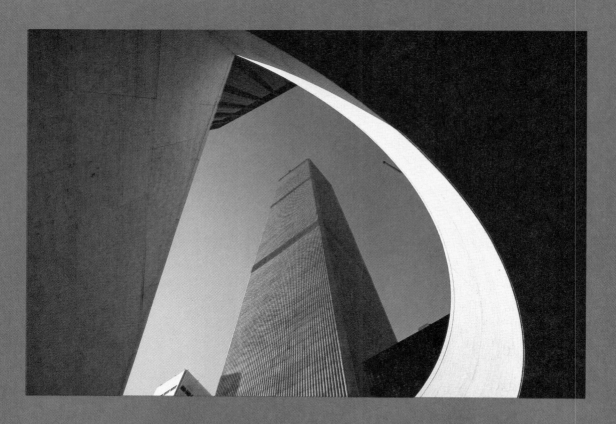

Writing Quadratic Equations in Standard Form

A quadratic equation is an equation in one variable in which the term of highest degree has degree two. These are quadratic equations.

$$4x^2 + 7x - 5 = 0 \qquad 3x^2 - \frac{1}{2}x = 9 \qquad 5y^2 = -6y$$

An equation of the form $ax^2 + bx + c = 0$ where a, b, and c are real number constants and $a > 0$, is called a quadratic equation in standard form.

EXAMPLES
Write each equation in standard form and determine a, b, and c.

1. $3y^2 - \frac{1}{2}y = 9$

   Standard form: $3y^2 - \frac{1}{2}y - 9 = 0 \quad a = 3, b = -\frac{1}{2}, c = -9$

2. $-5x^2 = 6x$
   Standard form: $5x^2 + 6x = 0 \quad a = 5, b = 6, c = 0$

   1. $x^2 - 7x = 0; a = 1, b = -7, c = 0$
   2. $x^2 + 9x - 3 = 0; a = 1, b = 9, c = -3$
   3. $4x^2 + 2x + 4 = 0; a = 4, b = 2, c = 4$

TRY THIS Write in standard form and determine a, b, and c.

1. $x^2 = 7x$ 　 2. $3 - x^2 = 9x$ 　 3. $3x + 5x^2 = x^2 - 4 + x$

Equations of the Form $ax^2 = k$

When b is 0 we have an equation of the form $ax^2 = k$. We first solve for x^2 and then take the principal square root of each side.

EXAMPLES
Solve.

3. $3x^2 = 18$

   $x^2 = 6$

   $|x| = \sqrt{6}$ 　 Taking principal square root of each side

   $x = \sqrt{6}$ 　 or 　 $x = -\sqrt{6}$

Both roots check, $3(\sqrt{6})^2 = 18$ and $3(-\sqrt{6})^2 = 18$.

4. $-3x^2 + 7 = 0$

$\quad\quad -3x^2 = -7$

$\quad\quad\quad x^2 = \dfrac{7}{3}$

$\quad\quad\quad |x| = \sqrt{\dfrac{7}{3}}$ Taking principal square root of each side

$\quad\quad x = \sqrt{\dfrac{7}{3}}\quad$ or $\quad x = -\sqrt{\dfrac{7}{3}}$

$\quad\quad x = \sqrt{\dfrac{7}{3} \cdot \dfrac{3}{3}}\quad$ or $\quad x = -\sqrt{\dfrac{7}{3} \cdot \dfrac{3}{3}}$ Rationalizing the denominators

$\quad\quad x = \dfrac{\sqrt{21}}{3}\quad$ or $\quad x = -\dfrac{\sqrt{21}}{3}$ The solutions are $\dfrac{\sqrt{21}}{3}$ and $-\dfrac{\sqrt{21}}{3}$.

When solving an equation such as $x^2 = k$ where $k \geq 0$, we must take the principal square root on both sides. Since $|x| = x$ or $-x$, we will always have $x = \sqrt{k}$ or $x = -\sqrt{k}$. Thus from now on we will not include the absolute value step. We can use the notation $x = \pm\sqrt{k}$ to show both the positive and negative root.

TRY THIS Solve.

4. $2x^2 = 20$ **5.** $3x^2 = 5$ **6.** $4x^2 = -100$ **7.** $9x^2 = 0$

4. $\sqrt{10}, -\sqrt{10}$
5. $\pm\dfrac{\sqrt{15}}{3}$
6. No solution
7. 0

Equations of the Form $ax^2 + bx = 0$

In a quadratic equation when c is 0 (and $b \neq 0$) we can factor and use the principle of zero products.

EXAMPLE 5
Solve.

$\quad\quad 20x^2 - 15x = 0$

$\quad\quad 5x(4x - 3) = 0$ Factoring

$\quad\quad 5x = 0\quad$ or $\quad 4x - 3 = 0$ Using the principle of zero products

$\quad\quad\; x = 0\quad\quad$ or $\quad\quad x = \dfrac{3}{4}$

The solutions are 0 and $\frac{3}{4}$. A quadratic equation of this type will always have 0 as one solution and a nonzero number as the other solution.

TRY THIS Solve.

8. $3x^2 + 5x = 0$ **9.** $10x^2 - 6x = 0$ 8. $\frac{-5}{3}, 0$ 9. $\frac{3}{5}, 0$

Exercises

Write standard form and determine a, b, and c.

1. $x^2 - 3x + 2 = 0$ 1, -3, 2   **2.** $x^2 - 8x - 5 = 0$ 1, -8 **3.** $2x^2 = 3$ 2, 0, -3

4. $5x^2 = 9$ 5, 0, -9 5. $7x^2 = 4x - 3$ 7, -4, 3   6. $9x^2 = x + 5$ 9, -1, -5

7. $5 = -2x^2 + 3x$ 2, -3, 5 **8.** $2x = x^2 - 5$ 1, -2, -5 **9.** $2x - 1 = 3x^2 + 7$ 3, -2, 8

Solve.

10. $x^2 = 121$ ± 11 11. $x^2 = 10$ $\pm\sqrt{10}$ 12. $5x^2 = 35$ $\pm\sqrt{7}$

13. $3x^2 = 30$ $\pm\sqrt{10}$ 14. $5x^2 = 3$ $\pm\frac{\sqrt{15}}{5}$ 15. $2x^2 = 5$ $\pm\frac{\sqrt{10}}{2}$

16. $4x^2 - 25 = 0$ $\pm\frac{5}{2}$ 17. $9x^2 - 4 = 0$ $\pm\frac{2}{3}$ 18. $3x^2 - 49 = 0$ $\pm\frac{7\sqrt{3}}{3}$

19. $5x^2 - 16 = 0$ $\pm\frac{4\sqrt{5}}{5}$ 20. $4y^2 - 3 = 9$ $\pm\sqrt{3}$ 21. $49y^2 - 16 = 0$ $\pm\frac{4}{7}$

22. $25y^2 - 36 = 0$ $\pm\frac{6}{5}$ 23. $5x^2 - 100 = 0$ $\pm 2\sqrt{5}$ **24.** $100x^2 - 5 = 0$ $\pm\frac{\sqrt{5}}{10}$

Solve.

25. $x^2 + 7x = 0$ 0, -7 26. $x^2 + 5x = 0$ 0, -5 27. $3x^2 + 6x = 0$ 0, -2

28. $4x^2 + 8x = 0$ 0, -2 29. $5x^2 - 2x = 0$ 0, $\frac{2}{5}$ 30. $3x^2 - 7x = 0$ 0, $\frac{7}{3}$

31. $4x^2 + 4x = 0$ 0, -1 32. $2x^2 - 2x = 0$ 0, 1   33. $10x^2 - 30x = 0$ 0, 3

34. $10x^2 - 50x = 0$ 0, 5   35. $55x^2 - 11x = 0$ 0, $\frac{1}{5}$ 36. $33x^2 + 11x = 0$ 0, $-\frac{1}{3}$

37. $14x^2 - 3x = 0$ 0, $\frac{3}{14}$ 38. $17x^2 - 8x = 0$ 0, $\frac{8}{17}$ 39. $3x^2 - 81x = 0$ 0, 27

Extension

Solve.

40. $t(t - 5) = 14$ -2, 7   41. $m(3m + 1) = 2$ $\frac{2}{3}$, -1

42. $3y^2 + 8y = 12y + 15$ 3, $-\frac{5}{3}$ 43. $18 + 2z = z^2 - 5z$ -2, 9

44. $t(9 + t) = 4(2t + 5)$ 4, -5 45. $16(p - 1) = p(p + 8)$ 4

46. $(2x - 3)(x + 1) = 4(2x - 3)$ $\frac{3}{2}$, 3 **47.** $(3x - 1)(2x + 1) = 3(2x + 1)$ $\frac{4}{3}$, $-\frac{1}{2}$

48. $5m^2 + 500 = 844.45$ ± 8.3 **49.** $\frac{x}{4} = \frac{9}{x}$ ± 6 **50.** $1 = \frac{1}{3}x^2$ $\pm\sqrt{3}$

51. $\frac{x}{9} = \frac{36}{4x}$ ± 9 **52.** $\frac{4}{m^2 - 7} = 1$ $\pm\sqrt{11}$ **53.** $x^2 + \sqrt{3}x = 0$ $-\sqrt{3}$, 0

54. $\sqrt{5}y^2 - y = 0$ $\frac{\sqrt{5}}{5}$, 0   **55.** $\sqrt{7}x^2 + \sqrt{3}x = 0$ **56.** $\sqrt{5}y^2 - y = 0$ $\frac{\sqrt{5}}{5}$, 0

                                $-\frac{\sqrt{21}}{7}$, 0

Challenge

57. The formula $s = 16t^2$ gives the distances traveled by a freely
    falling object dropped from rest. The time of the fall in
    seconds is t. Find the time in seconds for an object to fall
    1000 feet. 7.9 sec

13–2 Factoring and Binomial Squares

Equations of the Form $ax^2 + bx + c = 0$

When neither b nor c is 0 we can sometimes solve by factoring.

EXAMPLE

Solve.

1. $y^2 - 5y + 6 = 6y - 18$
    $y^2 - 11y + 24 = 0$ Standard form $ax^2 + bx + c = 0$
    $(y - 8)(y - 3) = 0$ Factoring

    $y - 8 = 0$ or $y - 3 = 0$
    $y = 8$ or $y = 3$

TRY THIS Solve.

  1. $3x^2 + x - 2 = 0$ 2. $x^2 + 4x + 8 = 8x + 29$ 1. $-1, \frac{2}{3}$ 2. $7, -3$

Squares of Binomials

We can extend the principal square root method of solution to quadratic equations of the form $(x + a)^2 = k$.

EXAMPLES

Solve.

2. $(x - 5)^2 = 9$
    $x - 5 = 3$ or $x - 5 = -3$ Taking principal square root
    $x = 8$ or $x = 2$

The solutions are 8 and 2.

3. $(x + 2)^2 = 7$
    $x + 2 = \sqrt{7}$ or $x + 2 = -\sqrt{7}$ Taking principal square root
    $x = -2 + \sqrt{7}$ or $x = -2 - \sqrt{7}$

The solutions are $-2 \pm \sqrt{7}$.

4. $x^2 + 16x + 64 = 17$ Factor the perfect square trinomial.
    $(x + 8)^2 = 17$

    $x + 8 = \sqrt{17}$ or $x + 8 = -\sqrt{17}$

The solutions are $-8 \pm \sqrt{17}$.

TRY THIS Solve.

3. $(x − 3)^2 = 16$ **4.** $(x + 3)^2 = 10$ **5.** $(x − 1)^2 = 5$

6. $x^2 − 14x + 49 = 3$ **7.** $x^2 + 22x + 121 = 169$

Solving Problems

The number of diagonals, d, of a polygon of n sides is given by

$$d = \frac{n^2 − 3n}{2}.$$

If, for example, a polygon has 6 sides, it has

$$\frac{6^2 − 3 \cdot 6}{2} \quad \text{or} \quad 9 \text{ diagonals.}$$

EXAMPLE 5

Suppose we know that a polygon has 27 diagonals. How many sides does it have?

We substitute 27 for d and solve for n.

$$\frac{n^2 − 3n}{2} = d$$

$$\frac{n^2 − 3n}{2} = 27 \quad \text{Substituting 27 for } d$$

$$n^2 − 3n = 54$$
$$n^2 − 3n − 54 = 0$$
$$(n − 9)(n + 6) = 0$$

$$n − 9 = 0 \quad \text{or} \quad n + 6 = 0$$
$$n = 9 \qquad\qquad n = −6.$$

Since the number of sides cannot be negative, −6 cannot be a solution. But 9 checks, so the polygon has 9 sides (it is a nonagon).

TRY THIS How many sides has a polygon with the given number of diagonals?

8. 20 8 **9.** 44 11

Interest problems can lead to quadratic equations. If you put money in a savings account you will receive interest at the end of the year. At the end of the second year you will receive interest on both the original amount and the interest. This is also called compounding interest annually . An amount of money P is invested at interest rate r. In t years it will grow to the amount A given by

$$A = P(1 + r)^t.$$

EXAMPLES

Solve.

6. $1000 invested at 16% for 2 years compounded annually will grow to what amount?

$$
\begin{aligned}
A &= P(1 + r)^t \\
&= 1000(1 + 0.16)^2 \quad \text{Substituting } P = 1000, r = 0.16, t = 2 \\
&= 1000(1.16)^2 \\
&= 1000(1.3456) \\
&= 1345.60 \quad \text{The amount is \$1345.60}
\end{aligned}
$$

7. $256 is invested at interest rate r compounded annually. In two years its grows to $289. What is the interest rate?

$$
\begin{aligned}
A &= P(1 + r)^t \\
289 &= 256(1 + r)^2 \quad \text{Substituting } A = 289, P = 256, t = 2 \\
\frac{289}{256} &= (1 + r)^2
\end{aligned}
$$

$\frac{17}{16} = 1 + r$ or $-\frac{17}{16} = 1 + r$ Taking principal square root

$\frac{1}{16} = r$ or $-\frac{33}{16} = r$

Since the interest rate cannot be negative, only $\frac{1}{16}$ is a solution. $\frac{1}{16} = 0.0625 = 6.25\%$. The interest rate must be 6.25% for $256 to grow to $289 in two years.

TRY THIS Solve.

10. Suppose $400 is invested at interest rate r compounded annually and grows to $529 in two years. What is the interest rate?   15%

13–2	

Exercises

Solve.   1. 4, 12   2. 4, −12   3. −1, −6   4. −1, −5   5. 3, −7   6. 2, −9

1. $x^2 - 16x + 48 = 0$ **2.** $x^2 + 8x - 48 = 0$ **3.** $x^2 + 7x + 6 = 0$

4. $x^2 + 6x + 5 = 0$ **5.** $x^2 + 4x - 21 = 0$ **6.** $x^2 + 7x - 18 = 0$

7. $x^2 - 9x + 14 = 0$ ₂,₇   **8.** $x^2 - 8x + 15 = 0$ ₃,₅   **9.** $x^2 + 10x + 25 = 0$ ₋₅

10. $x^2 + 6x + 9 = 0$ ₋₃   **11.** $x^2 - 2x + 1 = 0$ ₁   **12.** $x^2 - 8x + 16 = 0$ ₄

13. $2x^2 - 13x + 15 = 0$ $\frac{3}{2}$,5   **14.** $6x^2 + x - 2 = 0$ $-\frac{2}{3}$,$\frac{1}{2}$ **15.** $3a^2 - 10a - 8 = 0$ 4,$-\frac{2}{3}$

16. $9b^2 - 15b + 4 = 0$ $\frac{4}{3}$,$\frac{1}{3}$ **17.** $3x^2 - 7x = 20$ 4,$-\frac{5}{3}$ **18.** $6x^2 - 4x = 10$ $\frac{5}{3}$,-1

19. $2x^2 + 12x = -10$ ₋₁,₅   **20.** $12x^2 - 5x = 2$ $\frac{2}{3}$,$-\frac{1}{4}$ **21.** $6x^2 + x - 1 = 0$ $\frac{1}{3}$,$-\frac{1}{2}$

Solve.

22. $(x - 2)^2 = 49$ 9,-5 **23.** $(x + 1)^2 = 6$ $-1 \pm \sqrt{6}$ **24.** $(x + 3)^2 = 21$ $-3 \pm \sqrt{21}$

25. $(x - 3)^2 = 6$ $3 \pm \sqrt{6}$ **26.** $(x + 13)^2 = 8$ $-13 \pm 2\sqrt{2}$ **27.** $(x - 13)^2 = 64$ 21,5

28. $(x - 7)^2 = 12$ $7 \pm 2\sqrt{3}$ **29.** $(x + 1)^2 = 14$ $-1 \pm \sqrt{14}$ **30.** $(x + 9)^2 = 34$ $-9 \pm \sqrt{34}$

Solve.

31. $x^2 + 2x + 1 = 81$ **32.** $x^2 - 2x + 1 = 16$ **33.** $x^2 + 4x + 4 = 29$

34. $y^2 + 16y + 64 = 15$ **35.** $x^2 - 3x + 9 = 91$ **36.** $x^2 - 14x + 49 = 19$

31. $-10, 8$
32. $-3, 5$
33. $-2 \pm \sqrt{29}$
34. $-8 \pm \sqrt{15}$
35. $\frac{3 \pm \sqrt{337}}{2}$
36. $7 \pm \sqrt{19}$

How many sides has a polygon with the given number of diagonals. Use

$$d = \frac{n^2 - 3n}{2}.$$

37. 5 ₅   **38.** 35 ₁₀   **39.** 14 ₇   **40.** 54 ₁₂

The first amount is invested at interest rate r compounded annually and grows to the second amount in two years. Find the interest rate. Use $A = P(1 + r)^t$.

41. $P = 100$, $A = 121$ 10%   **42.** $P = 2560$, $A = 3610$ 18.75%   **43.** $P = 6250$, $A = 7290$ 8%

44. $P = 2500$, $A = 3600$ 20%   **45.** $P = 1000$, $A = 1267.88$ 12.6%   **46.** $P = 4000$, $A = 5267.03$ 14.75%

Extension

Solve.

47. $4m^2 - (m + 1)^2 = 0$ **48.** $(y - b)^2 = 4b^2$ **49.** $2(3x + 1)^2 = 8$

50. $5(5x - 2)^2 - 7 = 13$ **51.** $9x^2 - 24x + 16 = 2$ **52.** $64y^2 + 48y + 9 = 100$

53. $\frac{x - 1}{9} = \frac{1}{x - 1}$ **54.** $\frac{5}{y + 4} - \frac{3}{y - 2} = 4$ **55.** $0.81x^2 + 0.36x + 0.04 = 5.76$

47. 1, $\frac{-1}{3}$ $\frac{22}{9}, \frac{-26}{9}$
48. 3b, $-b$
49. $\frac{1}{3}$, -1
50. $\frac{2}{5}(1 \pm \sqrt{5})$
51. $\frac{1}{3}(4 \pm \sqrt{2})$
52. $\frac{-13}{8}, \frac{7}{8}$
53. 4, -2
54. 1, $\frac{-5}{2}$

Challenge

56. For $2000 to double itself in two years, what would the interest rate have to be? $2P = P(1 + r)^2$, $(1 + r)^2 = 2$, $r = \sqrt{2} - 1 = 0.4142$ or 41.42%

57. In two years you want to have $3000. How much do you need to invest now if you can get an interest rate of 15.75% compounded annually? $2239.13

58. Solve $y^4 - 4y^2 + 4 = 0$. (Hint: Let $x = y^2$, Solve for x, then solve for y after finding x.) $x = 2, y = \pm\sqrt{2}$

Completing the Square

We have seen that a quadratic equation of the form $(x + h)^2 = d$ can be solved by taking the principal square root on both sides. Thus, if we can write a quadratic expression as the square of a binomial, we can solve as before. For instance, we can make $x^2 + 10x$ the square of a binomial by adding the proper number to it. This process is called completing the square.

$$x^2 + 10x$$
$$\downarrow$$
$$\frac{10}{2} = 5 \quad \text{Taking half the } x\text{-coefficient}$$
$$\downarrow$$
$$5^2 = 25 \quad \text{Squaring}$$
$$\downarrow$$
$$x^2 + 10x + 25 \quad \text{Adding}$$

The trinomial $x^2 + 10x + 25$ is a perfect square trinomial. It is the square of $x + 5$.

EXAMPLES

1. Complete the square.

$$x^2 - 18$$
$$\downarrow$$
$$(-9)^2 = 81 \quad \text{Taking half the } x\text{-coefficient and squaring}$$
$$\downarrow$$
$$x^2 - 18x + 81 \quad \text{The trinomial } x^2 - 18x + 81 \text{ is the square of } x - 9.$$

2. Complete the square.

$$x^2 - 5x$$
$$\downarrow$$
$$\left(\frac{-5}{2}\right)^2 = \frac{25}{4}$$
$$\downarrow$$
$$x^2 - 5x + \frac{25}{4} \qquad x^2 - 5x + \frac{25}{4} \text{ is the square of } x - \frac{5}{2}$$

TRY THIS Complete the square.

1. $x^2 - 8x$ 2. $x^2 + 10x$ 3. $y^2 + 7y$ 4. $m^2 - 3m$

1. $x^2 - 8x + 16 = (x - 4)^2$
2. $x^2 + 10x + 25 = (x + 5)^2$
3. $y^2 + 7y + \frac{49}{4} = \left(y + \frac{7}{2}\right)^2$
4. $m^2 - 3m + \frac{9}{4} = \left(m - \frac{3}{2}\right)^2$

Solving Quadratic Equations

We can use the technique of completing the square to solve quadratic equations.

EXAMPLE 3

Solve by completing the square.

$$x^2 - 4x - 7 = 0$$
$$x^2 - 4x = 7 \quad \text{Adding 7 on both sides}$$
$$x^2 - 4x + 4 = 7 + 4 \quad \text{Adding 4 to complete the square: } \left(\frac{-4}{2}\right)^2 = 4$$
$$(x - 2)^2 = 11$$

$$x - 2 = \sqrt{11} \quad \text{or} \quad x - 2 = -\sqrt{11}$$
$$x = 2 + \sqrt{11} \quad \text{or} \quad x = 2 - \sqrt{11}$$

The solutions are $2 \pm \sqrt{11}$.

TRY THIS Solve by completing the square.

5. $x^2 + 8x + 12 = 0$ 6. $x^2 - 10x + 22 = 0$ 7. $y^2 + 6y - 1 = 0$

5. $-2, -6$
6. $5 \pm \sqrt{3}$
7. $-3 \pm \sqrt{10}$

For many quadratic equations, the leading coefficient is not 1, so we can use the multiplication principle to make it 1.

EXAMPLE 4

Solve by completing the square.

$$2x^2 - 3x - 1 = 0$$
$$x^2 - \frac{3}{2}x - \frac{1}{2} = 0 \quad \text{Multiplying by } \frac{1}{2} \text{ to make the } x^2\text{-coefficient 1}$$

$$x^2 - \frac{3}{2}x = \frac{1}{2}$$

$$x^2 - \frac{3}{2}x + \frac{9}{16} = \frac{1}{2} + \frac{9}{16} \quad \text{Adding } \left(-\frac{3}{4}\right)^2$$

$$\left(x - \frac{3}{4}\right)^2 = \frac{8}{16} + \frac{9}{16}$$

$$\left(x - \frac{3}{4}\right)^2 = \frac{17}{16}$$

$$x - \frac{3}{4} = \frac{\sqrt{17}}{4} \quad \text{or} \quad x - \frac{3}{4} = -\frac{\sqrt{17}}{4}$$

$$x = \frac{3}{4} + \frac{\sqrt{17}}{4} \quad \text{or} \quad x = \frac{3}{4} - \frac{\sqrt{17}}{4}$$

The solutions are $\dfrac{3 \pm \sqrt{17}}{4}$.

8. $2x^2 + 3x - 3 = 0$ 9. $3x^2 - 2x - 3 = 0$ 8. $\dfrac{-3 \pm \sqrt{33}}{4}$ 9. $\dfrac{1 \pm \sqrt{10}}{3}$

13–3

Exercises

Solve by completing the square.

1. $x^2 - 6x - 16 = 0$ 2. $x^2 + 8x + 15 = 0$

3. $x^2 + 22x + 21 = 0$ 4. $x^2 + 14x - 15 = 0$

5. $x^2 - 2x - 5 = 0$ 6. $x^2 - 4x - 11 = 0$

7. $x^2 - 22x + 102 = 0$ 8. $x^2 - 18x + 74 = 0$

9. $x^2 + 10x - 4 = 0$ 10. $x^2 - 10x - 4 = 0$

11. $x^2 - 7x - 2 = 0$ 12. $x^2 + 7x - 2 = 0$

13. $x^2 + 3x - 28 = 0$ 14. $x^2 - 3x - 28 = 0$

15. $x^2 + \frac{3}{2}x - \frac{1}{2} = 0$ 16. $x^2 - \frac{3}{2}x - 2 = 0$

17. $2x^2 + 3x - 17 = 0$ 18. $2x^2 - 3x - 1 = 0$

19. $3x^2 + 4x - 1 = 0$ 20. $3x^2 - 4x - 3 = 0$

21. $2x^2 - 9x - 5 = 0$ 22. $2x^2 - 5x - 12 = 0$

23. $4x^2 + 12x - 7 = 0$ 24. $6x^2 + 11x - 10 = 0$

Extension

Complete the square.

25. $x^2 - ax$
    $x^2 - ax + \frac{a^2}{4}$

26. $x^2 - (2b - 4)x$
    $x^2 - (2b - 4)x + (b - 2)^2$

27. $ax^2 + bx$
    $ax^2 + bx + \frac{b^2}{4a^2}$

Find all middle terms which complete the square.

28. $x^2 + ? + 36$ 29. $x^2 + ? + 55$ 30. $x^2 + ? + 128$

31. $4x^2 + ? + 16$ 32. $x^2 + ? + c$ 33. $ax^2 + ? + c$

34. $4a^2 + ? + 9c$ 35. $5y^2 + ? + 23c$ 36. $a^2x^2 + ? + 1 - a$

Challenge

Solve for x by completing the square.

37. $x^2 - ax - 6a^2 = 0$ 38. $x^2 + 4bx + 2b = 0$

39. $x^2 - x - c^2 - c = 0$ 40. $3x^2 - bx + 1 = 0$

41. $ax^2 + 4x + 3 = 0$ 42. $4x^2 + 4x + c = 0$

43. $kx^2 + mx + n = 0$ 44. $b^2x^2 - 2bx + c^2 = 0$

1. $-2, 8$
2. $-5, -3$
3. $-21, -1$
4. $-15, 1$
5. $1 \pm \sqrt{6}$
6. $2 \pm \sqrt{15}$
7. $11 \pm \sqrt{19}$
8. $9 \pm \sqrt{7}$
9. $-5 \pm \sqrt{29}$
10. $5 \pm \sqrt{29}$
11. $\dfrac{7 \pm \sqrt{57}}{2}$
12. $\dfrac{-7 \pm \sqrt{57}}{2}$
13. $-7, 4$
14. $-4, 7$
15. $\dfrac{-3 \pm \sqrt{17}}{4}$
16. $\dfrac{3 \pm \sqrt{41}}{4}$
17. $\dfrac{-3 \pm \sqrt{145}}{4}$
18. $\dfrac{3 \pm \sqrt{17}}{4}$
19. $\dfrac{-2 \pm \sqrt{7}}{3}$
20. $\dfrac{2 \pm \sqrt{13}}{3}$
21. $-\frac{1}{2}, 5$
22. $-\frac{3}{2}, 4$
23. $-\frac{7}{2}, \frac{1}{2}$
24. $-\frac{5}{2}, \frac{2}{3}$
28. $\pm 12x$
29. $\pm 2\sqrt{55}$
30. $\pm 16\sqrt{2}$
31. $\pm 16x$
32. $\pm 2\sqrt{c}$
33. $\pm 2\sqrt{ac}$
34. $\pm 12\sqrt{ac}$
35. $\pm 2\sqrt{115cy}$
36. $\pm 2ax\sqrt{1 - a}$
37. $3a, -2a$
38. $-2b \pm \sqrt{2b}$
39. $c + 1$
40. $\dfrac{b}{6} \pm \dfrac{\sqrt{b^2 - 12}}{6}$
41. $\dfrac{-2 \pm \sqrt{4 - 3a^2}}{a}$
42. $\dfrac{1 \pm \sqrt{1 - c}}{2}$
43. $\dfrac{-m + \sqrt{m^2 - 4nk}}{2k}$
44. $\dfrac{1 \pm \sqrt{1 - c^2}}{b}$

The Quadratic Formula

Using the Quadratic Formula

Each time you solve quadratic equations by completing the square you follow the same steps. By looking at these steps we can find a formula for solving them.

$$ax^2 + bx + c = 0, \, a > 0$$

Let's solve by completing the square.

$$x^2 + \frac{b}{a}x + \frac{c}{a} = 0 \quad \text{Multiplying by } \frac{1}{a}$$

$$x^2 + \frac{b}{a}x = -\frac{c}{a} \quad \text{Adding } -\frac{c}{a}$$

Half of $\frac{b}{a}$ is $\frac{b}{2a}$. The square is $\frac{b^2}{4a^2}$. We add $\frac{b^2}{4a^2}$ on both sides.

$$x^2 + \frac{b}{a}x + \frac{b^2}{4a^2} = -\frac{c}{a} + \frac{b^2}{4a^2}$$

$$\left(x + \frac{b}{2a}\right)^2 = -\frac{4ac}{4a^2} + \frac{b^2}{4a^2} \quad \text{or} \quad \frac{b^2 - 4ac}{4a^2}$$

$$x + \frac{b}{2a} = \sqrt{\frac{b^2 - 4ac}{4a^2}} \quad \text{or} \quad x + \frac{b}{2a} = -\sqrt{\frac{b^2 - 4ac}{4a^2}} \quad \text{Taking principal square root}$$

Since $a > 0$, $\sqrt{4a^2} = 2a$. Then

$$x + \frac{b}{2a} = \frac{\sqrt{b^2 - 4ac}}{2a} \quad \text{or} \quad x + \frac{b}{2a} = \frac{-\sqrt{b^2 - 4ac}}{2a}, \text{ so}$$

$$x = \frac{-b + \sqrt{b^2 - 4ac}}{2a} \quad \text{or} \quad x = \frac{-b - \sqrt{b^2 - 4ac}}{2a}.$$

The two solutions are the same except for the sign of the radical term. Thus, we can use the $\pm$ notation.

The quadratic formula: $x = \dfrac{-b \pm \sqrt{b^2 - 4ac}}{2a}$

EXAMPLE 1

Solve $5x^2 - 8x = -3$ using the quadratic formula. First find standard form and determine a, b, and c.

$$5x^2 - 8x + 3 = 0 \quad \text{Standard form}$$
$$a = 5, b = -8, c = 3$$

Then use the quadratic formula.

$$x = \frac{-b \pm \sqrt{b^2 - 4ac}}{2a}$$

$$x = \frac{-(-8) \pm \sqrt{(-8)^2 - 4 \cdot 5 \cdot 3}}{2 \cdot 5} \quad \text{Substituting for } a, b, \text{ and } c$$

$$x = \frac{8 \pm \sqrt{64 - 60}}{10} \quad \text{Simplifying the radicand}$$

$$x = \frac{8 \pm \sqrt{4}}{10} = \frac{8 \pm 2}{10}$$

$$x = \frac{8 + 2}{10} \quad \text{or} \quad x = \frac{8 - 2}{10}$$

$$x = \frac{10}{10} = 1 \quad \text{or} \quad x = \frac{6}{10} = \frac{3}{5}$$

The solutions are 1 and $\frac{3}{5}$.

Steps for Solving Quadratic Equations

1. Try factoring.
2. If it is not possible to factor or factoring seems difficult, use the quadratic formula. The solutions of a quadratic equation can always be found using the quadratic formula. They cannot *always* be found by factoring.

TRY THIS Solve by the quadratic formula.

1. $2x^2 = 4 - 7x$ **2.** $3m^2 - 8 = 10m$ 1. $\frac{1}{2}, -4$ 2. $4, -\frac{2}{3}$

The expression under the radical, $b^2 - 4ac$, is called the discriminant If $b^2 - 4ac < 0$ the equation has no real-number solutions. When using the quadratic formula it is wise to compute the discriminant first.

EXAMPLE 2

Solve $x^2 - x + 2 = 0$ using the quadratic formula.

Compute the discriminant: $a = 1, b = -1, c = 2$.
$b^2 - 4ac = (-1)^2 - 4 \cdot 1 \cdot 2 = -7$

The discriminant is negative, so there are no real number solutions.

EXAMPLE 3

Solve $3x^2 = 7 - 2x$ using the quadratic formula. Use Table 1 to approximate the solutions to the nearest tenth.

Find standard form: $3x^2 + 2x - 7 = 0$.

Compute the discriminant: $a = 3, b = 2, c = -7$.
$b^2 - 4ac = 2^2 - 4 \cdot 3 \cdot (-7) = 88$

The discriminant is positive, so there are solutions. They are given by

$$x = \frac{-2 \pm \sqrt{88}}{6} \qquad \text{Substituting into the quadratic formula}$$

$$x = \frac{-2 \pm \sqrt{4 \cdot 22}}{6}$$

$$x = \frac{-2 \pm 2\sqrt{22}}{6}$$

$$x = \frac{2(-1 \pm \sqrt{22})}{2 \cdot 3} \qquad \text{Factoring out 2 in the numerator and denominator}$$

$$x = \frac{-1 \pm \sqrt{22}}{3}.$$

The solutions are $\dfrac{-1 + \sqrt{22}}{3}$ and $\dfrac{-1 - \sqrt{22}}{3}$.

Substituting 4.690 for $\sqrt{22}$, we find the solutions are

$$\frac{-1 + 4.690}{3} = 1.2 \quad \text{and} \quad \frac{-1 - 4.690}{3} = 1.9 \text{ each to the nearest tenth.}$$

TRY THIS Solve using the quadratic formula. Use Table 1 to approximate the solutions to the nearest tenth.

3. $2x^2 - 4x = 5$ **4.** $x^2 + 5x = -3$ 3. 2.9, -0.9   4. 0.7, -4.3

| **13-4** | |

Exercises

Solve using the quadratic formula.   13. $5 \pm \sqrt{3}$ 14. $-3 \pm \sqrt{10}$

1. $x^2 - 4x = 21$ -3, 7   **2.** $x^2 + 7x = 18$ -9, 2   **3.** $x^2 = 6x - 9$ 3

4. $x^2 = 8x - 16$ 4   **5.** $3y^2 - 2y - 8 = 0$ $-\frac{4}{3}, 2$ **6.** $3y^2 - 7y + 4 = 0$ 1, $\frac{4}{3}$

7. $4x^2 + 12x = 7$ $-\frac{7}{2}, \frac{1}{2}$ **8.** $4x^2 + 4x = 15$ $-\frac{5}{2}, \frac{3}{2}$ **9.** $x^2 - 9 = 0$ -3, 3

10. $x^2 - 4 = 0$ -2, 2   **11.** $x^2 - 2x - 2 = 0$ $1 \pm \sqrt{3}$ **12.** $x^2 - 4x - 7 = 0$ $2 \pm \sqrt{11}$

13. $y^2 - 10y + 22 = 0$ **14.** $y^2 + 6y - 1 = 0$ **15.** $x^2 + 4x + 4 = 7$ $-2 \pm \sqrt{7}$

16. $x^2 - 2x + 1 = 5$ 17. $3x^2 + 8x + 2 = 0$ 18. $3x^2 - 4x - 2 = 0$

19. $2x^2 - 5x = 1$ 20. $2x^2 + 2x = 3$ 21. $4y^2 - 4y - 1 = 0$

22. $4y^2 + 4y - 1 = 0$ 23. $3x^2 + 5x = 0$ 24. $5x^2 - 2x = 0$ 16. $1 \pm \sqrt{5}$

25. $2t^2 + 6t + 5 = 0$ 26. $4y^2 + 3y + 2 = 0$ 27. $4x^2 = 100$ 17. $\dfrac{-4 \pm \sqrt{10}}{3}$

28. $5t^2 = 80$ 29. $3x^2 = 5x + 4$ 30. $2x^2 + 3x = 1$ 18. $\dfrac{2 \pm \sqrt{10}}{3}$

31. $2y^2 - 6y = 10$ 32. $5m^2 = 3 + 11m$ 33. $3p^2 + 2p = 3$ 19. $\dfrac{5 \pm \sqrt{33}}{4}$

20. $\dfrac{-1 \pm \sqrt{7}}{2}$

Solve using the quadratic formula. Use Table 1 to approximate the
solutions to the nearest tenth.   21. $\dfrac{1 \pm \sqrt{2}}{2}$

34. $x^2 - 4x - 7 = 0$ 35. $x^2 + 2x - 2 = 0$ 36. $y^2 - 6y - 1 = 0$

37. $y^2 + 10y + 22 = 0$ 38. $4x^2 + 4x = 1$ 39. $4x^2 = 4x + 1$

40. $3x^2 + 4x - 2 = 0$ 41. $3x^2 - 8x + 2 = 0$ 42. $2y^2 + 2y - 3 = 0$

22. $\dfrac{-1 \pm \sqrt{2}}{2}$ 25. No real-number solutions

Extension

Solve.

23. $-\frac{5}{3}, 0$ 26. No real-number solutions   29. $\dfrac{5 \pm \sqrt{73}}{6}$

24. $0, \frac{2}{5}$ 27. $-5, 5$

28. $-4, 4$ 30. $\dfrac{-3 \pm \sqrt{17}}{4}$

43. $5x + x(x - 7) = 0$ 44. $x(3x + 7) - 3x = 0$ 31. $\dfrac{3 \pm \sqrt{29}}{2}$

45. $3 - x(x - 3) = 4$ 46. $x(5x - 7) = 1$ 32. $\dfrac{11 \pm \sqrt{181}}{10}$

47. $(y + 4)(y + 3) = 15$ 48. $(y + 5)(y - 1) = 27$ 33. $\dfrac{-1 \pm \sqrt{10}}{3}$

49. $x^2 + (x + 2)^2 = 7$ 50. $x^2 + (x + 1)^2 = 5$ 34. $-1.3, 5.3$

35. $-2.7, 0.7$

51. $(x + 2)^2 + (x + 1)^2 = 0$ 52. $(x + 3)^2 + (x + 1)^2 = 0$ 36. $-0.2, 6.2$

37. $-6.7, -3.3$

53. $ax^2 + 2x = 3$ 54. $2bx^2 - 5x + 3b = 0$ 38. $-1.2, 0.2$

39. $-0.2, 1.2$

55. $4x^2 - 4cx + c^2 - 3d^2 = 0$ 56. $0.8x^2 + 0.16x - 0.09 = 0$ 40. $-1.7, 0.4$

41. $0.3, 2.4$

57. $bdx^2 + bcx - ac = adx$ 58. $\frac{1}{2}x^2 + bx + \left(b - \frac{1}{2}\right) = 0$ 42. $-1.8, 0.8$

43. $0, 2$

44. $-\frac{4}{3}, 0$

59. **a.** In $ax^2 + bx + c = 0$, $b^2 > 4ac$. Will the equation have
real-number solutions? Does it make any difference whether
b is positive, negative, or zero?   Yes; no   45. $\dfrac{3 \pm \sqrt{5}}{2}$

46. $\dfrac{7 \pm \sqrt{69}}{10}$

b. In $ax^2 + bx + c = 0$, $ac < 0$. Will the equation have
real-number solutions? Does b make any difference?   Yes; no   47. $\dfrac{-7 \pm \sqrt{61}}{2}$

48. $-8, 4$

c. In $ax^2 + bx + c = 0$, a and c are both positive. When will
the equation have real-number solutions?   When $b^2 \geq 4ac$ 49. $\dfrac{-2 \pm \sqrt{10}}{2}$

50. $-2, 1$

51. No real-number solutions

52. No real-number solutions

Challenge

53. $-1 \pm \sqrt{3a + 1}$

60. Use the two roots given by the quadratic formula to find a
formula for the sum of the solutions for any quadratic
equation. What is the product of the solution? Without
solving, tell the sum and product of the solutions for
$2x^2 + 5x - 3 = 0$. $\dfrac{-2b}{2a} = \dfrac{-10}{4}$, $\dfrac{c}{a} = \dfrac{-3}{2}$ 54. $\dfrac{5 \pm \sqrt{25 - 24b^2}}{4b}$

55. $\dfrac{c \pm \sqrt{3}d}{2}$

56. $0.25, -0.45$

57. $\dfrac{a}{b}, \dfrac{-c}{d}$

61. One solution to the equation $2x^2 + bx - 3 = 0$ is known to
be -5. Use the results of the preceding problem to find the
other solution. $b = 9.4$, so $x = 0.3$ 58. $-1, -2b + 1$

Solving Fractional and Radical Equations

Fractional Equations

Recall that we solve fractional equations by multiplying both sides by the LCM of all the denominators. This sometimes results in a quadratic equation.

EXAMPLE 1
Solve.

$$\frac{3}{x - 1} + \frac{5}{x + 1} = 2$$

$$(x - 1)(x + 1)\left(\frac{3}{x - 1} + \frac{5}{x + 1}\right) = 2(x - 1)(x + 1)$$

LCM is $(x - 1)(x + 1)$.

$$(x - 1)(x + 1)\frac{3}{x - 1} + (x - 1)(x + 1)\frac{5}{x + 1} = 2(x - 1)(x + 1)$$

$$3(x + 1) + 5(x - 1) = 2(x - 1)(x + 1)$$
$$3x + 3 + 5x - 5 = 2(x^2 - 1)$$
$$8x - 2 = 2x^2 - 2$$
$$-2x^2 + 8x = 0$$
$$2x^2 - 8x = 0 \quad \text{Multiplying by } -1$$
$$2x(x - 4) = 0 \quad \text{Factoring}$$

$$2x = 0 \quad \text{or} \quad x - 4 = 0$$
$$x = 0 \quad \text{or} \quad x = 4$$

Check:
$$\frac{3}{x - 1} + \frac{5}{x + 1} = 2 \qquad \frac{3}{x - 1} + \frac{5}{x + 1} = 2$$

$$\frac{3}{0 - 1} + \frac{5}{0 + 1} \;\Big|\; 2 \qquad \frac{3}{4 - 1} + \frac{5}{4 + 1} \;\Big|\; 2$$
$$-3 + 5 \qquad\qquad 1 + 1$$
$$2 \;\Big| \qquad\qquad\qquad 2 \;\Big|$$

Both number check. The solutions are 0 or 4.

TRY THIS Solve.

1. $\dfrac{2}{x + 2} + \dfrac{3}{x - 2} = 1$ 6, −1

Radical Equations

We can solve some radical equations by first using the principle of squaring to find a quadratic equation. When we do this we must be sure to check.

EXAMPLE 2

Solve.

$$x - 5 = \sqrt{x + 7}$$
$$(x - 5)^2 = (\sqrt{x + 7})^2 \quad \text{Principle of squaring}$$
$$x^2 - 10x + 25 = x + 7$$
$$x^2 - 11x + 18 = 0$$
$$(x - 9)(x - 2) = 0$$
$$x = 9 \quad \text{or} \quad x = 2$$

Check:

$x - 5 = \sqrt{x + 7}$		$x - 5 = \sqrt{x + 7}$	
$9 - 5$	$\sqrt{9 + 7}$	$2 - 5$	$\sqrt{2 + 7}$
4	4	-3	3

The number 9 checks, but 2 does not. Thus, the solution is 9.

EXAMPLE 3

We must first get the radical expression alone on one side before squaring both sides.

Solve.

$$\sqrt{27 - 3x} + 3 = x$$
$$\sqrt{27 - 3x} = x - 3 \quad \text{Adding} -3 \text{ to get the radical alone on one side}$$
$$(\sqrt{27 - 3x})^2 = (x - 3)^2 \quad \text{Principle of squaring}$$
$$27 - 3x = x^2 - 6x + 9$$
$$0 = x^2 - 3x - 18$$
$$0 = (x - 6)(x + 3)$$
$$x = 6 \quad \text{or} \quad x = -3$$

Check:

$\sqrt{27 - 3x} + 3 = x$		$\sqrt{27 - 3x} + 3 = x$	
$\sqrt{27 - 3 \cdot 6} + 3$	6	$\sqrt{27 - 3 \cdot (-3)} + 3$	-3
$\sqrt{9} + 3$		$\sqrt{27 + 9} + 3$	
6		$\sqrt{36} + 3$	
		9	

There is only one solution, 6.

TRY THIS Solve.

2. $\sqrt{x + 2} = 4 - x$ ₂ **3.** $\sqrt{30 - 3x} + 4 = x$ ₇

Formulas

Solve each formula for the given variable.

EXAMPLES

4. Solve $V = 3.5\sqrt{h}$ for h.

$$V = 3.5\sqrt{h}$$
$$V^2 = (3.5)^2(\sqrt{h})^2 \quad \text{Squaring both sides}$$
$$V^2 = 12.25h$$

$$\frac{V^2}{12.25} = h \quad \text{Multiplying by } \frac{1}{12.25} \text{ to get } h \text{ alone}$$

5. Solve $T = 2\pi\sqrt{\dfrac{L}{g}}$ for g.

$$T = 2\pi\sqrt{\frac{L}{g}}$$

$$T^2 = (2\pi)^2\left(\sqrt{\frac{L}{g}}\right)^2 \quad \text{Squaring both sides}$$

$$T^2 = \frac{4\pi^2 L}{g}$$

$$gT^2 = 4\pi^2 L$$

$$g = \frac{4\pi^2 L}{T^2} \quad \text{Multiplying by } \frac{1}{T^2}$$

TRY THIS Solve each formula for the given variable.

4. $r = 2\sqrt{5L}$; L **5.** $T = 2\pi\sqrt{\dfrac{L}{g}}$; L **6.** $c = \sqrt{\dfrac{E}{m}}$; m **7.** $A = \pi r^2$; r

4. $\dfrac{r^2}{20}$

5. $\dfrac{t^2 g}{4\pi^2}$

6. $\dfrac{E}{c^2}$

7. $\sqrt{\dfrac{A}{\pi}}$

EXAMPLE 6

Solve $A = P(1 + r)^2$ for r.

$$A = P(1 + r)^2$$

$$\frac{A}{P} = (1 + r)^2 \quad \text{Multiplying by } \frac{1}{P}$$

$$\sqrt{\frac{A}{P}} = 1 + r \quad \text{Taking the square root on both sides}$$

$$-1 + \sqrt{\frac{A}{P}} = r$$

TRY THIS Solve for the given variable.

8. $C = P(d - 1)^2$; d $1 + \sqrt{\dfrac{C}{P}}$

Exercises

Solve each fractional equation.

1. $x - 3 = \dfrac{5}{x - 3}$ $3 \pm \sqrt{5}$ **2.** $x + 2 = \dfrac{3}{x + 2}$ $-2 \pm \sqrt{3}$ **3.** $\dfrac{x^2}{x - 4} - \dfrac{7}{x - 4} = 0$ $\pm\sqrt{7}$

4. $\dfrac{x^2}{x + 3} - \dfrac{5}{x + 3} = 0$ $\pm\sqrt{5}$ **5.** $\dfrac{y + 2}{y} = \dfrac{1}{y + 2}$ No solution   **6.** $\dfrac{8}{x - 2} + \dfrac{8}{x + 2} = 3$ $6, -\frac{2}{3}$

7. $\dfrac{24}{x - 2} + \dfrac{24}{x + 2} = 5$ $10, -\frac{8}{5}$ **8.** $1 + \dfrac{12}{x^2 - 4} = \dfrac{3}{x - 2}$ 1 **9.** $\dfrac{5}{t - 3} - \dfrac{30}{t^2 - 9} = 1$ 2

Solve each radical equation.

10. $x - 7 = \sqrt{x - 5}$ 9 **11.** $\sqrt{x + 7} = x - 5$ 9 **12.** $\sqrt{x + 18} = x - 2$ 7

13. $x - 9 = \sqrt{x - 3}$ 12 **14.** $\sqrt{5x + 21} = x + 3$ 3 **15.** $\sqrt{2x + 3} = 6 - x$ 3

16. $x = 1 + 6\sqrt{x + 9}$ **17.** $\sqrt{2x - 1} + 2 = x$ 5 **18.** $x + 4 = 4\sqrt{x + 1}$ $0, 8$
$25, 13$

Solve each formula for the given variable.

19. $c^2 = a^2 + b^2$; a **20.** $E = mc^2$; c **21.** $c = \sqrt{a^2 + b^2}$; b

22. $N = 2.5\sqrt{A}$; A **23.** $V = \pi r^2 h$; r **24.** $S = \frac{1}{2}gt^2$; t

19. $a = \sqrt{c^2 - b^2}$ 21. $b = \sqrt{c^2 - a^2}$ 23. $r = \sqrt{\dfrac{V}{\pi h}}$

Extension
20. $c = \sqrt{\dfrac{E}{m}}$ 22. $A = \dfrac{N^2}{6.25}$ 24. $t = \sqrt{\dfrac{2S}{g}}$

Solve.

25. $\dfrac{1}{x} + \dfrac{1}{x + 6} = \dfrac{1}{4}$ $6, -4$ **26.** $\dfrac{1}{x} + \dfrac{1}{x + 6} = \dfrac{1}{5}$ $2 \pm \sqrt{34}$ **27.** $\dfrac{1}{x} + \dfrac{1}{x + 1} = \dfrac{1}{3}$ $\dfrac{5 \pm \sqrt{37}}{2}$

28. $\dfrac{1}{1 + x} - 1 = \dfrac{5x}{x^2 + 3x + 2}$ $0, -7$ **29.** $\sqrt{x + 3} = \dfrac{8}{\sqrt{x - 9}}$ 13 **30.** $\dfrac{12}{\sqrt{5x + 6}} = \sqrt{2x + 5}$ 2

31. The circumference C of a circle is given by $C = 2\pi r$.
   a. Solve $C = 2\pi r$ for r. $\frac{C}{2\pi}$
   b. Express the area $A = \pi r^2$ in terms of the circumference C. $A = \pi\left(\dfrac{C}{2\pi}\right)^2 = \dfrac{C^2}{4\pi}$

Challenge
32. $2\sqrt{x - 1} - \sqrt{3x - 5} = \sqrt{x - 9}$ 10 **33.** $\sqrt{y + 1} - \sqrt{2y - 5} = \sqrt{y - 2}$ 3
34. Solve $x + 1 + 3\sqrt{x + 1} - 28 = 0$ using two methods.
   First use the principle of squaring. Second, let $y = \sqrt{x + 1}$.
   (Then $y^2 = x + 1$). Solve for y, then substitute to find x. 15
35. Solve $h = vt + 8t^2$ for t. $\dfrac{-v \pm \sqrt{v^2 + 32h}}{16}$

13–6 Solving Problems

We now use quadratic equations to solve more applied problems.

EXAMPLE 1

A picture frame measures 20 cm by 14 cm. 160 square centimeters of picture shows. Find the width of the frame.

First we make a drawing. Let x = the width of the frame. To translate, we recall that area is length × width.

$$lw = A$$
$$lw = 160$$
$$(20 - 2x)(14 - 2x) = 160$$
$$280 - 68x + 4x^2 = 160$$
$$4x^2 - 68x + 120 = 0$$
$$x^2 - 17x + 30 = 0$$
$$(x - 15)(x - 2) = 0 \quad \text{Factoring}$$
$$x = 15 \text{ or } \quad x = 2$$

We check in the original problem. 15 is not a solution because when $x = 15$, $20 - 2x = -10$, and the length of the picture cannot be negative. When $x = 2$, $20 - 2x = 16$. This is the length. When $x = 2$, $14 - 2x = 10$. This is the width. The area is 16×10, or 160. This checks, so the width of the frame is 2 cm

TRY THIS

1. A rectangular garden is 80 m by 60 m. Part of the garden is torn up to install a strip of lawn around the garden. The new area of the garden is 800 m². How wide is the strip of lawn? 20 m

EXAMPLE 2

The hypotenuse of a right triangle is 6 m long. One leg is 1 m longer than the other. Find the lengths of the legs. Round to the nearest tenth.

We first make a drawing. Let x = the length of one leg. Then $x + 1$ is the length of the other leg. To translate we use the Pythagorean property.

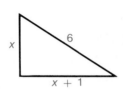

$$x^2 + (x + 1)^2 = 6^2$$
$$x^2 + x^2 + 2x + 1 = 36$$
$$2x^2 + 2x - 35 = 0$$

Since we cannot factor, we use the quadratic formula.

$$a = 2, b = 2, c = -35, \text{ so } b^2 - 4ac = 284$$

$$x = \frac{-b \pm \sqrt{b^2 - 4ac}}{2a} = \frac{-2 \pm \sqrt{284}}{4}$$

$$= \frac{-2 \pm \sqrt{4 \cdot 71}}{4} = \frac{-2 \pm 2 \cdot \sqrt{71}}{2 \cdot 2} = \frac{-1 \pm \sqrt{71}}{2}$$

The square root table gives an approximation: $\sqrt{71} \approx 8.426$.

$$\frac{-1 + \sqrt{71}}{2} \approx 3.7 \quad \frac{-1 - \sqrt{71}}{2} \approx -4.7$$

Since the length of a leg cannot be negative, -4.7 does not check. 3.7 does check. $(3.7)^2 + (4.7)^2 = 13.69 + 22.09 = 35.78$ and $\sqrt{35.78} \approx 5.98 \approx 6$. Thus, one leg is about 3.7 m long and the other is about 4.7 m long.

TRY THIS

2. The hypotenuse of a right triangle is 4 cm long. One leg is 1 cm longer than the other. Find the lengths of the legs. Round to the nearest tenth. 2.3 cm, 3.3 cm

EXAMPLE 3

The current in a stream moves at a speed of 2 km/h. A boat travels 24 km upstream and 24 km downstream in a total time of 5 hours. What is the speed of the boat in still water?

The distances are the same. Let r represent the speed of the boat in still water. Then, when traveling upstream the speed of the boat is $r - 2$. When traveling downstream, the speed of the boat is $r + 2$. We let t_1 represent the time it takes the boat to go upstream, and t_2 the time it takes to go downstream. We summarize in a chart.

	d	r	t
upstream	24	$r - 2$	t_1
downstream	24	$r + 2$	t_2

Since $d = rt$, we know that $t = \frac{d}{r}$. Then using the rows of the table, we have $t_1 = 24/(r - 2)$ and $t_2 = 24/(r + 2)$. Since the total time is 5 hours, $t_1 + t_2 = 5$, and we have

$$\frac{24}{r-2} + \frac{24}{r+2} = 5. \quad \text{LCM} = (r-2)(r+2).$$

$$(r-2)(r+2)\left(\frac{24}{r-2} + \frac{24}{r+2}\right) = (r-2)(r+2)5 \quad \text{Multiplying by the LCM}$$

$$24(r+2) + 24(r-2) = 5r^2 - 20$$
$$5r^2 - 48r - 20 = 0$$
$$(5r+2)(r-10) = 0 \quad \text{Factoring}$$

$$5r + 2 = 0 \quad \text{or} \quad r - 10 = 0 \quad \text{Principle of zero products}$$
$$5r = -2 \quad \text{or} \quad r = 10$$
$$r = -\frac{2}{5} \quad \text{or} \quad r = 10$$

Since speed cannot be negative, $-\frac{2}{5}$ cannot be a solution. But 10 checks, so the speed of the boat in still water is 10 km/h

TRY THIS

3. The speed of a boat in still water is 12 km/h. The boat travels 45 km upstream and 45 km downstream in a total time of 8 hours. What is the speed of the stream? (Hint: Let s = the speed of the stream. Then $12 - s$ is the speed upstream and $12 + s$ is the speed downstream.) 3 km/hr

---

13–6

Exercises

Solve.

1. A picture frame is 20 cm by 12 cm. There are 84 cm² of picture showing. Find the width of the frame. 3 cm

2. A picture frame is 18 cm by 14 cm. There are 192 cm² of picture showing. Find the width of the frame. 1 cm

3. The hypotenuse of a right triangle is 25 ft long. One leg is 17 ft longer than the other. Find the lengths of the legs. 7 ft, 24 ft

4. The hypotenuse of a right triangle is 26 yd long. One leg is 14 yd longer than the other. Find the lengths of the legs. 10 yd, 24 yd

5. The length of a rectangle is 2 cm greater than the width. The area is 80 cm². Find the length and width. 8 cm, 10 cm

6. The width of a rectangle is 4 cm less than the length. The area is 320 cm². Find the length and width. 20 cm, 16 cm

7. The length of a rectangle is twice the width. The area is 50 m². Find the length and width. 5 m, 10 m

8. The hypotenuse of a right triangle is 8 m long. One leg is 2 m longer than the other. Find the lengths of the legs. Round to the nearest tenth. 4.6 m, 6.6 m

9. The hypotenuse of a right triangle is 5 cm long. One leg is 2 cm longer than the other. Find the lengths of the legs. Round to the nearest tenth. 2.4 cm, 4.4 cm

10. The current in a stream moves at a speed of 3 km/h. A boat travels 40 km upstream and 40 km downstream in a total time of 14 hours. What is the speed of the boat in still water? 7 km/h

11. The current in a stream moves at a speed of 4 mi/h. A boat travels 4 mi upstream and 12 mi downstream in a total time of 2 hours. What is the speed of the boat in still water? 8 mi/h

12. The speed of a boat in still water is 10 km/h. The boat travels 12 km upstream and 28 km downstream in a total time of 4 hours. What is the speed of the stream? 4 km/h

13. An airplane flies 738 mi against the wind and 1062 mi with the wind in a total time of 9 hours. The speed of the airplane in still air is 200 mi/h. What is the speed of the wind? 36 mi/h

Extension

14. Find r in this figure. Round to the nearest hundredth. 2.41

15. What should the diameter d of a pizza be so it has the same area as two 10-inch pizzas? Do you get more to eat with a 15-inch pizza or two 10-inch pizzas? 14.14, a 15″ pizza

16. In this figure, the area of the shaded region is 24 cm². Find r if R = 6 cm. Round to the nearest hundredth. 5.33 cm

17. A ladder 10 ft long leans against a wall. The bottom of the ladder is 6 ft from the wall. How much would the lower end of the ladder have to be pulled away so that the top end would be pulled down the same amount? 2 ft

18. Trains A and B leave the same city at right angles at the same time. Train B travels 5 mi/h faster than train A. After 2 hr they are 50 mi apart. Find the speed of each train. 15 mi/h, 20 mi/h

19. Find the side of a square whose diagonal is 3 cm longer than a side. $3 + 3\sqrt{2}$ or 7.243 cm

20. Two pipes are connected to the same tank. When working together they can fill the tank in 2 hr. The larger pipe, working alone, can fill the tank in 3 hr less time than the smaller one. How long would the smaller one take, working alone, to fill the tank? $\frac{1}{x} + \frac{1}{x-3} = \frac{1}{2}$, $x = 6$ hr

Quadratic Functions

Graphing Quadratic Functions

A quadratic function is any function which can be described by a quadratic equation. For instance, $f(x) = x^2 + 5x + 3$ describes a quadratic function. In this case, x is the input and $x^2 + 5x + 3$ is the output. For each x in the domain of the function $f(x)$ gives the corresponding y-value.

EXAMPLE 1

Make a table of values and draw a graph of the quadratic function defined by $f(x) = x^2$. We choose numbers for x and find the corresponding values for y. Graph the ordered pairs (x, y), or $(x, f(x))$.

x	$f(x)$
3	9
2	4
1	1
0	0
1	1
2	4
3	9

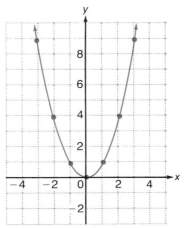

TRY THIS

1. Make a table of values and draw a graph of the quadratic function defined by $f(x) = x^2 - 1$.

Graphs of quadratic functions described by $y = ax^2 + bx + c$ (where $a \neq 0$) are always cup-shaped. These curves are called parabolas. Some parabolas are thin and others are wide but they all have the same general shape. They all have a line of symmetry. In Example 1 the line of symmetry is the y-axis. If you fold on this line, the two halves will match exactly. The arrows show that the curve goes on forever. In drawing parabolas be sure to plot enough points to see the general shape of each graph.

EXAMPLE 2

Graph $f(x) = -2x^2 + 3$.

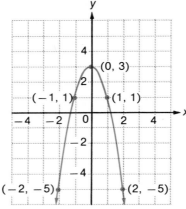

x	y
0	3
1	1
-1	1
2	-5
-2	-5

The graph in Example 1 opens upward and the coefficient of x^2 is 1, which is positive. The graph in Example 2 opens downward and the coefficient of x^2 is -2, which is negative.

> The graph of $f(x) = ax^2 + bx + c$ opens upward if $a > 0$. It opens downward if $a < 0$.

TRY THIS Without graphing tell whether the graph of the quadratic function opens upward or downward. Then graph the function.

2. $f(x) = -x^2 + 2x + 3$ **3.** $y = x^2 - 3x + 1$
Downward   Upward

Approximating Solutions of $ax^2 + bx + c = 0$

Graphing can be used to approximate the solutions of the equation

$$ax^2 + bx + c = 0.$$

We graph the function $f(x) = ax^2 + bx + c$. If the graph crosses the x-axis, the points of crossing will give us solutions.

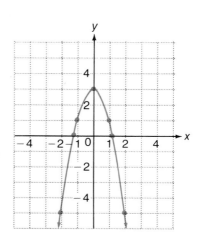

EXAMPLE 3

Approximate the solutions of $-2x^2 + 3 = 0$ by graphing.

The graph of $f(x) = -2x^2 + 3$ was found in Example 2. The graph crosses the x-axis at about $(-1.2, 0)$ and $(1.2, 0)$. So the solutions of the equation $-2x^2 + 3 = 0$ are about -1.2 and 1.2.

The solutions (if any) of the quadratic equation $ax^2 + bx + c = 0$ are the x-coordinates of the points where the graph of the quadratic function $f(x) = ax^2 + bx + c$ crosses the x-axis.

TRY THIS Approximate the solutions by graphing.

4. $x^2 - 4x - 4 = 0$ **5.** $-2x^2 - 4x + 1 = 0$
    $-0.8, 4.8$ $0.2, -2.2$

13–7

Exercises

Graph the following quadratic functions.

7. Upward	13. Upward	19. Downward	25. ± 2.2
8. Downward	14. Upward	20. Upward	26. ± 1.7
9. Downward	15. Downward	21. Downward	27. $0, -2$
10. Upward	16. Downward	22. Downward	28. $0, 2$
11. Downward	17. Upward	23. Downward	29. $2.3, -3.3$
12. Downward	18. Upward	24. Upward	30. $3.3, -2.3$

31. -5
32. 4
33. $-2.2, 0.2$
34. $0.2, -2.2$

1. $f(x) = \frac{1}{4}x^2$ **2.** $f(x) = 3x^2$ **3.** $y = -x^2 + 3$

4. $y = x^2 - 3$ **5.** $f(x) = -x^2 + x - 1$ **6.** $f(x) = x^2 + 2x$

Without graphing tell whether the graph of the function opens upward or downward. Then graph the function.

7. $y = 2x^2$ **8.** $y = -2x^2$ **9.** $f(x) = -x^2 - 1$

10. $f(x) = x^2 - 2$ **11.** $f(x) = -x^2 + 2x$ **12.** $f(x) = -x^2 - 2x$

13. $y = x^2 + x - 6$ **14.** $y = x^2 - x - 6$ **15.** $y = 8 - x - x^2$

16. $y = 8 + x - x^2$ **17.** $f(x) = x^2 + 2x + 1$ **18.** $f(x) = x^2 - 2x + 1$

19. $f(x) = -\frac{1}{2}x^2$ **20.** $f(x) = \frac{1}{2}x^2$ **21.** $y = -x^2 + 2x + 3$

22. $y = -x^2 - 2x + 3$ **23.** $y = -2x^2 - 4x + 1$ **24.** $y = 2x^2 + 4x - 1$

Approximate the solutions by graphing.

25. $x^2 - 5 = 0$ **26.** $x^2 - 3 = 0$ **27.** $x^2 + 2x = 0$

28. $x^2 - 2x = 0$ **29.** $8 - x - x^2 = 0$ **30.** $8 + x - x^2 = 0$

31. $x^2 + 10x + 25 = 0$ **32.** $x^2 - 8x + 16 = 0$ **33.** $-2x^2 - 4x + 1 = 0$

34. $2x^2 + 4x - 1 = 0$ **35.** $x^2 + 5 = 0$ **36.** $x^2 + 3 = 0$
                      Graph does not cross the x-axis   Graph does not cross the x-axis

Extension

37. For the graph of a linear function $f(x) = mx + b$ we know the y-intercept is b. Examine the graphs of the functions in Exercises 7-24. Describe the y-intercept of the graph of a quadratic function.   When the function is in standard form, the y-intercept is the constant term.

38. The graph of each quadratic function has either a high point (maximum) or low point (minimum). Examine the graphs in Exercise 7-24. What types of graphs have a maximum or minimum? Graphs that open upward have a minimum point. Graphs that open downward have a maximum point.

39. Examine the parabolas graphed in Exercises 7-24. Describe the axis of symmetry for each. Axis is parallel to y-axis and contains maximum or minimum point.

40. Use the same set of axes. Graph $y = x^2$, $y = 2x^2$, $y = 3x^2$ and $y = \frac{1}{2}x^2$. Describe the change in the graph of a quadratic function $y = ax^2$ as $|a|$ changes. As $|a|$ increases the graph widens.

41. Graph the equation $y = x^2 - x - 6$. Use your graph to approximate the solutions of $x^2 - x - 6 = 2$. (Hint: Graph $y = 2$ on the same set of axes as your graph of $y = x^2 - x - 6$.) $-2.4, 3.4$

42. Graph $y = 2x^2 - 4x + 7$. Use the graph to approximate the solutions of $2x^2 - 4x + 7 = 0$. Solve $2x^2 - 4x + 7 = 0$ using the quadratic formula. What do you think is true of any quadratic function whose graph does not cross the x-axis? If the graph of the function does not cross the x-axis, then the equation has no real-number solution.

43. What is the largest rectangular area that can be enclosed with 16 feet of fence?

$$2w + 2l = 16$$
$$w + l = 8$$
$$w = 8 - l$$

(Hint: Find $A = lw$ in terms of l. Graph the resulting quadratic function and find its maximum.) $A = lw$, $A = l(8 - l)$, $A = 8l - l^2$, maximum is at (4, 16), largest area is 4 by 4.

THE FREQUENCY OF A PENDULUM

The frequency of a pendulum is the number of times it makes a complete swing (forward and back) in one second. Given the length l_1 and frequency f_1 of a simple pendulum, it is possible to calculate the frequency f_2 of a second pendulum if you know its length l_2.

$$f_2 = \frac{f_1 \sqrt{l_1}}{\sqrt{l_2}}$$

You can verify this formula by experiment. Make two pendulums, one 3 feet long and one 2 feet long. To make a pendulum, tie one end of the string to a weight or rock. Tie the other end to a support. Measure the length from the support to the center of the weight.

Allow the 3-foot pendulum to swing out, but only a short distance. Count the number of complete swings it makes in 15 seconds. Calculate the frequency by dividing the number of swings by 15.

Use the formula above to calculate the frequency of the 2-foot pendulum. Then verify your answer experimentally by swinging the 2-foot pendulum.

CAREERS/Automobile Industry

You see a great-looking new car whiz past on the freeway. After determining the make and model, you are likely to begin framing some mathematical questions.

If you are interested in auto performance, you may wonder how quickly this car accelerates from 0 to 50 mph. If you are concerned with fuel economy, you may wonder how many miles per gallon the car delivers.

If you are a prospective car buyer, you may wonder what the cost of the car is—and what percentage of the cost is required as a down payment, what the interest rate on the balance would be, and so on. And if you are a highway patrol officer, you are checking to see how fast the vehicle is going, and figuring out by how much the driver is exceeding the speed limit!

The numbers and formulas that signify auto performance are of great importance to millions of Americans. They are talked about and used by people who design cars, people who sell them, and people who drive them on the job or for pleasure.

Complex algebraic equations are used to tell auto designers how effectively a newly-designed car will hold the road on a twisty course.

Other formulas are used with wind resistance data to determine *drag coefficient*, which indicates the effect of a new body design on mileage. Computers help with difficult calculations. Nevertheless, designers still must have a clear idea how the equations work in order to use the solutions in deciding on design improvements.

The exercises that follow are similar to those that must be solved by people who work with automobiles.

Exercises

Round answers to the nearest tenth of a unit.

1. The eyes of a driver in a sports car are 1 meter above the ground. The eyes of a driver in a van are 2.4 meters above the ground. Using the formula $V = 3.5\sqrt{h}$, find out how much farther to the horizon the van driver can see. (See Section 12–9.) 19.2 m

2. Designers have found that a heavy-duty braking system cuts stopping distance for one model of car by 20%. Using this information, revise the formula used to approximate the speed of a car that has left a skid mark of length L. The formula to be revised is $r = 2\sqrt{5L}$. (See Section 12–9.) $r = 4\sqrt{L}$

3. At 1:00 P.M. two truck-trailer rigs transporting new cars to dealers left the same factory on highways forming a right angle. Truck A traveled for 2 hours at an average speed of 38 mi/h. Truck B traveled for 3 hours at an average speed of 31 mi/h. Both trucks experienced breakdowns. One mechanic must repair both trucks; fortunately, a road runs straight from where truck A broke down to where truck B broke down.

a. How far apart are the two trucks? 120.1 mi

b. Assuming an average speed of 50 mi/h, how long will the mechanic take to get from the factory to the nearer truck? 1.5 hr

c. Assuming the same average speed, how long will it take the mechanic to go from there to the other truck? 2.4 hr

USING A CALCULATOR/Solving Quadratic Equations

EXAMPLE 1

A calculator with a square root key can be used to solve quadratic equations. Start by computing the discriminant.

Problem: Compute the discriminant for $4.38x^2 + 6.75x - 5.08 = 0$.

Write the formula: $b^2 - 4ac$

Substitute: $(6.75)^2 - 4(4.38)(-5.08)$

Enter: 6.75 $\boxed{x^2}$ $\boxed{-}$ 4 $\boxed{\times}$ 4.38 $\boxed{\times}$

Display: 6.75   45.5625   4   4.38   17.52

Enter: 5.08 $\boxed{+/-}$ $\boxed{=}$

Display: 5.08 -5.08 134.5641

Practice Problem: Compute the discriminant for
$$0.06x^2 - 0.05x - 0.07 = 0. \quad \text{\small 0.0193}$$

EXAMPLE 2

If the discriminant is positive, the equation has real solutions. Store the square root of the discriminant in the memory. Then use the positive square root to find the first solution.

Problem: Use $+\sqrt{134.5641}$ to find one solution of
$$4.38x^2 + 6.75x - 5.08 = 0.$$

Write the formula: $x = \dfrac{+\sqrt{b^2 - 4ac} - b}{2a}$

Substitute: $\dfrac{+\sqrt{134.5641} - 6.75}{2(4.38)}$

Enter: 134.5641 $\boxed{\sqrt{}}$ $\boxed{\text{Min}}$ $\boxed{-}$ 6.75

Display: 134.5641   11.600177   6.75

Enter: $\boxed{=}$ $\boxed{\div}$ 2 $\boxed{\div}$

Display: 4.8501767   2   2.4250884

Enter: 4.38 $\boxed{=}$

Display: 4.38   0.5536731

Practice Problem: Use the positive square root of the
discriminant to find one solution of
$$0.06x^2 - 0.05x - 0.07 = 0. \quad \text{\small 1.5743703}$$

EXAMPLE 3

To find the second solution of the equation, recall the square root of the discriminant from the memory and press the change sign key.

Problem:　　　　　　　Use $-\sqrt{134.5641}$ to find the second solution of
　　　　　　　　　　　$4.38x^2 + 6.75x - 5.08 = 0$.

Write the formula:　$x = \dfrac{-\sqrt{b^2 - 4ac} - b}{2a}$

Substitute:　　　　$\dfrac{-\sqrt{134.5641} - 6.75}{2(4.38)}$

Enter:　　　(MR)　　　　　(+/−)　　　(−)　6.75　　(=)

Display:　11.600177　−11.600177　　　6.75　−18.350177

Enter:　　(÷) 2　　　(÷)　　　4.38　　(=)

Display:　　　2　−9.1750884　4.38　−2.094769

Practice Problem:　Use the negative square root of the
　　　　　　　　discriminant to find a second solution of
　　　　　　　　$0.06x^2 - 0.05x - 0.07 = 0$.　−0.741037

Compare the three formulas below.

$$x = \frac{\pm\sqrt{b^2 - 4ac} - b}{2a} \qquad x = \pm\sqrt{b^2 - 4ac} - \frac{b}{2a} \qquad x = \frac{(\pm\sqrt{b^2 - 4ac} - b)a}{2}$$

The formula on the left is the quadratic formula and will give the correct solutions to a quadratic equation. The middle formula is incorrect. It is the result you will get if you forget to press the equals key before dividing by 2a. The formula on the right is also incorrect. You will get this result if you divide by 2 and then multiply by a, instead of dividing by 2 and also dividing by a.

CHAPTER 13　Review

Review the material in the chapter. Then see how you have done by trying these review exercises. If you miss an exercise, restudy the indicated lesson.

13–1　Solve.

1. $8x^2 = 24$ $\sqrt{3}, -\sqrt{3}$ **2.** $2x^2 = 0$ 0　**3.** $5x^2 - 7x = 0$ $0, \frac{7}{5}$
4. $3x^2 - 4x = 0$ $0, \frac{4}{3}$ **5.** $5x^2 = 40$ $2\sqrt{2}, -2\sqrt{2}$ **6.** $9x^2 = 0$ 0

13–2　Solve.

7. $5x^2 - 8x + 3 = 0$　　**8.** $3y^2 + 5y = 2$　　**9.** $(x + 8)^2 = 13$

7. $\frac{3}{5}, 1$
8. $\frac{1}{3}, -2$
9. $-8 \pm \sqrt{13}$

10. The hypotenuse of a right triangle is 5 m long. One leg is 3 m longer than the other. Find the lengths of the legs. Round to the nearest tenth. 1.7 m; 4.7 m

11. $1000 is invested at interest rate r. In 2 years it grows to $1690. What is the interest rate? 30%

12. $4000 is invested at interest rate r. In 2 years it grows to $6250. What is the interest rate? 25%

13–3 Solve by completing the square.

13. $x^2 - 2x - 10 = 0$ **14.** $9x^2 - 6x - 9 = 0$ 13. $1 \pm \sqrt{11}$

15. $3x^2 - 2x - 5 = 0$ **16.** $2x^2 + 7x - 1 = 0$ 14. $\dfrac{1 \pm \sqrt{10}}{3}$

15. $\frac{5}{3}, -1$

13–4 Solve using the quadratic formula.

16. $\dfrac{-7 \pm \sqrt{57}}{4}$

17. $x^2 + 6x - 9 = 0$ **18.** $4x^2 - 8x + 1 = 0$ 17. $-3 \pm 3\sqrt{2}$ 19. $\dfrac{3 \pm \sqrt{33}}{2}$

19. $x^2 - 3x - 6 = 0$ **20.** $5x^2 + 3x - 4 = 0$ 18. $\dfrac{2 \pm \sqrt{3}}{2}$ 20. $\dfrac{-3 \pm \sqrt{89}}{10}$

Use Table 1 to approximate the solutions of each equation to the nearest tenth.

21. $x^2 - 5x + 2 = 0$ **22.** $4x^2 + 8x + 1 = 0$ 21. 4.6, 0.4

22. $-1.9, -0.1$

13–5 Solve.

23. $\dfrac{15}{x} - \dfrac{15}{x + 2} = 2$ 3, -5 **24.** $x + \dfrac{1}{x} = 2$ 1

25. $\sqrt{x - 3} = 7$ 52

26. $\sqrt{3x + 4} = \sqrt{2x + 14}$ 10

27. Solve for T: $V = \dfrac{1}{2}\sqrt{1 + \dfrac{T}{L}}$ $T = L(4V^2 - 1)$

13–6 Solve.

28. The length of a rectangle is 3 m greater than the width. The area is 70 m². Find the length and width. Width 7 m, length 10 m

29. The width of a rectangle is 4 m less than the length. The area is 16.25 m². Find the length and width. Width 2.5 m, length 6.5 m

13–7

30. Graph $f(x) = x^2 - 2$.

31. Tell whether the graph of $f(x) = 5 - 4x - x^2$ opens upward or downward. Downward

32. Approximate the solutions of $f(x) = x^2 - 4x - 2$ by graphing. 4.4, -0.4

Solve.

1. $7x^2 = 35$ $\pm\sqrt{5}$

2. $7x^2 + 8x = 0$ $0, -\frac{8}{7}$

3. $x^2 + 2x - 48 = 0$ $8, -6$

4. $3y^2 + 5y = 2$ $\frac{1}{3}, -2$

5. $(x + 8)^2 = 13$ $\pm\sqrt{13} - 8$

6. $(x - 1)^2 = 8$ $\pm2\sqrt{2} + 1$

7. $x^2 + 4x - 10 = 0$

8. $x^2 - 3x - 7 = 0$

9. $x^2 - x - 3 = 0$

7. $\dfrac{-2 \pm \sqrt{14}}{}$

8. $\dfrac{3 \pm \sqrt{37}}{2}$

9. $\dfrac{1 \pm \sqrt{13}}{2}$

10. $3x^2 - 7x + 1 = 0$

11. $x - \dfrac{2}{x} = 1$ $2, -1$

12. $\dfrac{4}{x} - \dfrac{4}{x + 2} = 1$ $2, -4$

10. $\dfrac{7 \pm \sqrt{37}}{6}$

13. $\sqrt{x + 1} = 6$ 35

14. $\sqrt{6x + 1} = \sqrt{5x + 13}$ 12

15. The length of a rectangle is 5 m greater than the width. The area is 104 m². Find the length and width. 8 m, 13 m

16. Tell whether the graph $f(x) = x^2 + 4x + 2$ opens upward or downward. Then graph the function. Upward

Challenge

17. Solve this system for x. Use the substitution method.

$x - y = 2$ $1 \pm \sqrt{5}$
$xy = 4$

Ready for Trigonometry?

2–6 Write decimal notation. Approximate to four decimal places.

1. 0.9375
2. 1.0833
3. 0.2941
4. 0.9600
5. 0.6154
6. 0.3846

1. $\dfrac{15}{16}$ 2. $\dfrac{13}{12}$ 3. $\dfrac{5}{17}$ 4. $\dfrac{24}{25}$ 5. $\dfrac{8}{13}$ 6. $\dfrac{15}{39}$

3–5 Translate to an equation. Then solve and check.

7. One angle of a triangle is three times as large as another. The third angle is twice the sum of the other two angles. What are the measures of the three angles? 15°, 45°, 120°

8. One angle of a triangle is six times as large as another. The measure of the third angle is 84° greater than that of the smallest angle. What are the measures of the three angles? 12°, 72°, 96°

11–7 Solve.

9. $\dfrac{4}{5} = \dfrac{x}{20}$ 16 10. $\dfrac{9}{10} = \dfrac{2}{t}$ $2\frac{2}{9}$ 11. $\dfrac{14}{20} = \dfrac{3}{m}$ $4\frac{2}{7}$ 12. $\dfrac{5}{9} = \dfrac{y}{11}$ $6\frac{1}{9}$

14

CHAPTER FOURTEEN

Trigonometry

Similar Triangles

Similar triangles have the same shape, but need not be the same size nor positioned the same way.

$\triangle ABC$ is similar to $\triangle DEF$, or, $\triangle ABC \sim \triangle DEF$.

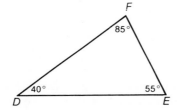

In similar triangles we identify corresponding angles and sides. Notice that angles A and D have the same measure, angles B and E have the same measure, and angles C and F have the same measure.

Corresponding Angles	**Corresponding Sides**
$\angle A$ and $\angle D$	$\overline{AB}$ and $\overline{DE}$
$\angle B$ and $\angle E$	$\overline{BC}$ and $\overline{EF}$
$\angle C$ and $\angle F$	$\overline{CA}$ and $\overline{FD}$

> The lengths of the corresponding sides of a pair of similiar triangles are proportional. Corresponding angles are the same size.

EXAMPLE 1

$\triangle ABC \sim \triangle RST$. Write several true proportions. The small letters are the lengths of the sides.

These proportions are true.

$$\frac{a}{r} = \frac{b}{s}, \frac{c}{t} = \frac{a}{r}, \text{ and } \frac{b}{s} = \frac{c}{t}.$$

There are others.

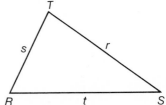

1. $\triangle PQR \sim \triangle XYZ$. Write three true proportions.

$p/x = q/y, r/z = p/x, q/y = r/z$; there are others.

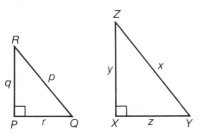

Right Triangles

Trigonometry is concerned with right triangles. A right triangle has one angle of 90°, usually marked with a small square. Two right triangles are similar whenever an acute angle of one is the same size as an acute angle of the other.

EXAMPLE 2
Which right triangles are similar?

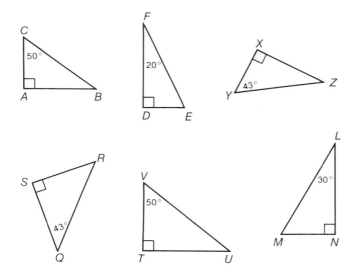

$\triangle ABC \sim \triangle TUV$ and $\triangle XYZ \sim \triangle SQR$

EXAMPLE 3

Suppose it is known that $\triangle XYZ \sim \triangle ABC$. Find the length a.

 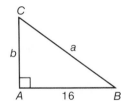

Since the triangles are similar the corresponding sides are proportional.

Thus

$$\frac{a}{5} = \frac{16}{4}.$$

$4a = 80$

$a = 20$ Solving the proportion

The length a is 20.

TRY THIS

2. $\triangle RST \sim WXY$. Find the length x.   75

 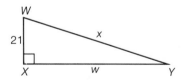

Trigonometric Ratios

For any right triangle six ratios of pairs of sides are possible.

$$\frac{a}{c}, \frac{b}{c}, \frac{a}{b}, \frac{b}{a}, \frac{c}{a}, \frac{c}{b}$$

These six ratios are called *trigonometric ratios*. Any right triangle similar to $\triangle ABC$ would have six trigonometric ratios equal to these.

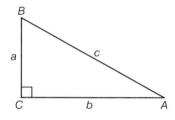

EXAMPLE 4

Find the trigonometric ratios for △PQR. The six trigonometric
ratios are

$$\frac{15}{39}, \frac{36}{39}, \frac{15}{36}, \frac{36}{15}, \frac{39}{15}, \frac{39}{36}$$

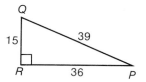

TRY THIS

3. Find the six trigonometric ratios for △PQR.

$$\frac{20}{29}, \frac{21}{29}, \frac{20}{21}, \frac{21}{20}, \frac{29}{20}, \frac{29}{21}$$

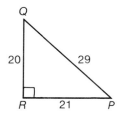

14—1

Exercises

1. △ABC ~ △DEF. Name the
corresponding sides and angles.

2. △PQR ~ △WXY. Name the
corresponding sides and angles.

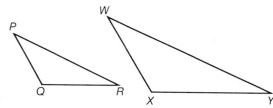

3. △STU ~ △LMN. Write three
true proportions. Answers may vary.
$t/m = u/n, s/u = l/n, u/t = n/m$

4. △FGH ~ △JKL. Write three
true proportions. Answers may vary.
$g/k = f/j, h/l = g/k, j/l = f/h$

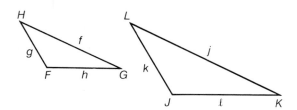

5. $\triangle ABC \sim \triangle DEF$. Find the length f. 16

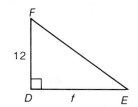

6. $\triangle LMN \sim \triangle HJK$. Find the length h. $3\sqrt{89}$

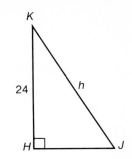

For each of the following find the six trigonometric ratios.

7.

8.

9.

7. $\frac{12}{15}, \frac{9}{15}, \frac{12}{9}, \frac{9}{12}, \frac{15}{12}, \frac{15}{9}$
8. $\frac{5}{\sqrt{89}}, \frac{8}{\sqrt{89}}, \frac{5}{8}, \frac{8}{5}, \frac{\sqrt{89}}{5}, \frac{\sqrt{89}}{8}$
9. $\frac{4}{7}, \frac{\sqrt{33}}{7}, \frac{4}{\sqrt{33}}, \frac{\sqrt{33}}{4}, \frac{7}{4}, \frac{7}{\sqrt{33}}$

Extension

Assume that the three sides of $\triangle RST$ are 12, 16, and 20.

10. If $\triangle DEF$ is similar to $\triangle RST$, and the longest side of $\triangle DEF$ is 30, what are the lengths of the other two sides? 18 and 24

11. If $\triangle XYZ \sim \triangle RST$, and the shortest side of $\triangle XYZ$ is 6, what are the lengths of the other two sides? 8, 10

Challenge

12. There are three right triangles in this figure. Name them, writing the right angle first. $\triangle BAC, \triangle DAB, \triangle DBC$

13. Which of these proportions are true?

$\dfrac{\overline{AB}}{\overline{BC}} = \dfrac{\overline{AC}}{\overline{DB}}$ No

$\dfrac{\overline{AC}}{\overline{AB}} = \dfrac{\overline{BC}}{\overline{BD}}$ Yes

$\dfrac{\overline{BD}}{\overline{BC}} = \dfrac{\overline{AB}}{\overline{BC}}$ Yes

14. If $\dfrac{\overline{AD}}{\overline{AB}} = \dfrac{\overline{AB}}{\overline{AC}}$, find the length of $\overline{AD}$. 36

15. If $\dfrac{\overline{AD}}{\overline{BD}} = \dfrac{\overline{BD}}{\overline{DC}}$, find the length of $\overline{DC}$. 64

The Sine Function

The first trigonometric function we study is called the sine function. The sine function assigns to an acute angle A the trigonometric ratio $\frac{a}{c}$.

The *sine* of A: $\sin A = \dfrac{\text{length of opposite side}}{\text{length of hypotenuse}} = \dfrac{a}{c}$

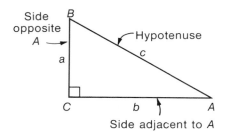

EXAMPLE 1

In $\triangle ABC$, find $\sin B$. Write this value to four decimal places.

$\sin B = \dfrac{\text{length of opposite side}}{\text{length of hypotenuse}} = \dfrac{15}{17}$

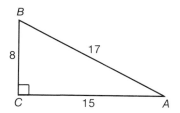

$\frac{15}{17} = 0.8824$, and so $\sin B = 0.8824$.

TRY THIS

1. In $\triangle PQR$, find $\sin R$ to four decimal places.

0.2195

The Cosine Function

The cosine function assigns to any acute angle A of a right triangle ABC the trigonometric ratio $\frac{b}{c}$.

The *cosine* of A: $\cos A = \dfrac{\text{length of adjacent side}}{\text{length of hypotenuse}} = \dfrac{b}{c}$

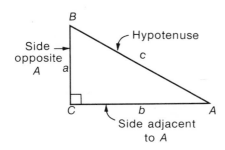

EXAMPLE 2

In $\triangle CLF$, find $\cos F$. Write this value to four decimal places.

$$\cos F = \frac{\text{length of adjacent side}}{\text{length of hypotenuse}} = \frac{32}{40}$$

$$\frac{32}{40} = \frac{4}{5} = 0.8000$$

$$\cos F = 0.8000$$

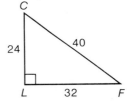

TRY THIS

2. In $\triangle DEF$, find $\cos D$ to four decimal places.

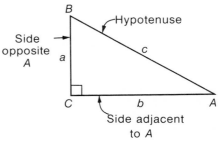

The Tangent Function

The tangent function assigns to any acute angle A of a right triangle ABC the ratio $\frac{a}{b}$.

The *tangent* of A:

$$\tan A = \frac{\text{length of opposite side}}{\text{length of adjacent side}} = \frac{a}{b}$$

EXAMPLE 3

In $\triangle RST$, find tan S. Write this value to four decimal places.

$$\tan S = \frac{\text{length of opposite side}}{\text{length of adjacent side}} = \frac{25}{60}$$

$$\frac{25}{60} = \frac{5}{12} = 0.4167$$

$$\tan S = 0.4167$$

TRY THIS

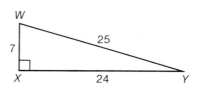

3. In $\triangle WXY$, find tan Y. $\frac{7}{24}$

14–2	

Exercises

In each of the following triangles, express the sine as a ratio.

1. In $\triangle DEF$, find sin F. $\frac{\sqrt{3}}{2}$ 2. In $\triangle PQR$, find sin P. $\frac{\sqrt{33}}{7}$

    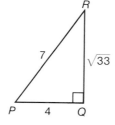

3. In $\triangle ABC$, find sin A. $\frac{4}{5}$ 4. In $\triangle PQR$, find sin R. $\frac{8}{17}$

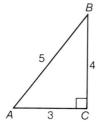

5. In △*RST*, find sin *T* to four decimal places. 0.4706

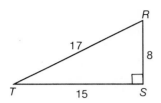

6. In △*PQR*, find sin *Q* to four decimal places. 0.9231

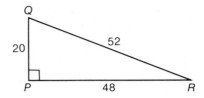

In each of the following triangles find the cosine. Express the cosine as a ratio.

7. Find cos *S*. $\frac{44}{55}$

8. Find cos *B*. $\frac{9}{15}$

9. Find cos *F*. $\frac{20}{52}$

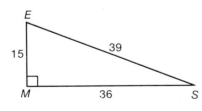

10. Find cos *Z*. $\frac{40}{58}$

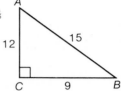

In each of the following triangles, find the cosine to four decimal places.

11. Find cos *S*. 0.9231

12. Find cos *R*. 0.9692

In each of the following triangles find the tangent. Express the tangent as a ratio.

13. Find tan *R*. $\frac{40}{42}$

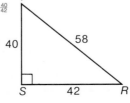

14. Find tan *T*. $\frac{45}{28}$

15. Find tan P. $\frac{60}{11}$

16. Find tan A. $\frac{10}{24}$

In each of the following triangles, find the tangent to four decimal places.

17. Find tan P. 0.5333

18. Find tan S.

0.9524

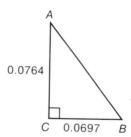

Extension

Use a calculator to solve.

19. In $\triangle PQR$, find cos R to four decimal places. 0.2925

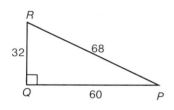

20. In $\triangle ABC$ find tan B to four decimal places. 1.0961

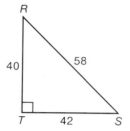

Use the Pythagorean Theorem to find the length of the hypotenuse of a triangle with legs of the given lengths.

21. 9 and 12 15   **22.** 4 and 6 7.211   **23.** 5 and 13 13.9284

24. 16 and 30 34   **25.** 24 and 32 40   **26.** 18 and 36 40.2492

Challenge

Use a calculator to test the following relationships.

27. In exercise 19, find $(\sin R)^2$. Then find $(\cos R)^2$. Is the sum of these two numbers close to 1? Test other triangles to see if this relationship is always true for any acute angle A in a right triangle: $(\sin A)^2 + (\cos A)^2 = 1$ Yes, $\left(\frac{a}{c}\right)^2 + \left(\frac{b}{c}\right)^2 = \frac{a^2 + b^2}{c^2}$, since $a^2 + b^2 = c^2$ this ratio = 1.

Using a Trigonometric Function Table

Reading a Table

The values of trigonometric functions have been computed for angle measures between 0° and 90°. A part of a 4-decimal-place table of these approximate values is shown below. The complete table is Table 2 in the back of the book.

Degrees	Sin	Cos	Tan
56°	0.8290	0.5592	1.4826
57°	0.8387	0.5446	1.5399
58°	0.8480	0.5299	1.6003
59°	0.8572	0.5150	1.6643

EXAMPLE 1
Find sin 58°.

First find 58° in the Degree column. Then find the entry in the Sin column opposite 58°. This is 0.8480. So, sin 58° ≈ 0.8480.

EXAMPLE 2
Find tan 59°.

The entry in the Tan column opposite 59° is 1.6643. So, tan 59° ≈ 1.6643.

TRY THIS Use the table above.
1. Find sin 57°.   2. Find cos 59°.   3. Find tan 56°.

1. 0.8387
2. 0.5150
3. 1.4826

Finding Angles

EXAMPLE 3
Suppose cos $A = 0.5592$. Find A.

In the Cos column find the entry 0.5592. Find the entry in the Degree column opposite 0.5592. This is 56°. So, $A = 56°$.

TRY THIS Use the table above.
4. Suppose sin $B = 0.8480$. Find B. 58° 5. Suppose tan $A = 1.6003$. Find A. 58°

EXAMPLE 4

Suppose sin $B = 0.8391$. Find B to the nearest degree.

In the Sin column the entry 0.8387 is closest to 0.8391. So, $B = 57°$ to the nearest degree.

TRY THIS Use the table on the previous page.

6. Suppose sin $A = 0.8293$. Find A to the nearest degree. 6. 56°
7. Suppose tan $B = 1.5404$. Find B to the nearest degree. 7. 57°

14–3

Exercises

Use Table 2 to find these trigonometric function values.

1. sin 38°	**2.** sin 47°	**3.** tan 56°	**4.** tan 84°	**5.** cos 9°
6. cos 31°	**7.** sin 60°	**8.** sin 30°	**9.** tan 45°	**10.** tan 55°
11. cos 1°	**12.** cos 89°	**13.** sin 71°	**14.** sin 45°	**15.** sin 15°

1. 0.6157
2. 0.7314
3. 1.4826
4. 9.5144
5. 0.9877
6. 0.8572
7. 0.8660
8. 0.5000
9. 1.0000
10. 1.4281
11. 0.9998
12. 0.0175
13. 0.9455
14. 0.7071
15. 0.2588

Use Table 2 to find A for the following function values of A.

16. sin $A = 0.2588$ 15° **17.** sin $A = 0.9397$ 70° **18.** cos $A = 0.8572$ 31°

19. cos $A = 0.1564$ 81° **20.** tan $A = 0.4877$ 26° **21.** tan $A = 2.2460$ 66°

22. cos $A = 0.7547$ 41° **23.** cos $A = 0.9816$ 11° **24.** tan $A = 9.5144$ 84°

25. tan $A = 1.1918$ 50° **26.** sin $A = 0.7193$ 46° **27.** sin $A = 0.0872$ 5°

For the following function values of A use Table 2 to find A to the nearest degree.

28. sin $A = 0.1746$ 10° **29.** sin $A = 0.8753$ 61° **30.** tan $A = 2.9064$ 71°

31. tan $A = 0.7824$ 38° **32.** cos $A = 0.8749$ 29° **33.** cos $A = 0.4234$ 65°

34. tan $A = 9.5234$ 84° **35.** tan $A = 2.8011$ 70° **36.** sin $A = 0.9948$ 84°

Extension

37. One degree is 60 minutes (60′). The value of the trigonometric function of an angle measured in degrees and minutes can be approximated using the idea of proportion.

    For example, sin 37°10′ must lie between sin 37° and 38°. It is reasonable to assume that sin 37°10′ would be $\frac{10}{60}$ of the difference between sin 37° and sin 38°. Find sin 37°10′, sin 37°20′, sin 37°50′. 0.6041, 0.6064, 0.6134

14-4 Solving Triangle Problems

EXAMPLE 1
In the right triangle ABC, $B = 61°$ and $c = 20$ cm. Find b.

The sine function relates the opposite side and the hypotenuse.

$$\sin B = \frac{b}{c}$$

$$\sin 61° = \frac{b}{20}$$

$$0.8746 \approx \frac{b}{20} \qquad \text{Finding sin 61° in the table}$$

$$20(0.8746) \approx b$$

$$17.492 \approx b$$

b is about 17.5 cm.

TRY THIS

1. In right triangle ABC, $B = 42°$ and $c = 10$ cm. Find b.

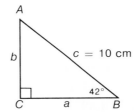

6.7 cm

EXAMPLE 2
In right triangle DEF, $D = 25°$ and $f = 18$ km. Find e.

$$\cos D = \frac{f}{e}$$

$$\cos 25° = \frac{18}{e}$$

$$0.9063 \approx \frac{18}{e} \qquad \text{Finding cos 25° in the table}$$

$$0.9063e \approx 18$$

$$e \approx \frac{18}{0.9063}$$

$$e \approx 19.8609$$

e is about 19.9 km.

TRY THIS

2. In right triangle DEF, $D = 36°$ and $f = 30$ m. Find e. 37.1 m

---

Trigonometric functions can sometimes help to solve problems. We translate the information into a right triangle diagram.

EXAMPLE 3

The angle of elevation of a jetliner is 12°. The distance to the jetliner is 16 km. How high is the jetliner?

Let the height of the jetliner be h.

$$\sin 12° = \frac{h}{16}$$

$$0.2079 \approx \frac{h}{16} \quad \text{Finding sin 12° in the table}$$

$$16(0.2079) \approx h$$
$$3.3264 \approx h$$

The height of the jetliner is about 3.3 km.

EXAMPLE 4

A fire warden's tower is 43 m tall. The angle of depression from the top of the tower to a fire in the woods is 5°. How far away from the base of the tower is the fire?

Let d be the distance from the fire to the base of the tower.

$$\tan 5° = \frac{43}{d}$$

$$0.0875 \approx \frac{43}{d} \quad \text{Finding tan 5° in the table}$$

$$0.0875d \approx 43$$
$$d \approx 491.4286$$

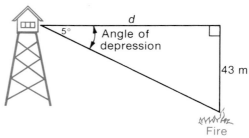

The distance to the fire is about 491.4 m.

TRY THIS

3. A kite is flown with 180 m of string. The angle of elevation of the kite is 58°. How high is the kite? 152.6 m

---

| **14−4** | |

Exercises

Solve the following triangle problems.

1. $B = 38°$ and $c = 37$ cm. Find b. 22.8 cm

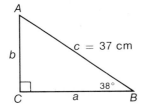

2. $B = 57°$ and $c = 24$ cm. Find b. 20.1 cm

3. $D = 39°$ and $f = 42$ cm. Find e. 54.0 cm

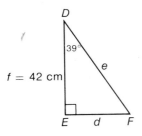

4. $D = 18°$ and $f = 16$ cm. Find e. 16.8 cm

5. $k = 18$ cm and $g = 26$ cm.
Find K to the nearest degree. 35°

6. $k = 29$ cm and $g = 41$ cm.
Find K to the nearest degree. 35°

Solve the following problems. Draw a picture first.

7. The angle of elevation of an airplane is 9°. The distance to the plane is 21 km. How high is the plane? 3.3 km

8. A kite is flown with 210 m of string. The angle of elevation of the kite is 61°. How high is the kite? 183.7 m

9. The top of a lighthouse is 110 m above the level of the water. The angle of depression from the top of the lighthouse to a fishing boat is 18°. How far from the base of the lighthouse is the fishing boat? 338.6 m

10. An observation tower is 98 m tall. The angle of depression from the top of the tower to a historical marker is 23°. How far from the base of the tower is the marker? 230.9 m

11. A flagpole casts a shadow 4.6 m long. The angle of elevation of the sun is 49°. How high is the flagpole? 5.3 m

12. A water tower casts a shadow 23 m long. The angle of elevation of the sun is 52°. How tall is the water tower? 29.4 m

13. The firing angle of a missile is 28°. About how high is it after it has traveled 450 m? 211.3 m

14. A rocket is launched at an angle of 34°. About how high is it after it has traveled 670 m? 374.7 m

15. A pilot in a plane 3 km above the ground estimates the angle of depression to a runway is 51°. How far is the pilot from the runway? 3.9 km

16. A balloonist 1.4 km above the ground estimates the angle of depression to a highway intersection to be 37°. How far is the balloonist from the intersection? 2.3 km

17. Karen is walking to the Texas Commerce Center which she knows is 1002 ft tall. The angle to the top of the building measures 7°. How far does she have to walk? 8160 ft (1.55 mi)

18. A person atop a 20 ft wall needs to know the distance from the bottom of the wall to the edge of a stream. The angle of depression to the stream edge is 52°. How far is the stream from the wall? 6.5 ft

Extension

It can be shown that the area of a triangle equals one half the product of two adjacent sides times the sine of the angle between them. Use this formula, area of $\triangle ABC = \frac{1}{2}bc \sin \angle A$, to find the area of the following triangles to the nearest tenth.

19. $\triangle ABC$ where $\angle A = 50°$, $b = 12$, and $c = 8$. 36.8

20. $\triangle MNP$ where $\angle N = 67°$, $m = 40$, and $p = 52$. 957.3

21. $\triangle XYZ$ where $\angle Z = 12°$, $x = 18$, and $y = 18$. 33.7

22. $\triangle GHJ$ where $\angle J = 24°$, $g = 6$, and $h = 6$. 7.3

Challenge

23. Draw an acute triangle ABC with side a opposite $\angle A$, b opposite $\angle B$, etc. Prove that $\frac{1}{2}bc \sin A$ is the area of the triangle. (Hint: Draw an altitude h.) Draw h so that it makes a right angle with side b. Then $\sin A = \frac{h}{c}$, so $A = \frac{1}{2}bc \sin A = \frac{1}{2}bc\left(\frac{h}{c}\right) = \frac{1}{2}bh$.

CAREERS/Shipping Industry

Shipping via waterways has, for thousands of years, been the cheapest, most efficient way of moving large quantities of materials across great distances. Unlike highways and railways, natural waterways cost nothing to build. And, because water helps support the load, less energy is required to move the goods or materials.

For example, tons of coal can be floated down a river on a barge with a tiny engine. Transportation of the same cargo by rail would require several times the amount of energy that is used by the barge's engine. Transportation by truck would involve another geometric increase in the amount of energy expended.

Numbers representing time and distance are of great importance to people working in the shipping industry. Shipping schedules are established on the basis of algebraic formulas involving time and distance. These formulas yield estimated travel time. Wind patterns and currents can affect the speed of ships, so workers must take these factors into account when calculating probable arrival times. Algebraic formulas are used for these calculations, too.

Volume measurements have special importance to workers selling space on cargo ships. To get the greatest amount of revenue for a voyage, a salesperson must know the exact volume of cargo space available on the ship. If the ship sails with empty cargo space, the fees paid by shippers may not cover the cost of the voyage. If, on the other hand, the salesperson sells more space than is actually available, the shipping company is likely to make enemies of the people whose goods must be left behind.

The exercises that follow resemble those that people involved with cargo shipping must solve on the job.

Exercises

Round answers to the nearest tenth of a unit.

1. A ship has been sailing on an incorrect course for 25 km. Its course has been 15° W of the correct course. What is the distance now between where the ship is and the nearest point on the correct course? (See Section 14-5.)

2. A river barge's flagpole casts a shadow 8.9 m long. The angle of elevation of the sun is 37°. Will the barge be able to go under a bridge with clearance of 20 m? Assume that the deck of the barge is 2 m above the surface of the river. (See Section 14–5.) Yes

3. The pilot of a rescue plane spots a burning ship; the pilot estimates the angle of depression to be 30°. Instruments tell the pilot that the plane is 1.2 km above the ground. How far must the pilot fly to be directly above the burning ship? (See Section 14–5.) 2.1 km

4. Two ships leave the same harbor at the same time. Both ships sail straight courses at the same speed. When plotted on a flat map, the two courses form a 24° angle. When the ships have traveled 100 km, approximately how far apart will they be? (See Section 14–5.) 42.5 km

Review the material in the chapter. Then see how you have done by trying these review exercises. If you miss an exercise, restudy the indicated lesson.

14–1

1. $\triangle PQR \sim \triangle STV$. Name the corresponding sides and angles.

$\overline{PQ}$ and $\overline{ST}$; $\overline{QR}$ and $\overline{TV}$
$\overline{RP}$ and $\overline{VS}$; $\angle P$ and $\angle S$
$\angle Q$ and $\angle T$; $\angle R$ and $\angle V$

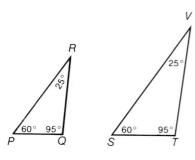

2. $\triangle ABC \sim \triangle DEF$. Find f. $f = 16$

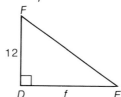

3. In $\triangle XYZ$, find $\sin Z$ to four decimal places. 0.3846

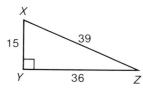

4. In $\triangle PQR$, find $\cos R$ to four decimal places. 0.8823

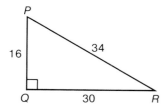

5. In $\triangle XYZ$, find tan X to four decimal places. 0.2550

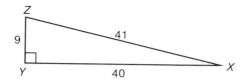

14–3   Use Table 2 in the back of the book for Exercises 6–11.

6. Find sin 27°. 0.4540

7. Find cos 65°. 0.4226

8. Find tan 88°. 28.6363

9. Sin $A = 0.6947$. Find A. 44°

10. Cos $B = 0.8572$. Find B. 31°

11. Tan $X = 1.0000$. Find X. 45°

14–4

12. In right triangle CLF, L is the right angle, $C = 46°$, and $l = 40$ cm. Find c. Use Table 2. 28.8 cm

13. In right triangle XYZ, Z is the right angles, $x = 23°$, and $z = 30$ cm. Find y. Use Table 2. 27.6 cm

14. In right triangle ABC, C is the right angle, $b = 70$ km and $a = 120$ km. Find B to the nearest degree. Use Table 2. 30°

14–4

15. A kite is flown with 225 m of string. The angle of elevation of the kite is 56°. How high is the kite? 186.5 m

16. The top of the lighthouse is 120 m above the water level. The angle of depression from the top of the lighthouse to a motorboat is 20°. How far from the base of the lighthouse is the motorboat? 4.37 m

---

CHAPTER 14   Test

1. $\triangle PQR \sim \triangle WXY$. If $q = 25$, $r = 65$, $p = 60$, and $z = 75$, find w and s. $w = 195$, $s = 180$

2. In $\triangle ABC$, find sin A to four decimal places. <small>0.8823</small>

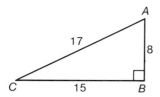

3. In $\triangle DEF$, find cos F to four decimal places. <small>0.3846</small>

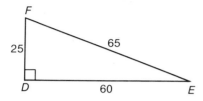

4. In $\triangle RST$, find tan R to four decimal places. <small>0.5333</small>

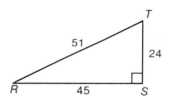

Use Table 2 for Exercises 5–8.

5. Find sin $13°$. <small>0.225</small> **6.** Find cos $52°$. <small>0.616</small>

7. Sin $A = 0.9659$. Find A. <small>75°</small>

8. Tan $B = 0.6009$. Find B. <small>31°</small>

9. In right triangle GHK, K is the right angle, $H = 41$, and $k = 60$ cm. Find h. Use Table 2. <small>39.36</small>

10. In right triangle MNQ, N is the right angle, $M = 18°$, and $n = 60$ m. Find q. Use Table 2. <small>57.06</small>

11. In right triangle PQR, R is the right angle, $q = 85$ km and $p = 140$ km. Find Q to the nearest degree. Use Table 2. <small>31°</small>

12. The angle of elevation of a hang glider is $15°$. The distance to the hang glider is 2 km. How high is the hang glider? <small>0.536 km</small>

13. An observation tower is 95 m tall. The angle of depression from the top of the tower to a monument is $26°$. How far from the base of the tower is the monument? <small>46.335 m</small>

Challenge

14. Use the formula area of $\triangle ABC = \frac{1}{2}bc \sin \angle A$ to find the area of $\triangle ABC$ where $\angle A = 60°$, $b = 8$, and $c = 16$. $32\sqrt{3}$ or 55.4

CHAPTERS 1–14   Cumulative Review

1–3   Evaluate.

1. $(x - 3)^2 + 5$ for $x = 10$. 54

2. $(y - 1)^2 + (y + 6)^2$ for $y = 4$ 109

3. $(x - y)^2 + 2(x + y)$ for $x = 10$ and $y = 2$. 88

1–4   Use commutative and associative laws to write an equivalent expression.

4. $(x + 2) + (y + 7)$ **5.** $6(xy)$ **6.** $2 + a + b$ **7.** $2x + 2y$

2–3, 2–4   Add.

8. $-12.8 + 2.6 + -11.9 + 6.2 + 0.9$ -15

9. $-\frac{1}{8} - 4 - \frac{3}{4} + 2\frac{1}{2} - 6\frac{1}{4}$ $-12\frac{5}{8}$

10. $2 + 6x - 14 - 5x$ $x - 12$ **11.** $12x - 7 + 8x - 13$ $20x - 20$

12. $4m + 9 - 6m - 13$ **13.** $18a + 16b + 2a - 10b$ $20a + 6b$
$-2m - 4$

2–6   Divide.

14. $-\frac{4}{7} \div \frac{1}{14}$ -8 **15.** $\frac{8}{9} \div \frac{1}{3}$ $\frac{8}{3}$ **16.** $\frac{1}{6} \div -\frac{7}{18}$ $-\frac{3}{7}$

2–9   Translate to an equation and solve.

17. What percent of 52 is 13? 25%   **18.** What percent of 86 is 129? 150%

19. 60 is what percent of 720? $8\frac{1}{3}$%   **20.** 12 is what percent of 0.5? 2400%

21. 110% of what number is 11? 10   **22.** What is 25% of 16? 4

2–10   Which axiom or property guarantees each statement?

23. $-5(x + 1) = -5x + 5$ Distributive

24. $xy + 3 = yx + 3$ Commutative for multiplication

25. $a + (b + c) = (b + c) + a$ Commutative for addition

26. $a(b + c) = (b + c)a$ Commutative for multiplication

Solve.

27. $3x - 12 = 2x$ 12

28. $-\frac{7}{8}x + 7 = \frac{3}{8}x - 3$ −8

29. $0.6x - 1.8 = 1.2x$ 3

30. Three fifths of the automobiles entering the city each morning will be parked in city parking lots. If there are 3654 such parking spaces, how many cars enter the city each morning? 6090

31. Solve $A = \pi r^2$ for r. $\sqrt{\frac{A}{\pi}}$

32. Solve $A = 2\pi r^2 + 2\pi rh$ for h. $\frac{A - 2\pi r^2}{2\pi r}$

Simplify.

33. $a^4 \cdot a^6$ a^{10} **34.** $\frac{4m^5}{m^3}$ $4m^2$ **35.** $(2y^6)^3$ $8y^{18}$ **36.** $\left(\frac{x}{y^3}\right)^2$ $\frac{x^2}{y^6}$

Simplify.

37. $-3x^2 - 4x - 6x^2 + 3x$ $-9x^2 - x$

38. $2m^3 - 9 + 5m^3 - 10m^2 + 10$ $7m^3 - 10m^2 + 1$

39. $(-6a^2 - a + 3) - (a^3 - 10a^2 + a + 3)$ $-a^3 + 4a^2 - 2a$

Multiply.

40. $(4b - 1)(4b + 3)$ $16b^2 - 8b - 3$

41. $(2m + 3)(m - 6)$ $2m^2 - 9m - 18$

42. $(7y + 6)(3y - 1)$ $21y^2 + 11y - 6$

43. $(a + 2)^2$ $a^2 + 4a + 4$

44. $(a - 3)^2$ $a^2 - 6a + 9$

45. $(3m + 5)^2$ $9m^2 + 30m + 25$

Factor.

46. $m^3 - m$ $m(m + 1)(m - 1)$

47. $49x^2 - 64$ $(7x + 8)(7x - 8)$

48. $m^4 - 1$ $(m^2 + 1)(m + 1)(m - 1)$

49. $2x^2 + 13x - 99$ $(2x - 9)(x + 11)$

50. $7m^2 - 8m + 1$ $(m - 1)(7m - 1)$

51. $9x^2 - 24x + 16$ $(3x - 4)^2$

52. $y^3 - y^2 + 2y - 2$ $(y^2 + 2)(y - 1)$

53. $x^4 + x^3 - 5x - 5$ $(x^3 - 5)(x + 1)$

54. $9x^4 - 30x^2y + 25y^2$ **55.** $a^5 - a^3y - a^2y^3 + y^4$ $(a^3 - y^3)(a^2 - y)$
$(3x^2 - 5y)^2$
56. $x^5 - 2x^3 + x$ $x(x^2 - 1)^2$ **57.** $100x^3 + 60x^2 + 9x$ $x(10x + 3)^2$

6–4

58. Solve for y: $2y + 6 = ky - 1$ $\frac{-7}{2+k}$

59. Solve for x: $mx + kx = 9 + km$ $\frac{9 + km}{m + k}$

7–3 Graph each equation.

60. $x + y = 5$

61. $2x + 3y = -1$

62. $-y = 7$

7–5 Find the slope and y-intercept of each equation.

63. $0.4x - 0.3y = 10$ $m = 0.4$, y-intercept $= -10$

64. $100x = 1250 - 200y$ $m = -\frac{1}{2}$, y-intercept $= 6.25$

65. $\frac{1}{3}y - \frac{1}{2}x + \frac{1}{6} = 0$ $m = \frac{3}{2}$, y-intercepts $= -\frac{1}{2}$

7–6 Write an equation for each line.

66. The line through $(0, 10)$ and parallel to the x-axis. $y = 10$

67. The line through the origin and $(-3, 3)$ $y = -x$

68. The line with slope of $-\frac{2}{3}$ that crosses the x-axis at -7. $y = -\frac{2}{3}x - \frac{14}{3}$ or $2x + 3y = -14$

69. The line with x-intercept 6 and y-intercept -1. $-6y + x = 6$ or $y = \frac{1}{6}x - 1$

Find the indicated output for the function
8–1 $f(x) = 2x^2 + 7x - 4$.

70. $f(0)$ -4 **71.** $f\left(\frac{1}{2}\right)$ 0 **72.** $f(-4)$ 0 **73.** $f(-2)$ -10

8–2

74. Write ordered pairs that belong to the function $y = 2|x| - x$ for the domain $\{-2, -1, 0, 1, 2\}$ $(-2, 6), (-1, 3), (0, 0), (1, 1), (2, 2)$

8–4, 8–5 Solve.

75. Myra's weekly pay varies directly as the number of hours she works. If her pay is $40 for 8 hours work, what is the constant of variation? 5

76. The force F required to keep a car from skidding on a curve varies directly as the car's speed S and its mass m, and inversely as the radius of the curve. Write an equation of variation for F. $F = \frac{kSm}{r}$

9–1 Which of these pairs are solutions of the following systems: $(0, 0)$, $(-2, 1)$, $(4, 3)$, $(1, 1)$?

77. $5x - 2y = 12$ 78. $2y = 6$ (4, 3)
     $3x + 8y = 2$ (-2, 1) $-3x = -12$

79. $x + 8y = 6$ (-2, 1)
     $3x + 6y = 0$

9–2 Solve these systems.

80. $y = x - 6$ (2, -4)
     $x + y = -2$

81. $\frac{1}{2}x + 2y = 9$ (-2, 5)
     $x - \frac{1}{2}y = -\frac{9}{2}$

82. $3x - 2y = -10$ $(-3, \frac{1}{2}, 4)$
     $x + 6y + 2z = 8$
     $-z = -4$

9–3 to 9–5 Solve.

83. The difference of two numbers is 14. Three times the larger number is 45 less than four times the smaller. What are the two numbers? 87, 101

84. The sum of two numbers is -11. Six times the greater is 4 less than one fifth the smaller. What are the numbers? (-1, -10)

85. In 15 years Judy will be three times as old as Joseph. Five years ago the difference in their ages was 50. How old are Judy and Joseph? 60 and 10

86. An airplane whose speed in still air is 530 miles per hour carries enough gas for 10 hours of flight. On a certain flight it flies against a wind of 30 miles per hour, and with a wind of 30 miles per hour on the return flight. How far can the plane fly without refueling? Approximately 2642 miles.

87. For the school festival, 600 tickets were sold, student tickets at $1.60 and adult tickets at $2.25. If the total amount received was $1122.50, how many tickets of each kind were sold? 250 student, 350 adult

88. A candy shop mixes nuts worth $1.10 per pound with another variety worth $0.80 per pound to make 42 pounds of a mixture worth $0.90 per pound. How many pounds of each kind of nuts must be used? 14, 28

10–1 to 10–3   Solve.

89. $x - 9 < 12$ $x < 21$ **90.** $3a + 8 \geq -5 + 2a$ $a \geq -13$

91. $x - 6 < -4$ $x < 2$ **92.** $6y \leq 3$ $y \leq \frac{1}{2}$ **93.** $3c - 6 < 5c$ $c > \frac{5}{2}$

94. $7y + 2 > 5y - 8$ $y > -5$

95. $23 - 7x - 3x \geq -11$ $x \leq \frac{17}{5}$

96. $23 - 19y - 3y \geq -12$ $y \geq \frac{35}{32}$

97. $20 + 3x < 5x + 4x - 4$ $x > 4$

10–4   Solve.

98. The width of a rectangle is 15 *cm*. What length will make the area at least 225 *cm*? 15

10–5   Graph on a number line.

99. $x + 2 > 11$ $x > 9$ **100.** $3x + 5 < 29$ $x < 8$ **101.** $|x| \leq 4$ $-4 \leq x \leq 4$

103. $|x - 6| \leq 10$ $-4 \leq x \leq 16$ **104.** $2|x| \geq 6$ $-3 \leq x \leq 3$ **105.** $-|x| > 0$ (no points)

Graph in a plane.

106. $x + 2y > 0$ **107.** $|x| < 5$ **108.** $|x| < -1$ no points

Solve these systems by graphing.

109. $x - y > 6$ $\quad y \geq -2$ **110.** $x \geq 0$ $\quad y \leq 0$ **111.** $y < 2x$ $\quad y < 3x$

11–1   Multiply.

112. $\dfrac{-5}{3x - 4} \cdot \dfrac{-6}{5x + 6}$ **113.** $\dfrac{x + 3}{x^2 - 2} \cdot \dfrac{x + 3}{x^2 - 2}$ 112. $\dfrac{30}{15x^2 - 2x - 24}$

Simplify.

113. $\dfrac{x^2 + 6x + 9}{x^4 - 4x^2 + 4}$

114. $\dfrac{x^2 - 25}{x^2 + x - 20}$ $\dfrac{x - 5}{x - 4}$ **115.** $\dfrac{2x^2 + 6x + 4}{4x^2 + 12x + 16}$ $\dfrac{x + 2}{2(x + 3)}$

Multiply and simplify.

116. $\dfrac{x^2 - 6x}{x - 6} \cdot \dfrac{x + 3}{x}$ $x + 3$ **117.** $\dfrac{x^2 + 5x + 6}{x^2 + x - 6} \cdot \dfrac{x^2 - 3x + 2}{x^2 + x - 2}$ 1

11–2   Divide and simplify.

118. $\dfrac{x^2 + 2x - 15}{x^2 + 4x - 5} \div \dfrac{x^2 - x - 6}{x^2 + x - 2}$ $\dfrac{1}{x + 2}$

119. $\dfrac{x^2 - 4}{x^2 - 4x + 4} \div \dfrac{2x - 4}{x^2 + 4}$ $\dfrac{2(x + 2)}{x^2 + 4}$

11–3 Divide.

120. $(32x^5 - 16x^4 + 40x^3) \div (-8x^2)$ $-4x^3 + 2x^2 - 5x$

121. $(x^3 - x^2 + x - 1) \div (x - 1)$ $x^2 + 1$ **122.** $(x^3 - 64) \div (x - 4)$ $x^2 + 4x + 16$

11–4 to 11–6 Simplify.

123. $\dfrac{2x^2}{2x - 1} - \dfrac{1 - x}{2x - 1}$ $x + 1$ $\dfrac{x^2}{x - 3} + \dfrac{9}{3 - x}$ $x + 3$

124. $\dfrac{2x^2 - 15}{x^2 - 4x + 3} + \dfrac{x^2 - 2x}{4x - 3 - x^2}$ $\dfrac{x + 5}{x - 1}$

125. $\dfrac{x - 5}{x} - \dfrac{x}{x - 5}$ **126.** $\dfrac{3}{12 + x - x^2} - \dfrac{2}{x^2 - 9}$ 125. $\dfrac{-10x + 25}{x(x - 5)}$ 126. $\dfrac{-5x + 17}{(x - 4)(x + 3)(x - 3)}$

127. $\dfrac{1}{2x + 1} + \dfrac{1}{x - 2} - \dfrac{5}{4x^2 - 6x + 4}$ **128.** $\dfrac{\dfrac{3}{x} + \dfrac{1}{2x}}{\dfrac{1}{3x} - \dfrac{3}{4x}}$ 127. $\dfrac{3}{2x + 1}$ 128. $\dfrac{-42}{5}$

11–7 Solve.

129. $\dfrac{6x - 2}{2x - 1} = \dfrac{9x}{3x + 1}$ $\dfrac{2}{9}$ **130.** $\dfrac{2x}{x + 1} = 2 - \dfrac{5}{2x}$ -5

11–8 Solve.

131. In checking records a contractor finds that crew *A* can pave a certain length of highway in 8 hours. Crew *B* can do the same job in 10 hours. How long would it take if they worked together? $4\frac{4}{9}$ hours

132. One boat travels 5 *km/h* slower than another. While one boat travels 85 *km*, the other travels 110 *km*. Find their speeds. 17 km, 22 km

133. Two women were partners in a store, one investing $50,000 and the other $38,000. They agreed to share the profits in the ratio of the amounts invested. The profits for the first year were $11,000. How much should each receive? $6250, $4750

12–1 Simplify.

134. $\sqrt{49}$ 7 **135.** $-\sqrt{81}$ -9

Identify each number as rational or irrational.

136. $-\sqrt{8}$ Irrational **137.** $0.383838\ldots$ Rational **138.** $2.010010001\ldots$ Irrational

Determine whether each of the following is a sensible replacement in $\sqrt{12 - x}$.

139. -7 Yes **140.** 14 No **141.** $x \le 12$ Yes

12–2 Simplify.

142. $\sqrt{c^2 d^2}$ $|cd|$ **143.** $\sqrt{(x + 1)^2}$ $|x + 1|$ **144.** $\sqrt{64x^2}$ $8|x|$

12–3   Multiply.

145. $\sqrt{\dfrac{2}{3}}\sqrt{\dfrac{9}{8}}$ **146.** $\sqrt{x}\sqrt{x-1}$ **147.** $\sqrt{a+b}\sqrt{a-b}$ 145. $\frac{1}{2}\sqrt{3}$ 146. $\sqrt{x^2-x}$ 147. $\sqrt{a^2-b^2}$

Factor. Simplify where possible.

148. $\sqrt{150}$ **149.** $\sqrt{9y}$ **150.** $\sqrt{16x-16}$
148. $5\sqrt{6}$ 149. $3\sqrt{y}$ 150. $4\sqrt{x-1}$

12–4   Simplify.

151. $\sqrt{243x^3y^2}$ **152.** $\sqrt{25y+10y^2+y^3}$ 151. $9xy\sqrt{3x}$ 152. $(y+5)\sqrt{y}$

Multiply and simplify.

153. $\sqrt{4xy^2}\sqrt{8x^2y}$ **154.** $\sqrt{32ab}\sqrt{6a^4b^2}$ 153. $4xy\sqrt{2xy}$ 154. $8a^2b\sqrt{3ab}$

12–5   Simplify.

155. $-\sqrt{\dfrac{100}{81}}$ $-\frac{10}{9}$ **156.** $\sqrt{\dfrac{18}{32}}$ $\frac{3}{4}$ **157.** $\sqrt{\dfrac{64}{x^2}}$ $\frac{8}{x}$

Rationalize the denominator.

158. $\sqrt{\dfrac{1}{6}}$ $\frac{\sqrt{6}}{6}$ **159.** $\sqrt{\dfrac{5}{18}}$ $\frac{1}{6}\sqrt{10}$ **160.** $\sqrt{\dfrac{x^2}{27}}$ $\frac{x\sqrt{3}}{9}$

12–6   Divide and simplify.

161. $\dfrac{\sqrt{2}}{\sqrt{7}}$ **162.** $\dfrac{\sqrt{42x^6}}{\sqrt{6x}}$ 161. $\frac{1}{7}\sqrt{14}$ 162. $x^2\sqrt{7x}$

12–7   Simplify.

163. $13\sqrt{a}$ 164. $(9y-2)\sqrt{y}$

163. $6\sqrt{a}+7\sqrt{a}$

164. $\sqrt{81y^3}-\sqrt{4y}$ $(3x^2-x^2y-2y)\sqrt{y}$

165. $3x\sqrt{x^2y}-x\sqrt{x^2y^3}-2\sqrt{y^3}$

12–8

166. In a right triangle, $a=9$ and $c=41$. Find the length of side b.   40

12–9   Solve.

167. $\sqrt{5x+1}-3=5$ $\frac{63}{5}$

168. $\sqrt{x+9}=\sqrt{2x-3}$ 12

13–1, 13–2   Solve.

169. $3x^2=30$ **170.** $3x^2-7x=0$ 169. $\sqrt{10},\ -\sqrt{10}$ 170. $0,\ \frac{7}{3}$

171. $6x^2+x-2=0$ $\frac{1}{2},\ -\frac{2}{3}$

172. $(x-3)^2=6$ $3\pm\sqrt{6}$

173. $x^2-10x-4=0$ $5\pm\sqrt{29}$

13–3

174. Solve by completing the square: $9x^2 - 12x - 2 = 0$. $\frac{2 \pm \sqrt{6}}{3}$

13–4

175. Solve using the quadratic formula: $2y^2 + 6y - 5 = 0$. $\frac{-3 \pm \sqrt{19}}{2}$

176. Use the square root table to approximate the solutions of $4x^2 = 4x + 1$ to the nearest tenth. $1.2, -0.2$

13–5 Solve.

177. $\frac{x + 2}{x^2 - 2} = \frac{2}{2 - x}$ **178.** $2\sqrt{x^2 - 1} = x - 1$ 177. $\pm\frac{2\sqrt{6}}{3}$ 178. 1

13 – 5

179. Solve $A = -\pi r^2 - 4\pi rh$ for r. $r = \frac{-\pi \pm 2\sqrt{4\pi^2 - \pi A}}{2\pi}$

13–6 Solve.

180. The speed of a boat in still water is 8 *km/h*. It travels 60 *km* upstream and 60 *km* downstream in a total time of 16 hours. What is the speed of the stream?   2 km/h

181. The width of a rectangle is half its length. The area is 32 *mm²*. Find the length and the width.   Length, 8 mm; width, 4 mm

13–7

182. Approximate the solutions of $8 + x - x^2 = 0$ by graphing.   3.4, −2.4

14–1

183. $\triangle RST \sim \triangle ABC$. Find the length c. $\frac{1}{2}\sqrt{33}$

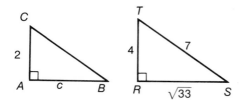

14–2

184. In $\triangle RST$, find sin S, cos S, and tan S to four decimal places.
0.5714, 0.8207, 0.6962

14–4

185. In $\triangle XYZ$, $X = 29°$ and $y = 18$ m. Find z.   15.7 m

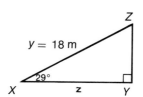

COMPUTER APPENDIX

The following sections give an introduction to programming in BASIC. The topics covered are:

Writing Expressions and Numbers in BASIC
Introduction to BASIC programs
INPUT Statements
READ and DATA Statements
IF . . . THEN Statements
Loops and FOR . . . NEXT Statements
Programs for Quadratic Equations
Programs for Quadratic Functions
Programs for Systems of Equations
Programs for Trigonometry

Writing Expressions and Numbers in BASIC

In order to use a computer, we must use a computer language. One of the most common computer languages is called BASIC. There are different versions of BASIC, so minor changes may be necessary for a particular computer.

In BASIC, as in algebra, variables are quantities whose value may change. A BASIC variable can be specified by a single letter, or a single letter followed by a single digit.

X   Y   Y8   A1   P2

There are five arithmetic operations in BASIC.

Operation	Basic Symbol
Exponentiation	^
Multiplication	*
Division	/
Addition	+
Subtraction	−

In BASIC we write

P^2	as	P ^ 2
$3X$	as	3 * X
$Y \div 2$	as	Y / 2
$S + 4$	as	S + 4
$X - Y$	as	X - Y

We evaluate BASIC expressions just as we do algebraic expressions. For example, when P = 5,

P ^ 2	means 5^2	or 25
3 * P	means 3×5	or 15
P / 2	means $5 \div 2$	or 2.5
P + 4 + 8	means $5 + 4 + 8$	or 17

To represent numbers in BASIC we use signs and decimal points, but not commas. We do not use fractional notation. Here are some examples.

−29   7.92   4923   .666666667

BASIC uses a type of exponential notation for large numbers.

1.23456789E + 05: The "E + 05" means "times 10^5" so
                  1.23456789E + 05 means 123456.789.

4.789789789E + 09: The "E + 09" means "times 10^9" so
                   4.789789789E + 09 means 4789789789.

Exercises

Represent these numbers in BASIC.

1. 19,937   2. -32.17 3. $4\frac{1}{2}$ 4. 33,550,336   5. 10^6
   19937 -32.17 4.5   33550336   1E + 06

Determine whether these are acceptable variables in BASIC. If not, tell why not.

6. X Yes   7. B33 No; letter and two digits   8. AB2 No; two letters and digit   9. Y2 Yes   10. RST No; three letters

Write each expression in BASIC.

11. X^3 12. 4AB   13. $T - 5$ 14. $\frac{X}{2}$ 15. $7 + B + C$
    X ^ 3   4 * A * B   T − 5   X/2   7 + B + C

Evaluate each BASIC expression.

16. 12 * 35 * 2 840   17. 2091/17 123   18. 16 ^ 4 65536   19. 135 − 18 117

Evaluate each BASIC expression using the values given.

20. 25 * X for X = 2 50   21. Y ^ 4 for Y = 6 1296   22. 135 − T for T = 5 130
23. 343 / P for P = 7 49   24. S + 1 + 2 + 3 for S = 10 16

Introduction to BASIC Programs

A computer program in BASIC consists of a series of numbered statements. The numbers specify the order in which we tell the computer to consider the statements. We usually number by tens so that additional statements can be inserted later if necessary. Here is a program.

10 LET X = 5	The LET statement assigns a value to a variable.
20 LET Y = 3	
30 LET Z = X − Y	Z is assigned the value that is computed on the right of the equals sign.
40 PRINT X, Y, Z	The PRINT statement tells the computer what to write.
50 END	The END statement (not required on all computers) ends the program.
OUTPUT 5 3 2	

The PRINT statement, as in line 40, can be written in various ways to provide different outputs as shown in this table.

Statement	Output
PRINT 987	987 The computer prints the number.
PRINT 9,8,7	9　8　7 Commas give wide spacing.
PRINT 9;8;7	9 8 7 Semicolons close in the spacing (or eliminate it on some computers).
PRINT 9-6	3 The computer prints the difference.
PRINT 4 / 5	.8 The computer prints the quotient in decimal notation.
PRINT	The computer leaves a blank line.
PRINT "X+Y"	X+Y The computer prints exactly what is enclosed in quotation marks.
PRINT "9-6"	9-6
PRINT "ALGEBRA IS EASY."	ALGEBRA IS EASY.

In order to run a program, we must use system commands correctly. System commands are executed immediately. They do not need line numbers because they are not part of the BASIC program. Here are some examples.

NEW   deletes all previous statements.
LIST lists the program currently in memory.
RUN   starts the execution of the program currently in memory.

To enter and run a program, we type the following.

NEW   This will clear out any statements in memory.
Program steps   These must be numbered.
RUN   This will start the execution of the program.

We press RETURN at the end of each line. We type LIST if we wish to see the program steps listed, for example if we made an error and need to correct it.

Exercises

1. If you have a computer, enter and run the program in this section. Remember, you must type it exactly as shown and you must use system commands correctly.

2. Revise the program in Exercise 1 so that $Z = X \div Y$. 30 LET Z = X/Y

Determine the output for each program. If you have a computer, enter and run the program.

3.
```
10  LET R = 55
20  LET T = 7.5
30  LET D = R*T
40  PRINT "DISTANCE EQUALS"; D
50  END
```
DISTANCE EQUALS 412.5

4.
```
10  LET D = 450
20  LET G = 19.2
30  LET M =D/G
40  PRINT "MILES PER GALLON EQUALS"; M
50  END
```
MILES PER GALLON EQUALS 23.4375

5.
```
10  LET S1 = 25
20  LET S2 = 16
30  LET S3 = 42
40  LET S4 = 52
50  LET P = S1 + S2 + S3 + S4
60  PRINT "PERIMETER OF THE QUADRILATERAL IS"; P
70  END
```
PERIMETER OF THE QUADRILATERAL IS 135

6.
```
10  LET B = 14.32
20  LET H = 9.5
30  LET A = B*H
40  PRINT "AREA OF THE RECTANGLE IS"; A
50  END
```
AREA OF THE RECTANGLE IS 136.04

7. Write a program using LET and PRINT statements that will find the sum, difference, product, and quotient of two numbers, N1 and N2.

8. Write a program using LET and PRINT statements that will find the sum of six test scores and find their average.

7. Answers may vary. Any numbers may be used for N1 and N2.
```
10  LET N1 = 20
20  LET N2 = 30
30  PRINT N1 + N2,
    N1 − N2, N1 * N2, N1/N2
40  END
```

8. Answers may vary. Any numbers may be used for T1–T6.
```
10   LET T1 = 95
20   LET T2 = 80
30   LET T3 = 98
40   LET T4 = 72
50   LET T5 = 86
60   LET T6 = 92
70   LET S = T1 + T2 + T3
     + T4 + T5 + T6
80   LET A = S/6
90   PRINT "SUM IS"; S,
     "AVERAGE IS"; A
100  END
```

INPUT Statements

BASIC uses the LET statement to assign values to variables and expressions. The INPUT statement can also be used to do this. We use an INPUT statement if we want to assign the values when the program is run. This allows us to use the same program over and over with different values assigned to the variable(s).

```
10  PRINT "INPUT BASE AND HEIGHT"      After run, the computer prints: INPUT BASE
                                       AND HEIGHT.
20  INPUT B, H                         The computer prints: ? (We type in the values
                                       separated by a comma.)
30  LET A = B * H
40  LET P = 2 * B + 2 * H              The computer computes A and P.
50  PRINT "AREA IS"; A
60  PRINT "PERIMETER IS"; P            The computer prints the values of A and P.
70  END
```

The variables listed in the INPUT statement *must* be separated by commas and so must the values typed in. Also there must be a one-to-one correspondence between the variables listed in the INPUT statement and the values typed in.

Note that in line 40, P = 2 * B + 2 * H, the multiplications are done first, then the addition. The order in which the computer performs operations is the same as in algebra.

1. Operations within parentheses first.
2. Exponentiations in order from left to right.
3. Multiplication and division from left to right.
4. Addition and subtraction from left to right.

This order is important when we evaluate expressions.

When $X = 2$: $X \char94 3 + 3 * X - 5$ means $X^3 + 3X - 5$ or $2^3 + (3 \cdot 2) - 5$ or
$$8 + 6 - 5 = 9$$

When $Y = 5$: $Y \char94 2 + 2 * Y - (Y + 4)/3$ means $Y^2 + 2Y - \dfrac{Y + 4}{3}$ or
$$5^2 + 2(5) - \dfrac{5 + 4}{3}$$
$$= 25 + 10 - 3 = 32$$

Exercises

1. If you have a computer, enter and run the program in this section. Try different values for the base and height of the rectangle. Answers may vary.

2. If you have a computer, enter and run this program. Try different values for the number of gallons. Answers may vary.

```
10  PRINT ""ENTER THE NUMBER OF GALLONS"
20  INPUT G
30  LET L = G * 3.785
40  PRINT G; "GALLONS ="; L; "LITERS"
50  END
```

3. Write a program using the INPUT statement that will find area and circumference of a circle. Area = πr^2. Circumference = $2\pi r$. Use 3.14159 as π. If you have a computer, enter and run the program.

```
3. Answers may vary.
10  PRINT "TYPE IN
    RADIUS OF A CIRCLE"
20  INPUT R
30  LET P = 3.14159
40  LET A = P * R ^ 2
50  LET C = 2 * P * R
60  PRINT "AREA ="; A,
    'CIRCUMFERENCE ="; C
70  END
```

Evaluate each BASIC expression.

  4. $3 \hat{} 2 + 2 \hat{} 3$ 17   5. $(12 * 2)/6$ 4   6. $8 + 2 \hat{} 3 - 6$ 10   7. $2 \hat{} 4 + (-3) \hat{} 3$ -11

Evaluate each BASIC expression using the values given.

  8. $(T + 5) \hat{} 3$ for $T = 2$ 343   9. $Y + 4/(2 * Y)$ for $Y = 6$ 6.3333333
 10. $P1 \hat{} 2 + P1 - 5$ for $P1 = 10$ 105   11. $X2 + 8/2$ for $X2 = 7$ 11
 12. $4 \hat{} N1 + 3 \hat{} N1$ for $N1 = 3$ 91   13. $Q + 2 \hat{} Q/4$ for $Q = 4$ 8

READ and DATA Statements

The READ and DATA statements may be used to assign values to variables.

```
10  READ F
```
READ tells the computer to go to the data statement and read a value for F.

```
20  LET C=5/9 * {F - 32}
30  PRINT F; "F=" C; "C"
40  DATA 77
50  END
```
DATA supplies the value for F.

The computer will repeat the process if we list more data in line 40 and insert a GO TO statement. A GO TO statement directs the computer to go to the line indicated and continue through the program.

  When we insert the lines

```
35  GO TO 10
40  DATA 77, -13, 95, -22, 32
```

and run the program, the computer will print this output.

```
 77 F =  25 C
-13 F = -25 C
 95 F =  35 C
-22 F = -30 C
 32 F =   0 C
```

When it runs out of data it prints: OUT OF DATA ERROR IN 10

The following program uses READ/DATA statements to compute the slope of a line given two points of the line. It also uses a REM (remark) statement which reminds us of the purpose of the program. Although REM statements are printed in the listing of the program, they are ignored during execution of the program.

```
10 REM PROGRAM WILL COMPUTE SLOPE GIVEN TWO POINTS
20 READ X1,Y1,X2,Y2
30 LET M = {Y2 - Y1}/{X2 - X1}
40 PRINT "SLOPE ="; M
50 GO TO 20
60 DATA 4,-4,-3,-2,3,5,1,1,-1,2,-2,4
70 END
```

2–4. Answers may vary.

2.
```
10  REM EVALUATE
    EXPRESSION
20  READ X
30  PRINT 5 * X ^ 2 + 3 * X
    - 1
40  DATA 7, 0, -2, 100, 15
50  END
```
Output:
```
265
-1
13
50299
1169
```

3.
```
10  REM ORDERED PAIR
    SOLUTIONS
20  READ X
30  LET Y = 3 * X - 1
40  PRINT "(" X "," Y ")"
50  GO TO 20
60  DATA -5, 0, 33, -16,
    50
70  END
```
Output:
```
(-5, -16)
(0, -1)
(34, 101)
(-16, -49)
(50, 149)
```

Since four variables are named in the READ statement, the computer reads four values in the DATA statement. The next time around it reads the next four values, and so on, until it runs out of values to read.

Exercises

1. If you have a computer, enter and run the programs in this section. Try different values for the variables.

2. Write a program using READ/DATA that will print the value of the expression $5X^2 + 3X - 1$ when X = 7, 0, -2, 100, and 15. Use a REM statement for clarification.

3. Write a program using READ/DATA that will print ordered pair solutions to Y = 3X - 1 when X = -5, 0, 33, -16, and 50. Use a REM statement for clarification.

4. Write a program using READ/DATA which will print N, N^2, and N^3 when N = 13, -6, 1000, -2, and 28. Use a REM statement for clarification.

4.
```
10  REM PRINT N, ITS
    SQUARE, ITS CUBE
20  READ N
30  PRINT N, N ^ 2, N ^ 3
40  GO TO 20
50  DATA 13, -6, 1000, -2,
    28
60  END
```
Output:

13	169	2197
-6	36	-216
1000	1000000	1E + 09
-2	4	-8
28	784	21952

IF . . . THEN Statements

In BASIC a computer makes a decision by means of an IF . . .THEN statement. Its usual form is as follows.

IF (relationship) THEN (line number)

When the statement following the IF is true, the computer goes to the line named after THEN. When it is not true, the computer continues on to the next line. Here is an example.

```
10  REM X AND X CUBE FOR X <= 12
20  LET X = 1
30  PRINT X, X ^ 3          The computer prints the values for X and X³
                            starting with X = 1.
40  LET X = X + 1           X is assigned a new value, X + 1.
50  IF X > 12 THEN 70       When X > 12, the computer goes to line 70. When X is not
                            greater than 12, the computer reads the next line.
60  GO TO 30
70  END
```

The example above used the symbol ">" in line 50 just as it is
used in algebra. However, the symbol for "less than or equal to" in
line 10 is different from algebra. Here are the BASIC symbols for
equality and inequality relations.

```
= EQUALS                <= is less than or equal to
< IS LESS THAN          >= is greater than or equal to
> IS GREATER THAN       <> is not equal to
```

We can use the IF . . . THEN statement in a program to determine
whether an ordered pair is a solution of the equation $Y = 2X + 1$.
Note how the "is not equal to" symbol is used in line 40.

```
10  REM DETERMINE WHETHER ORDERED PAIR IS A SOLUTION
20  PRINT "INPUT X,Y"
30  INPUT X,Y
40  IF Y <> 2 * X + 1 THEN 70
50  PRINT "{"X;",","Y;"} IS A SOLUTION"
60  GO TO 80
70  PRINT "{"X;",","Y;"} IS NOT A SOLUTION"
80  END
```

Exercises

1. If you have a computer, enter and run the programs in this
   section. Try different values for the variables. Answers may vary.

2. Revise the program that determines whether an ordered pair is a
   solution to an equation to test these ordered pairs in the
   equation $Y = \frac{2}{3}X - 1$. 40 IF Y <> 2/3 * X - 1 THEN 70

   $(0,1)$ Yes $(9,5)$ Yes $(3,6)$ No $(6,3)$ Yes $(4,7)$ No $(-1,-3)$ No

3. Revise the slope program in the previous section on READ and
   DATA statements by using an IF . . . THEN statement to tell the
   computer what to do when X1 = X2.

   3. Answers may vary.
   25 IF X1 = X2 THEN 55
   55 PRINT "THERE IS NO
       SLOPE"
   56 GO TO 20

4. Write a program using an IF . . . THEN statement that will determine the absolute value of a number. Use READ/DATA statements to assign the values.

4. Answers may vary.

10	PRINT "NUMBER", "ABSOLUTE VALUE"
20	READ N
30	PRINT N,
40	IF N >= 0 THEN 60
50	LET N = −N
60	PRINT N
70	GO TO 20
80	DATA 35, −98, 2.4, −73.9, −5, 0, 1
90	END

Output:

NUMBER	ABSOLUTE VALUE
35	35
−98	98
2.4	2.4
−73.9	73.9
−5	5
0	0
−1	1

?OUT OF DATA ERROR IN 20

Loops and FOR . . . NEXT Statements

In previous chapters we have used BASIC statements to perform repetitive operations. A sequence of instructions that is repeated over and over is called a loop. FOR . . . NEXT statements are useful in constructing loops.

The following program uses a FOR . . . NEXT loop (lines 20–40) to print the integers from 1 to 25 and their reciprocals.

```
10  REM 1 INTEGERS THROUGH 25 AND RECIPROCALS
20  FOR X = 1 TO 25      The computer begins the loop with X as 1.
30  PRINT X,1/X          The computer executes line 30.
40  NEXT X               The computer increases X by one and goes through the loop again.
50  END
```

The process of adding one to X and executing line 30 continues through X = 25. Then the program ends. The range of values for X may be any values needed.

If we wanted the computer to print the square roots of the integers from 1 to 25, we could use a loop and the built-in computer function for square root, SQR(X). Line 30 could be revised to the following.

```
30  PRINT X, SQR(X)
```

Then the computer would print this output.

```
1    1
2    1.41421356
3    1.73205081
.    .
.    .
.    .
```

There are many other built-in functions. These are the most useful to us in algebra.

Function	Definition
INT(X)	Greatest integer less than or equal to X
ABS(X)	Absolute value of X
SQR(X)	Square root of X

In the next program we use a loop and built-in functions to find pairs of factors for the number 16.

```
10 REM FACTOR PAIRS FOR 16
20 LET N = 16
30 FOR D = 1 TO SQR(N)   The divisor D is assigned the value one.
40 LET Q = N/D   The quotient Q is computed.
50 IF Q = INT(Q) THEN 70   If the quotient is an integer, the computer goes to line
60 GO TO 80             70. If the quotient is not an integer, the computer
70 PRINT D "AND" Q "ARE FACTORS"   reads the next line (line 60).
80 NEXT D
90 END
```

The process of adding 1 to D and then dividing into N continues through $\sqrt{N}$. The computer prints this output.

```
1 AND 16 ARE FACTORS
2 AND 8 ARE FACTORS
4 AND 4 ARE FACTORS
```

Exercises

1. If you have a computer, enter and run the two programs in this section. Try different values for the variables. Answers may vary.

2. Write a program using a FOR . . . NEXT loop and the SQR function that will compute $V = 3.5\sqrt{H}$. Use the first ten positive integers as H.

3. Write a program using the INT function that will determine whether an integer is even or odd.

4. Write a program using the ABS function to find the distance between these pairs of numbers on the number line.

   -8 and -92 -5 and 15 0 and 27 49 and -4 -10 and 10

   Remember, the distance between two numbers A and B can be expressed as $|A - B|$.

5. Write a program using a FOR . . . NEXT loop that will add the integers from 1 to 25 and print their sum.

2–5. Answers may vary.

2.
```
10 REM DISTANCE (KM)
   YOU CAN SEE
20 FOR H = 1 TO 10
30 LET V = 3.5 * SQR(H)
40 PRINT "WHEN H=" H,
   "V=" V
50 NEXT H
60 END
```

3.
```
10 REM EVEN OR ODD
20 PRINT "INPUT N"
30 INPUT N
40 IF N/2 = INT(N/2) THEN
   70
50 PRINT N "IS ODD"
60 GO TO 80
70 PRINT N "IS EVEN"
80 END
```

4.
```
10 REM DISTANCE ON
   NUMBER LINE
20 READ N1,N2
30 LET D = ABS(N1 − N2)
40 PRINT "DISTANCE
   BETWEEN"; N1 "AND"
   N2 "IS"; D
50 GO TO 20
60 DATA −8, −92, −5, 15,
   0, 27, 49, −4, −10, 10
70 END
```

5.
```
10 REM SUM OF 25
   INTEGERS
20 LET S = 0
30 FOR N = 1 TO 25
40 LET S = S + N
50 NEXT N
60 PRINT "THE SUM IS"; S
70 END
```

Programs for Solving Quadratic Equations

We can use the computer to solve quadratic equations. To solve equations of the form $AX^2 + BX + C = 0$, $A \neq 0$, we have learned to use the quadratic formula

$$X = \frac{-B \pm \sqrt{B^2 - 4AC}}{2A}$$

The following BASIC program solves these equations.

$$5X^2 - 8X + 3 = 0$$
$$X^2 - 4X - 21 = 0$$
$$2X^2 + 6X + 5 = 0$$

Note that the DATA statement lists the numbers in the exact order that they appear in the equations.

```
10   REM SOLVE BY QUADRATIC FORMULA
20   READ A,B,C
30   IF B ^ 2 - 4 * A * C < 0 THEN 80
40   LET X1 = {-B + SQR{B ^ 2 - 4 * A * C}}/{2 * A}
50   LET X2 = {-B - SQR{B ^ 2 - 4 * A * C}}/{2 * A}
60   PRINT "THE SOLUTIONS ARE ";X1;" AND " X2
70   GO TO 20
80   PRINT "NO REAL-NUMBER SOLUTIONS"
90   GO TO 20
100  DATA 5, -8, 3, 1, -4, -21, 2, 6, 5
110  END
```

Additional DATA statements could contain values for more equations, if necessary.

We can use quadratic equations to solve certain compound interest problems. The computer can be programmed to find the total amount,

$$A = P(1 + R)^T$$

for many different principal amounts with the use of a FOR . . . NEXT loop (lines 40–70).

```
10   REM INTEREST COMPOUNDED ANNUALLY
20   LET R = .12
30   LET T = 2
40   FOR P = 100 TO 125
50   LET A = P * {1 + R} ^ T
60   PRINT "$"; P; "GROWS TO $"; A
70   NEXT P
80   END
```

Exercises

1. If you have a computer, enter and run the programs in this section.

2. Solve these equations in the quadratic formula program.

$3X^2 + 2X - 7 = 0$ 1,230/3859, -1.89680525

$X^2 + 9X + 14 = 0$ $-2, -7$

1. Output for first program:
THE SOLUTIONS ARE 1
AND .6
THE SOLUTIONS ARE 7
AND -3
NO REAL-NUMBER
SOLUTIONS

Output for second program:
$100 GROWS TO $125.44;
$101 GROWS TO $126.6944;
$102 GROWS TO $127.9488;
$103 GROWS TO $129.2032;
$104 GROWS TO $130.4576;
$105 GROWS TO $131.712;
$106 GROWS TO $132.9664;
$107 GROWS TO $134.2208;
$108 GROWS TO $135.4752;
$109 GROWS TO $136.7296;
$110 GROWS TO $137.984;
$111 GROWS TO $139.2384;
$112 GROWS TO $140.4928;
$113 GROWS TO $141.7472;
$114 GROWS TO $143.0016;
$115 GROWS TO $144.256;
$116 GROWS TO $145.5104;
$117 GROWS TO $146.7648;
$118 GROWS TO $148.0192;
$119 GROWS TO $149.2736;
$120 GROWS TO $150.528;
$121 GROWS TO $151.7824;
$122 GROWS TO $153.0368;
$123 GROWS TO $154.2912;
$124 GROWS TO $155.5456;
$125 GROWS TO $156.8

3. Try these values in the compound interest program:

    a. R = 13.5%   **b.** R = 11%
       P = 500 TO 510   P = 1 TO 15

4. Revise the compound interest program to find the amount after two years at 15% for every $1000 from $5000 to $20,000. To do this, the FOR statement must contain a STEP other than 1: FOR P = 5000 TO 20000 STEP 1000. This causes the computer to step or "jump" by 1000 instead of by one.

3a.

Output:
$500 GROWS TO $644.112501;
$501 GROWS TO $645.400726;
$502 GROWS TO $646.688951;
$503 GROWS TO $647.977176;
$504 GROWS TO $649.265401;
$505 GROWS TO $650.553626;
$506 GROWS TO $651.841851;
$507 GROWS TO $653.130076;
$508 GROWS TO $654.418301;
$509 GROWS TO $655.706526;
$510 GROWS TO $656.994751

Programs for Solving Quadratic Equations

The graph of a quadratic function $AX^2 + BX + C$, $A \neq 0$, is a parabola. Sometimes we want to know the vertex, the line of symmetry, and the maximum or minimum value of the parabola.

  The coordinates of the vertex of the parabola are (X, Y) where

$$X = \frac{-B}{2A} \text{ and } Y = \frac{4AC - B^2}{4A}$$

The equation of the line of symmetry is $X = \frac{-B}{2A}$.

The maximum or minimum value occurs at the vertex of the parabola. If A is positive, there is a minimum value, Y. If A is negative, there is a maximum value, Y.

  We can use the computer to determine these answers. The DATA statement in the following program contains values from these equations.

$$F(X) = -2X^2 + 10X - 7, F(X) = 4X^2 + 8X - 3, F(X) = -X^2 - 4X + 3$$

```
10   REM LINE OF SYMMETRY, VERTEX, MAX OR MIN
20   READ A, B, C
30   IF A = 0 THEN 160
40   LET X = -B / (2 * A)
50   PRINT "LINE OF SYMMETRY IS X= ";X
60   LET Y = (4 * A * C - B ^ 2) / (4 * A)
70   PRINT "VERTEX IS (";X;",";Y;")"
80   LET S = SGN(A)
90   IF S = +1 THEN 120
100  PRINT "MAXIMUM VALUE IS "; Y
110  GO TO 20
120  PRINT "MAXIMUM VALUE IS "; Y
130  GO TO 20
140  DATA -2,10,-7,4,8,-3,-1,-4,3
150  DATA 0,0,0
160  END
```

3b.

Output:
$1 GROWS TO $1.2321;
$2 GROWS TO $2.4642;
$3 GROWS TO $3.6963;
$4 GROWS TO $4.92840001;
$5 GROWS TO $6.16050001;
$6 GROWS TO $7.39260001;
$7 GROWS TO $8.62470001;
$8 GROWS TO $9.85680002;
$9 GROWS TO $11.0889;
$10 GROWS TO $12.321;
$11 GROWS TO $13.5531;
$12 GROWS TO $14.7852;
$13 GROWS TO $16.0173;
$14 GROWS TO $17.2494;
$15 GROWS TO $18.4815

4.
20   LET R = .15
30   LET T = 2

40   FOR P = 5000 TO 20000
     STEP 1000

.
.

Output:
$5000 GROWS TO $6612.5;
$6000 GROWS TO $7935;
$7000 GROWS TO $9257.5;
$8000 GROWS TO $10580;
$9000 GROWS TO $11902.5;
$10000 GROWS TO $13225;
$11000 GROWS TO $14547.5;
$12000 GROWS TO $15870;
$13000 GROWS TO $17192.5;
$14000 GROWS TO $18515;
$15000 GROWS TO $19837.5;
$16000 GROWS TO $21160;
$17000 GROWS TO $22482.5;
$18000 GROWS TO $23805;
$19000 GROWS TO $25127.5;
$20000 GROWS TO $26450

Note how lines 30 and 150 are used to stop the READ procedure. The use of trailer or "dummy" values in line 150 avoids the OUT OF DATA IN 20 printout when the computer runs out of data to read. Three dummy values are used because the READ statement contains three variables. In selecting dummy values, be sure to use ones that are obviously not valid values.

Also note the use of the built-in function SGN (X) in line 80.

Exercises

1. If you have a computer, enter and run the program in this section.

2. Add a new DATA statement to the program in this section. Use the values from these functions.

$$F(X) = 3X^2 - 24X + 50, \quad F(X) = X^2 - 6X + 4$$

3. A simple way to use the computer to plot certain parabolas is to use the TAB(X) function. The TAB function tells the computer to print at the specific position determined by X. Enter and run this program to graph the parabola $Y = X^2 + 1$. Note that the X- and Y-axes are rotated.

```
10  REM PARABOLA
20  FOR X = -6 TO 6
30  LET Y = X ^ 2 + 1
40  PRINT TAB{Y}; "*"
50  NEXT X
60  END
```

There are other ways to plot graphs on a computer, but they require more sophisticated commands.

4. Revise the program in Exercise 3 to graph these parabolas.

   a. $F(X) = X^2 + 0.5X + 1$ **b.** $F(X) = \frac{1}{4}X^2 + 16$

1. Output:
   LINE OF SYMMETRY IS
   X = 2.5
   VERTEX IS (2.5, 5.5)
   MAXIMUM VALUE IS 5.5
   LINE OF SYMMETRY IS
   X = -1
   VERTEX IS (-1, -7)
   MINIMUM VALUE IS -7
   LINE OF SYMMETRY IS
   X = -2
   VERTEX IS (-2, 7)
   MAXIMUM VALUE IS 7

2. 140 DATA 3, -24, 50, 1, -6, 4
   Output:
   LINE OF SYMMETRY IS
   X = 4
   VERTEX IS (4, 2)
   MINIMUM VALUE IS 2
   LINE OF SYMMETRY IS
   X = 3
   VERTEX IS (3, -5)
   MINIMUM VALUE IS -5

4. a. 30 LET Y = X ^ 2 + .5 * X + 1
   b. 30 LET Y = .25 * X ^ 2 + 16

Programs for Systems of Equations

We can use the computer to find some ordered pair solutions to a system of two quadratic equations. Recall that FOR . . . NEXT loops are useful in performing repetitive operations. Sometimes a loop is programmed within another loop. These loops, placed one inside the other, are called nested loops.

The following program uses nested loops to find integer values of X and Y (from -5 to 5) that are solutions of this system of quadratic equations.

$$2X^2 + 5Y^2 = 22$$
$$3X^2 - Y^2 = -1$$

```
10  REM INTEGER SOLUTIONS
20  FOR X = -5 TO 5
30  FOR Y = -5 TO 5
40  IF 2 * X ^ 2 + 5 * Y ^ 2 <> 22 THEN 70
50  IF 3 * X ^ 2 - Y ^ 2 <> -1 THEN 70
60  PRINT " {";X;",",";Y;"} IS A SOLUTION"
70  NEXT Y
80  NEXT X
90  END
```

The computer assigns X the first value, -5. With X as -5, the computer tests $Y = -5, -4, -3, \ldots 5$ in the two equations. If the pair of values solves the system, the computer prints it, otherwise it goes on to the next Y. After $Y = 5$, the computer assigns the next value for X, -4, and tests $Y = -5, -4, -3, \ldots 5$ again. The process continues through $X = 5$. After $X = 5$, the computer goes to line 90, which ends the program.

In the FOR statements in lines 20 and 30, we chose a particular range of values for X and Y. This range may be any that we choose. We may also use the STEP option in the FOR statement to tell the computer to increment by a number other than one. For example, STEP 0.5, STEP -1, STEP 10, and so on.

A simple example is the following program, which finds the sums of all possible combinations of even numbers from 0 to 10. We use STEP 2 to tell the computer to "step" by two. (When the STEP statement is omitted, the computer steps by one.)

```
10  REM SUMS OF EVENS
20  FOR W1 = 0 TO 10 STEP 2
30  FOR W2 = 0 TO 10 STEP 2
40  PRINT W1; "+" ;W2; "=";  W1 + W2,
50  NEXT W2
60  NEXT W1
70  END
```

1. Output for first program:
   $(-2, -2)$ IS A SOLUTION
   $(-1, 2)$ IS A SOLUTION
   $(1, -2)$ IS A SOLUTION
   $(1, 2)$ IS A SOLUTION
   Output for second program:

$0 + 0 = 0$	$0 + 2 = 2$	$0 + 4 = 4$
$0 + 6 = 6$	$0 + 8 = 8$	$0 + 10 = 10$
$2 + 0 = 2$	$2 + 2 = 4$	$2 + 4 = 6$
$2 + 6 = 8$	$2 + 8 = 10$	$2 + 10 = 12$
$4 + 0 = 4$	$4 + 2 = 6$	$4 + 4 = 8$
$4 + 6 = 10$	$4 + 8 = 12$	$4 + 10 = 14$
$6 + 0 = 6$	$6 + 2 = 8$	$6 + 4 = 10$
$6 + 6 = 12$	$6 + 8 = 14$	$6 + 10 = 16$
$8 + 0 = 8$	$8 + 2 = 10$	$8 + 4 = 12$
$8 + 6 = 14$	$8 + 8 = 16$	$8 + 10 = 18$
$10 + 9 = 10$	$10 + 2 = 12$	$10 + 4 = 14$
$10 + 6 = 16$	$10 + 8 = 18$	$10 + 10 = 20$

2. a. 40 IF 2 * Y ^ 2 - 3
        * X ^ 2 <> 6
        THEN 70
   50 IF 5 * Y ^ 2 - 2
        * X ^ 2 <> 53
        THEN 70
   b. 40 IF X ^ 2 + 4 * Y ^
        2 <> 20 THEN 70
   50 X * Y <> 4 THEN
        70

Exercises

1. If you have a computer, enter and run the programs in this computer section.

2. Revise the first program to find integer solutions to these systems of equations for values of X and Y from -5 to 5.
   a. $2Y^2 - 3X^2 = 6$ **b.** $X^2 + 4Y^2 = 20$ **c.** $X^2 + Y^2 = 25$
   $5Y^2 + 2X^2 = 53$ $XY = 4$ $3X - 4Y = 0$

c. 40 IF X ^ 2 + Y ^ 2
       <> 25 THEN 70
   50 IF 3 * X - 4 * Y
       <> 0 THEN 70

3. We can use nested loops to print a type of bar graph of values for certain equations. Enter and run this program.

```
10  REM BAR GRAPH
20  FOR X = -5 TO 5 STEP .5
30  LET Y = X ^ 2 + X + 3
40  FOR I = 1 TO Y
50  PRINT "*";
60  NEXT I
70  PRINT
80  NEXT X
90  END
```

4. Revise the program in Exercise 3 to print a bar graph for these equations.

    a. $Y = X^2 + 4$ **b.** $Y = X^2 - X + 1$

5. Write a program using nested loops with STEP statements to print the prime numbers from 100 to 200.

Programs for Trigonometry

Computers have built-in functions for some trigonometric functions. Usually available in BASIC are SIN(X), COS(X), and TAN(X), where the angle X is measured in radians. One degree equals $\frac{\pi}{180}$ radians.

We can use the computer to evaluate functions for any angle. Here is a short program using a FOR . . . NEXT loop that lists values for selected angles from 0° to 80°. Since the computer measures angles in radians, we enter the value C in line 20 to convert radians to degrees.

```
10  PRINT "DEGREES"; TAB (10) "RADIANS"; TAB (24) "SINE"
20  LET C = 3.14159 / 180
30  FOR D = 0 TO 80 STEP 10
40  PRINT D; TAB (10) D * C; TAB (24) SIN (D * C)
50  NEXT D
60  END
```

Note the TAB function in lines 10 and 40. TAB(X) tells the computer to print at the specific position named by the X within the parentheses. It is useful in printing results in neat columns.

In Section 14–4 we solved triangle problems. In the Extension Exercises for that section, we used the formula $\frac{1}{2}BC \sin \angle A$ to find the area of triangles. We can use a BASIC program to do these com-

(right margin)

3.
```
************************
******************
****************
***********
*********
*******
*****
***
***
**
***
***
*****
******
*********
***********
**************
*****************
********************
***********************
****************************
*********************************
```

4. a. 30 LET Y = X ^ 2 + 4
   b. 30 LET Y = X ^ 2 − X + 1

5. Answers may vary.
```
10  REM PRIMES 100 TO
    200
20  FOR X = 101 TO 200
    STEP 2
30  FOR I = 3 TO SQR(X)
    STEP 2
40  IF X / I = INT(X / I)
    THEN 70
50  NEXT I
60  PRINT X,
70  NEXT X
80  END
```
Output:
```
101   103   107
109   113   127
131   137   139
149   151   157
163   167   173
179   181   191
193   197   199
```

putations. Here we use A1, B1, and C1 to denote the angles of a triangle (C1 being the right angle), and A, B, and C to denote the sides opposite angles A1, B1, and C1 respectively. Given A1, C1, and C, we solve the triangles.

```
10   LET K = 3.14159 / 180
20   READ A1, C1, A
30   IF A1 = 0 THEN 200
40   REM COMPUTE THIRD ANGLE
50   LET B1 = 180 - (A1 + C1)
60   REM COMPUTE OTHER TWO SIDES
70   LET A = C * SIN (A1 * K)
80   LET B = C * SIN (B1 * K)
90   REM COMPUTE AREA
100  LET R = .5 * B * C * SIN (A1 * K)
110  PRINT "ANGLES:"A1;TAB(15)B1;TAB(28)C1
120  PRINT "SIDES:" A;TAB(15)B;TAB(28)C
130  PRINT "AREA:" R
140  PRINT
150  GO TO 20
160  DATA 40, 90, 15
170  DATA 58, 90, 10
180  DATA 25, 90, 6.2
190  DATA 0, 0, 0
200  END
```

1. Output for first program:

DEGREES	RADIANS	SINE
0	0	0
10	.174532778	.173648033
20	.349065556	.342019866
30	.523598333	.499999597
40	.698131111	.642787158
50	.872663889	.766043969
60	1.04719667	.866024961
70	1.22172944	.939692268
80	1.39626222	.984807548

Output for second program:

```
ANGLES:   40          50          90
SIDES:    9.64181415  11.4906667  15
AREA:     55.3954361

ANGLES:   58          32          90
SIDES:    8.48048096  5.29919264  10
AREA:     22.4698512

ANGLES:   25          65          90
SIDES:    2.62023322  5.61910828  6.2
AREA:     7.36168710
```

The DEFINE statement (DEF) is a user-defined function. It is used when the same calculation must be performed several times. Its form is as follows.

DEF FNA(X) = (Expression written by user) FNA is the name of the function (FN followed by any letter.) X is the dummy variable. Once the function has been defined, and the computer finds a reference to it, the computer takes the value indicated, as in PRINT FNA(10), assigns it to X, and evaluates the expression.

Exercises

1. If you have a computer, enter and run the programs in this section.

2. Revise the first program to print cosine and tangent values for angles from 0° to 45° in increments of five.

3. Revise the DATA statement in the second program for different values of A1 and A.

4. Determine how the DEFINE statement (DEF) can be used to simplify the program for solving triangles.

2.
```
10  PRINT "DEGREES";
    TAB(10) "COS";
    TAB(24) "TAN"
    ⋮
30  FOR D = 0 TO 45
    STEP 5
40  PRINT D; TAB(10)
    COS(D * C); TAB(24)
    TAN(D * C)
```

3. Answers may vary.

4. Answers may vary. For example this function may be used to express angles in degrees.
DEF FNA(X) = X * 3.14159 / 180

TABLES

TABLE 1: Squares and Square Roots

N	N^2	$\sqrt{N}$	N	N^2	$\sqrt{N}$
1	1	1	51	2,601	7.141
2	4	1.414	52	2,704	7.211
3	9	1.732	53	2,809	7.280
4	16	2	54	2,916	7.348
5	25	2.236	55	3,025	7.416
6	36	2.449	56	3,136	7.483
7	49	2.646	57	3,249	7.550
8	64	2.828	58	3,364	7.616
9	81	3	59	3,481	7.681
10	100	3.162	60	3,600	7.746
11	121	3.317	61	3,721	7.810
12	144	3.464	62	3,844	7.874
13	169	3.606	63	3,969	7.937
14	196	3.742	64	4,096	8
15	225	3.873	65	4,225	8.062
16	256	4	66	4,356	8.124
17	289	4.123	67	4,489	8.185
18	324	4.243	68	4,624	8.246
19	361	4.359	69	4,761	8.307
20	400	4.472	70	4,900	8.367
21	441	4.583	71	5,041	8.426
22	484	4.690	72	5,184	8.485
23	529	4.796	73	5,329	8.544
24	576	4.899	74	5,476	8.602
25	625	5	75	5,625	8.660
26	676	5.099	76	5,776	8.718
27	729	5.196	77	5,929	8.775
28	784	5.292	78	6,084	8.832
29	841	5.385	79	6,241	8.888
30	900	5.477	80	6,400	8.944
31	961	5.568	81	6,561	9
32	1,024	5.657	82	6,724	9.055
33	1,089	5.745	83	6,889	9.110
34	1,156	5.831	84	7,056	9.165
35	1,225	5.916	85	7,225	9.220
36	1,296	6	86	7,396	9.274
37	1,369	6.083	87	7,569	9.327
38	1,444	6.164	88	7,744	9.381
39	1,521	6.245	89	7,921	9.434
40	1,600	6.325	90	8,100	9.487
41	1,681	6.403	91	8,281	9.539
42	1,764	6.481	92	8,464	9.592
43	1,849	6.557	93	8,649	9.644
44	1,936	6.633	94	8,836	9.695
45	2,025	6.708	95	9,025	9.747
46	2,116	6.782	96	9,216	9.798
47	2,209	6.856	97	9,409	9.849
48	2,304	6.928	98	9,604	9.899
49	2,401	7	99	9,801	9.950
50	2,500	7.071	100	10,000	10

TABLE 2: Values of Trigonometric Functions

Degrees	Sin	Cos	Tan	Degrees	Sin	Cos	Tan
0°	0.0000	1.0000	0.0000				
1°	0.0175	0.9998	0.0175	46°	0.7193	0.6947	1.0355
2°	0.0349	0.9994	0.0349	47°	0.7314	0.6820	1.0724
3°	0.0523	0.9986	0.0524	48°	0.7431	0.6691	1.1106
4°	0.0698	0.9976	0.0699	49°	0.7547	0.6561	1.1504
5°	0.0872	0.9962	0.0875	50°	0.7660	0.6428	1.1918
6°	0.1045	0.9945	0.1051	51°	0.7771	0.6293	1.2349
7°	0.1219	0.9925	0.1228	52°	0.7880	0.6157	1.2799
8°	0.1392	0.9903	0.1405	53°	0.7986	0.6018	1.3270
9°	0.1564	0.9877	0.1584	54°	0.8090	0.5878	1.3764
10°	0.1736	0.9848	0.1763	55°	0.8192	0.5736	1.4281
11°	0.1908	0.9816	0.1944	56°	0.8290	0.5592	1.4826
12°	0.2079	0.9781	0.2126	57°	0.8387	0.5446	1.5399
13°	0.2250	0.9744	0.2309	58°	0.8480	0.5299	1.6003
14°	0.2419	0.9703	0.2493	59°	0.8572	0.5150	1.6643
15°	0.2588	0.9659	0.2679	60°	0.8660	0.5000	1.7321
16°	0.2756	0.9613	0.2867	61°	0.8746	0.4848	1.8040
17°	0.2924	0.9563	0.3057	62°	0.8829	0.4695	1.8807
18°	0.3090	0.9511	0.3249	63°	0.8910	0.4540	1.9626
19°	0.3256	0.9455	0.3443	64°	0.8988	0.4384	2.0503
20°	0.3420	0.9397	0.3640	65°	0.9063	0.4226	2.1445
21°	0.3584	0.9336	0.3839	66°	0.9135	0.4067	2.2460
22°	0.3746	0.9272	0.4040	67°	0.9205	0.3907	2.3559
23°	0.3907	0.9205	0.4245	68°	0.9272	0.3746	2.4751
24°	0.4067	0.9135	0.4452	69°	0.9336	0.3584	2.6051
25°	0.4226	0.9063	0.4663	70°	0.9397	0.3420	2.7475
26°	0.4384	0.8988	0.4877	71°	0.9455	0.3256	2.9042
27°	0.4540	0.8910	0.5095	72°	0.9511	0.3090	3.0777
28°	0.4695	0.8829	0.5317	73°	0.9563	0.2924	3.2709
29°	0.4848	0.8746	0.5543	74°	0.9613	0.2756	3.4874
30°	0.5000	0.8660	0.5774	75°	0.9659	0.2588	3.7321
31°	0.5150	0.8572	0.6009	76°	0.9703	0.2419	4.0108
32°	0.5299	0.8480	0.6249	77°	0.9744	0.2250	4.3315
33°	0.5446	0.8387	0.6494	78°	0.9781	0.2079	4.7046
34°	0.5592	0.8290	0.6745	79°	0.9816	0.1908	5.1446
35°	0.5736	0.8192	0.7002	80°	0.9848	0.1736	5.6713
36°	0.5878	0.8090	0.7265	81°	0.9877	0.1564	6.3138
37°	0.6018	0.7986	0.7536	82°	0.9903	0.1392	7.1154
38°	0.6157	0.7880	0.7813	83°	0.9925	0.1219	8.1443
39°	0.6293	0.7771	0.8098	84°	0.9945	0.1045	9.5144
40°	0.6428	0.7660	0.8391	85°	0.9962	0.0872	11.4301
41°	0.6561	0.7547	0.8693	86°	0.9976	0.0698	14.3007
42°	0.6691	0.7431	0.9004	87°	0.9986	0.0523	19.0811
43°	0.6820	0.7314	0.9325	88°	0.9994	0.0349	28.6363
44°	0.6947	0.7193	0.9657	89°	0.9998	0.0175	57.2900
45°	0.7071	0.7071	1.0000	90°	1.0000	0.0000	

TABLE 3: Geometric Formulas

Rectangle
Area: $A = \ell w$
Perimeter: $P = 2\ell + 2w$

Parallelogram
Area: $A = bh$

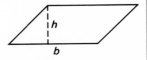

Square
Area: $A = s^2$
Perimeter: $P = 4s$

Trapezoid
Area: $A = \frac{1}{2}h(a + b)$

Triangle
Area: $A = \frac{1}{2}bh$
Sum of Angle Measures:
$A + B + C = 180°$

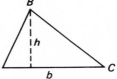

Circle
Area: $A = \pi r^2$
Circumference:
$C = \pi d = 2\pi r$

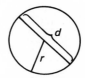

Right Triangle
Pythagorean Property:
$a^2 + b^2 = c^2$

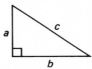

Rectangular Solid
Volume: $V = \ell wh$

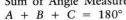

TABLE 4: Symbols

{ }	set braces	$\geq$	is greater than or equal to
$\cap$	the intersection of	$\{x \mid x > 1\}$	the set of all real numbers x
$\cup$	the union of		such that $x > 1$
$\subset$	is a subset of	$\sqrt{}$	principle square root
$\varnothing$	the empty set	$\approx$	is approximately equal to
b^n	nth power of b	$\pm$	plus or minus
$<$	is less than	π	pi, approximately 3.14
$>$	is greater than	$\triangle$	triangle
$\mid n \mid$	absolute value of n	$\angle$	angle
$-n$	additive inverse of n	$\sim$	is similar to
(x, y)	ordered pair	sin A	the sine of A
$f(x)$	f of x, the value of f at x	cos A	the cosine of A
$\leq$	is less than or equal to	tan A	the tangent of A

GLOSSARY

Absolute value   The absolute value of a number is its distance from 0 on the number line.

Addition method   A method of solving systems of equations in which the equations are added in order to eliminate a variable.

Addition Principle   For equations: If an equation $a = b$ is true, then $a + c = b + c$ is true for any number c. For inequalities: if any number is added on both sides of a true inequality we get another true inequality.

Additive identity   Zero is the additive identity for addition. When we add 0 to any number we get that same number.

Additive inverse   If the sum of two numbers is 0, they are additive inverses of each other.

Additive property of 0   Adding 0 to any number gives the same number.

Adjacent side   In a right triangle, the leg next to a given angle.

Algebraic expression   A symbol made up of variables, numerals, and operations signs.

Antecedent   *See* If, then statement.

Ascending order   A polynomial is in ascending order if the term with the smallest exponent (often the constant term) is first, the term with the next greatest exponent is second, and so on.

Associative laws   Addition: For any numbers a, b, and c, $a + (b + c) = (a + b) + c$. Multiplication: $(a \cdot b) \cdot c = a \cdot (b \cdot c)$.

Average   To average two numbers, find their sum and then divide by two.

Axiom   A property assumed or accepted without proof.

Base   In exponential notation n^x, n is the base.

Binomial   A polynomial with just two terms.

Coefficient   In any term, the coefficient is the number that is multiplied by the variable. In $-3x$, the coefficient is -3; in x^4 the coefficient is 1.

Common factor   A factor that is common to all the terms in an expression.

Commutative laws   Addition: For any numbers a and b, $a + b = b + a$. Multiplication: $a \cdot b = b \cdot a$.

Completing the square   Adding one or more terms to an expression to make it the square of a binomial.

Complex fractional expression   A fractional expression that has a fractional expression in its numerator, denominator or both.

Consecutive integers   Integers next to each other in counting order, such as 3 and 4.

Consequent   *See* If-then statement.

Constant term   A term with no variable.

Constant of variation   Whenever a situation gives rise to a relation $y = kx$ or $y = \frac{k}{x}$ where x and y are the variables, k is the constant of variation.

Coordinates   The numbers associated with a point on a number line or in a plane.

Cosine ratio   In a right triangle, the ratio of the length of the adjacent side to the length of the hypotenuse.

Degree   A unit used to measure angles. There are $90°$ in a right angle.

Degree   The degree of a term (monomial) is the sum of the exponents of the variables. The degree of a polynomial is the greatest degree of any of its terms.

Denominator   In $\frac{a}{b}$, b is the denominator.

Descending order   A polynomial is in descending order of exponents if the term with the largest exponent is first, the term with the next smaller exponent is second, and so on.

Difference of two squares   Any expression of the form $A^2 - B^2$.

Direct variation   A function that can be described by an equation $y = kx$, for some constant k.

Discriminant For a quadratic equation $ax^2 + bx + c = 0$, the expression $b^2 - 4ac$ is called the discriminant.

Distributive law The distributive law of multiplication over addition: For any numbers a, b, and c, $(a + b) \cdot c = a \cdot c + b \cdot c$.

Domain *See* Function.

Element (of a set) An object that belongs to a set.

Empty set The set with no members.

Equation A statement of equality between two expressions.

Equivalent expressions Expressions that represent the same number for all sensible replacements of the variables.

Evaluate an expression Replace each variable in the expression by a given value and simplify the result.

Even integer Any integer that has 2 as a factor.

Exponent In exponential notation n^x, x is the exponent.

Factor When two or more numbers (or expressions) are multiplied, each of the numbers is a factor of the product.

Factor To factor a number or expression means to express it as a product.

Fractional equation An equation containing at least one fractional expression.

Fractional expression A quotient of polynomials.

Function A correspondence or rule that assigns to each member of one set (called the *domain*) exactly one member of some set (called the *range*).

Graph The graph of an equation (or inequality) is the set of all points whose coordinates satisfy the equation or (inequality).

Greatest common factor The greatest integer that is a factor of two or more integers.

Half-plane If a straight line is drawn in a plane, the set of points on one side of the line is a half-plane.

Hypotenuse In a right triangle, the side opposite the right angle.

Identity An equation that is true for all sensible replacements of the variables.

If-then statement A conditional statement made up of two parts: If . . . , then . . . . The "if" part is called the *antecedent*. The "then" part is called the *consequent*.

Inequality A sentence formed by placing $>$, $<$, $\geq$, or $\leq$ between two expressions.

Infinite set An endless set.

Integer Any natural number, the additive inverse of a natural number, or zero.

Intercept In the graph of an equation in two variables, the point where the graph crosses an axis.

Intersection of sets The intersection of two sets is the set of all members that are common to both.

Inverse of a sum property The inverse of a sum is the sum of the inverses.

Inverse variation A function that can be described by an equation $y = \frac{k}{x}$, $k \neq 0$, and k is a constant.

Irrational number A number that cannot be named by fractional notation $\frac{a}{b}$, $b \neq 0$, where a and b are integers.

Least common denominator The smallest number that is a multiple of each denominator.

Legs In a right triangle, the two shorter sides.

Like terms Terms with exactly the same variables with exactly the same exponents.

Line of symmetry In any figure, an axis that divides the figure, so that if it is folded on the line of symmetry the two halves will match.

Linear equation   An equation in which the variables occur to the first power only.

Linear function   Any function that can be described by a linear equation.

Linear inequality   An inequality in which the variables occur to the first power only.

Monomial   A numeral or constant, a variable to some power, or a product of a numeral and a variable to a power.

Multiplication principle   For equations: If an equation $a = b$ is true, then $a \cdot c = b \cdot c$ is true for any number c. For inequalities: If we multiply on both sides of a true inequality by a positive number, we get another true inequality. If we multiply by a negative number, the inequality sign must be reversed to get another true inequality.

Multiplicative property of 0   The product of any number and 0 is 0.

Multiplicative identity   The number 1 is the multiplicative identity. For any number n, $n \cdot 1 = n$.

Multiplicative inverse   *See* Reciprocal.

Natural number   The numbers we use for counting. They are 1, 2, 3, 4 and so on.

Negative number   A number less than 0.

Nonrepeating decimal   Decimal notation that does not repeat endlessly.

Number of arithmetic   A number that can be named with fractional notation $\frac{a}{b}$, where a and b are whole numbers.

Numeral   A symbol we write to name a number.

Numerator   In $\frac{a}{b}$, a is the numerator.

Odd integer   Any integer that does not have 2 as a factor.

Opposite side   In a triangle, the side not adjacent to a given angle.

Ordered pair   A set of two elements in which the order is specified.

Parabola   The graph of the quadratic equation $ax^2 + bx + c = 0$, $a \neq 0$, is a parabola.

Parallel lines   Lines on the same plane that do not meet.

Perfect square   A number (or expression) that is the square of another number (or expression).

Perpendicular lines   Two lines that intersect to form right angles.

Plot a point   To mark the graph of an ordered pair on the coordinate plane.

Point-slope equation   A nonvertical line that contains a point (x_1, y_1) and has slope m has an equation $y - y_1 = m(x - x_1)$.

Polynomial   A sum of monomials.

Positive number   A number greater than zero.

Power   A number that can be named with exponential notation as n^x.

Prime number   An integer with exactly two different factors, itself and 1.

Principle square root   The nonnegative square root of a number.

Principle of squaring   If an equation $a = b$ is true, then the equation $a^2 = b^2$ is true.

Principle of zero products   A product is 0 if and only if at least one of the factors is 0. An equation with 0 on one side and with factors on the other can be solved by finding those numbers that make the factors 0.

Property of −1   Negative one times a number or expression is the additive inverse of that number or expression.

Proportion   An equality of ratios or rates. The numbers in a true proportion are said to be *proportional*.

Quadrant   One of the four regions into which the coordinate axes divide the plane.

Quadratic equation   An equation in which the term of highest degree has degree two.

Quadratic formula   A formula for finding the solutions of a quadratic equation $ax^2 + bx + c = 0$. The formula is
$$x = \frac{-b \pm \sqrt{b^2 - 4ac}}{2a}.$$

Quadratic function   Any function that can be described by a quadratic equation.

Quotient   The quotient $\frac{a}{b}$ is the number (if it exists) which when multiplied by b gives a.

Radical   The symbol $\sqrt{}$ is called a radical symbol. Any expression that contains a radical is called a *radical expression*.

Radicand   The expression under a radical.

Range   *See* Function.

Rate   A ratio of two different kinds of measures.

Ratio   The quotient of two numbers or measures of the same kind.

Rational number   Any number that can be expressed in the form $\frac{a}{b}$ where a and b are integers, $b \neq 0$.

Rationalizing the denominator   Simplifying a radical expression so that there are no radicals in the denominator and only whole numbers or variables in the radicand.

Real number   The real numbers consist of the rational numbers and the irrational numbers. There is a real number for each point of the number line.

Reciprocal   Two expressions are reciprocals if their product is 1. A reciprocal is also called a *multiplicative inverse*.

Relation   Any set of ordered pairs.

Repeating decimal   Decimal notation that repeats endlessly.

Replacement set   The set of all values that may replace the variables in a sentence.

Sensible replacement   Any value in a replacement that doesn't make a radicand negative or result in division by zero.

Set   A collection of numbers. Each number in the set is called an *element*.

Similar triangles   Similar triangles have the same shape, but not necessarily the same size.

Simplifying   Replacing an expression by a simpler expression.

Sine ratio   In a right triangle, the ratio of the length of the opposite side to the length of the hypotenuse.

Slope-intercept equation   A line with slope m and y-intercept b has an equation $y = mx + b$.

Slope of a line   A number that tells how steeply the line slants. The ratio of rise to run.

Solution   Any number that makes an equation or inequality true.

Solution set   The set of all replacements that make a sentence true.

Square root   The number c is a square root of a if $c^2 = a$.

Standard form   Standard form of a linear equation is $ax + by = c$. Standard form of a quadratic equation is $ax^2 + bx + c = 0$.

Statement   A sentence that is either true or false.

Substitute   To replace a variable with a number or expression.

Substitution method   A method of solving systems of equations in which one equation is solved for one of the variables and the result is substituted in the other equation.

System   A set of equations (or inequalities).

Tangent ratio   In a right triangle, the ratio of the length of the opposite side to the length of the adjacent side.

Term   In an expression or polynomial, the terms are separated by plus signs.

Theorem   A property that can be proved.

Trigonometric function   A function that uses one of the six trigonometric ratios to assign values to the measures of the acute angles of a right triangle.

Trigonometric ratio   The sine, cosine, or tangent ratio; or their reciprocals.

Trinomial square   The square of a binomial.

Union of sets   The union of two sets is the set of all members that are in either or both sets.

Value of a function   A member of the range of the function.

Variable   A letter (or other symbol) used to stand for one or several numbers.

Whole number   Any natural number or 0.

SELECTED ANSWERS

The following pages contain answers for all TRY THIS Exercises, odd-numbered Exercises, and odd-numbered Chapter Review Exercises.

Chapter 1

Section 1-1 TRY THIS

1. $8 **2.** $30 **3.** $21 **4.** 4 **5.** $\frac{14}{5}$ **6.** $7y$
7. $8 + x$ or $x + 8$ **8.** $x + 7$ **9.** $y - 9$

Exercise Set 1-1

1. 23, 28, 41, 52 **3.** 36 **5.** 42 **7.** 3 **9.** 1
11. 6 **13.** 2 **15.** $\frac{1}{2}$ **17.** 20 **19.** $b + 6$
21. $c - 9$ **23.** $q + 6$ **25.** $a + b$ **27.** $y - x$
29. $w + x$ **31.** $n - m$ **33.** $r + s$ **35.** $2x$ **37.** $5t$
39. $3b$ **41.** $m + 1$ **43.** $h - 43$ **45.** $y + 2x$
47. $2x - 3$ **49.** $b - 2$ **51.** lw **53.** 6 **55.** 6
57. 9 **59.** d **61.** $2v$ **63.** $n + 0.10n$

Section 1-2 TRY THIS

1. $9 + x$ **2.** qp **3.** $yx + t$, $t + xy$, or $t + yx$
4. $\frac{28}{20}$ **5.** $\frac{yz}{2xz}$ **6.** $\frac{2}{3}$ **7.** $\frac{8}{3}$ **8.** $\frac{8}{7}$ **9.** $\frac{1}{2}$ **10.** 4
11. $\frac{5y}{3}$ **12.** $\frac{1}{8n}$

Exercise Set 1-2

1. $8 + y$ **3.** nm **5.** $9 + yx$, $yx + 9$, $xy + 9$
7. $ba + c$, $c + ba$, $c + ab$ **9.** $\frac{40}{48}$ **11.** $\frac{600}{700}$
13. $\frac{st}{20t}$ **15.** $\frac{2}{5}$ **17.** $\frac{7}{2}$ **19.** $\frac{1}{7}$ **21.** 8 **23.** y
25. $\frac{1}{9y}$ **27.** $\frac{8}{3b}$ **29.** $\frac{p}{2}$ **31.** $\frac{9z}{19t}$ **33.** No
35. Yes **37.** Yes **39.** No **41.** $\frac{2}{3}$ **43.** $\frac{3sb}{2}$
45. $\frac{r}{g}$ **47.** No. ($12 \div 4$ does not equal $4 \div 12$)

Section 1-3 TRY THIS

1. $5 \cdot 5 \cdot 5 \cdot 5$ **2.** $x \cdot x \cdot x \cdot x \cdot x$ **3.** $5y \cdot 5y \cdot 5y \cdot 5y$
4. 9^3 **5.** y^5 **6.** $(4y)^3$ **7.** 100 **8.** 32 **9.** 0
10. 4 **11.** 1 **12.** 29 **13.** 40

Exercise Set 1-3

1. $2 \cdot 2 \cdot 2 \cdot 2$ **3.** $(1.4) \cdot (1.4) \cdot (1.4) \cdot (1.4)$
5. $n \cdot n \cdot n \cdot n \cdot n$ **7.** $7p \cdot 7p$ **9.** $19k \cdot 19k \cdot 19k \cdot 19k$
11. $10pq \cdot 10pq \cdot 10pq$ **13.** 10^6 **15.** x^7
17. $(3y)^4$ **19.** 27 **21.** 19 **23.** 256 **25.** 10^2
27. 5^2 **29.** 14 **31.** 225 **33.** 729; 81
35. 3375; 375 **37.** 1225; 245 **39.** 16,900; 3380
41. $(3a)^3 (2b)^2$ **43.** 9 **45.** 81

Section 1-4 TRY THIS

1. 11 **2.** 27 **3.** 6 **4.** 225 **5.** 75 **6.** 32

7. 512 **8.** 8 **9.** 36 **10.** 16 **11.** 4 **12.** 139
13. 120 **14.** $\frac{1}{5}$ **15.** 8 **16.** 63 **17.** 20 **18.** 72
19. $(a + b) + 2$ **20.** $(3 \cdot v) \cdot w$ **21.** $(4 \cdot t) \cdot u$,
$(t \cdot 4) \cdot u$, $u \cdot (4 \cdot t)$ **22.** $(r + 2) + s$, $(2 + r) + s$,
$s + (2 + r)$, $2 + (r + s)$

Exercise Set 1-4

1. 19 **3.** 86 **5.** 7 **7.** 6 **9.** 12 **11.** 324
13. 100 **15.** 512 **17.** 22 **19.** 1 **21.** 4
23. 60 **25.** 125 **27.** 96 **29.** 500 **31.** $\frac{11}{5}$
33. 3 **35.** $5 + (x + y)$ **37.** $6 \cdot (x \cdot y)$
39-45. Answers may vary. **39.** $3 + (x + y)$,
$3 + (y + x)$, $(x + 3) + y$ **41.** $(6 + x) + y$,
$(x + 6) + y$, $y + (6 + x)$ **43.** $a \cdot (b \cdot 5)$, $(a \cdot 5) \cdot b$,
$(b \cdot a) \cdot 5$ **45.** $(5 \cdot x) \cdot y$, $(x \cdot 5) \cdot y$, $y \cdot (x \cdot 5)$
47. Any number except 0 **49.** Any number except 2
51. $x^2 + 7$ **53.** $(x + 7)^2$ **55.** $\frac{x + 3}{x^2}$ **57.** $2(x - 1)$
59. Neither. $6 - (10 - 7) \neq (6 - 10) - 7$;
$10 \div (5 \div 5) \neq (10 \div 5) \div 5$

Section 1-5 TRY THIS

1a. 28 **1b.** 28 **2a.** 77 **2b.** 77 **3a.** 54 **3b.** 54
4. $5y + 15$ **5.** $4x + 4y + 4z$ **6.** $6x + 12y + 30$
7. $5(x + 2)$ **8.** $3(4 + x)$ **9.** $3(2x + 4 + 3y)$
10. $5(x + 2y + 1)$ **11.** $3(3x + y)$
12. $5(1 + 2x + 3y)$ **13.** $8y$ **14.** $11x + 8y$
15. $14p + 13q$ **16.** $8x^2$ **17.** $8x + 10y$
18. $9x + 10y$ **19.** $7s + 13w^2$

Exercise Set 1-5

1. $2b + 10$ **3.** $7 + 7t$ **5.** $3x + 3$ **7.** $4 + 4y$
9. $30x + 12$ **11.** $7x + 28 + 42y$ **13.** $2(x + 2)$
15. $5(6 + y)$ **17.** $7(2x + 3y)$ **19.** $5(x + 2 + 3y)$
21. $9(x + 3)$ **23.** $3(3x + y)$ **25.** $8(a + 2b + 8)$
27. $11(x + 4y + 11)$ **29.** $19a$ **31.** $11a$
33. $8x + 9z$ **35.** $7x + 15y^2$ **37.** $101a + 92$
39. $11a + 11b$ **41.** $14u^2 + 13t + 2$
43. $50 + 6t + 8y$ **45.** $1b$ or b **47.** $\frac{13}{4}y$ or $3\frac{1}{4}y$
49. $P(1 + rt)$ **51.** $\frac{3}{2}$ **53.** $6x + 6x^2 + 3x^3 = $
$3x(2 + 3x + x^2)$ **55.** $7x + 7xy + 7y = $
$7(x + xy + y)$ **57.** Answers may vary.

Section 1-6 TRY THIS

1. False **2.** True **3.** Neither **4.** Example: 1, 2,
or 3 **5.** 7 **6.** 6 **7.** 4 **8.** 5 **9.** 72 **10.** 4.9
11. $\frac{1}{5}$ **12.** 12 **13.** $\frac{25}{3}$ **14.** 4.5

Exercise Set 1-6

1. 15 **3.** 19 **5.** 9 **7.** 30 **9.** 20 **11.** 7
13. 17 **15.** 86 **17.** 377 **19.** 2818 **21.** 5.66

23. $\frac{5}{7}$ **25.** 6 **27.** $\frac{5}{4}$ **29.** 0.24 **31.** 3.1 **33.** 8.5
35. 18 **37.** $\frac{5}{4}$ **39.** $\frac{3}{25}$ **41.** 8 **43.** 8
45-47. Answers may vary. **45.** $3x = 2$ **47.** $12x = 0$

Section 1−7 TRY THIS

1. $x + 397 = 1821$; 1424 **2.** $16x = 496$; 31
3. $7x = 168$; 24 **4.** $755 = 637 + x$; 118
5. $1.16x = 14{,}500$; 12,500

Exercise Set 1−7

1. $60 + x = 112, x = 52$ **3.** $x + 29 = 171$,
$x = 142$ **5.** $7x = 2233, x = 319$ **7.** $42x = 2352$,
$x = 56$ **9.** $8 - x = 5, x = 3$ **11.** $x + 37 = 101$,
$x = 64$ **13.** $x + 48 = 115, x = 67$ **15.** $12x = 3.12, x = \$0.26$ **17.** $80x = 53{,}400, x = 667.5$
19. $2.5x = 16.6, x = 6.64$ **21.** $x + 13.5 = 78.3$,
$x = 64.8°C$ **23.** $391x = 150{,}000{,}000, x = 383{,}631.7$ km **25.** $59°F$ **27.** $36x = 3.14 + 6.13$;
$25.75¢$ **29.** $2.54x = 100$; 39.37 in.
31. $x + (x + 1) = 13$; \$7

Chapter 1 Review

1. 15 **3.** 5 **5.** $z - 8$ **7.** $x - 1$ **9.** ba **11.** $\frac{12}{30}$
13. $\frac{5}{12}$ **15.** $2m \cdot 2m \cdot 2m$ **17.** 9 **19.** 32
21. $(m \cdot 4) \cdot n$ **23.** Answers may vary.
25. $40x + 24y + 16$ **27.** $4(9x + 4 + y)$
29. $60x + 12b$ **31.** $\frac{1}{8}$ **33.** 26 **35.** $9x = 3033$,
$x = 337$

Chapter 2

Section 2−1 TRY THIS

1. $-12, 15$ **2.** $8, -5$ **3.** $-3, 128$ **4.** $>$ **5.** $>$
6. $<$ **7.** 17 **8.** 8 **9.** 14 **10.** 21

Exercise Set 2−1

1. $+5, -12$ **3.** $-17, +12$ **5.** $-1286, +29{,}028$
7. $+750, -125$ **9.** $+20, -150, +300$ **11.** $>$
13. $>$ **15.** $>$ **17.** $<$ **19.** $>$ **21.** $>$ **23.** 7
25. 11 **27.** 4 **29.** 325 **31.** 3 **33.** $-23, -17$,
$0, 4$ **35.** $20 > -25$ **37.** $+60 > +20$ **39.** In
either case, a lower number is better than a greater
one. **41.** $-1, 0, 1$ **43.** $<$ **45.** $=$ **47.** $<$
49. $=$ **51.** $-100, -5, 0, 1^7, |3|, \frac{14}{4}, 4, |-6|, 7^1$

Section 2−2 TRY THIS

1. Answers may vary. **6.** $>$ **7.** $>$ **8.** $<$ **9.** $<$
10-15. Answers may vary. **10.** $\frac{45}{10}$ **11.** $\frac{-3}{2}$
12. $\frac{-10}{1}$ **13.** $\frac{-143}{10}$ **14.** $\frac{0}{1}$ **15.** $\frac{-1}{100}$

Exercise Set 2−2

7. $<$ **9.** $>$ **11.** $>$ **13.** $<$ **15.** $\frac{-7}{1}$ **17.** $\frac{-3}{1}$
19. $\frac{-81}{10}$ **21.** $\frac{-5333}{1000}$ **23.** $\frac{-5}{6}$ **25.** $\frac{-68}{100}$ or $\frac{-17}{25}$
27. 3 **29.** $\frac{-1}{4}$ **31.** $\frac{-11}{18}, \frac{11}{18}$ **33.** no value
35. ~ 0.9 **39a.** 1 **39b.** $\frac{1}{9}$

Section 2−3 TRY THIS

1. -8 **2.** -5 **3.** -7.2 **4.** $-\frac{16}{5}$ **5.** -9 **6.** -6
7. -5 **8.** 0 **9.** 7 **10.** 1 **11.** -4 **12.** 0
13. -20 **14.** -25 **15.** 53 **16.** 13 **17.** -7
18. -23 **19.** 11 **20.** 2.3 **21.** -7.7 **22.** 0
23. -58 **24.** -56 **25.** -14 **26.** 19 **27.** -54
28. 0 **29.** 7.4 **30.** $\frac{8}{3}$ **31.** $-14, 14$ **32.** $-1, 1$
33. $19, -19$ **34.** $6, -6$ **35.** 34 meters

Exercise Set 2−3

1. -7 **3.** -4 **5.** 0 **7.** -8 **9.** -7 **11.** -27
13. 0 **15.** -42 **17.** -43 **19.** -2 **21.** 5
23. $\frac{-25}{7}$ **25.** -11 **27.** $\frac{7}{16}$ **29.** 39 **31.** 50
33. -1093 **35.** -24 **37.** 9 **39.** 26.9 **41.** -9
43. $\frac{14}{3}$ **45.** -0.101 **47.** -65 **49.** $\frac{5}{3}$
51. $+8$ yards **53.** 77,320 profit **55.** \$2.41
57. When x is negative **59.** Positive **61.** Positive
63. Minus 8, the additive inverse of 8, or negative 8
65. No value **67.** 21

Section 2−4 TRY THIS

1. -8 **2.** -6 **3.** -5 **4.** -9 **5.** -9 **6.** -5
7. -5 **8.** -9.7 **9.** -9.7 **10.** -5 **11.** 10
12. -21 **13.** 9 **14.** -5.2 **15.** -9 **16.** 21.6
17. $5x + 5$ **18.** $y - 500$ dollars

Exercise Set 2−4

1. -4 **3.** -7 **5.** -6 **7.** 0 **9.** 0 **11.** 14
13. 11 **15.** -14 **17.** 5 **19.** -7 **21.** -1
23. 18 **25.** -5 **27.** -49 **29.** -193 **31.** 500
33. -2.8 **35.** -3.53 **37.** $\frac{-1}{2}$ **39.** 0 **41.** $\frac{-41}{30}$
43. $\frac{-1}{156}$ **45.** 37 **47.** -62 **49.** -139 **51.** 6
53. $10x + 7$ **55.** $15x + 66$ **57.** $-\$330.54$
59. $y + \$215.50$ **61.** 116 m **63.** False. $3 - 0 \neq 0 - 3$ **65.** True **67.** True by definition
69. Both. Subtraction is the addition of an inverse.
71. $-[-(-5)] = -5, -\left\{-[-(-5)]\right\} = 5$. If the
number of signs is odd, the number is negative, if
even, the number is positive.

Section 2−5 TRY THIS

1. $20, 10, 0, -10, -20$ **2.** -18 **3.** -100
4. -90 **5.** $-\frac{3}{2}$ **6.** $-10, 0, 10, 20$ **7.** 20 **8.** 72

9. 12.6   **10.** $\frac{3}{56}$ **11.** -140 **12.** -90 **13.** 120
14. -6 **15.** No. $-800 + 900 \neq 0$ or $-900 + 800 \neq 0$

Exercise Set 2–5

1. -16 **3.** -42 **5.** -24 **7.** -72 **9.** 16
11. 42   **13.** -120 **15.** -238 **17.** 1200   **19.** 98
21. $\frac{-2}{45}$ **23.** 1911   **25.** 50.4   **27.** $\frac{10}{189}$ **29.** -960
31. 17.64   **33.** $\frac{5}{784}$ **35.** 0   **37.** No. $170(-7) +$
$150(8) \neq 0$ **39.** Yes   **41.** 72   **43.** -6 **45.** 1944
47. -32 **49.** 13   **51.** -79 **53.** If odd number of
factors, negative; if even, positive
55. Yes. $(-a)(-b) = (-1)(a)(-1)(b) = (-1)^2(ab) =$
$1ab = ab$ **57a.** $2(10) + 2(9) + 2(8) + 2(7) +$
$2(6) + 2(5) + 2(4) + 2(3) + 2(2) + 2(1) - 10x = 0$,
$10x = 110, x = 11$ lbs   **57b.** $20w = 110, w = 5.5$,
5.5 ft from the center

Section 2–6 TRY THIS

1. -5 **2.** -3 **3.** 4   **4.** $-\frac{13}{5}$ **5.** $-\frac{9}{4}$ **6.** 5
7. $-\frac{8}{9}$ **8.** Not possible   **9.** $\frac{6}{3}$ **10.** $\frac{1}{-4}$ **11.** $\frac{1}{-2.6}$
12. 2.3   **13.** $\frac{y}{x}$ **14.** $-6(5)$ **15.** $-5(\frac{1}{7})$
16. $(x^2 - 2)\frac{1}{3}$ **17.** $13(-\frac{3}{2})$ **18.** $-15x$
19. $\frac{-4}{7}(-\frac{5}{3})$ **20.** $a(\frac{1}{b})$ **21.** ab **22.** $\frac{11}{20}$
23. $\frac{-12}{5}$ **24.** -16.2 **25.** -26.2

Exercise Set 2–6

1. -6 **3.** -13 **5.** -2 **7.** 4   **9.** -8 **11.** 2
13. $\frac{-108}{9}$ **15.** -8 **17.** None   **19.** $\frac{-88}{9}$
21. $\frac{7}{15}$ **23.** $\frac{13}{47}$ **25.** $\frac{1}{13}$ **27.** $\frac{1}{4.3}$ **29.** 7.1
31. $\frac{q}{p}$ **33.** $4y$ **35.** $\frac{3b}{2a}$ **37.** $3(\frac{1}{19})$ **39.** $6(\frac{-1}{13})$
41. $13.9(\frac{-1}{1.5})$ **43.** $x \cdot y$ **45.** $\frac{1}{5}(3x + 4)$
47. $(5a - b)(\frac{1}{5a + b})$ **49.** $\frac{-9}{8}$ **51.** $\frac{5}{3}$ **53.** $\frac{9}{14}$
55. $\frac{9}{64}$ **57.** -2 **59.** $\frac{11}{13}$ **61.** -16.2 **63.** $\frac{69}{25}$
65. -8 **67.** $\frac{95}{77}$ **69.** 1   **71.** No, $\frac{4}{2} \neq \frac{2}{4}$
73. Yes, this is true for 1 and also for -1.   **75.** You
get the original number. The reciprocal of the reciprocal is the original number.

Section 2–7 TRY THIS

1. $8y - 56$ **2.** $\frac{5}{6}x - \frac{5}{6}y - \frac{35}{6}z$ **3.** $-5x + 15y -$
$40z$ **4.** $4(x - 2)$ **5.** $3(x - 2y - 5)$
6. $b(x - y + z)$ **7.** $-2(y - 4z + 1)$
8. $4(3z - 4x - 1)$ **9.** $5a, -4b, 3$ **10.** $-5y, -3x, 5z$

11. $3x$ **12.** $6y$ **13.** $0.59m$ **14.** $3x + 3y$
15. $-4x - 5y - 14$

Exercise Set 2–7

1. 7   **3.** 12   **5.** -12.71 **7.** $7x - 14$
9. $-7y + 14$ **11.** $45x + 54y - 72$ **13.** $-4x +$
$12y + 8z$ **15.** $-3.72x + 9.92y - 3.41$
17. $8(x - 3)$ **19.** $8(4 - y)$ **21.** $2(4x + 5y - 11)$
23. $a(x - 7)$ **25.** $a(x - y + z)$ **27.** $4x, 3z$
29. $7x, 8y, -9z$ **31.** $12x, -13.2y, \frac{5}{8}z, -4.5$
33. $8x$ **35.** $5n$ **37.** $4x + 2y$ **39.** $7x + y$
41. $0.8x + 0.5y$ **43.** $\frac{3}{5}x + \frac{3}{5}y$ **45.** $8(x - y)$
47. $3(a + b) - 7a$ or $3b - 4a$ **49.** $2500(x + y)$
51. $5420(41\frac{1}{8} - 37\frac{3}{4})$ or $5420(41\frac{1}{8}) - 5420(37\frac{3}{4})$
Her loss is $18,292.50.

Section 2–8 TRY THIS

1. $-x - 2$ **2.** $-5x - 2y - 8$ **3.** $-6 + t$
4. $4a - 3t + 10$ **5.** $-18 + m + 2n + 4t$
6. $2x - 9$ **7.** $8x - 4y + 4$ **8.** $-9x - 8y$
9. $-16a + 18$ **10.** -1 **11.** 4   **12.** $2x - y + 4$

Exercise Set 2–8

1. $-2x - 7$ **3.** $-5x + 8$ **5.** $-4a + 3b - 7c$
7. $-6x + 8y - 5$ **9.** $-3x + 5y + 6$
11. $8x + 6y + 43$ **13.** $5x - 3$ **15.** $-3a + 9$
17. $5x - 6$ **19.** $-19x + 2y$ **21.** $9y - 25z$ **23.** 7
25. -40 **27.** 19   **29.** $12x + 30$ **31.** $3x + 30$
33. $9x - 18$ **35.** $6y - (-2x + 3a - c)$
37. $6m - (-3n + 5m - 4b)$ **39.** $-4z$ **41.** $x - 3$

Section 2–9 TRY THIS

1. 64%   **2.** $16\frac{2}{3}$%   **3.** 225   **4.** 50   **5.** Let $x =$
the former price. Former price + increase = new
price, $x + 0.12x = 20,608$, $1.12x = 20,608$, $x =$
18,400. Check: 12% of 18,400 is 2208. 18,400 plus
2208 is 20,608.

Exercise Set 2–9

1. 25   **3.** 24   **5.** 150   **7.** 2.5   **9.** 546   **11.** 125
13. 0.8   **15.** 5   **17.** 86.4%   **19.** $800   **21.** 36,
436   **23.** 7200   **25.** 26%   **27.** 90%   **29.** 12
31. 345% or 3.45   **33.** 2.5%
35. $(16.41)(1.06)(1.15) = \$20.00$ **37.** 40%, 70%,
95%   **39.** 125% of $8800 = 11,000$.
$\frac{11,000 - 8800}{11,000} = \frac{2200}{11,000} = 20\%$ **41.** 40%. Successive 20% discounts means you pay 80% of 80%, or
64%, which is only a 36% discount.
43a. $\frac{100\%}{\frac{4}{10}\%} = 250$ **43b.** $\frac{90\%}{\frac{4}{10}\%} = 225$ and Big Louie,
or 226 people.   **45.** 0.0000006%   **47.** Seven.
$(0.9)^7 = 47.8\%$

Section 2−10 TRY THIS

1. Comm. for add.   **2.** Add. inverses, add. prop. of zero   **3.** Asso. law for add., comm. law for add.
4. Distributive law   **5.** Add. prop. of zero, comm. law for add.   **6.** Asso. law for add., reciprocals, add. inverses   **7.** Prop. of 1, distrib., add. inverses
8. Reflexive   **9.** Transitive   **10.** Symmetric
11. 2. Distributive law, 3. Distributive law
12. 4. Distributive law, 6. Multiplicative prop. of 1, 7. Additive inverses

Exercise Set 2−10

1. Comm. of add.   **3.** Distrib.   **5.** Add. inv., add. prop. of zero   **7.** Add. inv.   **9.** Asso. of mult.
11. Distrib.   **13.** Axiom of reciprocals
15. Reflexive   **17.** Comm. of mult.   **19.** 1. Property of zero, 3. Asso. law of addition, 5. Distributive law, 7. Mult. property of zero, 8. Add. property of zero   **21.** No. $1 + 3 = 4$; 4 is not in the set of odd whole numbers.   **23.** Yes   **25.** $-(a - b) = -[a + (-b)]$, Subtr. rule; $-[a + (-b)] = -a + -(-b)$, Inverse of a sum; $-a + -(-b) = -a + b$, Mult.; $-a + b = b + (-a)$, Comm., add.; $b + (-a) = b - a$, Subtr. rule.

Chapter 2 Review

1. $-45, 72$ **3.** $>$ **5.** 91   **9.** $<$ **11.** 3.5
13. -5 **15.** $\frac{3}{4}$ **17.** 5   **19.** 4   **21.** -7.9 **23.** 8
25. $11y - 16$ **27.** 54   **29.** $-\frac{2}{7}$ **31.** $\frac{8}{3}$ **33.** $\frac{2y}{x}$
35. -3 **37.** $15x - 35$ **39.** $4x + 15$ **41.** $2(x - 7)$
43. $5(x + 2)$ **45.** $7a - 3b$ **47.** $5x - y$
49. $3a + 9$ **51.** $-2b + 21$ **53.** 6   **55.** 250
57. Distributive law

Chapter 3

Section 3−1 TRY THIS

1. -5 **2.** -11 **3.** 9   **4.** 6   **5.** 13.2   **6.** -10
7. Let x = amount of old rental cost. Amount of old rental cost increased by \$32 = \$475, $x + 32 = 475$, $x = 443$. Check: \$443 plus \$32 increase is \$475.

Exercise Set 3−1

1. 4   **3.** 11   **5.** -14 **7.** -18 **9.** 15   **11.** -14
13. 2   **15.** 20   **17.** -6 **19.** $\frac{7}{3}$ **21.** $\frac{-21}{12}$
23. $\frac{41}{24}$ **25.** $\frac{-1}{20}$ **27.** 5.1   **29.** 12.4   **31.** 51
33. 58   **35.** 2,952,515   **37.** -10 **39.** Any value
41. $x = 1 - c - a$ **43.** 13 or -13 **45.** Subtraction is addition of inverses.   **47.** $\frac{-5}{17}$

Section 3−2 TRY THIS

1. 5   **2.** $-\frac{7}{4}$ **3.** 14   **4.** -6 **5.** -50 **6.** -12
7. $-\frac{5}{4}$ **8.** Let x = cost of 1 bottle. Cost of 1 bottle times 12 bottles = \$6.72, $x \cdot 12 = 6.72$, $12x = 6.72$, $x = 0.56$. Check: $\$0.56 \times 12 = \$6.72$.

Exercise Set 3−2

1. 6   **3.** 9   **5.** 12   **7.** -40 **9.** 1   **11.** -7
13. -6 **15.** 6   **17.** -63 **19.** 36   **21.** -21
23. $\frac{-3}{5}$ **25.** $\frac{3}{2}$ **27.** $\frac{9}{2}$ **29.** 7   **31.** -7 **33.** 8
35. 15.9   **37.** -56 **39.** \$42.50   **41.** 670 mi/h
43. 2900   **45.** 2956   **47.** 267   **49.** 237.5
51. 286   **53.** 5   **55.** $\frac{a^2 + 1}{c}$ **57.** Any value
59. $x = 3$ or -3 **61.** Division is multiplication of reciprocals.

Section 3−3 TRY THIS

1. 5   **2.** -4 **3.** 13   **4.** -1 **5.** 3   **6.** 4   **7.** 1
8. 2   **9.** 2   **10.** 9   **11.** Let x = a number. 3 times a number minus 5 is 10, $3 \cdot x - 5 = 10$, $3x - 5 = 10$, $3x = 15$, $x = 5$.

Exercise Set 3−3

1. 5   **3.** 8   **5.** 10   **7.** 14   **9.** -8 **11.** -8
13. -7 **15.** 15   **17.** 24   **19.** 6   **21.** 4   **23.** 6
25. 5   **27.** -3 **29.** 1   **31.** -20 **33.** 6   **35.** 7
37. 7   **39.** 2   **41.** 5   **43.** 2   **45.** 10   **47.** 4
49. 4 m, 2 m   **51.** .19   **53.** -10 **55.** 40
57. 30 m, 90 m, 360 m   **59.** 3.5   **61.** -2
63. x = cost of game, $3x + 2x + 2(0.75) = 9$, \$1.50
65. $x = 3$, $y = -5$ **67.** $x = 0.13$, $y = -0.324$
69. Amazon 6437, Nile 6671   **71.** They can do $\frac{1}{3} + \frac{1}{6} = \frac{1}{2}$ the job in one day, or the entire job in 2 days.

Section 3−4 TRY THIS

1. 2   **2.** 3   **3.** -2 **4.** $-\frac{1}{2}$ **5.** 2   **6.** -4.3
7. Let x = even integer. Then $x + 2$ = next even integer. An even integer + twice next even integer = 40, $x + 2(x + 2) = 40$, $x + 2x + 4 = 40$, $3x = 36$, $x = 12$, $x + 2 = 14$. Check: The sum of 12 and twice 14 is 40.   **8.** Let x = the number (no.). $\frac{1}{6}$ of the no. $+ \frac{1}{4}$ of the no. $= \frac{1}{2}$ of the no. $- 3$, $\frac{1}{6} \cdot x + \frac{1}{4} \cdot x = \frac{1}{2} \cdot x - 3$, $12(\frac{1}{6}x + \frac{1}{4}x) = 12(\frac{1}{2}x - 3)$, $2x + 3x = 6x - 36$, $x = 36$.

Exercise Set 3−4

1. 6   **3.** 2   **5.** 6   **7.** 8   **9.** 4   **11.** 1   **13.** 17
15. -8 **17.** -3 **19.** -3 **21.** 2   **23.** 5   **25.** -1
27. $\frac{-4}{3}$ **29.** $\frac{2}{5}$ **31.** -2 **33.** -4 **35.** 0.8   **37.** 3
39. 28   **41.** 4   **43.** 37, 39   **45.** 56, 58   **47.** 35,

36, 37   **49.** 61, 63, 65   **51.** 30, 45   **53.** 65, 90
55. 27, 49   **57.** 22.5°   **59.** 28°, 84°, 68°
61. 17.5   **63.** $\frac{24}{19}$ **65.** $\frac{10}{7}$ **67.** 6   **69.** $\frac{1}{3}$

Section 3−5 TRY THIS

1. Let x = original amount. Original amount + interest = \$8287.50, $x + 0.105x = 8287.50$, $1.105x = 8287.50$, $x = 7500$.   **2.** Let m = no. of miles. \$19.95 + 0.18 times no. of miles = \$50, $19.95 + 0.18 \cdot m = 50$, $0.18m = 30.05$, $m = 166.94$.   **3.** Let x = marked price. Marked price − reduction = \$8050, $x − 0.3x = 8050$, $0.7x = 8050$, $x = 11,500$. Check: 30% of \$11,500 is \$3450. \$11,500 minus \$3450 is \$8050.

Exercise Set 3−5

1. \$5600   **3.** 252.9 mi   **5.** \$16   **7.** 3.6 billion
9. 10   **11.** $4s + 7 = 1863 − 1776$, $s = 20$ **13.** 19¢
15. 12 cm, 9 cm   **17.** 30   **19.** 7.5%   **21.** 5 half dollars, 10 quarters, 20 dimes, 60 nickels

Section 3−6 TRY THIS

1. $I = \frac{E}{R}$ **2.** $d = \frac{C}{\pi}$ **3.** $c = 4A − a − b − d$
4. $n = \frac{y}{r}$

Exercise Set 3−6

1. $\frac{A}{h}$ **3.** $\frac{d}{t}$ **5.** $\frac{I}{rt}$ **7.** $\frac{F}{m}$ **9.** $\frac{P − 2l}{2}$ **11.** $\frac{A}{\pi}$
13. $\frac{2A}{h}$ **15.** $\frac{E}{c^2}$ **17.** $3A − a − c$ **19.** $\frac{3k}{v}$
21. $\frac{2.5H}{N}$ **23.** $\frac{360A}{\pi r^2}$ **25.** $\frac{5}{9}(F − 32)$ **27.** $\frac{c − b}{a}$
29. $\frac{1}{A}$ **31.** $\frac{b}{d}$ **33.** $\frac{9}{20} − 2n$ **35.** $\frac{y}{1 − b}$
37. $\frac{1}{d} − e$ **39.** $\frac{m − ax^2 − c}{x}$ **41.** Yes

Section 3−7 TRY THIS

1. 20   **2.** $\frac{5}{2}$ **3.** $\frac{14}{3}$ **4.** 250 km

Exercise Set 3−7

1. 1   **3.** $\frac{27}{2}$ **5.** $\frac{18}{5}$ **7.** 25   **9.** $\frac{5}{2}$ **11.** $\frac{55}{9}$ **13.** 40
15. $\frac{4}{15}$ min   **17.** $\frac{1}{60}$ min, or 1 sec   **19.** $\frac{45}{4} = \frac{x}{1}$, $x =$
$11\frac{3}{4}$ oz   **21.** $4\frac{2}{7}$, $4\frac{3}{7}$, $52\frac{1}{7}$, $52\frac{2}{7}$

Section 3−8 TRY THIS

1. 1. $3x + 5 = 20$, Hypothesis; 2. $3x = 15$, Add. prin.; 3. $x = 5$, Mult. prin.; 4. If $3x + 5 = 20$, then $x = 5$, Statements 1-3.   **2.** If $x = 10$, then $3x + 7 = 37$.   **3.** If $x > 12$, then $x > 15$.   **4.** Prove: If $x = 5$, then $3x + 5 = 20$, 1. $x = 5$, Hypothesis; 2. $3x = 15$, Mult.

prin.; 3. $3x + 5 = 20$, Add. prin.; 4. If $x = 5$, then $3x + 5 = 20$, Statements 1-3.   **5a.** 1. $6y − 12 = 30$, Hypothesis; 2. $6y = 42$, Add. prin.; 3. $y = 7$, Mult. prin.; 4. If $6y − 12 = 30$, then $y = 7$, Statements 1-3.
5b. 1. $y = 7$, Hypothesis; 2. $6y = 42$, Mult. prin.; 3. $6y − 12 = 30$, Add. prin.; 4. If $y = 7$, then $6y − 12 = 30$, Statements 1-3.   **6a.** 1. $8x + 17 = 81$, Hypothesis; 2. $8x = 64$, Add. prin.; 3. $x = 8$, Mult. prin.; 4. If $8x + 17 = 81$, then $x = 8$, Statements 1-3.
6b. $8(8) + 17 = 64 + 17 = 81$

Exercise Set 3−8

1. 1. $8x − 12 = 68$, Hypothesis; 2. $8x = 80$, Add. prin.; 3. $x = 10$, Mult. prin.; 4. If $8x − 12 = 68$, then $x = 10$, Statements 1-3.   **3.** 1. $\frac{x}{2} + 3 = 15$, Hypothesis; 2. $\frac{x}{2} = 12$, Add. prin.; 3. $x = 24$, Mult. prin.; 4. If $\frac{x}{2} + 3 = 15$, then $x = 12$, Statements 1-3.
5. If $x = 6$, then $x + 3 = 9$.   **7.** If schools are closed, then it is snowing.   **9.** 1. $x = 10$, Hypothesis; 2. $8x = 80$, Mult. prin.; 3. $8x − 12 = 68$, Add. prin.; 4. If $x = 10$, then $8x − 12 = 68$, Statements 1-3.

11. 1. $x = 24$, Hypothesis; 2. $\frac{x}{2} = 12$, Mult. prin.; 3. $\frac{x}{2} + 3 = 15$, Add. prin.; 4. If $x = 24$, then $\frac{x}{2} + 3 = 15$, Statements 1-3.   **13.** $(x = 3)$ **15.** $(m = 11)$
17. $(x = 16)$ **19.** $(y = 7)$ **21.** $(m = −18)$
23. $(x = 4)$ **25.** a is $−b$ **27.** Any a between $−3$ and 0   **29.** $x = 1$, Hypothesis, $x \cdot x = 1 \cdot x$, Mult. prin., $x \cdot x = x$, Prop. of 1; if $x = 0$, $x \cdot x = x$ is true but $0 = 1$ is false.

Chapter 3 Review

1. $−22$ **3.** 1   **5.** 7   **7.** $−192$ **9.** $−5$ **11.** 4
13. 3 m, 5 m   **15.** 6   **17.** 12   **19.** 57, 59
21. \$220   **23.** $h = \frac{3V}{B}$ **25.** $A = \frac{3V}{r}$ **27.** 702 km

Chapter 4

Section 4−1 TRY THIS

1. y^5 **2.** $(4y)^7$ **3.** a^{15} **4.** 7^9 **5.** $\frac{1}{x^8}$ **6.** 1
7. $\frac{1}{y^4}$ **8.** 5^{54} **9.** n^{24} **10.** $256y^{12}$
11. $243x^{20}y^{35}z^{30}$ **12.** $49x^{18}y^{12}$ **13.** $−y^{45}$

Exercise Set 4−1

1. 2^7 **3.** 8^{14} **5.** x^7 **7.** 9^{38} **9.** $(3y)^{12}$
11. $(7y)^{17}$ **13.** 7^3 **15.** 8^6 **17.** y^4 **19.** $\frac{1}{16^6}$
21. $\frac{1}{m^6}$ **23.** $\frac{1}{(8x)^4}$ **25.** $18^0 = 1$ **27.** 1   **29.** 3^{12}

31. 6^{72} 33. x^{60} 35. n^{105} 37. $25a^{10}$
39. $81x^{20}y^{36}z^{12}$ 41. x^{200} 43. $(2^2)^3 \cdot 2^3 \cdot 2^4 = 2^{13}$ 45. No, $(5y)^0 = 1$ and $5(y)^0 = 5$. 47. $\frac{1}{5}$
49. 3^{11} 51. 1 53. $\frac{1}{\frac{1}{2}}$ or 2 55. $3^{0-2} = \frac{3^0}{3^2} = \frac{1}{3^2}$
57. No, $(a^b)^c = a^{(bc)}$, $b \cdot c \neq b^c$. 59. 9^2 or 81

Section 4-2 TRY THIS

1. $5y^6, 8y^4, 9y^5, 12, 6y$ 2. $-6x^3, 5x^5, -2x^3, -103$
3. monomial 4. none 5. binomial 6. trinomial
7. $-10x^3 + 2x - 24$ 8. $6x^2 - x - 7$ 9. $x^3 + 3x^2 - 1$ 10. $-\frac{1}{4}x^5 + 2x^2$ 11. 4, 2, 1, 0; 4
12. 5, 3, 1, 0; 5 13. 5, -6, 1, -1, -4

Exercise Set 4-2

1. $5x^3, -6x, -3$ 3. $-2, -3y, 7y^2, -3y^3$ 5. binomial 7. none 9. binomial 11. $-8x$ 13. $-x^2$
15. $11x^3 + 4$ 17. $4x^4 + 5$ 19. $-9x^4 + 5$
21. $6x^2 - 3x$ 23. $\frac{1}{6}x^3 + 2x + 4$ 25. $-x^3$ 27. 1, 0; 1 29. 2, 1, 0; 2 31. 4, 2, 1, 0; 4 33. 1, 2, 0, 3; 3 35. 2, -4 37. 3, -5, 2 39. 5, 1, -1, 2
41. 7, -4, -4, 5 43. Answers may vary, ex. $\frac{1}{2}y^4 + \frac{3}{5}y - 2$ 45. Three ax^4 terms 47. $5x^9 + 4x^8 + x^2 + 5x$ 49. not a monomial; $\frac{5}{y}$ not a monomial; $\sqrt{x}$ not a monomial; $\frac{y^2+3}{y} = y + \frac{3}{y}$, $\frac{3}{y}$ not a monomial 51. $n(n+2) - 3 = n^2 + 2n - 3$

Section 4-3 TRY THIS

1. $6x^7 + 3x^5 - 2x^4 + 4x^3 + 5x^2 + x$ 2. $7x^5 - 5x^4 + 2x^3 + 4x^2 - 3$ 3. $-14t^7 - 10t^3 + 7t^2 - 14$
4. $-2x^2 - 3x + 2$ 5. $10x^4 - 7x - 5.5$ 6. first degree term 7. third, second, first degree, and constant term 8. second, first degree term 9. third degree term 10. -19 11. -14 12. -13
13. $2(-4)^2 + 5(-4) - 4 = 32 - 20 - 4 = 8$
14. $0.005(55)^2 - 0.35(55) + 28 = 0.005(3025) - 19.25 + 28 = 15.125 - 19.25 + 28 = 23.875$. The cost is 23.875¢ per mile.

Exercise Set 4-3

1. $x^5 + 6x^3 + 2x^2 + x + 1$ 3. $15x^9 + 7x^8 + 5x^3 - x^2 + x$ 5. $-5y^8 - y^7 + 9y^6 + 8y^3 - 7y^2$ 7. $x^6 + x^4$ 9. $13x^3 - 9x + 8$ 11. $-5x^2 + 9x$
13. $12x^4 - 2x + \frac{1}{4}$ 15. 2nd, 1st degree terms
17. 3rd, 2nd degree, constant 19. no missing terms
21. -18 23. 19 25. -12 27. 2 29. 4
31. 11 33. 448.6 35. $x^2 - 16$ 37. 99, 1; 50, 50; 99, 1 39. 384, 225, 25

Section 4-4 TRY THIS

1. $x^2 + 7x + 3$ 2. $24x^4 + 5x^3 + x^2 + 1$ 3. $2x^2 - 7x - 1$ 4. $8x^3 - 2x^2 - 8x - 3.5$ 5. $-8x^4 + 4x^3 - 10x^2 + 5x - 16$ 6. $-2x^3 + 2x^2 - 7x + 3$
7. $8 \cdot 16 + 8 \cdot 8 + 8 \cdot 4 = 224$ 8. $x \cdot 2x + x \cdot x + x \cdot \frac{1}{2}x = 2x^2 + x^2 + \frac{1}{2}x^2 = 3\frac{1}{2}x^2$ 9. $3\frac{1}{2}(8)^2 = 3\frac{1}{2} \cdot 64 = 224$

Exercise Set 4-4

1. $-x + 5$ 3. $x^2 - 5x - 1$ 5. $3x^5 + 13x^2 + 6x - 3$ 7. $-4x^4 + 6x^3 + 6x^2 + 2x + 4$ 9. $12x^2 + 6$
11. $5x^4 - 2x^3 - 7x^2 - 5x$ 13. $9x^8 + 8x^7 - 3x^4 + 2x^2 - 2x + 5$ 15. $-\frac{1}{2}x^4 + \frac{2}{3}x^3 + x^2$
17. $0.01x^5 + x^4 - 0.2x^3 + 0.2x + 0.06$
19. $-3x^4 + 3x^2 + 4x$ 21. $3x^5 - 3x^3 + x^2 + 3x$ 23. $5x^3 - 9x^2 + 4x - 7$ 25. $\frac{1}{4}x^4 - \frac{1}{4}x^3 + \frac{3}{2}x^2 + 6\frac{3}{4}x + 1$ 27. $-x^4 + 3x^3 - 6x^2 + 2x + 1$
29. $x^4 + 4x^2 + 12x - 1$ 31. $x^5 - 6x^4 + 4x^3 - x^2 + 1$ 33. 0 35. $3x^5 + x^4 + 10x^3 + x^2 + 3x - 6$
37a. $3x^2 + x^2 + x^2 + 4x = 5x^2 + 4x$ 37b. 57, 352
39. $x + (x + 5) + (x + 10) - 3(2) = 69, x = 20$, $x + 5 = 25, x + 10 = 30$ 41. $25 + 65 + 45 + 117 = 252$ 43. $20 + 5(m - 4) + 4(m - 5) + (m - 4)(m - 5) = m^2$ 45. $(ax + b) + (cx + d) = (a + c)x + (b + d); (cx + d) + (ax + b) = (c + a)x + (d + b)$. Both equal $ax + cx + b + d$.
47. $(a_nx^n + a_{n-1}x^{n-1} + \cdots + a_1x + a_0) + (b_nx^n + b_{n-1}x^{n-1} + \cdots + b_1x + b_0) = (a_n + b_n)x^n + (a_{n-1} + b_{n-1})x^{n-1} + \cdots + (a_1 + b_1)x + (a_0 + b_0)$

Section 4-5 TRY THIS

1. $-12x^4 + 3x^2 - 4x$ 2. $13x^6 - 2x^4 + 3x^2 - x + \frac{5}{13}$ 3. $-4x^3 + 6x - 3$ 4. $5x^4 + 3x^2 - 7x + 5$
5. $3x^2 + 5$ 6. $-5x^3 + 2x + 8$ 7. $4x^3 - 14x^2 + 7x + 2$ 8. $-8x^4 - 5x^3 + 8x^2 - 1$ 9. $x^3 - x^2 - \frac{4}{3}x - 1$ 10. $2x^3 + 5x^2 - 2x - 5$ 11. $-x^5 - 2x^3 + 3x^2 - 2x + 2$

Exercise Set 4-5

1. $5x$ 3. $x^2 - 10x + 2$ 5. $-12x^4 + 3x^3 - 3$
7. $-3x + 7$ 9. $-4x^2 + 3x - 2$ 11. $4x^4 + 6x^2 - \frac{3}{4}x + 8$ 13. $2x^2 + 14$ 15. $-2x^5 - 6x^4 + x + 2$
17. $9x^2 + 9x - 8$ 19. $\frac{3}{4}x^3 - \frac{1}{2}x$ 21. $0.06x^3 - 0.05x^2 + 0.01x + 1$ 23. $3x + 6$ 25. $4x^3 - 3x^2 + x + 1$ 27. $11x^4 + 12x^3 - 9x^2 - 8x$ 29. $-4x^5 + 9x^4 + 6x^2 + 16x + 6$ 31. $x^4 - x^3 + x^2 - x$

35. $11a^2 - 18a - 4$ 37. $-10y^2 -$
9. $-3y^4 - y^3 + 5y - 2$ 41. $m^2 -$
$- 28$ 43. $y^2 - 2(y - 2) - 2(y - 2) -$
$- 4y + 4$ 45a. A zero polynomial, or 0
ach term, the coefficients are real numbers;
n of real numbers is not commutative, so
$a_n x^n - b_n x^n = (a_n - b_n)x^n$ which $\neq (b_n - a_n)x^n$.
45c. No, $a_n - (b_n - c_n) = a_n - b_n + c_n$ and
$(a_n - b_n) - c_n = a_n - b_n - c_n$.

Section 4 – 6 TRY THIS

1. $-15x$ 2. $-x^2$ 3. x^2 4. $-x^5$ 5. $12x^7$
6. $-8x^{11}$ 7. $7y^5$ 8. 0   9. $8x^2 + 16x$
10. $-15x^5 + 6x^3 - 21x^2$ 11. $40t^5 - 15t^4 +$
$20t^3 - 45t^2 - 55t$ 12. $8x^3 - 12x^2 + 16x$
13. $10y^6 - 8y^5 - 10y^4 + 16y^3$ 14. $x^2 - 3x - 40$
15. $x^2 - 9x + 20$ 16. $5x^2 - 17x - 12$
17. $6y^2 - 19y + 15$

Exercise Set 4 – 6

1. $42x^2$ 3. x^4 5. $-x^8$ 7. $6x^6$ 9. $28t^8$
11. $0.02x^{10}$ 13. $\frac{1}{15}x^4$ 15. 0   17. $8x^2 - 12x$
19. $-10x^3 + 5x^2$ 21. $-4x^4 + 4x^3$ 23. $4y^7 -$
$24y^6$ 25. $20x^{38} - 50x^{25} + 25x^{14}$ 27. $-66y^{108} +$
$42y^{58} - 66y^{49} + 360y^{12} - 54y^8$ 29. $x^2 + 7x + 10$
31. $x^2 + 4x - 12$ 33. $x^2 - 10x + 21$ 35. $x^2 -$
36 37. $2x^2 + 12x + 18$ 39. $9x^2 - 24x + 16$
41. $4y^2 - 1$ 43. $x^2 + \frac{17}{6}x + 2$ 45. $a^2 - 2ab + b^2$
47. $25y^2 + 60y + 36$ 49. $84t^2 + 32t - (6t^2 - 8t) =$
$78t^2 + 40t$ 51a. $2x^2 + 18x + 36$ 51b. 0
53a. $2x^2 + 4x - 30$ 53b. 0   55. 3   57. 0

Section 4 – 7 TRY THIS

1. $x^4 + 3x^3 + x^2 + 15x - 20$ 2. $6x^5 - 6x^4 + x^3 +$
$14x^2 - 35x$ 3. $3x^4 + 13x^3 - 3x^2 + 18x + 4$
4. $20x^4 - 21x^3 + 36x^2 - 30x - 16$ 5. $8x^5 +$
$4x^4 - 20x^3 - 16x^2 + 7x + 10$ 6. $3x^7 - 3x^6 -$
$4x^5 + 10x^4 - 5x^3 - 3x^2 - 10$

Exercise Set 4 – 7

1. $x^3 - 1$ 3. $4x^3 + 14x^2 + 8x + 1$ 5. $3y^4 -$
$6y^3 - 7y^2 + 18y - 6$ 7. $x^6 + 2x^5 - x^3$
9. $-10x^5 - 9x^4 + 7x^3 + 2x^2 - x$ 11. $x^4 - x^2 -$
$2x - 1$ 13. $4x^4 + 8x^3 - 9x^2 - 10x + 8$ 15. $6t^4 +$
$t^3 - 16t^2 - 7t + 4$ 17. $-4x^4 + 6x^3 - 2x^2 - 13x +$
10 19. $x^9 - x^5 + 2x^3 - x$ 21. $x^4 - 1$ 23. $x^4 -$
$2x^3 - 4x^2 + 9$ 25. $x^3 + 3x^2y + 3xy^2 + y^3$
27. Coefficients are from Pascal's triangle. $x^5 +$
$5x^4y + 10x^3y^2 + 10x^2y^3 + 5xy^4 + y^5$ 29. $x^4 +$

$+ x^3 + x^2 + x + 1$ 31. $x^5 + x^4 + x^3 + x^2 + x + 1$
33. $dc + be = 1$; $(ax^2 + 5x + 7)(3x - 4)$ or
$(ax^2 + \frac{1}{2}x + \frac{3}{2})(\frac{1}{2}x + \frac{1}{2})$

Section 4 – 8 TRY THIS

1. $x^2 + 7x + 12$ 2. $x^2 - 2x - 15$ 3. $2x^2 + 9x +$
4 4. $2x^3 - 4x^2 - 3x + 6$ 5. $12x^5 + 10x^3 +$
$6x^2 + 5$ 6. $y^6 - 49$ 7. $-2x^8 + 2x^6 - x^5 + x^3$
8. $x^2 - \frac{16}{25}$ 9. $x^4 + x^2 + 0.25$ 10. $8 + 2x^2 - 15x^4$
11. $30x^5 - 3x^4 - 6x^3$ 12. $x^2 - 4$ 13. $x^2 - 49$
14. $9t^2 - 25$ 15. $4x^6 - 1$

Exercise Set 4 – 8

1. $x^3 + x^2 + 3x + 3$ 3. $x^4 + x^3 + 2x + 2$ 5. $x^2 -$
$x - 6$ 7. $9x^2 + 15x + 6$ 9. $5x^2 + 4x - 12$
11. $9x^2 - 1$ 13. $4x^2 - 6x + 2$ 15. $x^2 - \frac{1}{16}$
17. $x^2 - 0.01$ 19. $2x^3 + 2x^2 + 6x + 6$
21. $-2x^2 - 11x + 6$ 23. $x^2 + 14x + 49$ 25. $1 -$
$x - 6x^2$ 27. $x^5 + 3x^3 - x^2 - 3$ 29. $x^3 - x^2 -$
$2x + 2$ 31. $3x^6 - 6x^2 - 2x^4 + 4$ 33. $6x^7 +$
$18x^5 + 4x^2 + 12$ 35. $8x^6 + 65x^3 + 8$ 37. $4x^3 -$
$12x^2 + 3x - 9$ 39. $4x^6 + 4x^5 + x^4 + x^3$
41. $x^2 - 16$ 43. $4x^2 - 1$ 45. $25m^2 - 4$
47. $4x^4 - 9$ 49. $9x^8 - 16$ 51. $x^{12} - x^4$
53. $x^8 - 9x^2$ 55. $x^{24} - 9$ 57. $4x^{16} - 9$
59. $20^2 - 2^2$ or 396   61. $8y^3 + 72y^2 + 160y$
63. -7 65. $-2\frac{1}{2}$ 67. -5 69. $a^2 + 10a + 24$
71. $16x^4 - 1$ 73. $\frac{1}{17}$ 75a. $w(w + 1)(w + 2) =$
$w^3 + 3w^2 + 2w$ 75b. $l(l - 1)(l + 1) = l^3 - l$
75c. $h(h - 1)(h - 2) = h^3 - 3h^2 + 2h$ 77. Each
trip is $0.70 + 3\frac{6}{7}(7)(0.10) = 3.40$, $3.40(11x + 6) =$
$37.40x + 20.40$.

Section 4 – 9 TRY THIS

1. $x^2 + 4x + 4$ 2. $y^2 - 18y + 81$ 3. $16x^2 -$
$40x + 25$ 4. $a^2 - 8a + 16$ 5. $25x^4 + 40x^2 + 16$
6. $16x^4 - 24x^3 + 9x^2$ 7. $x^2 + 11x + 30$ 8. $x^2 -$
16 9. $-8x^5 + 20x^4 + 40x^2$ 10. $81x^4 + 18x^2 + 1$
11. $4x^2 + 6x - 40$ 12. $3x^3 - 14x^2 - x + 6$

Exercise Set 4 – 9

1. $x^2 + 4x + 4$ 3. $x^2 - 6x + 9$ 5. $4x^2 - 4x + 1$
7. $9x^4 + 6x^2 + 1$ 9. $x^2 - x + \frac{1}{4}$ 11. $9x^2 + \frac{9}{2}x +$
$\frac{9}{16}$ 13. $t^2 - 6t + 9$ 15. $x^6 + 2x^3 + 1$
17. $64x^2 - 16x^3 + x^4$ 19. $x^2 - 16x + 64$
21. $x^2 - 64$ 23. $x^2 - 3x + 40$ 25. $4x^3 + 24x^2 -$
$12x$ 27. $4x^4 - 2x^2 + \frac{1}{4}$ 29. $36a^6 - 1$
31. $-9x^2 + 4$ 33. $36x^8 + 48x^4 + 16$ 35. $-6x^5 -$
$48x^3 + 54x^2$ 37. $12q^5 + 6q^3 - 2q^2 - 1$

39. $\frac{9}{16}x^2 + \frac{9}{4}x + 2$ **41.** $4x^3 + 13x^2 + 22x + 15$
43. $3x^5 - 14x^4 + 13x^3 - 20x^2$ **45a.** ac, ad, bc, bd
45b. $ac + ad + bc + bd$ **45c.** $ac + ad + bc + bd$,
equal   **47.** $a^2 + (a+1)^2 + (a+2)^2 = 3a^2 + 65$,
$a = 10, a + 1 = 11, a + 2 = 12$ **49.** $100(x^2 + x) +$
25. Add the first digit to its square, multiply by 100,
add 25.

Chapter 4 Review

1. 7^6 **3.** $(3x)^{14}$ **5.** $\frac{1}{6^5}$ **7.** y^{12} **9.** $9t^8$

11. $3x^2, 6x, \frac{1}{2}$ **13.** Trinomial   **15.** Monomial
17. $-\frac{1}{4}x^3 + 4x^2 + 7$ **19.** 3, 1, 0; 3   **21.** 6, 17
23. $-2x^3 - 3x + 2$ **25.** 2nd degree, constant
27. 16   **29.** $2x^5 - 6x^4 + 2x^3 - 2x^2 + 2$ **31.** $w^2 +$
$4w$ or $l^2 - 4l$ **33.** $x^5 - 3x^3 - 2x^2 + 8$ **35.** $-12x^3$
37. $x^2 - 3x - 28$ **39.** $x^2 - 1.05x + 0.225$
41. $12x^3 - 23x^2 + 13x - 2$ **43.** $x^7 + x^5 - 3x^4 +$
$3x^3 - 2x^2 + 5x - 3$ **45.** $9x^4 - 16$ **47.** $x^2 -$
$18x + 81$ **49.** $9x^4 - 12x^3 + 4x^2$

Chapter 5

Section 5–1 TRY THIS

1-3. Answers may vary.   **1.** $(4x^2)(2x^2), (4x)(2x^3),$
$(8x)(x^3)$ **2.** $(2x)(3x^4), (x^2)(6x^3), (2x^3)(3x^2)$
3. $(6x)(2x), (-6x)(-2x), (4x)(3x)$ **4.** $x(x+3)$
5. $x^2(3x^4 - 5x + 2)$ **6.** $3x^2(3x^2 - 5x + 1)$
7. $\frac{1}{4}(3x^3 + 5x^2 + 7x - 1)$
8. $7x^3(5x^4 - 7x^3 + 2x^2 - 9)$

Exercise Set 5–1

1-5. Answers may vary.   **7.** $x(x-4)$ **9.** $2x(x+3)$
11. $x^2(x+6)$ **13.** $8x^2(x^2-3)$ **15.** $2(x^2+x-4)$
17. $17x(x^4 + 2x^2 + 3)$ **19.** $x^2(6x^2 - 10x + 3)$
21. $x^2(x^3 + x^2 + x - 1)$ **23.** $2x^3(x^4 - x^3 - 32x^2 + 2)$
25. $0.8x(2x^3 - 3x^2 + 4x + 8)$
27. $\frac{x^3}{3}(5x^3 + 4x^2 + x + 1)$ **29.** No   **31.** No
33. No   **35.** Yes   **37.** Yes   **39.** $3t$ **41.** $24t^2$
43. no common factor

Section 5–2 TRY THIS

1. Yes   **2.** No   **3.** No   **4.** No   **5.** Yes   **6.** Yes
7. $(x+3)(x-3)$ **8.** $(y+8)(y-8)$
9. $8y^2(2+y^2)(2-y^2)$ **10.** $x^4(8+5x)(8-5x)$
11. $5(1+2y^3)(1-2y^3)$ **12.** $(9x^2+1)(9x^2-1) =$
$(9x^2+1)(3x+1)(3x-1)$ **13.** $x^4(49-25x^6) =$
$x^4(7+5x^3)(7-5x^3)$

Exercise Set 5–2

1-9. 1 and 7   **11.** $(x+6)(x-6)$
13. $(x+1)(x-1)$ **15.** $(5x+2)(5x-2)$
17. $(3a+4)(3a-4)$ **19.** $6(2x+3)(2x-3)$
21. $x(4+9x)(4-9x)$ **23.** $x^2(x^7+3)(x^7-3)$
25. $(5a^2+3)(5a^2-3)$ **27.** $(11a^4+10)(11a^4-10)$
29. $(10y^3+7)(10y^3-7)$
31. $(x^2+4)(x+2)(x-2)$
33. $5(x^2+4)(x+2)(x-2)$
35. $(x^4+1)(x^2+1)(x+1)(x-1)$
37. $(x^4+9)(x^2+3)(x^2-3)$ **39.** $(\frac{1}{5}+x)(\frac{1}{5}-x)$
41. $(2+\frac{1}{3}y)(2-\frac{1}{3}y)$ **43.** $(1+a^2)(1+a)(1-a)$
45. $3x^3(x+2)(x-2)$ **47.** $2x(3x+\frac{2}{5})(3x-\frac{2}{5})$
49. $x(x+\frac{1}{1.3})(x-\frac{1}{1.3})$ **51.** $(0.8x+1.1)(0.8x-1.1)$
53. $x(x+6)$ **55.** $3(a-1)(3a+11)$
57. $(y^4+16)(y^2+4)(y+2)(y-2)$
59. $\frac{1}{x^2}(x^2+1)(x+1)(x-1)$ **61.** irred.
63. prime irred.   **65.** prime irred.

Section 5–3 TRY THIS

1. Yes   **2.** Yes   **3.** No   **4.** Yes   **5.** No   **6.** Yes
7. Yes   **8.** Yes   **9.** $(x+1)^2$ **10.** $(x-1)^2$
11. $(x+2)^2$ **12.** $(5x-7)^2$ **13.** $(4x-7)^2$
14. $3(16x^2+40x+25) = 3(4x+5)^2$

Exercise Set 5–3

1-9. 1   **11.** $(x-8)^2$ **13.** $(x+7)^2$ **15.** $(x+1)^2$
17. $(x-2)^2$ **19.** $(y+3)^2$ **21.** $2(x-10)^2$
23. $x(x+12)^2$ **25.** $3(2x+3)^2$ **27.** $(8-7x)^2$
29. $(a^2+7)^2$ **31.** $(y^3-8)^2$ **33.** $(3x^5+2)^2$
35. $(a^3-1)^2$ **37.** $(\frac{1}{3}a+\frac{1}{2})^2$ **39.** $x(27x^2-13)$
41. No   **43.** $2x(3x+1)^2$ **45.** $2(81x^2-41)$
47. No   **49.** $(9+x^2)(3+x)(3-x)$ **51.** $(a+3)^2$
53. $(7x+4)^2$ **55.** $(a+1)^2$ **57.** No.
$(x+3)^2(x-3)^2 = [(x+3)(x-3)]^2 = (x^2-9)^2 =$
$x^4 - 18x^2 + 81$ **59.** $(x^n+5)^2$ **61.** $(y+3)^2 -$
$(x+4)^2 = (y+x+7)(y-x-1)$ **63.** 16
65. $x^2 + a^2x + a^2 = x^2 + 2ax + a^2, a^2x = 2ax, a = 2$

Section 5–4 TRY THIS

1. $(x+4)(x+3)$ **2.** $(x+9)(x+4)$
3. $(x-5)(x-3)$ **4.** $(x-5)(x-4)$
5. $(x+6)(x-2)$ **6.** $(x-6)(x+2)$
7. $(x+7)(x-2)$ **8.** $(x-6)(x+5)$

Exercise Set 5–4

1. $(x+5)(x+3)$ **3.** $(x+4)(x+3)$ **5.** $(x-3)^2$
7. $(x+7)(x+2)$ **9.** $(b+4)(b+1)$ **11.** $(x+\frac{1}{3})^2$
13. $(d-5)(d-2)$ **15.** $(y-10)(y-1)$
17. $(x+7)(x-6)$ **19.** $(x+2)(x-9)$

21. $(x + 2)(x - 8)$ **23.** $(y + 5)(y - 9)$
25. $(x + 9)(x - 11)$ **27.** $(c + 8)(c - 7)$
29. $(a + 7)(a - 5)$ **31.** $(x + 10)^2$
33. $(x - 25)(x + 4)$ **35.** $(x - 24)(x - 3)$
37. $(x - 16)(x - 9)$ **39.** $(a + 12)(a - 11)$
41. $(x - 15)(x - 8)$ **43.** $(12 + x)(9 - x)$ **45.** 15,
27, 51   **47.** $(x + \frac{1}{4})(x - \frac{3}{4})$ **49.** $(x + 5)(x - \frac{5}{7})$

Section 5–5 TRY THIS

1. $(3x + 2)(2x + 1)$ **2.** $(4x - 1)(2x + 3)$
3. $(6x + 1)(x - 7)$ **4.** $2(x - 1)(x + 3)$
5. $2(2x + 3)(x - 1)$ **6.** $3(2x - 1)(x + 3)$

Exercise Set 5–5

1. $(2x + 1)(x - 4)$ **3.** $(5x - 9)(x + 2)$
5. $(2x + 7)(3x + 1)$ **7.** $(3x + 1)(x + 1)$
9. $(2x + 5)(2x - 3)$ **11.** $(2x + 1)(x - 1)$
13. $(3x + 8)(3x - 2)$ **15.** $(3x + 1)(x - 2)$
17. $(3x + 4)(4x + 5)$ **19.** $(7x - 1)(2x + 3)$
21. $(3x + 4)(3x + 2)$ **23.** $(7 - 3x)^2$
25. $(x + 2)(24x - 1)$ **27.** $(7x + 4)(5x - 11)$
29. $2(5 - x)(2 + x)$ **31.** $4(3x - 2)(x + 3)$
33. $6(5x - 9)(x + 1)$ **35.** $2(3x + 5)(x - 1)$
37. $(3x + 1)(x + 1)$ **39.** $4(3x - 2)(x + 3)$
41. $(2x + 1)(x - 1)$ **43.** $(3x + 8)(3x - 2)$
45. $5(3x + 1)(x - 2)$ **47.** $(3x + 4)(4x + 5)$
49. $(7x - 1)(2x + 3)$ **51.** $(8x - 1)(7x - 1)$
53. $(3 - 2x)(2 - 3x)$ **55.** $(5x^2 - 3)(3x^2 - 2)$
57. $3x(2x - 3)(3x + 1)$ **59.** not factorable
61. $(3x + 7)(3x - 7)(3x - 7)$
63. $(-3x^m + 4)(5x^m - 2)$ **65.** $x(x^n - 1)^2$
67. $(2y + 10)(2y + 8) = 2(y + 5) \cdot 2(y + 4) =$
$4(y + 5)(y + 4)$

Section 5–6 TRY THIS

1. $(4x + 1)(2x^2 + 3)$ **2.** $(2x - 3)(2x^2 - 3)$
3. $(x + 1)(x + 1)(x - 1)$ **4.** $(x + 2)(x - 2)(3x^3 - 1)$

Exercise Set 5–6

1. $(x + 3)(x^2 + 2)$ **3.** $(x + 3)(2x^2 + 1)$
5. $(2x - 3)(4x^2 + 3)$ **7.** $(3x - 4)(4x^2 + 1)$
9. $(x + 8)(x^2 - 3)$ **11.** $(7x + 9)(2x^2 - 3)$
13. $(x - 4)(2x^2 - 9)$ **15.** $(4x - 3)(6x^2 - 5)$
17. $(x + 5)(x + 1)(x - 1)$
19. $(x - 3)(4x + 5)(4x - 5)$ **21.** $(2x^2 + 3)(2x^3 + 3)$
23. $(x^2 + 1)(x + 1)(x + 1)(x - 1)(x - 1)$
25. $(ax^n + b)(cx^m + d)$ **27.** $x(x + 1)^2 -$
$(x^2 + 1)^2 = x^4 + 2x^3 + x^2 - (x^4 + 2x^2 + 1) = 2x^3 -$
$2x^2 + x^2 - 1 = 2x^2(x - 1) + (x + 1)(x - 1) =$
$(2x^2 + x + 1)(x - 1)$

Section 5–7 TRY THIS

1. $3(m^2 + 1)(m + 1)(m - 1)$ **2.** $(x^3 + 4)^2$

3. $2x^2(x + 3)(x + 1)$ **4.** $(x + 4)(3x^2 - 2)$
5. $8x(x + 5)(x - 5)$

Exercise Set 5–7

1. $2(x + 8)(x - 8)$ **3.** $(a - 5)^2$ **5.** $(2x - 3)(x - 4)$
7. $x(x + 12)^2$ **9.** $(x - 2)(x + 2)(x + 3)$
11. $6(2x + 3)(2x - 3)$ **13.** $4x(x - 2)(5x + 9)$
15. not factorable   **17.** $x(x - 3)(x^2 + 7)$
19. $x^3(x - 7)^2$ **21.** $-2(x - 2)(x + 5)$ **23.** not
factorable   **25.** $4(x^2 + 4)(x + 2)(x - 2)$
27. $(y^4 + 1)(y^2 + 1)(y + 1)(1 - y)$
29. $x^3(x - 3)(x - 1)$ **31.** $(6a - \frac{5}{4})^2$
33. $(a + 1)(a + 1)(a - 1)(a - 1)$ **35.** $(3.5x - 1)^2$
37. $5(x + 1.8)(x + 0.8)$ **39.** $(y - 2)(y + 3)(y - 3)$
41. $(a + 4)(a^2 + 1)$ **43.** $(y^3 + 1)(y^2 + y + 1)$ or
$(y + 1)(y^4 + y^3 + 1)$ **45.** Yes. $a^3 + 3a^2 + 9a + 27$
or $(a^2 + 9)(a + 3)$

Section 5–8 TRY THIS

1. $3, -4$ **2.** $7, 3$ **3.** $0, \frac{17}{3}$ **4.** $-\frac{1}{4}, \frac{2}{3}$ **5.** $0, 5,$
-2 **6.** $3, -2$ **7.** $7, -4$ **8.** 3 **9.** $0, 4$
10. $-\frac{4}{5}, \frac{4}{5}$

Exercise Set 5–8

1. $-8, -6$ **3.** $3, -5$ **5.** $-12, 11$ **7.** $0, -5$
9. $0, 13$ **11.** $0, -10$ **13.** $-\frac{5}{2}, -4$ **15.** $\frac{1}{3}, -2$
17. $-\frac{1}{5}, 3$ **19.** $4, \frac{1}{4}$ **21.** $0, \frac{2}{3}$ **23.** $0, 18$
25. $\frac{1}{9}, \frac{1}{10}$ **27.** $2, 6$ **29.** $\frac{1}{3}, 20$ **31.** $0, \frac{2}{3}, \frac{1}{2}$
33. $-5, -1$ **35.** $2, -9$ **37.** $5, 3$ **39.** $0, 8$
41. $0, -19$ **43.** $4, -4$ **45.** $\frac{2}{3}, -\frac{2}{3}$ **47.** -3
49. 4 **51.** $0, \frac{6}{5}$ **53.** $-1, \frac{5}{3}$ **55.** $\frac{2}{3}, -\frac{1}{4}$ **57.** $7,$
-2 **59.** $\frac{9}{8}, -\frac{9}{8}$ **61.** $-3, 1$ **63.** $\frac{5}{4}, \frac{2}{3}$ **65.** $4, -5$
67. $9, -3$ **69.** $\frac{1}{8}, -\frac{1}{8}$ **71.** $4, -4$ **73a.** $x^2 +$
$2x - 3 = 0$ **73b.** $x^2 - 2x - 3 = 0$ **73c.** $x^2 -$
$4x + 4 = 0$ **73d.** $x^2 - 7x + 12 = 0$ **73e.** $x^2 +$
$x - 12 = 0$ **73f.** $x^2 - x - 12 = 0$ **73g.** $x^2 + 7x +$
$12 = 0$ **73h.** $x^2 - x + \frac{1}{4}$ or $4x^2 - 4x + 1 = 0$
73i. $x^2 - 25 = 0$ **73j.** $x^3 - \frac{14}{40}x^2 - \frac{1}{40}x$ or
$40x^3 - 14x^2 - x = 0$

Section 5–9 TRY THIS

1. 7 or 8   **2.** 0 or 1   **3.** 5 or -5 **4.** 5 or -4
5. 6 or -6 **6.** $l(l - 2) = 15$, 5 cm, 3 cm   **7.** 21,
22; $-21, 22$ **8.** 342   **9.** 9

Exercise Set 5–9

1. $-\frac{3}{4}$ or 1   **3.** 2 or 4   **5.** 13 and 14, -13 and -14
7. 12 and 14, -12 and -14 **9.** 15 and 17, -15 and
-17 **11.** 12 m, 8 m   **13.** 5   **15.** 4 cm, 14 cm
17. 6 m   **19.** 5 and 7   **21.** 506   **23.** 12   **25.** 780

27. 20   **29.** 5 ft   **31a.** 2 seconds   **31b.** 4.2 seconds   **33.** 7 m   **35a.** 26, 28, 30   **35b.** $-29, -27, -25$ **37.** 12, 4   **39.** 30 cm by 15 cm

Chapter 5 Review

1. Answers may vary.   **3.** $x(x-3)$
5. $4x^4(2x^2 - 8x + 1)$ **7.** $(2x-5)(2x+5)$
9. $3(x-3)(x+3)$ **11.** $(4x^2+1)(2x+1)(2x-1)$
13. $(x+7)^2$ **15.** $(5x-2)^2$ **17.** $3(2x+5)^2$
19. $(x+6)(x-2)$ **21.** $(2x+1)(x-4)$
23. $2(3x+4)(x-6)$ **25.** $(x^3-2)(x+4)$
27. $5(1+2x^3)(1-2x^3)$ **29.** $-7, 5$ **31.** $\frac{2}{3}, 1$
33. $8, -2$ **35.** 16, 18, or $-16, -18$ **37.** $\frac{5}{2}$ or -2

Chapter 6

Section 6–1 TRY THIS

1. -7940 **2.** -176 **3.** 357.96 cm^2 **4.** $5xy^4 - 3xy^3 - 7xy^2 + 3xy$ **5.** $-2 + 5xy^2z + 2x^2yz + 5x^3yz^2$ **6.** $2x^2y - 2x^2 + 3xy^2 + 3xy$

Exercise Set 6–1

1. -1 **3.** -19 **5.** -1 **7.** $12,950.29$
9. 44.4624 in^2 **11.** $4, 2, 2, 0; 4$ **13.** $5, 5, 0; 5$
15. $4, 4, 4, 4, 4; 4$ **17.** $-y^3 - xy^2 + 5x^2y$
19. $-y^3 - xy^2 + x^3$ **21.** $4n^2 - 3mn^3 + 5m^2n - m^4n$ **23.** $3y^2 + 2xy + x^2$ **25.** $-11uv^2 + 7u^2v + 5uv$ **27.** a **29.** Answers may vary.   **31.** $5x^2y^4$
33-35. Answers may vary.   **37.** 549.5 cm^2
39. 2.304 liters   **41.** 2   **43.** $\dfrac{n-5}{2}$

Section 6–2 TRY THIS

1. $14x^3y + 7x^2y - 3xy - 2y$ **2.** $-2p^2q^4 + 2p^2q^2 + 6pq^2 + 3p - 3q$ **3.** $-8s^4t + 6s^3t^2 + 2s^2t^3 - s^2t^2$
4. $x^5y^5 + 2x^4y^2 + 3x^3y^3 + 5x^2$ **5.** $p^5q + 3pq^3 - 4p^3q^3 + 6q^4$ **6.** $3x^3y + 6x^2y^3 + 2x^3 + 4x^2y^2$
7. $2x^2 - 11xy + 15y^2$ **8.** $16x^2 + 40xy + 25y^2$
9. $9x^4 - 12x^3y^2 + 4x^2y^4$ **10.** $4x^2y^4 - 9x^2$
11. $16y^2 - 9x^2y^4$ **12.** $9y^2 + 24y + 16 - 9x^2$
13. $4a^2 - 25b^2 - 10bc - c^2$

Exercise Set 6–2

1. $3xy - 4ab$ **3.** $x^2 - 4xy + 3y^2$ **5.** $5p^4q^2 + 4p^3q - 7p - 2q$ **7.** $-xy + 2ab$ **9.** $3x^3 - x^2y + xy^2 - 3y^3$ **11.** $-5p^3q^2 + 5p^2q + 17$ **13.** $-5b$
15. $6z^2 + 7zu - 3u^2$ **17.** $x^2y^2 + 3xy - 28$
19. $a^4 + a^3 - a^2y - ay + a + y - 1$ **21.** $a^6 - b^2c^2$

23. $a^4 + a^2b^2 + b^4$ **25.** $a^4 - b^4$ **27.** $12x^2y^2 + 2xy - 2$ **29.** $12 - c^2d^2 - c^4d^4$ **31.** $m^3 + m^2n - mn^2 - n^3$ **33.** $x^9y^9 - x^6y^6 + x^5y^5 - x^2y^2$
35. $x^2 + xy^3 - 2y^6$ **37.** $9a^2 + 12ab + 4b^2$
39. $9a^4b^2 - 6a^2b^3 + b^4$ **41.** $a^2b^2 + 2abcd + c^2d^2$
43. $-5x^3 - 30x^2y - 45xy^2$ **45.** $x^2 - y^2$
47. $c^4 - d^2$ **49.** $a^2b^2 - c^2d^4$ **51.** $x^2 + 2xy + y^2 - 9$ **53.** $p^8 - m^4n^4$ **55.** $a^2 - b^2 - 2bc - c^2$
57. $9x^2 - 25y^2 - 10y - 1$ **59.** $4xy - 4y^2$
61. $\pi x^2 + 2xy$ **63.** $x^3 + 3x^2y + 3xy^2 + y^3$
65. $x^4 + 4x^3y + 6x^2y^2 + 4xy^3 + y^4$ **67.** $x^5 + 5x^4y + 10x^3y^2 + 10x^2y^3 + 5xy^4 + y^5$ **69.** 7
71. $5, 6$ **73.** 8   **75.** $(x - 2y)^2 - (x - 2y - 2z)^2 = 4xz - 4z^2 - 8yz$

Section 6–3 TRY THIS

1. $x^2(x^2y^2 + 2x + 3y)$ **2.** $2p^4q^2(5p^2 - 2pq + q^2)$
3. $(3a + 4x^2)(3a - 4x^2)$
4. $2(5xy^2 + 2a)(5xy^2 - 2a)$
5. $5(1 + x^2y^2)(1 + xy)(1 - xy)$ **6.** $(x^2 + y^2)^2$
7. $(2x - 3y)^2$ **8.** $(x^3 + 2y)^2$
9. $(xy + 4)(xy + 1)$ **10.** $2(x^2y^3 + 5)(x^2y^3 - 2)$
11. $(x^2 - y)(a - b)$ **12.** $(a - 2b)(3 + 5a)$

Exercise Set 6–3

1. $12n^2(1 + 2n)$ **3.** $5cd(cd + 2)$ **5.** $rt(r + t)$
7. $\pi r(r + h)$ **9.** $3a^2b^2(4a^2b^2 - 3ab + 2)$
11. $(xy + 5)(xy - 5)$ **13.** $(cd + t)(cd - t)$
15. $(4a^2b + c)(4a^2b - c)$ **17.** $(8z + 5cd)(8z - 5cd)$
19. $5(t + 2m)(t - 2m)$ **21.** $16a^2(a + 1)(a - 1)$
23. $(3c - d)^2$ **25.** $(7m^2 - 8n)^2$ **27.** $(y^2 + 5z^2)^2$
29. $(0.2a^2 + 0.3b^2)^2$ **31.** $(\frac{1}{2}a + \frac{1}{3}b)^2$
33. $p(2p + q)^2$ **35.** $(x + 3y)(x - y)$
37. $(n + 35r)(n - 12r)$ **39.** $(ab - 5)(ab + 2)$
41. $n^4(mn + 8)(mn - 4)$ **43.** $ab^2(b^2 + b - 1)$
45. $-(p + 10t)^2$ **47.** $(d - 3bc)^2$ **49.** $2a(a - b)$
51. $6m(7m + 3n)(m - n)$ **53.** $5(a + b)(c - d)$
55. $3a(5a + 2b)^2$ **57.** $(x - y + 1)(x - 1)$
59. $(x + y)(x - 1)$ **61.** $(b + c)(x + 2)$
63. $(2x + z)(x - 2)$ **65.** $(3y + p)(2y - 1)$
67. $(2a + 3b - 1)(2a - 3b)$ **69.** $(c + 3d)(x - 2y)$
71. $(a^2b^2 + 4)(ab + 2)(ab - 2)$
73. $(1 + 4x^6y^6)(1 + 2x^3y^3)(1 - 2x^3y^3)$
75. $(a - 1)(y + 1)(y - 1)$
77. $2(x^2 + 3y)(x + 2y)(x - 2y)$
79. $-(y + 3x + 5)(y + 3x - 5)$ **81.** $y = 3x$ or $-3x$
83. $x = 1$ or -1 or $y = 0$
85a. $(x - y)(x^2 + xy + y^2)$
85b. $(x + y)(x^2 - xy + y^2)$
85c. $(x - y)(x + y)(x^2 + xy + y^2)(x^2 - xy + y^2)$
85d. $(x - y)(x^4 + x^3y + x^2y^2 + xy^3 + y^4)$

Section 6−4 TRY THIS

1. $\dfrac{b^2 + 3}{a}$ 2. $\dfrac{6}{b}$ 3. $\dfrac{2 - ab}{a + b}$ 4. $-3b - 2a - 8$

Exercise Set 6−4

1. $\dfrac{2a - 12}{3}$ 3. $\dfrac{3b - 1}{2}$ 5. $\dfrac{c}{rt}$ 7. $b + 4$ 9. $a + b$

11. $\dfrac{c}{2a - b}$ 13. $a - b$ 15. $\dfrac{a + b + 11}{3}$ 17. $b + 2$

19. $\dfrac{7b}{4}$ 21. 2 23. $m + n$ 25. $\dfrac{ab + 3}{b - a}$

27. $\dfrac{d + c}{2}$ 29. $\dfrac{-(d + c)}{2}$ 31. $d - 1$ 33. a, b

35. $a, -b, c$ 37. $a, -a$ 39. $c, -a$ 41. $\dfrac{-b}{2}, \dfrac{b}{3}$

43. $-d, \dfrac{3d}{4}$ 45. $b, -b$ 47. $0, 2, -2, 3, -3$

49. $k - 1, 1 - k$

Section 6−5 TRY THIS

1. $\dfrac{fd^2}{km}$ 2. $\dfrac{h^2}{3} - \dfrac{2v}{\pi h}$ 3. 30 cm 4. 33 cm

Exercise Set 6−5

1. $r = \dfrac{S}{2\pi k}$ 3. $b = \dfrac{2A}{k}$ 5. $n = \dfrac{S + 360}{180}$

7. $b = \dfrac{6V - Bk - 4kM}{k}$ 9. $r = \dfrac{S - a}{S - l}$

11. $h = \dfrac{2A}{b_1 + b_2}$ 13. $a = \dfrac{v^2 pL}{r}$ 15. $b_1 = \dfrac{2A - hb_2}{h}$

17. $E = \dfrac{180A}{\pi r^2}$ 19. $M = -\dfrac{V + hB + hc}{4h}$

21. $L = \dfrac{ay}{v^2 p}$ 23. $p = \dfrac{ar}{v^2 L}$ 25. $n = \dfrac{a}{c(1 + b)}$

27. $F = \dfrac{9C + 160}{5}$ 29. $g = \dfrac{fm + t}{m}$ 31. 13 cm

33. 0.625 amp 35. 45 37. \$102.18

Chapter 6 Review

1. 29 3. 3, 3, 0; 3 5. $a^3 + 3a^2 b + 3ab^2 + b^3$
7. $x^2 y^2 + 4x^2 yz^3$ 9. $18s^2 t^3 + 6st^2 + s^2 t^2 + 7$
11. $3x^3 + 3x^2 y - 4xy - 4y^2$ 13. $p^2 - 16t^4$
15. $(4xy + 1)(4xy - 1)$ 17. $(2x + 3y)(4x - y)$
19. $x = -3a$ 21. $p = \dfrac{A}{prt}$

Chapter 7

Section 7−1 TRY THIS

11. Both coordinates are negative. 12. x-coordinate
is positive, y-coordinate is negative. 13. first
14. third 15. fourth 16. second 17. (4, 3),
$(-4, -3), (2, -4), (1, 5), (-2, 0), (0, 3)$

Exercise Set 7−1

17. second 19. fourth 21. third 23. first
25. negative, positive 27. $A(3, 3), B(0, -4)$,
$C(-5, 0), D(-1, -1), E(2, 0)$ 29-37. Answers may
vary. 29. Ex. $(-2, -2), (0, 0), (1, 1)$ 31. Ex.
$(-1, 1), (0, 0)$ 33. Ex. $(-3, 0), (-2, 1), (1, 4)$
35. Ex. $(2, 3), (4, 1), (0, 5)$ 37. Ex. $(-2, 8)$,
$(-1, 7), (0, 6), (1, 5)$ 39. 26

Section 7−2 TRY THIS

1. No 2. Yes 3. Answers may vary. Ex. (0, 3),
$(1, 5), (-1, 1), (-2, -1)$

Exercise Set 7−2

1. Yes 3. No 5. Yes 7-15. Answers may vary.
35. $(0, 6), (1, 5), (2, 4), (3, 3), (4, 2), (5, 1), (6, 0)$
37. $5n + 10d = 195$; Ex. in (d, n) form, (10, 19),
(0, 39), (15, 9) 39. Ex. $(-3, 3), (2, 2), (0, 0)$
41. $68x + 76y = 864$, let $x = y$, 6 hr each machine

Exercise Set 7−3

37. $y = 0$ 39. $y = -5$ 41. $y = 2.8$ 43. e; b and
g, a and f; b

Section 7−4 TRY THIS

1. slope $= \dfrac{2}{5}$ 2. slope $= -\dfrac{5}{3}$ 3. $\dfrac{7}{6}$ 4. $\dfrac{4}{7}$ 5. $-\dfrac{1}{2}$
6. $-\dfrac{15}{14}$ 7. 0 8. No slope 9. $-\dfrac{1}{3}$

Exercise Set 7−4

1. $m = 0$ 3. $m = -\dfrac{4}{5}$ 5. $m = 2$ 7. 3 9. $-\dfrac{9}{7}$
11. 7 13. $-\dfrac{2}{3}$ 15. -2 17. 3 19. $\dfrac{4}{3}$ 21. 2
23. No slope 25. Zero slope 27. No slope
29. Zero slope 31. The slopes are the same.
33. 6 35. 12 37. 39% 39. Yes, the slopes of
any two points are the same.

Section 7−5 TRY THIS

1. $-\dfrac{4}{5}$ 2. $-\dfrac{3}{8}$ 3. $-\dfrac{1}{5}$ 4. $\dfrac{5}{4}$ 5. 5, (0, 0)
6. $-\dfrac{3}{2}, (0, -6)$ 7. 2, $(0, -\dfrac{17}{2})$ 8. $-\dfrac{3}{4}, (0, \dfrac{15}{4})$
9. $-\dfrac{7}{5}, (0, -\dfrac{22}{5})$

Exercise Set 7−5

1. $-\dfrac{3}{2}$ 3. $-\dfrac{1}{4}$ 5. 2 7. $\dfrac{4}{3}$ 9. $\dfrac{1}{2}$ 11. $\dfrac{1}{2}$ 13. $\dfrac{7}{5}$
15. $-\dfrac{2}{3}$ 17. $-\dfrac{8}{9}$ 19. $-4, (0, -9)$ 21. $-\dfrac{2}{3}, (0, 3)$
23. $-\dfrac{8}{7}, (0, -3)$ 25. 3, $(0, -\dfrac{5}{3})$ 27. $-\dfrac{3}{2}, (0, -\dfrac{1}{2})$
43. Lines are parallel. 45. -2 47. 7, (0, −8)

Section 7−6 TRY THIS

1. $y = 5x - 18$ 2. $y = -3x - 5$ 3. $y = -\dfrac{2}{3}x + \dfrac{22}{3}$

4. $y = \frac{9}{2}x + \frac{17}{2}$ **5.** $y = 6x - 13$ **6.** $y = -\frac{2}{3}x + \frac{14}{3}$
7. $y = x + 2$ **8.** $y = 2x + 4$

Exercise Set 7−6

1. $y = 5x - 5$ **3.** $y = \frac{3}{4}x + \frac{5}{2}$ **5.** $y = x - 8$
7. $y = -3x - 9$ **9.** $y = \frac{3}{4}x$ **11.** $y = \frac{5}{6}x + \frac{16}{3}$
13. $y = \frac{1}{4}x + \frac{5}{2}$ **15.** $y = -\frac{1}{2}x + 4$
17. $y = -\frac{3}{2}x + \frac{13}{2}$ **19.** $y = \frac{2}{5}x - 2$
21. $y = \frac{3}{4}x - \frac{5}{2}$ **23.** $y = 3x - 9$ **25.** $y = \frac{3}{2}x - 2$
27. $bx + ay - ab = 0$ **29.** -1 **31.** Answers may vary. Ex. $y = x - 6$

Section 7−7 TRY THIS

1. The y-intercept of a line is the point where the line crosses the y-axis. Thus, the x-coordinate of the point is 0. Let $x = 0$ in the equation $y = mx + b$. $y = (0)x + b$, $y = 0 + b$, $y = b$. Thus b is the y-intercept. **2.** Suppose that (x_1, y_1) and (x_2, y_2) are any two points on a vertical line. The slope of the line is $\frac{y_2 - y_1}{x_2 - x_1}$. Since the line is vertical, the x-coordinates are the same, so slope is $\frac{y_2 - y_1}{0}$. Division by 0 is not allowed, so the line has no slope.

Exercise Set 7−7

1. Given a nonvertical line containing point (x_1, y_1) and having slope m. Let (x, y) be any other point on the line. Then $m = \frac{y - y_1}{x - x_1}$. Multiplying each side of the equation by $x - x_1$ (Mult. prin.), we have $m(x - x_1) = y - y_1$, or $y - y_1 = m(x - x_1)$.

Chapter 7 Review

5. third   **7.** $(-3, 6)$ **9.** $(5, -2)$ **11.** No   **17.** $\frac{3}{2}$
19. 0   **23.** $y = -2x + 4$ **25.** $y = \frac{1}{2}x - 1$

Chapter 8

Section 8−1 TRY THIS

1. Yes   **2.** Yes   **3.** $8, -5, 1$ **4.** $0, -10, 2$
5. $11, 35, 5$ **6.** $-1, 5, 20$

Exercise Set 8−1

1. Yes   **3.** Yes   **5.** No   **7.** $8, 12, -4$ **9.** $-6, 15, 72$ **11.** $6, -10, 16$ **13.** $2, 9, 4$ **15.** $4, 5, 3$
17. $1, 91, 98$ **19.** $-3, -2, 78$ **21.** \$45.15
23. \$54.24   **25.** $1.606, 1.909, 4.03$ **27.** $70, 220, 10,020$ **29.** $5, 8, 11, 14$ **31.** $0, 2$ **33.** 8

35. -186 **37.** $f(x) = \frac{15}{4}x - \frac{13}{4}$ **39.** No. One flip may correspond to 0 or 1 heads.

Section 8−2 TRY THIS

3. Yes   **4.** No   **5.** No

Exercise Set 8−2

15. Yes   **17.** No   **21.** Yes. (The domain excludes 0.)   **23.** If $|a|$ increases, the graph is stretched horizontally; if b increases, the graph is moved upwards.

Section 8−3 TRY THIS

1. Input 9 hours, output \$18.35 cost

Exercise Set 8−3

1. $c = 35 + 0.21k$, input 340 km, output \$106.40 cost   **3.** $L = \frac{1}{3}w + 40$, input 15 kg, output 45 cm
5. $c = 5.50 + 4.25h$, input 4.5 hr, output \$24.63 cost
7. $c = 6.50 + 3.90h$, input 7.5 hr, output \$35.75 cost
9. \$8.70   **11.** A nonvertical straight line   **13.** A horizontal line

Section 8−4 TRY THIS

1. $y = 7x$ **2.** $y = 0.625x$ **3.** $46\frac{2}{3}¢, 1\frac{17}{18}¢$
4. 79.2 kg

Exercise Set 8−4

1. $y = 4x$ **3.** $y = 1.75x$ **5.** $y = 3.2x$ **7.** $y = \frac{2}{3}x$
9. \$183.75   **11.** 22   **13.** $16\frac{2}{3}$ kg   **15.** 68.4 kg
17. Yes   **19.** No   **21.** No   **23.** $C = kr$ $(k = 2\pi)$
25. $C = kA$ **27.** $S = kV^6$ **29.** $P = kRI^2$

Section 8−5 TRY THIS

1. $y = \frac{63}{x}$ **2.** $y = \frac{900}{x}$ **3.** 8 hr   **4.** $7\frac{1}{2}$ hr

Exercise Set 8−5

1. $y = \frac{75}{x}$ **3.** $y = \frac{80}{x}$ **5.** $y = \frac{1}{x}$ **7.** $y = \frac{1050}{x}$
9. $y = \frac{0.06}{x}$ **11.** $5\frac{1}{3}$ hr   **13.** 320 kg   **15.** 54 min
17. $C = \frac{k}{N}$ **19.** $I = \frac{k}{R}$ **21.** $I = \frac{k}{d^2}$ **23.** Yes
25. No   **27.** $F = \frac{kSm}{r}$

Chapter 8 Review

1. No   **3.** $2, -4, -7$ **5.** $-7, 1, 2$ **9.** No
11. $c = 0.35 + 0.25m$; input 5, output 1.60; cost is \$1.60   **13.** $y = \frac{1}{2}x$ **15.** \$247.50   **17.** $y = \frac{30}{x}$
19. $y = \frac{0.65}{x}$ **21.** 5 hours

Chapter 9

Section 9-1 TRY THIS

1. Yes   **2.** No   **3.** $(-2, -1)$ **4.** $(0, 5)$

Exercise Set 9-1

1. Yes   **3.** No   **5.** Yes   **7.** Yes   **9.** Yes
11. $(2, 1)$ **13.** $(-12, 11)$ **15.** $(4, 3)$
17. $(-3, -3)$ **19.** No solution   **21.** $(2, 2)$
23. $(5, 3)$ **25.** Infinitely many solutions
27. $A = 2, B = 2$ **29.** The slopes are equal, the
intercepts are equal.   **31.** Non-integer solutions are
difficult to approximate from graphs. Other methods
are needed, $(\frac{2}{3}, \frac{3}{7})$.

Section 9-2 TRY THIS

1. $(3, 2)$ **2.** $(1, -3)$ **3.** $(\frac{24}{5}, -\frac{8}{5})$ **4.** $(\frac{5}{2}, 5)$
5. 63, 21   **6.** 85, 17

Exercise Set 9-2

1. $(1, 3)$ **3.** $(1, 2)$ **5.** $(4, 3)$ **7.** $(-2, 1)$
9. $(-1, -3)$ **11.** $(\frac{17}{3}, \frac{16}{3})$ **13.** $(\frac{25}{8}, -\frac{11}{4})$
15. $(-3, 0)$ **17.** $(6, 3)$ **19.** No solution   **21.** 15,
12   **23.** 37, 21   **25.** 28, 12   **27.** 120 m, 80 m
29. 100 yd, $53\frac{1}{3}$ yd   **31.** $(10, -2)$ **33.** No
35. $w = \dfrac{y - 16}{4}$ **37.** $(30, 50, 100)$ **39.** The

x-terms drop out and leave $15 = 15$. The lines coincide, so all solutions to one equation are solutions of
the system.

Section 9-3 TRY THIS

1. $(3, 2)$ **2.** $(1, -1)$ **3.** $(1, 4)$ **4.** $(3, \frac{13}{11})$
5. $(1, 1)$ **6.** $(13, 3)$ **7.** $(1, -1)$ **8.** $(2, -4)$
9. 126, 90   **10.** 75 miles

Exercise Set 9-3

1. $(9, 1)$ **3.** $(3, 5)$ **5.** $(3, 0)$ **7.** $(-\frac{1}{2}, 3)$
9. $(-1, \frac{1}{5})$ **11.** No solution   **13.** $(-3, -5)$
15. $(4, 5)$ **17.** $(4, 1)$ **19.** $(4, 3)$ **21.** $(1, -1)$
23. $(-3, -1)$ **25.** $(2, -2)$ **27.** $(5, \frac{1}{2})$ **29.** 56, 36
31. 68, 47   **33.** 150 mi   **35.** $137°, 43°$ **37.** $62°$,
$28°$ **39.** 480, 340   **41.** $(5, 2)$ **43.** $(1, -1)$
45. $(525, 1000)$ **47.** $\left(\dfrac{b-c}{1-a}, \dfrac{b-ac}{1-a} \right)$ **49.** $(4, 3)$
51a. $x = \dfrac{ce - bf}{ae - bd}, y = \dfrac{af - cd}{ae - bd}$ **51b.** $(2722.4, 1.4)$

Section 9-4 TRY THIS

1. 16, 20   **2.** 16 km   **3.** 4   **4.** 14, 21   **5.** 14

Exercise Set 9-4

1. 69 nickels, 81 dimes   **3.** 18, 9   **5.** \$1.15, \$0.95
7. 28, 10   **9.** 16, 14   **11.** 10 rock, 14 blue   **13.** 73
15. 3200 bumper stickers, 1800 cycles   **17.** 12 rabbits, 23 pheasants   **19.** $5x + 2y = 43$, 74 is the only
possible solution.   **21.** glove \$79.95, bat \$14.50,
ball \$4.55

Section 9-5 TRY THIS

1. 168 km   **2.** 275 km/h   **3.** $35t + 40t = 200$, $t =$
$2\frac{2}{3}$ h   **4.** $d = 35t$, $d + 15 = 40t$, $t = 3$ h, $d = 105$ mi

Exercise Set 9-5

1. 2 hr   **3.** 4.5 hr   **5.** $7\frac{1}{2}$ hours after first train
leaves   **7.** 14 km/h   **9.** 384 km   **11.** 330 km/h
13. 15 mi   **15.** ~317.03 km/h   **17.** 90 mi, 48 mi
19. 144 mi   **21.** 40 min

Section 9-6 TRY THIS

1. 7 quarters, 13 dimes   **2.** 8 dimes, 11 nickels
3. 135, 31   **4.** 75 kg of 90¢, 100 kg of \$1.60

Exercise Set 9-6

1. 70 dimes, 33 quarters   **3.** 300 nickels, 100 dimes
5. 203 adults, 226 children   **7.** 130 adults, 70 students   **9.** 40 g of A, 60 g of B   **11.** 43.75 L
13. 80 L of 30%, 120 L of 50%   **15.** 6 kg of cashews,
4 kg of pecans   **17.** 39   **19.** 12,500 at 12%, 14,500
at 13%   **21.** 10 at \$20, 5 at \$25   **23.** 40 lb silver,
80 lb lead   **25.** $4\frac{4}{7}$ liters

Chapter 9 Review

1. No   **3.** Yes   **5.** $(6, -2)$ **7.** $(2, -3)$ **9.** $(0, 5)$
11. $(1, -2)$ **13.** $(1, 4)$ **15.** $10, -2$ **17.** $(1, 4)$
19. $(-4, 1)$ **21.** $(-2, -6)$ **23.** $(2, -4)$
25. 12 and 15   **27.** 135 km/h   **29.** 40 L of each

Chapter 10

Section 10-1 TRY THIS

1a. Yes   **1b.** Yes   **1c.** Yes   **1d.** No   **1e.** No
2a. Yes   **2b.** No   **2c.** No   **2d.** Yes   **2e.** No
3. $x > 2$ **4.** $x < 13$ **5.** $x > 9$ **6.** $x < 2$
7. $x < -3$ **8.** $y \leq -3$ **9.** $y < -21$ **10.** $y > \frac{9}{8}$

Exercise Set 10-1

1a. No   **1b.** No   **1c.** No   **1d.** Yes   **3a.** No
3b. No   **3c.** Yes   **3d.** Yes   **5a.** No   **5b.** No

5c. Yes   **5d.** No   **7a.** Yes   **7b.** Yes   **7c.** Yes
7d. No   **9.** $x > -5$ **11.** $y > 3$ **13.** $x \leq -18$
15. $a < -6$ **17.** $x \leq 16$ **19.** $x > 8$ **21.** $y > -5$
23. $x > 2$ **25.** $x \leq -3$ **27.** $x \geq 13$ **29.** $x < 4$
31. $y \geq -11$ **33.** $c > 0$ **35.** $y \leq \frac{1}{4}$ **37.** $x > \frac{7}{12}$
39. $x > 0$ **41.** $r < -2$ **43.** $x \geq 1$ **45.** $x > -11.8$
47. $x \leq -1.2$ **49.** True   **51.** $x \geq 6$ **53.** Yes, if
$a > b$ and $b > c$, $a > c$. Yes, if $a \leq b$ and $b \leq c$, $a \leq c$.

Section 10–2 TRY THIS

1. $x < 8$ **2.** $y > 32$ **3.** $t < 28$ **4.** $s > 9$
5. $x \leq -6$ **6.** $y > -\frac{13}{5}$ **7.** $t > 5$ **8.** $n < -2$
9. $y \leq -\frac{1}{2}$ **10.** $x > -\frac{1}{18}$ **11.** $x \geq -\frac{5}{16}$
12. $y \leq \frac{3}{28}$

Exercise Set 10–2

1. $x < 7$ **3.** $y \leq 9$ **5.** $y > 12$ **7.** $x < \frac{13}{7}$
9. $y \geq \frac{15}{4}$ **11.** $y \leq \frac{1}{2}$ **13.** $y \geq -3$ **15.** $x < -3$
17. $y \geq -\frac{2}{5}$ **19.** $x \geq -6$ **21.** $y \geq -4$
23. $y < -60$ **25.** $x > 2$ **27.** $y \leq 2$ **29.** $x > \frac{17}{2}$
31. $y \leq \frac{31}{8}$ **33.** $y > -\frac{1}{21}$ **35.** $x \leq \frac{1}{7}$ **37.** $x \leq 0.9$
39. $x > 5.0625$ **41.** $y \geq 700$ **43.** $q > 180$
45. $x \leq -\frac{1}{112.5}$ **47.** False. $-2 > -3$ but $4 < 9$

Section 10–3 TRY THIS

1. $x > -\frac{1}{4}$ **2.** $x \leq -1$ **3.** $x \geq \frac{21}{5}$ **4.** $x > 6$
5. $y > \frac{19}{9}$ **6.** $y < \frac{3}{4}$ **7.** $x \leq \frac{8}{5}$ **8.** $x \geq -\frac{5}{4}$

Exercise Set 10–3

1. $x < 8$ **3.** $y \geq 6$ **5.** $x \leq 6$ **7.** $y > 4$
9. $x < -3$ **11.** $x \geq -2$ **13.** $y < -3$ **15.** $x > -3$
17. $y < -\frac{10}{3}$ **19.** $x \leq 7$ **21.** $x > -10$ **23.** $y < 2$
25. $y \geq 3$ **27.** $y > -2$ **29.** $y > -2$ **31.** $y \leq \frac{33}{7}$
33. $x < \frac{9}{5}$ **35.** $t \leq 0$ **37.** $y < \frac{2.2}{7}$ **39.** $x \leq 9$
41. $y \leq -3$ **43.** $x > \frac{8}{3}$ **45.** $x \leq -4a$ **47.** $x \geq \frac{3y}{2}$
49. $x \geq y$ and $x \leq y$, so $x = y$.

Section 10–4 TRY THIS

1. 94   **2.** $w \leq 34$ **3.** 16, 17

Exercise Set 10–4

1. 97   **3.** 9, 11   **5.** 8, 6   **7.** $n < 5$ **9.** $J > 15$,
$G > 12$ **11.** \$16.68, \$8.34   **13.** 20
15. $l \geq 18.75$ cm   **17.** $s \leq 8$ cm

Exercise Set 10–5

39. Never   **41.** positive   **43a.** Always true
43b. Always true   **43c.** Not true when $x \geq 0$
43d. Always true   **43e.** Not true when $-1 \leq x \leq 1$

43f. Not true when $x \leq 0$ **45.** Yes   **47a.** $-3, -2,$
$-1, 0, 1, 2, 3$ **47b.** $2b$ and zero, or $2b + 1$

Section 10–6 TRY THIS

1. Yes   **2.** No

Exercise Set 10–6

1. No   **3.** Yes   **43.** $xy \leq 0$

Exercise Set 10–7

21. $-x + 3y < 4$ and $-x + 3y > 4$, so there is no
solution   **27.** (5, 3), 19

Chapter 10 Review

1. Yes   **3.** Yes   **5.** $x < -11$ **7.** $y > -7$
9. $x \geq -\frac{1}{12}$ **11.** $x > -6$ **13.** $x > -\frac{9}{11}$ **15.** 86
17. $x < 1$ **19.** $x > 4$ or $x < -2$ **21.** No

Chapter 11

Section 11–1 TRY THIS

1. $\dfrac{x^2 + 5x + 6}{5x + 20}$ **2.** $\dfrac{-12}{4x^2 - 1}$ **3.** $\dfrac{2x^2 + x}{3x^2 - 2x}$
4. $\dfrac{x^2 + 3x + 2}{x^2 - 4}$ **5.** $\dfrac{8 - x}{y - x}$ **6.** $\dfrac{y + 2}{4}$ **7.** $\dfrac{2x + 1}{3x + 2}$
8. $\dfrac{x + 1}{2x + 1}$ **9.** $\dfrac{a - 2}{a - 3}$ **10.** $\dfrac{x - 5}{2}$

Exercise Set 11–1

1. $\dfrac{3x^2 + 12x}{2x - 2}$ **3.** $\dfrac{x^2 - 1}{x^2 + 4x + 4}$ **5.** $\dfrac{2x^2 + 5x + 3}{4x - 20}$
7. $\dfrac{a^2 - 3a - 10}{a^4 - 1}$ **9.** $\dfrac{x^2 - 1}{x^2 + 3x + 2}$ **11.** $\dfrac{3y^2 - y}{2y^2 + y}$
13. $\dfrac{a - 3}{a + 2}$ **15.** $\dfrac{t + 2}{2(t - 4)}$ **17.** $\dfrac{x + 5}{x - 5}$ **19.** $a + 1$
21. $\dfrac{x^2 + 1}{x + 1}$ **23.** $\dfrac{3}{2}$ **25.** $\dfrac{6}{t - 3}$ **27.** $\dfrac{a - 3}{a - 4}$
29. $\dfrac{t - 2}{t + 2}$ **31.** $\dfrac{x + 2}{x - 2}$ **33.** $\dfrac{a^2 - 9}{a^2 + 4a}$ **35.** $\dfrac{2a}{a - 2}$
37. $\dfrac{2}{y - 2}$ **39.** 1   **41.** $\dfrac{x^2 - 4}{x^2 - 1}$ **43.** $\dfrac{t - 2}{t - 1}$
45. $x + 2y$ **47.** $\dfrac{(t - 1)(t - 9)^2}{(t^2 + 9)(t + 1)}$ **49.** $\dfrac{x - y}{x - 5y}$
51. -2 **53.** 0, 2, 7

Section 11–2 TRY THIS

1. 8   **2.** $\dfrac{x^2 - 5x + 6}{x^2 + 10x + 25}$ **3.** $\dfrac{3x - 3}{2x^2 - 8}$ **4.** $\dfrac{x - 3}{x + 2}$
5. $x + 3$ **6.** $\dfrac{y + 1}{y - 1}$

Exercise Set 11-2

1. $\dfrac{15}{8}$ **3.** $\dfrac{15}{4}$ **5.** $\dfrac{a-5}{3a-3}$ **7.** $\dfrac{x^2+4x+4}{x}$ **9.** $\dfrac{3}{2}$

11. $\dfrac{c+1}{c-1}$ **13.** $\dfrac{y-3}{2y-1}$ **15.** $\dfrac{1}{c^2-10c+25}$

17. $\dfrac{t+5}{t-5}$ **19.** $\dfrac{a}{(c-3d)(2a+5b)}$ **21.** $\dfrac{-1}{b^2}$ **23.** x

25. $\dfrac{4}{x+7}$ **27.** $\dfrac{3(y+2)^3}{y(y-1)}$ **29.** $\dfrac{-1}{a}$

Section 11-3 TRY THIS

1. $2x^3+3x-\dfrac{5}{2}$ **2.** x^2+3x+2 **3.** $x-2$

4. $x+4+\dfrac{-1}{x-2}$ **5.** $x^2-3x+2+\dfrac{4}{x+3}$

6. x^2+x+1

Exercise Set 11-3

1. $3x^4-\dfrac{x^3}{2}+\dfrac{x^2}{8}-2$ **3.** $1-2u-u^4$ **5.** $5t^2+$
$8t-2$ **7.** $-4x^4+4x^2+1$ **9.** $6x^2-10x+\dfrac{3}{2}$

11. $-3rs-r+2s$ **13.** $x+2$ **15.** $x-5+\dfrac{-50}{x-5}$

17. $x-2+\dfrac{-2}{x+6}$ **19.** $x-3$ **21.** $x^4-x^3+x^2-$
$x+1$ **23.** $2x^2-7x+4$ **25.** x^3-6 **27.** x^3+
$2x^2+4x+8$ **29.** t^2+1 **31.** x^2+5 **33.** $a+$
$3+\dfrac{5}{5a^2-7a-2}$ **35.** $2x^2+x-3$ **37.** a^5+a^4b+
$a^3b^2+a^2b^3+ab^4+b^5$ **39.** $3a^{2h}+2a^h-5$ **41.** 2

Section 11-4 TRY THIS

1. $x-5$ **2.** $\dfrac{2(x-3)}{x-1}$ **3.** $\dfrac{x-5}{4}$ **4.** $\dfrac{3(x+1)}{x-3}$

5. $\dfrac{4y^2-3x^2-9}{3x-5}$

Exercise Set 11-4

1. $\dfrac{2(x-2)(x-1)}{2x-1}$ **3.** $\dfrac{-2(x-3)}{(x-1)^2}$ **5.** $\dfrac{11-5x}{6}$

7. $\dfrac{13}{a}$ **9.** $\dfrac{-2x+5}{4}$ **11.** 0 **13.** $\dfrac{x-2}{x-7}$

15. $\dfrac{t^2+4}{t-2}$ **17.** 0 **19.** $\dfrac{-2(5x+4)}{2x-3}$

21. $\dfrac{4x}{x^2-5x-8}$ **23.** $\dfrac{3x^2+2x-3}{(x-2)(x-3)}$ **25.** $\dfrac{-7x+6}{x-5}$

27. $\dfrac{10x+2}{2x-3}$ **29.** $\dfrac{x^2-7x+16}{(x+3)(x-3)}$ **31.** 0

33. $\dfrac{2b-a-c}{a-b+c}$ **35.** $\dfrac{x}{3x+1}$

Section 11-5 TRY THIS

1. $60x^3y^2$ **2.** $(y+1)^2(y+4)$ **3.** $(t^2+16)(t-2)$
4. $3(a+b)(a-b)$ **5.** $3x(x+1)^2(x-1)$
6. $\dfrac{56x^2+9x}{48}$ **7.** $\dfrac{x^2+6x-8}{(x-2)(x+2)}$

8. $\dfrac{4x^2-x+3}{x(x-1)(x+1)^2}$ **9.** $\dfrac{8x+88}{(x+16)(x+1)(x+8)}$

10. $\dfrac{-x^2+4}{x^2-16}$

Exercise Set 11-5

1. c^3d^2 **3.** $(x-y)(x+y)$ **5.** $6(y-3)$
7. $t(t+2)(t-2)$ **9.** $(x+2)(x-2)(x+3)$
11. $t(t+2)^2(t-4)$ **13.** $(a-1)^2(a+1)$
15. $(m-2)^2(m-3)$ **17.** $(3x+2)(3x-2)$
19. $10v(v+3)(v+4)$ **21.** $18x^3(x-2)^2(x+1)$
23. $6x^3(x+2)^2(x-2)$ **25.** $\dfrac{2x+5}{x^2}$ **27.** $\dfrac{41}{24r}$

29. $\dfrac{x^2+4xy+y^2}{x^2y^2}$ **31.** $\dfrac{6x}{(x-2)(x+2)}$

33. $\dfrac{11x+2}{3x(x+1)}$ **35.** $\dfrac{x^2+6x}{(x-4)(x+4)}$ **37.** $\dfrac{6}{z+4}$

39. $\dfrac{3x-1}{(x-1)^2}$ **41.** $\dfrac{11a}{10(a-2)}$ **43.** $\dfrac{2x^2+8x+16}{x(x+4)}$

45. $\dfrac{x^2+5x+1}{(x+1)^2(x+4)}$ **47.** $\dfrac{2x^2-4x+34}{(x-5)(x+3)}$

49. $\dfrac{3a+2}{(a-1)(a+1)}$ **51.** $\dfrac{2x+6y}{(x-y)(x+y)}$

53. $\dfrac{3x^2+19x-20}{(x+3)(x-2)^2}$ **55.** $\dfrac{-x-4}{6}$ **57.** $\dfrac{y-19}{4y}$

59. $\dfrac{7z-12}{12z}$ **61.** $\dfrac{-6x^2+13xy+3y^2}{2x^2y^2}$

63. $\dfrac{2x-40}{(x+5)(x-5)}$ **65.** $\dfrac{x+12}{(x-3)(x+3)}$

67. $\dfrac{3-5t}{2t(t-1)}$ **69.** $\dfrac{2s-st-s^2}{(t+s)(t-s)}$

71. $\dfrac{x-6}{(x+4)(x+6)}$ **73.** $\dfrac{16y+28}{15}$, $\dfrac{y^2+2y-8}{15}$

75. $\dfrac{(z+6)(2z-3)}{z^2-4}$ **77.** $\dfrac{11z^4-22z^2+6}{(2z^2-3)(z^2+2)(z^2-2)}$

79. $\dfrac{5x^2}{x^2+y^2}-\dfrac{2xy}{x^2+y^2}$ **81.** Every 60 years

Section 11-6 TRY THIS

1. $\dfrac{6x^2-2x-2}{3x(x+1)}$ **2.** $\dfrac{-10x+2}{3(x+2)(x-1)}$ **3.** $\dfrac{20}{21}$

4. $\dfrac{2(x+6)}{5}$ **5.** $\dfrac{7x^2}{3(2-x^2)}$ **6.** $\dfrac{x}{x-1}$

Exercise Set 11-6

1. $\dfrac{2}{y(y-1)}$ **3.** $\dfrac{z-3}{2z-1}$ **5.** $\dfrac{-3x+1}{(2x-3)(x+1)}$

7. $\dfrac{1}{2c-1}$ **9.** 0 **11.** $\dfrac{25}{4}$ **13.** $\dfrac{1+3x}{1-5x}$ **15.** $\dfrac{5}{3y^2}$

17. $\dfrac{x+y}{x}$ **19.** $\dfrac{(x-1)(3x-2)}{5x-3}$ **21.** $\dfrac{ac}{bd}$ **23.** x^5

25. $\dfrac{-2z(5z-2)}{(z+2)(-13z+6)}$

578 Selected Answers

Section 11−7 TRY THIS

1. $\frac{33}{8}$ **2.** 3 **3.** 1 **4.** 2 **5.** $-\frac{1}{8}$

Exercise Set 11−7

1. $\frac{47}{2}$ **3.** −6 **5.** $\frac{24}{7}$ **7.** −4; −1 **9.** 4, −4
11. 3 **13.** $\frac{14}{3}$ **15.** 10 **17.** 5 **19.** $\frac{5}{2}$ **21.** −1
23. $\frac{17}{2}$ **25.** No solution **27.** −5 **29.** $\frac{5}{3}$ **31.** $\frac{1}{2}$
33. No solution **35.** 7 **37.** $-\frac{1}{30}$ **39.** 2, −2
41. 4, −3 **43.** $\frac{4}{3}$, $-\frac{4}{3}$

Section 11−8 TRY THIS

1. $3\frac{3}{7}$ hr **2.** $34\frac{2}{7}$ km/h, $44\frac{2}{7}$ km/h **3.** −3
4. 2074 **5.** 769,231 **6.** 5.306 tons

Exercise Set 11−8

1. $1\frac{7}{8}$ hr **3.** $10\frac{2}{7}$ hr **5.** 30 km/h, 70 km/h
7. p: 80 km/h, f: 66 km/h **9.** $\frac{1}{2}x + \frac{1}{x} = \frac{51}{x}$, $x = 10$
11. 204 **13.** 420 **15a.** 1.992 tons **15b.** 14.94 kg
17. $\frac{92}{54} = \frac{24}{x}$, $x = 14\frac{2}{23}$ ft **19.** $9x + 17x = 104$,
$x = 4$, $\frac{36}{68}$ **21.** Ex. $\frac{B}{A} = \frac{D}{C}$, $\frac{A}{C} = \frac{B}{D}$, $\frac{C}{A} = \frac{D}{B}$, $\frac{D}{C} = \frac{B}{A}$,
equal **23.** 6, 8 **25.** $27\frac{3}{11}$ min or $\frac{5}{11}$ hr
27. Michelle 6 hr, Sal 3 hr, Kristen 4 hr

Section 11−9 TRY THIS

1. 1. $(ab) \cdot \left(\frac{1}{a} \cdot \frac{1}{b}\right) = \left[\left(a \cdot b \cdot \frac{1}{a}\right) \cdot \frac{1}{b}\right]$, Assoc. prop.;
2. $\left[\left(a \cdot b \cdot \frac{1}{a}\right) \cdot \frac{1}{b}\right] = \left[\left(a \cdot \frac{1}{a} \cdot b\right) \cdot \frac{1}{b}\right]$, Comm. prop.;
3. $\left[\left(a \cdot \frac{1}{a} \cdot b\right) \cdot \frac{1}{b}\right] = \left[\left(a \cdot \frac{1}{a}\right) \cdot \left(b \cdot \frac{1}{b}\right)\right]$, Assoc. prop.;
4. $\left[\left(a \cdot \frac{1}{a}\right) \cdot \left(b \cdot \frac{1}{b}\right)\right] = 1 \cdot 1$, Def. of reciprocal;
5. $1 \cdot 1 = 1$, Prop. of 1; 6. $(ab) \cdot \left(\frac{1}{a} \cdot \frac{1}{b}\right) = 1$, Statements 1-5. **2.** 3. Assoc. prop.; 4. Mult. of fractions;
5. Div. theorem; 6. Trans. prop. of equality

Exercise Set 11−9

1. 3. Distr. law; 4. Div. theorem; 5. Trans. prop. of
equality **3.** 1. $\frac{a}{b} \cdot \frac{b}{a} = \left(a \cdot \frac{1}{b}\right) \cdot \left(b \cdot \frac{1}{a}\right)$, Div. theorem;
2. $\left(a \cdot \frac{1}{b}\right) \cdot \left(b \cdot \frac{1}{a}\right) = \left(a \cdot \frac{1}{a}\right) \cdot \left(b \cdot \frac{1}{b}\right)$, Assoc. and
Comm. props.; 3. $\left(a \cdot \frac{1}{a}\right) \cdot \left(b \cdot \frac{1}{b}\right) = 1 \cdot 1 = 1$, Def. of
reciprocal, prop. of 1; 4. $\frac{a}{b} \cdot \frac{b}{a} = 1$, Statements 1-3;
5. The reciprocal of $\frac{a}{b}$ is $\frac{b}{a}$, Def. of reciprocal.

Chapter 11 Review

1. $\frac{3t^2 - 3t}{5t + 20}$ **3.** $\frac{x - 2}{x + 1}$ **5.** $\frac{a - 6}{5}$ **7.** −20t
9. $5x^2 - \frac{1}{2}x + 3$ **11.** $\frac{-3x + 18}{x + 7}$ **13.** $\frac{3}{x - 2}$
15. $30x^2y^2$ **17.** $(y^2 - 4)(y + 1)$ **19.** $\frac{2a}{a - 1}$
21. $\frac{-x^2 + x + 26}{(x - 5)(x + 5)(x + 1)}$ **23.** $\frac{z}{1 + z}$ **25.** 2
27. 240 km/h, 280 km/h **29.** 160

Chapter 12

Section 12−1 TRY THIS

1. 13, −13 **2.** −10 **3.** 16 **4.** Irrational
5. Rational **6.** Irrational **7.** Irrational
8. Rational **9.** Rational **10.** Rational
11. Irrational **12.** 2.236 **13.** 8.485

Exercise Set 12−1

1. 1, −1 **3.** 4, −4 **5.** 10, −10 **7.** 13, −13
9. 2 **11.** −3 **13.** −8 **15.** −15 **17.** −19
19. Irrational **21.** Irrational **23.** Rational
25. Irrational **27.** Rational **29.** Irrational
31. Rational **33.** Rational **35.** Rational
37. Rational **39.** Rational **41.** Irrational
43. Irrational **45.** 2.450 **47.** 4.359 **49.** 6.557
51. 2 **53.** −5, −6 **55.** $\sqrt{113}$ **57.** 1 is $(-1)^2$
and 1^3, 64 is 8^2 and 4^3. **59.** $\frac{12}{7}$

Section 12−2 TRY THIS

1. No **2.** Yes **3.** $a \geq 0$ **4.** $x \geq 3$ **5.** $x \geq \frac{5}{2}$
6. All replacements **7.** $|xy|$ **8.** $|xy|$ **9.** $|x - 1|$
10. $|x + 4|$ **11.** $5|y|$ **12.** $\frac{1}{2}|t|$

Exercise Set 12−2

1. $x \geq 0$ **3.** $t \geq 5$ **5.** $y \geq -8$ **7.** $x \geq -20$
9. $y \geq \frac{7}{2}$ **11.** any value **13.** $|t|$ **15.** $3|x|$ **17.** 7
19. $4|d|$ **21.** $|x + 3|$ **23.** $|a - 5|$ **25.** 6, −6
27. 3, −3 **29.** $3|a|$ **31.** $2\left|\frac{x^4}{y^3}\right|$ **33.** $\frac{13}{m^8}$
35. $m \geq 0$ and $m \leq -3$ **37.** $x \geq 2$ and $x \leq -3$
39. $x \geq 2$ and $x \leq -2$ **41.** a, b, e

Section 12−3 TRY THIS

1. 56 **2.** 44 **3.** $\sqrt{21}$ **4.** 5 **5.** $\sqrt{x^2 + x}$
6. $\sqrt{x^2 - 1}$ **7.** $4\sqrt{2}$ **8.** $5|x|$ **9.** $8\sqrt{t}$
10. $2a\sqrt{19}$ **11.** 16.585 **12.** 10.099

Exercise Set 12-3

1. $\sqrt{6}$ **3.** $\sqrt{12} = 2\sqrt{3}$ **5.** $\sqrt{\frac{3}{10}}$ **7.** 17
9. $\sqrt{75} = 5\sqrt{3}$ **11.** $\sqrt{2x}$ **13.** $\sqrt{0.72}$ **15.** $\sqrt{xt}$
17. $\sqrt{x^2 - 3x}$ **19.** $\sqrt{10x - 5}$ **21.** $\sqrt{x^2 + 3x + 2}$
23. $\sqrt{2x^2 - 2x - 12}$ **25.** $\sqrt{x^2 - 16}$ **27.** $\sqrt{x^2 - y^2}$
29. No real value **31.** $2\sqrt{3}$ **33.** $5\sqrt{3}$ **35.** $2\sqrt{5}$
37. $10\sqrt{2}$ **39.** $\sqrt{3}\sqrt{x}$ **41.** $3\sqrt{x}$ **43.** $4\sqrt{a}$
45. $8|y|$ **47.** $|x|\sqrt{13}$ **49.** $2|t|\sqrt{2}$ **51.** 11.180
53. 13.416 **55.** 18.972 **57.** 10.248 **59.** 17.320
61. 11.961 **63.** 44.720 **65.** 27.712
67. $\sqrt{3}\sqrt{x - 1}$ **69.** $\sqrt{x + 2}\sqrt{x - 2}$ **71.** $x\sqrt{x - 2}$
73. 0.1 **75.** x^2 **77.** 7, $7\sqrt{10}$, 70, $70\sqrt{10}$, 700;
Each is $\sqrt{10}$ times the last. **79.** = **81.** > **83.** >
85. = **87.** 20, 37.4, 54.8

Section 12-4 TRY THIS

1. $2\sqrt{15x}$ **2.** $3x\sqrt{5}$ **3.** $\sqrt{3}\,(x - 1)$ **4.** y^4
5. $(x + y)^7$ **6.** $t^7\sqrt{t}$ **7.** $3\sqrt{2y}$ **8.** $10x$
9. $4x^3y^2$ **10.** $5xy^2\sqrt{2xy}$

Exercise Set 12-4

1. $6\sqrt{5}$ **3.** $4\sqrt{3x}$ **5.** $12\sqrt{2y}$ **7.** $2x\sqrt{5}$
9. $\sqrt{2}(2x + 1)$ **11.** $\sqrt{y}(6 + y)$ **13.** x^3 **15.** x^6
17. $x^2\sqrt{x}$ **19.** $t^9\sqrt{t}$ **21.** $(y - 2)^4$
23. $2(x + 5)^5$ **25.** $6m\sqrt{m}$ **27.** $2a^2\sqrt{2a}$
29. $8x^3y\sqrt{7y}$ **31.** $3\sqrt{6}$ **33.** $3\sqrt{10}$ **35.** $6\sqrt{7x}$
37. $6\sqrt{xy}$ **39.** 10 **41.** $5b\sqrt{3}$ **43.** $2t$
45. $a\sqrt{bc}$ **47.** $2xy\sqrt{2xy}$ **49.** $6xy^3\sqrt{3xy}$
51. $10ab^2\sqrt{5ab}$ **53.** $a^2 - 5\sqrt{a}$ **55.** $6(x - 2)^2\sqrt{10}$
57. $0.2x^{2n}$ **59.** $7y^{13}x^{157}\sqrt{3xy}$ **61.** Only if $B = 0$
63. $y^{(n-1)/2}\sqrt{y}$ **65.** 2

Section 12-5 TRY THIS

1. $\frac{4}{3}$ **2.** $\frac{1}{5}$ **3.** $\frac{1}{3}$ **4.** $\frac{3}{4}$ **5.** $\frac{15}{16}$ **6.** $\frac{1}{7}\sqrt{21}$
7. $\sqrt{\frac{10}{16}} = \frac{1}{4}\sqrt{10}$ **8.** $\frac{1}{9}\sqrt{6}$ **9.** 0.534 **10.** 0.791
11. 0.624

Exercise Set 12-5

1. $\frac{3}{7}$ **3.** $\frac{1}{6}$ **5.** $-\frac{4}{9}$ **7.** $\frac{8}{17}$ **9.** $-\frac{3}{10}$ **11.** $\frac{3}{5}$
13. $\frac{1}{5}\sqrt{10}$ **15.** $\frac{1}{4}\sqrt{6}$ **17.** $\frac{1}{6}\sqrt{21}$ **19.** $\frac{1}{6}\sqrt{2}$
21. $\frac{1}{2}\sqrt{2}$ **23.** $\frac{2}{3}\sqrt{6}$ **25.** $\frac{1}{x}\sqrt{3x}$ **27.** $\frac{1}{y}\sqrt{xy}$
29. $\frac{x\sqrt{2}}{6}$ **31.** 0.577 **33.** 0.935 **35.** 0.289
37. 0.707 **39.** 0.592 **41.** 0.850 **43.** $\frac{6}{x}$ **45.** $\frac{3a}{25}$
47. $\frac{\sqrt{5}}{4}$ **49.** $\frac{\sqrt{5x}}{5x^2}$ **51.** $\frac{\sqrt{3ab}}{b}$ **53.** $\frac{\sqrt{70}}{100}$
55. 1.57, 3.14, 8.88, 11.10 **57.** 1 second

Section 12-6 TRY THIS

1. 1 **2.** $\frac{1}{3}\sqrt{3}$ **3.** $x\sqrt{6}$ **4.** $\frac{\sqrt{35}}{7}$ **5.** $\frac{\sqrt{xy}}{y}$
6. $\frac{4x^3\sqrt{3x}}{9}$

Exercise Set 12-6

1. 3 **3.** 2 **5.** $\sqrt{5}$ **7.** $\frac{1}{5}$ **9.** $\frac{2}{5}$ **11.** 2 **13.** $3y$
15. $x^2\sqrt{5}$ **17.** $\frac{1}{3}\sqrt{21}$ **19.** $\frac{3}{4}\sqrt{2}$ **21.** 2
23. $\frac{1}{2}\sqrt{5}$ **25.** $\frac{\sqrt{10}}{5}$ **27.** $\sqrt{2}$ **29.** $\frac{\sqrt{55}}{11}$ **31.** $\frac{\sqrt{21}}{6}$
33. $\frac{\sqrt{6}}{2}$ **35.** 5 **37.** $\frac{\sqrt{3x}}{x}$ **39.** $\frac{4y\sqrt{3}}{3}$ **41.** $\frac{a\sqrt{2a}}{4}$
43. $\frac{\sqrt{42x}}{3x}$ **45.** $\frac{3\sqrt{6}}{8c}$ **47.** $\frac{y\sqrt{xy}}{x}$ **49.** $\frac{\sqrt{2}}{4a}$
51. $\frac{\sqrt{6}}{9}$ **53.** $\frac{\sqrt{10}}{3}$ **55.** $\frac{8\sqrt{2}}{21}$ **57.** -44 **59.** 3

Section 12-7 TRY THIS

1. $12\sqrt{2}$ **2.** $5\sqrt{5}$ **3.** $-12\sqrt{10}$ **4.** $5\sqrt{6y}$
5. $\sqrt{x + 1}$ **6.** $\frac{3}{2}\sqrt{2}$ **7.** $\frac{2\sqrt{15}}{15}$ **8.** $2\sqrt{x}$

Exercise Set 12-7

1. $7\sqrt{2}$ **3.** $4\sqrt{5}$ **5.** $13\sqrt{x}$ **7.** $-2\sqrt{x}$ **9.** $25\sqrt{2}$
11. $\sqrt{3}$ **13.** $\sqrt{5}$ **15.** $13\sqrt{2}$ **17.** $3\sqrt{3}$
19. $-24\sqrt{2}$ **21.** $6\sqrt{2} - 6\sqrt{3}$ **23.** $(2 + 9x)\sqrt{x}$
25. $(3 - 2x)\sqrt{3}$ **27.** $3\sqrt{2x + 2}$
29. $(x + 3)\sqrt{x^3 - 1}$ **31.** $(-x^2 + 3xy + y^2)\sqrt{xy}$
33. $-2(a + b)\sqrt{2(a + b)}$ **35.** $\frac{2\sqrt{3}}{3}$ **37.** $\frac{13\sqrt{2}}{2}$
39. $\frac{\sqrt{6}}{6}$ **41.** $\frac{-\sqrt{3}}{18}$ **43a.** None **43b.** $\sqrt{10} + 5\sqrt{2}$
45. $16\sqrt{2}$ **47.** $11\sqrt{3} - 10\sqrt{2}$ **49.** 0
51. $\frac{x + 1}{x}\sqrt{x}$ **53.** $\left(2 - \frac{2}{a^2} + \frac{5a}{4}\right)\sqrt{2ab}$
55. x or y is 0, the other is any number
57. $\frac{24 + 3\sqrt{3} + 8\sqrt{2} + \sqrt{6}}{7}$

Section 12-8 TRY THIS

1. $\sqrt{65} = 8.062$ **2.** $\sqrt{75} = 8.660$ **3.** $\sqrt{10} = 3.162$
4. $\sqrt{175} = 5\sqrt{7} = 13.229$ **5.** $5\sqrt{13} = 18.028$ ft

Exercise Set 12-8

1. 17 **3.** $4\sqrt{2}$ **5.** 12 **7.** 4 **9.** 26 **11.** 12
13. 2 **15.** $\sqrt{2}$ **17.** 5 **19.** $3\sqrt{2}$ or 4.24 cm
21. $5\sqrt{10}$ or 15.81 m **23.** $90\sqrt{2}$ or 127.28 ft
25. $\frac{a^2}{4}\sqrt{3}$ **27.** $50\sqrt{10} \approx 158$ ft **29.** $\sqrt{193} \approx$
13.89 in. **31.** $10\sqrt{3}$ **33.** $\sqrt{1525} = 5\sqrt{61} \approx$
39.05 mi, 1.28 hr **35.** $\frac{\sqrt{3}}{2}$

Section 12−9 TRY THIS

1. $\frac{64}{3}$ **2.** $\frac{169}{20}$ **3.** 2 **4.** 66 **5.** 313.05 km
6. 15.652 km **7.** 303.76 m

Exercise Set 12−9

1. 25 **3.** 38.44 **5.** 397 **7.** 310.5 **9.** 5 **11.** 3
13. $\frac{17}{4}$ **15.** No value **17.** No value
19. 346.48 km **21.** 11,236 m **23.** 125, 245
25. 2 or -2 **27.** 49 **29.** 12 **31.** 7.30 ft **33.** $\frac{1}{2}$
35. 5 **37.** 0 or 4. -1 is not a solution. **39.** $\frac{t^2 g}{2}$
41. 50 g or 1610 ft

Chapter 12 Review

1. 6 **3.** 7 **5.** Irrational **7.** Irrational
9. Rational **11.** 1.732 **13.** $x \geq -7$ **15.** $|m|$
17. p **19.** $\sqrt{21}$ **21.** $\sqrt{x^2 - 9}$ **23.** $-4\sqrt{3}$
25. 10.392 **27.** $2x\sqrt{10}$ **29.** $\frac{5}{8}$ **31.** $\frac{7}{t}$ **33.** $\frac{1}{4}\sqrt{2}$
35. 0.354 **37.** $\frac{1}{5}\sqrt{15}$ **39.** $\frac{2}{3}\sqrt{3}$ **41.** $\sqrt{5}$
43. 25 **45.** 247.49 km

Chapter 13

Section 13−1 TRY THIS

1. $x^2 - 7x = 0; a = 1, b = -7, c = 0$ **2.** $x^2 + 9x - 3 = 0; a = 1, b = 9, c = -3$ **3.** $4x^2 + 2x + 4 = 0;$ $a = 4, b = 2, c = 4$ **4.** $\sqrt{10}, -\sqrt{10}$ **5.** $\pm\frac{\sqrt{15}}{3}$
6. No solution **7.** 0 **8.** $-\frac{5}{3}, 0$ **9.** $\frac{3}{5}, 0$

Exercise Set 13−1

1. $a = 1, b = -3, c = 2$ **3.** $2x^2 - 3 = 0, a = 2,$ $b = 0, c = -3$ **5.** $7x^2 - 4x + 3 = 0, a = 7,$ $b = -4, c = 3$ **7.** $2x^2 - 3x + 5 = 0, a = 2, b = -3,$ $c = 5$ **9.** $3x^2 - 2x + 8 = 0, a = 3, b = -2, c = 8$
11. $\sqrt{10}, -\sqrt{10}$ **13.** $\sqrt{10}, -\sqrt{10}$
15. $\frac{\sqrt{10}}{2}, -\frac{\sqrt{10}}{2}$ **17.** $\frac{2}{3}, -\frac{2}{3}$ **19.** $\frac{4\sqrt{5}}{5}, -\frac{4\sqrt{5}}{5}$
21. $\frac{4}{7}, -\frac{4}{7}$ **23.** $2\sqrt{5}, -2\sqrt{5}$ **25.** $0, -7$
27. $0, -2$ **29.** $0, \frac{2}{5}$ **31.** $0, -1$ **33.** $0, 3$
35. $0, \frac{1}{5}$ **37.** $0, \frac{3}{14}$ **39.** $0, 27$ **41.** $\frac{2}{3}, -1$
43. $-2, 9$ **45.** 4 **47.** $\frac{4}{3}, -\frac{1}{2}$ **49.** ± 6 **51.** ± 9
53. $-\sqrt{3}, 0$ **55.** $\sqrt{\frac{3}{7}}, 0$ **57.** 7.9 sec

Section 13−2 TRY THIS

1. $-1, \frac{2}{3}$ **2.** $7, -3$ **3.** $7, -1$ **4.** $-3 \pm \sqrt{10}$

5. $1 \pm \sqrt{5}$ **6.** $7 \pm \sqrt{3}$ **7.** $2, -24$ **8.** 8 **9.** 11
10. 15%

Exercise Set 13−2

1. 4, 12 **3.** $-1, -6$ **5.** $3, -7$ **7.** $2, 7$ **9.** -5
11. 1 **13.** $\frac{3}{2}, 5$ **15.** $4, -\frac{2}{3}$ **17.** $4, -\frac{5}{3}$
19. $-1, 5$ **21.** $\frac{1}{3}, -\frac{1}{2}$ **23.** $-1 \pm \sqrt{6}$ **25.** $3 \pm \sqrt{6}$
27. 21, 5 **29.** $-1 \pm \sqrt{14}$ **31.** $-10, 8$
33. $-2 \pm \sqrt{29}$ **35.** $\frac{3 \pm \sqrt{337}}{2}$ **37.** 5 **39.** 7
41. 10% **43.** 8% **45.** 20% **47.** $1, -\frac{1}{3}$
49. $\frac{1}{3}, -1$ **51.** $\frac{1}{3}(4 \pm \sqrt{2})$ **53.** $4, -2$
55. $\frac{22}{9}, -\frac{26}{9}$ **57.** $2239.13

Section 13−3 TRY THIS

1. $x^2 - 8x + 16 = (x - 4)^2$ **2.** $x^2 + 10x + 25 = (x + 5)^2$ **3.** $y^2 + 7y + \frac{49}{4} = (y + \frac{7}{2})^2$ **4.** $m^2 - 3m + \frac{9}{4} = (m - \frac{3}{2})^2$ **5.** $-2, -6$ **6.** $5 \pm \sqrt{3}$
7. $-3 \pm \sqrt{10}$ **8.** $\frac{-3 \pm \sqrt{33}}{4}$ **9.** $\frac{1 \pm \sqrt{10}}{3}$

Exercise Set 13−3

1. $-2, 8$ **3.** $-21, -1$ **5.** $1 \pm \sqrt{6}$ **7.** $11 \pm \sqrt{19}$
9. $-5 \pm \sqrt{29}$ **11.** $\frac{7 \pm \sqrt{57}}{2}$ **13.** $-7, 4$
15. $\frac{-3 \pm \sqrt{17}}{4}$ **17.** $\frac{-3 \pm \sqrt{145}}{4}$ **19.** $\frac{-2 \pm \sqrt{7}}{3}$
21. $-\frac{1}{2}, 5$ **23.** $-\frac{7}{2}, \frac{1}{2}$ **25.** $x^2 - ax + \frac{a^2}{4}$
27. $ax^2 + bx + \frac{b^2}{4a^2}$ **29.** $\pm 2\sqrt{55}$ **31.** $\pm 16x$
33. $\pm 2\sqrt{ac}$ **35.** $\pm 2\sqrt{115cy}$ **37.** $3a, -2a$
39. $c + 1$ **41.** $\frac{-2 \pm \sqrt{4 - 3a^2}}{a}$
43. $\frac{-m \pm \sqrt{m^2 - 4nk}}{2k}$

Section 13−4 TRY THIS

1. $\frac{1}{2}, -4$ **2.** $4, -\frac{2}{3}$ **3.** $2.9, -0.9$ **4.** $0.7, -4.3$

Exercise Set 13−4

1. $-3, 7$ **3.** 3 **5.** $-\frac{4}{3}, 2$ **7.** $-\frac{7}{2}, \frac{1}{2}$ **9.** $-3, 3$
11. $1 \pm \sqrt{3}$ **13.** $5 \pm \sqrt{3}$ **15.** $-2 \pm \sqrt{7}$
17. $\frac{-4 \pm \sqrt{10}}{3}$ **19.** $\frac{5 \pm \sqrt{33}}{4}$ **21.** $\frac{1 \pm \sqrt{2}}{2}$
23. $-\frac{5}{3}, 0$ **25.** No real-number solutions **27.** $-5, 5$
29. $\frac{5 \pm \sqrt{73}}{6}$ **31.** $\frac{3 \pm \sqrt{29}}{2}$ **33.** $\frac{-1 \pm \sqrt{10}}{3}$
35. $-2.7, 0.7$ **37.** $-6.7, -3.3$ **39.** $-0.2, 1.2$
41. $0.3, 2.4$ **43.** $0, 2$ **45.** $\frac{3 \pm \sqrt{5}}{2}$ **47.** $\frac{-7 \pm \sqrt{61}}{2}$

49. $\dfrac{-2 \pm \sqrt{10}}{2}$ **51.** No real-number solutions
53. $-1 \pm \sqrt{3a + 1}$ **55.** $\dfrac{c \pm \sqrt{3}d}{2}$ **57.** $\dfrac{a}{b}, \dfrac{-c}{d}$
59a. Yes; no   **59b.** Yes; no   **59c.** When $b^2 \geq 4ac$
61. $b = 9.4$, so $x = 0.3$

Section 13–5 TRY THIS

1. 6, -1 **2.** 2   **3.** 7   **4.** $\dfrac{r^2}{20}$ **5.** $\dfrac{t^2 g}{4\pi^2}$ **6.** $\dfrac{E}{c^2}$
7. $\sqrt{\dfrac{A}{\pi}}$ **8.** $1 + \sqrt{\dfrac{c}{P}}$

Exercise Set 13–5

1. $3 \pm \sqrt{5}$ **3.** $\pm \sqrt{7}$ **5.** No solution   **7.** 10, $-\dfrac{2}{5}$
9. 2   **11.** 9   **13.** 12   **15.** 3   **17.** 5
19. $a = \sqrt{c^2 - b^2}$ **21.** $b = \sqrt{c^2 - a^2}$
23. $r = \sqrt{\dfrac{V}{\pi h}}$ **25.** 6, -4 **27.** $\dfrac{5 \pm \sqrt{37}}{2}$ **29.** 13
31a. $\dfrac{C}{2\pi}$ **31b.** $A = \pi\left(\dfrac{C}{2\pi}\right)^2 = \dfrac{C^2}{4\pi}$ **33.** 3
35. $\dfrac{-v \pm \sqrt{v^2 + 32h}}{16}$

Section 13–6 TRY THIS

1. 20 m   **2.** 2.3 cm, 3.3 cm   **3.** 3 km/hr

Exercise Set 13–6

1. 3 cm   **3.** 7 ft, 24 ft   **5.** 8 cm, 10 cm   **7.** 5 m,
10 m   **9.** 2.4 cm, 4.4 cm   **11.** 8 mi/h   **13.** 36 mi/h
15. 14.14, a 15-in. pizza   **17.** 2 ft   **19.** $3 + 3\sqrt{2}$ or
7.243 cm

Section 13–7 TRY THIS

2. Downward   **3.** Upward   **4.** 4.8, -0.8
5. 0.2, -2.2

Exercise Set 13–7

7. Upward   **9.** Downward   **11.** Downward
13. Upward   **15.** Downward   **17.** Upward
19. Downward   **21.** Downward   **23.** Downward
25. ± 2.2 **27.** 0, -2 **29.** 2.3, -3.3 **31.** -5
33. -2.2, 0.2   **35.** Graph does not cross the x-axis
37. When the function is in standard form the
y-intercept is the constant term.   **39.** Axis is parallel
to y-axis and contains maximum or minimum point.
41. -2.4, 3.4   **43.** $A = lw$, $A = l(8 - l)$, $A = 8l - l^2$,
maximum is at (4, 16), largest area is 4 by 4.

Chapter 13 Review

1. $\sqrt{3}, -\sqrt{3}$ **3.** 0, $\dfrac{7}{5}$ **5.** $2\sqrt{2}, -2\sqrt{2}$ **7.** $\dfrac{3}{5}$, 1
9. $-8 \pm \sqrt{13}$ **11.** 30%   **13.** $1 \pm \sqrt{11}$ **15.** $\dfrac{5}{3}, -1$

17. $-3 \pm 3\sqrt{2}$ **19.** $\dfrac{3 \pm \sqrt{33}}{2}$ **21.** 4.6, 0.4
23. 3, -5 **25.** 52   **27.** $T = L(4V^2 - 1)$
29. Width 2.5 m, length 6.5 m   **31.** Downward

Chapter 14

Section 14–1 TRY THIS

1. $\dfrac{p}{x} = \dfrac{q}{y}, \dfrac{r}{z} = \dfrac{p}{x}, \dfrac{q}{y} = \dfrac{r}{z}$; there are others.   **2.** 75
3. $\dfrac{20}{29}, \dfrac{21}{29}, \dfrac{20}{21}, \dfrac{21}{20}, \dfrac{29}{20}, \dfrac{29}{21}$

Exercise Set 14–1

1. $\overline{AB}$ and $\overline{DE}$; $\overline{BC}$ and $\overline{EF}$; $\overline{AC}$ and $\overline{DF}$; $\angle A$ and $\angle D$;
$\angle B$ and $\angle E$; $\angle C$ and $\angle F$ **3.** Answers may vary.
$\dfrac{t}{m} = \dfrac{u}{n}, \dfrac{s}{u} = \dfrac{l}{n}, \dfrac{u}{t} = \dfrac{n}{m}$ **5.** 16   **7.** $\dfrac{12}{15}, \dfrac{9}{15}, \dfrac{12}{9}, \dfrac{9}{12}$,
$\dfrac{15}{12}, \dfrac{15}{9}$ **9.** $\dfrac{4}{7}, \dfrac{\sqrt{33}}{7}, \dfrac{4}{\sqrt{33}}, \dfrac{\sqrt{33}}{4}, \dfrac{7}{4}, \dfrac{4}{\sqrt{33}}$ **11.** 8, 10
13. No; Yes; Yes   **15.** 64

Section 14–2 TRY THIS

1. 0.2195   **2.** 0.3846   **3.** $\dfrac{7}{24}$

Exercise Set 14–2

1. $\dfrac{\sqrt{3}}{2}$ **3.** $\dfrac{4}{5}$ **5.** 0.4706   **7.** $\dfrac{44}{55}$ **9.** $\dfrac{20}{52}$
11. 0.9231   **13.** $\dfrac{40}{42}$ **15.** $\dfrac{60}{11}$ **17.** 0.5333
19. 0.2925   **21.** 15   **23.** 13.9284   **25.** 40
27. Yes, $\left(\dfrac{a}{c}\right)^2 + \left(\dfrac{b}{c}\right)^2 = \dfrac{a^2 + b^2}{c^2}$, since $a^2 + b^2 = c^2$
this ratio = 1.

Section 14–3 TRY THIS

1. 0.8387   **2.** 0.5150   **3.** 1.4826   **4.** 58°   **5.** 58°
6. 56°   **7.** 57°

Exercise Set 14–3

1. 0.6157   **3.** 1.4826   **5.** 0.9877   **7.** 0.8660
9. 1.0000   **11.** 0.9998   **13.** 0.9455   **15.** 0.2588
17. 70°   **19.** 81°   **21.** 66°   **23.** 11°   **25.** 50°
27. 5°   **29.** 61°   **31.** 38°   **33.** 65°   **35.** 70°
37. 0.6041, 0.6064, 0.6134

Section 14–4 TRY THIS

1. 6.7 cm   **2.** 37.1 m   **3.** 152.6 m

Exercise Set 14-4

1. 22.8 cm   **3.** 54.0 cm   **5.** $35°$ **7.** 3.3 km
9. 338.6 m   **11.** 5.3 m   **13.** 211.3 m   **15.** 3.9 km
17. 8160 ft (1.55 mi)   **19.** 36.8   **21.** 33.7
23. Draw h so that it makes a right angle with side b.
Then $\sin A = \frac{h}{c}$, so $A = \frac{1}{2}bc \sin A = \frac{1}{2}bc\left(\frac{h}{c}\right) = \frac{1}{2}bh$.

Chapter 14 Review

1. $\overline{PQ}$ and $\overline{ST}$; $\overline{QR}$ and $\overline{TV}$; $\overline{RP}$ and $\overline{VS}$; $\angle P$ and $\angle S$;
$\angle Q$ and $\angle T$; $\angle R$ and $\angle V$ **3.** 0.3846   **5.** 0.2550
7. 0.4226   **9.** $44°$ **11.** $45°$ **13.** 27.6 cm
15. 186.5 m

INDEX